A Manual of

Engineering Drawing

for Students and Draftsmen

The Engineering Drawing Series

ENGINEERING DRAWING

FRENCH AND VIERCK: *A Manual of Engineering Drawing for Students and Draftsmen,* 9th edition
Fundamentals of Engineering Drawing
Graphic Science

COOPER AND MACHOVINA: *Engineering Drawing Problems,* Series III, 11 × 17

GRANT: *Engineering Drawing Problems,* Series 1, 10 × 12

HILL: *Problems in Graphical Analysis,* 11 × 17

LEVENS AND EDSTROM: *Problems in Engineering Drawing,* Series V, 10 × 12

MCNEARY, WEIDHAAS, AND KELSO: *Creative Problems for Basic Engineering Drawing,* 11 × 17

VIERCK AND HANG: *Engineering Drawing Problems,* 8½ × 11
Fundamental Engineering Drawing Problems, 8½ × 11

FRENCH AND TURNBULL: *Lessons in Lettering: Book I, Vertical Single Stroke,* 3d edition, 9 × 6;
Book II, Inclined Single Stroke, 3d edition, 9 × 6

MCGRAW-HILL TEXT-FILMS FOR ENGINEERING DRAWING: *A Series of 10 Directly Correlated Motion Pictures with 9 Follow-up Filmstrips*

MECHANICAL DRAWING

FRENCH AND SVENSON: *Mechanical Drawing,* 6th edition

LEVENS AND EDSTROM: *Problems in Mechanical Drawing, First Course,* 2d edition, 8½ × 11
Problems in Mechanical Drawing, Second Course, 8½ × 11

MCGRAW-HILL TEXT-FILMS FOR MECHANICAL DRAWING: *A Series of 8 Directly Correlated Motion Pictures with 7 Follow-up Filmstrips and Mechanical Drawing Filmstrips (set 3)*

Thomas E. French, *Late Professor of Engineering Drawing,*
The Ohio State University, and **Charles J. Vierck,**
Visiting Professor of Engineering Graphics, University of Florida,
with the assistance of **Ralph S. Paffenbarger,** *Professor of Engineering Drawing,*
The Ohio State University

1960 NEW YORK TORONTO LONDON

A MANUAL OF ENGINEERING DRAWING FOR STUDENTS & DRAFTSMEN

Ninth Edition

McGRAW-HILL BOOK COMPANY, INC.

744

Library of Congress Catalog Card Number: 59-15458

First Edition (August, 1911): ten printings, 35,000
copies
Second Edition (July, 1918): twelve printings,
108,000 copies
Third Edition (May, 1924): ten printings, 96,000
copies
Fourth Edition (June, 1929): ten printings, 106,000
copies
Fifth Edition (April, 1935): sixteen printings,
148,000 copies
Sixth Edition (May, 1941): fourteen printings,
439,700 copies
Seventh Edition (August, 1947): seven printings,
291,099 copies
Eighth Edition (March, 1953): ten printings,
399,800 copies

Total Issue: 1,623,599

Preface to the Ninth Edition

SCIENTIFIC DISCOVERIES AND ADVANCES are accompanied by new methods, processes, and designs in all engineering fields. As engineering knowledge grows, greater demands are made of practicing engineers, and college curricula are being expanded to adequately prepare students. The teaching of all courses must be highly efficient in order to accomplish the total job in the same or only slightly more time than formerly.

In view of the general expansion in the field, the need for concise, accurate, and efficient communication of technical information has become ever more important. Nor is this need created alone by the actual bulk of material that must be transmitted; it is due also to the complexities that have come with advances in areas such as automation and control of processes, mechanisms, and electrical devices.

Industry is well aware of the need for improved communication, and executives have again and again pointed to the obligation of colleges and universities in providing adequate training in speaking, writing, and drawing. To meet today's needs, this text has been extensively revised to present engineering drawing in a direct and efficient manner. The text material has been brought up to date and conforms with the most recent standards. Presentation of many of the essentials has been revised and expanded for better explanation and coverage. A new writing style is employed to present the subject in a more positive, direct, and meaningful manner.

Illustrations have been redrawn or altered in many ways, and a number of new ones have been included. In many of the illustrations explanatory notes and reference letters have been added, and their use makes explanations in the text and in the greatly expanded captions more specific. The close correlation between the illustrations and the interpretations given will lead to better understanding for the student and help the teacher in explanations. Photographic illustrations add interest and clarify the material. The new two-column format and increased page size have been designed for flexibility in arranging the text, illustrations, and captions.

The organization of chapters has been revised to make for a more logical order and to consolidate related subjects. In Chap. 1 the subject of engineering drawing is outlined, with the aid of illustrations, so that the student may obtain a significant concept of it before studying the text proper. Chapters 2 to 9 explain and illustrate shape description; they include instruments and their use, applied geometry, lettering, orthographic drawing and sketching, pictorial drawing and sketching, auxiliary edge and normal views, and sections and conventions. In Chaps. 10 and 11 size description (dimensioning and tolerancing) are discussed. Chapter 12 explains the representation, dimensioning, and specifying of screw threads, fasteners, keys, rivets, and springs—necessary elements in making working drawings, which are explained in Chap. 13. Chapter 14 describes the construction of charts, graphs, and diagrams—a subject important in all engineering fields.

Chapters 15 to 18 give information on specialties—jigs and fixtures, welds, gears and cams, and piping—used in all fields. The practices peculiar to special fields are explained in Chaps. 19 to 21, which present drawings of electrical systems, structural and architectural drawings, and maps and topographic drawing. Chapter 22, on commercial practices and economies, discusses procedures that expedite and augment the graphic language. A comprehensive appendix contains all reference material needed for the problems.

To obtain authentic subject matter, personnel of industry and engineering education have been consulted. The following persons and companies have supplied text and problem material.

Procter & Gamble Co. (William Jaques); Cleveland Metal Specialties Co. (Al Gross); Industrial Nucleonics (Paul M. Werth); Philco Corporation (Harry Kenyon); Union Chain & Mfg. Co. (Ralph Young); Milton Beckberger, Erie County (Ohio) Engineer; General Motors Corp. (Roy P. Trowbridge); Radio Corporation of America (Sam H. Watson); Lincoln Electric Co. (Charles Herbruck); Jenkins Bros. (Alfred M. Street); Dodge Mfg. Co. (C. J. Shamo); Grinnell Co.; Sanders Associates, Inc.; Convair (H. F. conGoodat); Columbia-Southern Chemical Corp. (Dallas Dupre III); Lockheed Aircraft Corp. (T. C. Pritchard); Link-Belt Co. (R. F. Bergmann); Boeing Airplane Co. (W. I. Andrews); North American Aviation Corp. (Humphrey Keever); Curtiss Wright Corp. (Paul G. Clark).

The manuscript was reviewed and helpful suggestions were made by Professors Irwin Wladaver and E. W. Jackunski. Richard I. Hang contributed to the making of many of the new drawings.

Again available with this edition are the McGraw-Hill text-films designed especially for, and correlated with, the text and problems. These visual aids, consisting of motion pictures and filmstrips, have a high teaching value and illustrate certain principles and practices more effectively than can be done by a textbook alone.

There are problem books correlated directly with the text. Consultation materials are available to teachers.

Charles J. Vierck

Preface to the First Edition

THERE IS a wide diversity of method in the teaching of engineering drawing, and perhaps less uniformity in the courses in different schools than would be found in most subjects taught in technical schools and colleges. In some well-known instances the attempt is made to teach the subject by giving a series of plates to be copied by the student. Some give all the time to laboratory work; others depend principally upon recitations and homework. Some begin immediately on the theory of descriptive geometry, working in all the angles; others discard theory and commence with a course in machine detailing. Some advocate the extensive use of models; some condemn their use entirely.

Different courses have been designed for different purposes, and criticism is not intended, but it would seem that better unity of method might result if there were a better recognition of the conception that drawing is a real language, to be studied and taught in the same way as any other language. With this conception it may be seen that except for the practice in the handling and use of instruments, and for showing certain standards of execution, copying drawings does little more in the study as an art of expression of thought than copying paragraphs from a foreign book would do in beginning the study of a foreign language.

And it would appear equally true that good pedagogy would not advise taking up composition in a new language before the simple structure of the sentence is understood and appreciated; that is, "working drawings" would not be considered until after the theory of projection has been explained.

After a knowledge of the technic of expression, the "penmanship and orthography," the whole energy should be directed toward training in constructive imagination, the perceptive ability which enables one to think in three dimensions, to visualize quickly and accurately, to build up a clear mental image, a requirement absolutely necessary for the designer who is to represent his thoughts on paper. That this may be accomplished more readily by taking up solids before points and lines has been demonstrated beyond dispute.

It is then upon this plan, regarding drawing as a language, the universal graphical language of the industrial world, with its varied force of expression, its grammar and its styles, that this book has been built. It is not a "course in drawing," but a textbook, with exercises and problems in some variety from which selections may be made.

Machine parts furnish the best illustrations of principles, and have been used freely, but the book is intended for all engineering students. Chapters on architectural drawing and map drawing have been added, as in the interrelation of the professions every engineer should be able to read and work from such drawings.

In teaching the subject, part of the time, at least one hour per week, may profitably be scheduled for class lectures, recitations, and blackboard work, at which time there may be distributed "study sheets" or home plates of problems on the assigned lesson, to be drawn in pencil and returned at the next corresponding period. In the drawing-room period, specifications for plates, to be approved in pencil and some finished by inking or tracing, should be assigned, all to be done under the careful supervision of the instructor.

The judicious use of models is of great aid, both in technical sketching and, particularly, in drawing to scale, in aiding the student to feel the sense of proportion between the drawing and the structure, so that in reading a drawing he may have the ability to visualize not only the shape but the size of the object represented.

In beginning drawing it is not advisable to use large plates. One set of commercial drafting-room sizes is based on the division of a 36″ × 48″ sheet into 24″ × 36″, 18″ × 24″, 12″ × 18″, and 9″ × 12″. The size 12″ × 18″ is sufficiently large for first year work, while 9″ × 12″ is not too small for earlier plates.

Grateful acknowledgment is made of the assistance of Messrs. Robert Meiklejohn, O. E. Williams, A. C. Harper, Cree Sheets, F. W. Ives, W. D. Turnbull, and W. J. Norris of the staff of the Department of Engineering Drawing, The Ohio State University, not only in the preparation of the drawings, but in advice and suggestion on the text. Other members of the faculty of this University have aided by helpful criticism.

The aim has been to conform to modern engineering practice, and it is hoped that the practical consideration of the draftsman's needs will give the book permanent value as a reference book in the student's library.

The author will be glad to cooperate with teachers using it as a textbook.

Thomas E. French

Columbus, Ohio
June, 1911

Contents

Contents

Engineering Drawing Films

THE FOLLOWING 16-mm sound motion pictures are especially recommended for use with various chapters of this book:

According to Plan. An introduction to engineering drawing (9 min). *For Chap. 1.*

Orthographic Projection. Shape description and the principles of orthographic projection (18 min). *For Chap. 5.*

Pictorial Sketching. Basic principles of axonometric, oblique, and perspective pictorial sketching (11 min). *For Chap. 6.*

Auxiliary Views: Single Auxiliaries. Reviews orthographic projection and explains auxiliary projection (23 min). *For Chap. 7.*

Auxiliary Views: Double Auxiliaries. The theory and practice of double-auxiliary or oblique view (13 min). *For Chap. 7.*

Sections and Conventions. Theory and practice of sectioning and conventional principles (15 min). *For Chap. 8.*

Simple Developments. What simple developments are and how they are used (11 min). *For Chap. 9.*

Oblique Cones and Transition Developments. Animated drawings illustrate oblique cones and transitions (11 min). *For Chap. 9.*

Drawings and the Shop. Relationships between the drawing and production operations in the shop; basic machines (15 min). *For Chap. 10.*

Selection of Dimensions. Principles governing choice of dimensions and their applications (18 min). *For Chap. 11.*

Prints of these films may be purchased from Text-Film Department, McGraw-Hill Book Company, Inc.

A Manual of

Engineering Drawing

for Students and Draftsmen

1

Introduction

1.1. In beginning the study of engineering drawing (or engineering graphics, as it is now coming to be called), you are embarking upon a rewarding educational experience and one that will be of real value in your future career. When you have become proficient in it, you will have at your command a method of communication used in all branches of technical industry, a language unequaled for accurate description of physical objects.

The importance of this graphic language can be seen by comparing it with word languages. All who attend elementary and high school study the language of their country and learn to read, write, and speak it with some de-

gree of skill. In high school and college most students study a foreign language. These word languages are highly developed systems of communication. Nevertheless, any word language is inadequate for describing the size, shape, and relationship of physical objects. Study the photograph at the opening of this chapter and then try to describe it verbally so that someone who has not seen it can form an accurate and complete mental picture. It is almost impossible to do this. Even a picture such as Fig. 1.1, although possibly easier to describe, presents an almost insurmountable problem. Furthermore, in trying to describe either picture, you may want to use pencil and paper to sketch all or

FIG. 1.1. Try to describe in words the shape, the relative size, and the position of the objects in this picture.

3

a part in an attempt to make the word description more complete, meaningful, and accurate, or tend to use your hands, gesturing to aid in explaining shape and relationship. From this we can see that a word language is often without resources for accurate and rapid communication of shape and size and the relationships of components.

Engineering is applied science, and communication of physical facts *must* be complete and accurate. Quantitative relationships are expressed mathematically. The written word completes many descriptions. But whenever machines and structures are designed, described, and built, graphic representation is necessary. Although the works of artists (or photography and other methods of reproduction) would provide pictorial representation, they cannot serve as engineering descriptions. Shaded pictorial drawings and photographs are used for special purposes, but the great bulk of engineering drawings are made in line only, with separate views arranged in a logical system of projection. To these views, dimensions and special notes giving operations and other directions for manufacture are added. This is the language of engineering drawing, which can be defined as *the graphic representation of physical objects and relationships.*

As the foundation upon which all designing and subsequent manufacture are based, engineering graphics is one of the most important single branches of study in a technical school. Every engineering student must know how to make and how to read drawings. The subject is essential in all types of engineering practice, and should be understood by all connected with, or interested in, technical industry. All designs and directions for manufacture are prepared by draftsmen, professional writers of the language, but even one who may never make drawings must be able to read and understand them or be professionally illiterate. Thorough training in engineering graphics is particularly important for the engineer because he is responsible for and specifies the drawings required in his work and must therefore be able to interpret every detail for correctness and completeness.

Our object is to study the language of engineering graphics so that we can write it, expressing ourselves clearly to one familiar with it, and read it readily when written by another. To do this, we must know its basic theory and composition, and be familiar with its accepted conventions and abbreviations. Since its principles are essentially the same throughout the world, a person who has been trained in the practices of one nation can readily adapt himself to the practices of another.

This language is entirely graphic and written, and is interpreted by acquiring a visual knowledge of the object represented. A student's success with it will be indicated not alone by his skill in execution, but also by his ability to interpret lines and symbols and to visualize clearly in space.

In the remainder of this chapter we shall introduce briefly the various aspects of engineering drawing that will be discussed at length later. It is hoped that this preview will serve as a broad perspective against which the student will see each topic, as it is studied, in relation to the whole. Since our subject is a graphic language, illustrations are helpful in presenting even this introductory material; figures are used both to clarify the text and to carry the presentation forward.

1.2. ESSENTIALS OF DRAFTING: LINES AND LETTERING. Drawings are made up of lines that represent the surfaces, edges, and contours of objects. Symbols, dimensional sizes, and word notes are added to these lines, collectively making a complete description. Proficiency in the methods of drawing straight lines, circles, and curves, either freehand or with instruments, and the ability to letter word statements are fundamental to writing the graphic language. Furthermore, lines are connected according to the geometry of the object represented, making it necessary to know the geometry of plane and solid figures and to understand how to combine circles, straight lines, and curves to represent separate views of many geometric combinations.

THE USE OF INSTRUMENTS. Facility in the use of instruments makes for speed and accuracy.

LETTERING. The standard lettering for engineering drawings is known as "commercial Gothic." Both vertical and inclined styles are used.

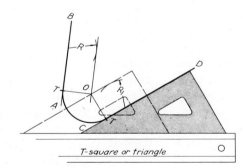

T-square or triangle

APPLIED GEOMETRY. A knowledge of, and facility in, the construction of lines and geometric figures promotes efficiency.

1.3. METHODS OF EXPRESSION. There are two fundamental methods of writing the graphic language: freehand and with instruments.

Freehand drawing is done by sketching the lines with no instruments other than pencils and erasers. It is an excellent method during the learning process because of its speed and because at this stage the study of projection is more important than exactness of delineation. Freehand drawings are much used commercially for preliminary designing and for some finished work. Instrument drawing is the standard method of expression. Most drawings are made "to scale," with instruments used to draw straight lines, circles, and curves con- cisely and accurately. Training in both freehand and instrument work is necessary for the engineer so that he will develop competence in writing the graphic language and the ability to judge work done under his direction.

FREEHAND DRAWINGS. The freehand method is fine for early study because it provides training in technique, form, and proportion. It is used commercially for economy.

INSTRUMENT DRAWINGS. Because of the necessity of drawing "to scale," most drawings are made with instruments.

1.4. METHODS OF SHAPE DESCRIPTION. Delineation of the *shape* of a part, assembly, or structure is the primary element of graphic communication. Since there are many purposes for which drawings are made, the engineer must select, from the different methods of describing shape, the one best suited to the situation at hand. Shape is described by projection, that is, by the process of causing an image to be formed by rays of sight taken in a particular direction from an object to a picture plane.

Following projective theory, two methods of *representation* are used: orthographic views and pictorial views.

For the great bulk of engineering work, the orthographic system is used, and this method, with its variations and the necessary symbols and abbreviations, constitutes an important part of this book. In the orthographic system, separate views arranged according to the projective theory are made to show clearly all details of the object represented. The figures that follow illustrate the fundamental types of orthographic drawings and orthographic views.

ONE-VIEW DRAWINGS. These are used whenever views in more than one direction are unnecessary, for example, for parts made of thin material.

TWO-VIEW DRAWINGS. Parts such as cylinders require only two views. More would duplicate the two already drawn.

THREE-VIEW DRAWINGS. Most objects are made up of combined geometric solids. Three views are required to represent their shape.

AUXILIARIES: EDGE AND NORMAL VIEWS. Auxiliaries are used to show the *normal view* (true size and shape) of an inclined surface (at an angle to two of the planes of projection), shown at left, or of a skew surface (inclined to all three planes of projection), shown at right.

SECTIONAL VIEWS.   These are used to clarify the representation of objects with complicated internal detail.

INTERSECTIONS.   Geometric surfaces or solids often are combined so that additional projection is needed to determine the line of intersection between the parts.

DEVELOPMENTS.   These are the projections of geometric surfaces into a flat pattern.

"Pictorial representation" designates the methods of projection resulting in a view that shows the object approximately as it would be seen by the eye. Pictorial representation is often used for presentation drawings, text, operation, and maintenance book illustrations, and some working drawings.

There are three main divisions of pictorial projection: axonometric, oblique, and perspective. Theoretically, axonometric projection is projection in which only one plane is used, the object being turned so that three faces show. The main axonometric positions are isometric, dimetric, and trimetric.

ISOMETRIC DRAWING.   This method is based on turning the object so that three mutually perpendicular edges are equally foreshortened.

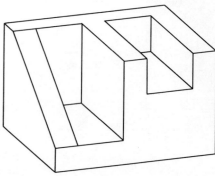

DIMETRIC DRAWING.   This method is based on turning the object so that two mutually perpendicular edges are equally foreshortened.

TRIMETRIC DRAWING. This method is based on turning the object so that three mutually perpendicular edges are all unequally foreshortened.

AXONOMETRIC PROJECTION FROM ORTHOGRAPHIC VIEWS. Pictorials—isometric, dimetric, or trimetric—may be obtained by projection from orthographic views. The views are located by a geometric method.

Oblique projection is a pictorial method used principally for objects with circular or curved features only on one face or on parallel faces; and for such objects the oblique is easy to draw and dimension. Perspective projection gives a result identical with what the eye or a single-lens camera would record.

OBLIQUE DRAWING. This pictorial method is useful for portraying cylindrical parts. Projectors are oblique to the picture plane. Cavalier and cabinet drawings are specific forms.

OBLIQUE PROJECTION FROM ORTHOGRAPHIC VIEWS. In this pictorial method views are arranged so that, by projection, an oblique drawing results.

PERSPECTIVE. In this method of pictorial projection angular and parallel forms are both used extensively.

1.5. METHODS OF SIZE DESCRIPTION. After delineation of shape, *size* is the second element of graphic communication, completing the representation of the object. Size is shown by "dimensions," which state linear distances, diameters, radii, and other necessary magnitudes.

DIMENSIONING ORTHOGRAPHIC DRAWINGS. Dimensions showing the magnitude and relative position of each portion of the object are placed on the view where each dimension is most meaningful.

DIMENSIONING PICTORIAL DRAWINGS. The descriptions of magnitudes and positions are shown on the pictorial by dimensions placed so as to be easily readable.

1.6. BASIC MACHINE ELEMENTS. Many machine elements occur repeatedly in all kinds of engineering work. Familiarity with these elements is necessary so that dimensioning and specifications on the drawings will be correct. The material that follows introduces basic machine elements and shop processes, so illustrating the principles of engineering drawing laid out in the previous sections.

SHARP V   AMERICAN NATIONAL (UNIFIED)   SQUARE   ACME

SCREW THREADS. Screw threads are used on fasteners, on devices for making adjustments, and for the transmission of power and motion. The screw thread is the most extensively used machine element.

FASTENERS. Bolts and screws in a wide variety of forms are used for fastenings. Familiarity with the standard sizes available and their drawing and specification is fundamental.

KEYS. Keys are used to prevent cylindrical elements such as gears and pulleys from rotating on their shafts.

RIVETS. Rivets are permanent fasteners. They are cylinders of metal with a head on one end. When placed in position, the opposite head is formed by impact.

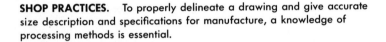

Compression Spring   Torsion Spring   Extension Spring

SPRINGS. A spring is an elastic body that stores energy when deflected. Basic forms are illustrated.

SHOP PRACTICES. To properly delineate a drawing and give accurate size description and specifications for manufacture, a knowledge of processing methods is essential.

1.7. SPECIAL FIELDS AND PRACTICES. The methods of projection, the choice of representational type (shape description), and the accompanying size description are more or less uniform in all fields because these are the elements of which all drawings are composed. However, for most special fields certain symbols and notation, drawing, and dimensioning practices have been standardized, and a knowledge of these is necessary so that drawings will be readily and efficiently understood.

The special practices or fields given in this book include: charts, graphs, and diagrams; various portions of mechanisms and systems; welding; electrical drawing; structural and topographic practices; and commercial practices and economies. Illustrative figures follow.

AMPLIFIER POWER OUTPUT REQUIRED TO COVER VARIOUS DISTANCES AS COMPARED TO THE SURROUNDING NOISE LEVEL

CHARTS, GRAPHS, AND DIAGRAMS. These are graphic plots for the analysis of engineering data or the presentation of statistics. Special standards designate preferred construction, lines, symbols, and lettering.

JIGS AND FIXTURES.   In modern high-quantity production these devices are used for holding parts during machining. Drawings are made to conform to tool-engineering standards.

REPRESENTATION OF WELDS.   Welds are represented by symbols standardized by the American Welding Society (AWS) and the American Standards Association (ASA).

GEARS.   Special practices include calculation of detailed sizes and their tabulation on drawings.

CAMS. Special practices include full-size layouts and also calculation and dimensioning of points on cam surfaces.

Note: All fittings 2"M.I. unless otherwise noted
All valves 2" Iron body.

PIPING. Piping drawings are made to scale or symbolically. Symbols for pipe, valves, fittings, and other details are standardized by the ASA.

DRAWINGS OF ELECTRICAL SYSTEMS. Most electrical drawings are made symbolically, using ASA standards.

STRUCTURES. Architectural standards of the American Institute of Architects (AIA) and structural standards of the American Institute of Steel Construction (AISC) prevail in the building industry.

MAPS AND TOPOGRAPHY. Maps and topographic drawings are made up chiefly of symbols.

COMMERCIAL PRACTICES AND ECONOMIES.   These include simplified drawing practices, special uses of reproduction processes, photography, and modelmaking.

1.8. TERMINOLOGY. During any course of study in engineering drawing the student must become thoroughly familiar with the terminology of design and construction. The glossary of technical, structural, architectural, and welding terms in the Appendix should be consulted as needed. Form the habit of never passing over a word without understanding its meaning completely.

1.9.   APPENDIX TABLES. Many details of engineering drawing depend upon specifications for drills, bolts and screws, fits, limits, pipe sizes, symbols, and other standards. It is important to become well acquainted with this material, which is given in the Appendix.

2

Instruments and Their Use

2.1. To record information on paper (or another surface), instruments and equipment are required. Since engineering drawing is entirely a graphic language, equipment is needed; even for drawings made freehand, pencils, erasers, and sometimes coordinate paper or other special items are used.

The lines made on drawings are *straight* or *curved* (including circles and arcs). They are made with drawing instruments, which are the necessary tools for laying down lines on a drawing in an accurate and efficient manner. In order to position the lines, a measuring device, a scale, is used.

The various instruments will be described in detail later, but the opening photograph of this chapter will serve as an introductory illustration. To draw straight lines, the T square (at the left), with its straight blade and perpendicular head, or a triangle (shown resting on the T-square blade) is used. A pencil is shown across the triangle. To draw circles, a compass is needed, placed here near the T-square head. To the right of the compass are shown dividers for spacing distances and a small bow compass for drawing small circles. To draw curved lines other than circles, a french curve (lower right) is used. In the center of the picture, across the T square and triangle, is a scale, for making measurements. Also shown (right) are pens for inking and an ink bottle in holder.

2 LAYERS OF BASSWOOD

BALSA CORE | BASSWOOD FRAME

2 LAYERS OF BASSWOOD

FIG. 2.1. Drawing board. This one is light and rigid. *Courtesy of Keuffel & Esser Co.*

2.2. SELECTION OF INSTRUMENTS. In selecting instruments and materials for drawing, secure the *best* you can afford. For one who expects to do work of professional grade, it is a mistake to buy inferior instruments. Sometimes a beginner is tempted to get cheap instruments for learning, expecting to buy better ones later. With reasonable care a set of good instruments will last a lifetime, whereas poor ones will be an annoyance from the start and worthless after short use. Since poor instruments can be difficult to distinguish from good ones, it is well to seek trustworthy advice before buying. Instruments have been greatly improved in recent years.

2.3. DRAWING BOARDS. The drawing surface may be the table top itself or a separate board. In either case the working surface should be made of well-

seasoned clear white pine or basswood, cleated to prevent warping. The working edge must be straight and should be tested with a steel straightedge. Some boards and table tops are supplied with a hardwood edge or a steel insert on the working edge, thus ensuring a better-wearing surface. Figure 2.1 illustrates a drawing board which, because of its design and the materials of which it is made, is rigid, sturdy, and light.

2.4. DRAWING PAPER. Drawing paper is made in a variety of qualities and may be had in sheets or rolls. White drawing papers that will not turn yellow with age or exposure are used for finished drawings, maps, charts, and drawings for photographic reproduction. For pencil layouts and working drawings, cream or buff detail papers are preferred as they are easier on the eyes and do not show soil so quickly as white papers. In general, paper should have sufficient grain, or "tooth," to take the pencil, be agreeable to the eye, and have a hard surface not easily grooved by the pencil, with good erasing qualities. Formerly imported papers were considered the best, but American mills are now making practically all the paper used in this country. Cheap manila papers should be avoided.

2.5. TRACING PAPER. Tracing papers are thin papers, *natural* or *transparentized,* on which drawings are traced, in pencil or ink, and from which blueprints or similar contact prints can be made. In most drafting rooms original drawings are penciled on tracing papers, and blueprints are made directly from these drawings, a practice increasingly successful because of improvements both in papers and in printing. Tracing papers

STANDARD PENCILS   SEMIAUTOMATIC PENCILS

A   B   C   D   E

FIG. 2.2. Drafting pencils. The semiautomatics are most convenient to use.

vary widely in color, thickness, surface, etc., and the grade of pencil and the technique must be adjusted to suit the paper, but with the proper combination, good prints can be obtained from such drawings.

2.6. TRACING CLOTH. Finely woven cloth coated with a special starch or plastic is used for making drawings in pencil or ink. The standard tracing cloth is used for inked tracings and specially made pencil cloth for pencil drawings or tracings. Cloth is more permanent than paper as it will stand more handling. Tracing and duplicating processes are described in Chap. 13.

2.7. DRAFTING TAPE. The paper to be used is usually attached to the drawing board by means of Scotch drafting tape, with a short piece stuck across each corner or with tape along the entire edge of the paper. Drafting tape is not the same as masking tape (made by the same company); the latter has a heavier coating of adhesive and does not come off the drawing paper so cleanly as the former.

2.8. THUMBTACKS. The best thumbtacks are made with thin heads and steel points screwed into them. Cheaper ones are made by stamping. Use tacks with tapering pins of small diameter, and avoid flat-headed (often colored) map pins, as the heads are too thick and the pins rather large.

2.9. PENCILS. The basic instrument is the graphite lead pencil, made in various hardnesses. Each manufacturer has special methods of processing designed to make the lead strong and yet give a smooth clear line. Figure 2.2 shows five varieties of pencils. At the left are two

FIG. 2.3. Accessories. These are used for fastening paper, sharpening pencils, and erasing.

ordinary pencils, with the lead set in wood. (*A*) is of American and (*B*) of foreign manufacture. Both are fine, but have the disadvantage that, in use, the wood must be cut away to expose the lead (a time-consuming job), and the pencil becomes shorter until the last portion must be discarded. Semiautomatic pencils, (*C*) to (*E*), with a chuck to clamp and hold the lead, are more convenient. (*C*) has a plastic handle and changeable tip (for indicating the grade of lead). (*D*) has an aluminum handle and indexing tip for indication of grade. (*E*) is the rather elegant Alteneder pencil with rosewood handle, hardened-steel chuck ring, and eraser. Drawing pencils are graded by numbers and letters from 6B, very soft and black, through 5B, 4B, 3B, 2B, B, and HB to F, the medium grade; then H, 2H, 3H, 4H, 5H, 6H, 7H, and 8H to 9H, the hardest. The soft (B) grades are used primarily for sketching and rendered drawings and the hard (H) grades for instrument drawings.

DROPPER BOTTLE IN
BOTTLEHOLDER

PLASTIC "SQUEEZE" DROPPER TUBE

FIG. 2.4. Standard bottle in holder; Leroy pen-filler cartridge. The cartridge is particularly convenient.

2.10. PENCIL POINTER. After the wood of the ordinary pencil is cut away with a pocketknife or mechanical sharpener, the lead must be formed to a long, conic point. A lance-tooth steel file, Fig. 2.3*A*, about 6 in. long is splendid for the purpose. Some prefer the standard sandpaper pencil-pointer pad, Fig. 2.3*B*.

2.11. ERASERS. The Ruby pencil eraser, Fig. 2.3*C*, large size with beveled ends, is the standard. This eraser not only removes pencil lines effectively but is better for ink than the so-called ink eraser, as it removes ink without seriously damaging the surface of paper or cloth. A good metal erasing shield, Fig. 2.3*D*, aids in getting clean erasures.

Artgum or a *soft*-rubber eraser, Fig. 2.3*E*, is useful for cleaning paper and cloth of finger marks and smears that spoil the appearance of the completed drawing.

2.12. PENHOLDERS AND PENS. The penholder should have a grip of medium size, small enough to enter the mouth of a drawing-ink bottle easily yet not so small as to cramp the fingers while in use. A size slightly larger than the diameter of a pencil is good.

An assortment of pens for lettering, grading from coarse to fine, may be chosen from those listed in Chap. 4.

A penwiper of lintless cloth or thin chamois skin should always be at hand for both lettering and ruling pens.

2.13. DRAWING INK. Drawing ink is finely ground carbon in suspension, with natural or synthetic gum added to make the mixture waterproof. Nonwaterproof ink flows more freely but smudges easily. Drawing ink diluted with distilled water or Chinese ink in stick form rubbed up

with water on a slate slab is used in making wash drawings and for very fine line work.

Bottleholders prevent the bottle from upsetting and ruining the drawing table or floor. They are made in various patterns; one is illustrated in Fig. 2.4. As a temporary substitute, the lower half of the paper container in which the ink is sold may be fastened to the table with a thumbtack, or a strip of paper or cloth with a hole for the neck of the bottle may be tacked down over the bottle. Several companies are now supplying ink in small-necked plastic bottles or tubes, Fig. 2.4, which are squeezed to supply the ink, a drop at a time. These containers prevent spillage and protect the ink from deterioration through evaporation or contamination.

2.14. THE T SQUARE. The fixed-head T square, Fig. 2.5, is used for all ordinary work. It should be of hardwood, and the blade should be perfectly straight. The transparent-edged blade is much the best. A draftsman will have several fixed-head squares of different lengths and will find an adjustable-head square of occasional use.

2.15. TRIANGLES. Triangles, Fig. 2.5, are made of transparent celluloid (fiberloid) or other plastic material. Through internal strains they sometimes lose their accuracy. Triangles should be kept flat to prevent warping. For ordinary work, a 6- or 8-in. 45° and a 10-in. 30-60° are good sizes.

2.16. SCALES. Scales, Figs. 2.6 to 2.9, are made in a variety of graduations to meet the requirements of many different kinds of work. For convenience, scales are classified according to their most common uses.

T SQUARE

45°
TRIANGLE

30–60°
TRIANGLE

FIG. 2.5. T square and triangles. These are standard equipment for drawing straight lines.

Mechanical Engineer's Scales. These are divided and numbered so that fractions of inches represent inches. The most common ranges are ⅛, ¼, ½, and 1 in. to the *inch*. These scales are known as the *size* scales because the designated reduction also represents the ratio of size, as, for example, *one-eighth* size. A full- and half-size scale is illustrated in Fig. 2.6. Mechanical engineer's scales are almost always "full divided," that is, the smallest divisions run throughout the entire length. They are often graduated with the marked divisions numbered from right to left, as well as from left to right, as shown in Fig. 2.6. Mechanical engineer's scales are used mostly for drawings of machine parts and small structures where the drawing size is never less than one-eighth the size of the actual object.

Civil Engineer's Scales. These are divided into decimals with 10, 20, 30, 40, 50, 60, and 80 divisions to the inch (Fig. 2.7). Such a scale is usually full divided and is sometimes numbered both from left to right and right to left. Civil engineer's scales are most used for plotting and drawing maps, although they are convenient for any work where divisions of the inch in tenths is required.

Architect's Scales. Divided into proportional feet and inches, these scales have divisions indicating ⅛, ¼, ⅜, ½, ¾, 1½, and 3 in. to the *foot* (Fig. 2.8). They are usually "open divided," that is, the units are shown along the entire length, but only the end units are subdivided into inches and fractions. These scales are much used by all engineers—mechanical, industrial, chemical, etc.—for both machine and structural drawings and are sometimes called *mechanical engineer's* scales.

A variety of special scales, made with divisions specified by the customer, are available from most instrument companies. Compared with standard scales, they are expensive.

FIG. 2.6. A mechanical engineer's full- and half-size scale. Divisions are in inches to sixteenths of an inch. (The half-size scale is on the back of the full-size scale.)

FIG. 2.7. A civil engineer's scale. Divisions are 10, 20, 30, 40, 50, and 60 parts to the inch.

FIG. 2.8. An architect's (or mechanical engineer's) scale. Reduction in size is based on proportion of a foot.

TRIANGULAR   OPPOSITE BEVEL

A   B   C   D   E   F

FIG. 2.9. Scale types. Flat scales are the most effective.

The "double-bevel" scale, (*E*), in the shorter lengths is convenient as a pocket scale, but it can be had in lengths up to 24 in.

Practically all drafting scales of good quality were formerly made of boxwood, either plain or with white edges of celluloid. Although metal scales have been available for more than thirty years, they were seldom used until about 1935, when drafting machines equipped with metal scales made rather important gains in popularity. Extruded medium-hard aluminum alloys are the preferred metals. The Second World War brought a period of considerable experimentation with various types of plastic for all kinds of drafting scales. Up to the present time the white-edge scale has retained a large measure of its popularity. Another type of scale is now getting considerable attention, a metal scale with a white plastic coating that carries the graduations. Both magnesium and aluminum have been used successfully. These scales have all the reading advantages of a white-edge boxwood scale together with the stability afforded by metal.

Scales are made with various cross-sectional shapes, as shown in Fig. 2.9. The triangular form, (*A*) and (*B*), has long been favored because it carries six scales as a unit and is very stiff. However, many prefer the flat types as being easier to hold flat to a board and having a particular working scale more readily available. The "opposite-bevel" scale, (*C*) and (*D*), is easier to pick up than the "flat-bevel" scale, (*F*); moreover, it shows only one graduation at a time.

2.17. CURVES. Curved rulers, called "irregular curves" or "french curves," are used for curved lines other than circle arcs. The patterns for these curves

FIG. 2.10. Irregular curves. These are used for drawing curves where the radius of curvature is not constant.

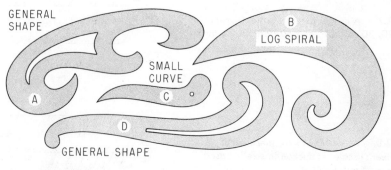

GENERAL SHAPE

B
LOG SPIRAL

SMALL CURVE

A   C   o

D

GENERAL SHAPE

DIVIDER   COMPASS, LENGTHENING BAR, PEN ATTACHMENT   BOW PEN, PENCIL AND DIVIDER   PEN

FIG. 2.11. The basic three-bow set. Large compass and dividers; bow pen, pencil, and dividers; ruling pen.

are laid out in parts of ellipses and spirals or other mathematical curves in various combinations. For the student, one ellipse curve of the general shape of Fig. 2.10*A* or *D* and one spiral, either a logarithmic spiral (*B*) or one similar to the one used in Fig. 2.60, is sufficient. (*C*) is a useful small curve.

2.18. THE "CASE" INSTRUMENTS.

We have so far, with the exception of curves, considered only the instruments (and materials) needed for drawing straight lines. A major portion of any drawing is likely to be circles and circle arcs, and the so-called "case" instruments are used for these. The basic instruments are shown in Fig. 2.11. At the left is a divider of the "hairspring" type (with a screw for fine adjustment), used for laying off or transferring measurements. Next is the large compass with lengthening bar and pen attachment. The three "bow" instruments are for smaller work. They are almost always made without the conversion feature (pencil to pen). The ruling pen, at the extreme right, is used for inking straight lines. A set of instruments of the type shown in Fig. 2.11 is known as a three-bow set.

Until recently the three-bow set was considered the standard, in design and number of pieces, for all ordinary drafting work. However, the trend now is for more rigid construction and fewer pieces. The 6-in. compass in Fig. 2.12 embraces practically a whole set in one instrument. Used as shown, the instrument is a pencil compass; with pencil replaced by pen, it is used to ink circles; with steel point installed in place of pencil point, it becomes a divider; the pen point, placed in the handle provided, makes a ruling pen; and there is a small metal container for steel points and lead. Similar instruments of other manufac-

PENCIL COMPASS

PEN HANDLE

PEN   LEADS, POINTS

FIG. 2.12. Large bow. It performs triple service as dividers, pen, and pencil compass. Pen leg in handle makes ruling pen.

BOW PENCIL

FAST-ACTION BOW

LARGE PENCIL COMPASS
WITH PEN AND
DIVIDER LEGS

FIG. 2.13. A very rugged bow.
Serves as dividers, or pen or
pencil compass.

FIG. 2.14. Three different designs of large bow
instruments. All are rigid and efficient.

DIVIDER
OR
COMPASS

PEN

ture are shown in Figs. 2.13 and 2.14. The instrument in the central part of Fig. 2.14 is a "quick-change" design (with vernier adjustment), a great convenience when changing from a very small setting to a large one.

Even though it is possible to find an instrument that serves practically all purposes, it is convenient to have several instruments, thus saving the time required to convert from pencil leg to ink leg or divider points. For this reason the newer more rigid instruments are also made as separate pieces in different sizes. Figure 2.15 shows the 6-in. dividers and large 6-in. bow compass; three 3-in. bow compasses, two with pencil and one with ink leg, which can also be used as dividers by changing attachments; and

pen points, which are used on the 6-in. compass or in a handle (not shown) to make a ruling pen.

The standard 6-in. compass will open to only approximately 5 in. The lengthening bar of the older-type compass (Fig. 2.11) will extend the radius to about 8 in. Lengthening bars for the newer spring-bow instruments are of the beam type. The instrument in Fig. 2.16 has a center point on the beam, thus employing the pencil and pen of the instrument itself, while the compass in Fig. 2.17 uses the center point of the instrument and separate pen and pencil attachments on the beam. A standard metal beam compass for drawing circles up to 16-in. radius is shown in Fig. 2.18.

Various ruling pens are shown in Fig.

DIVIDER   LARGE BOW

SMALL BOWS AND ATTACHMENTS

FIG. 2.15. A large- and small-bow set. Combines the advantages of both standard three-bow and large-bow designs.

BEAM

PENCIL   ADJUSTABLE POINT

FIG. 2.16. Extender for large bow. This type extends the range of its center point, with the pen or pencil on the bow.

FIG. 2.17. Extender for large bow. This type uses the center point of the bow and has its own pen and pencil attachments.

BEAM

POINT   PEN   PENCIL

BEAM

CONNECTOR   PEN

POINT   PENCIL

FIG. 2.18. A beam compass. This compass is adjustable for radii of 1 to 16 inches.

EXTENSION BEAM

2.19. (A) to (E) are standard types. Note that (D) uses the compass-pen leg in a handle. (F) is a contour pen, (G) is a border pen for wide lines, (H) and (I) are "railroad" pens for double lines, and (J) and (K) are border pens with large ink capacity.

All manufacturers supply instruments made up in sets, with leather or metal case. Figure 2.20 shows a standard three-bow combination and Fig. 2.21 a large-bow set with beam compass. The case in Fig. 2.22 is unique in that fillers may be removed to provide space for any combination of instruments desired at the time of purchase or for additions later.

2.19.   LETTERING DEVICES.   The Braddock-Rowe triangle and the Ames lettering instrument (Figs. 4.2A and B) are convenient devices used in drawing guide lines for lettering.

2.20.   CHECK LIST OF INSTRUMENTS AND MATERIALS.   Set of drawing instruments, including: 6-in. compass with fixed needle-point leg, removable pencil and pen legs, and lengthening bar; 6-in. hairspring dividers; 3½-in. bow pencil, bow pen, and bow dividers; two ruling pens; box of leads. Or large-bow set containing 6½-in. bow compass; 4½-in. bow compass; 6½-in. friction dividers and pen attachment for compass; 5½-in. ruling pen; beam compass with extension beam; box for extra leads and points

Drawing board
T square
45° and 30-60° triangles
Three mechanical engineer's scales, flat pattern, or the equivalent triangular scale
Lettering instrument or triangle
French curves
Drawing pencils, 6H, 4H, 2H, H, and F
Pocketknife or pencil sharpener
Pencil pointer (file or sandpaper)
Pencil eraser (Ruby)
Artgum or cleaning rubber
Penholder, pens for lettering, and penwiper
Bottle of drawing ink and bottleholder
Scotch drafting tape or thumbtacks
Drawing paper to suit
Tracing paper and cloth
Dustcloth or brush

To these may be added:

Civil engineer's scale
Protractor
Erasing shield
Slide rule
Six-foot steel tape
Clipboard or sketchbook
Hard Arkansas oiltone
Piece of soapstone
Cleaning powder or pad

FIG. 2.19.   Various ruling pens. Standard pens are all-purpose instruments. Special pens (F to K) are convenient and efficient for contours, double lines, and heavy lines.

CONTOUR PEN   BORDER PEN   RAILROAD PENS   BORDER PENS

STANDARD PENS

A   B   C   D   E   F   G   H   I   J   K

FIG. 2.20. A three-bow set, in case. It contains large dividers, large compass with extension bars and pen attachment, two ruling pens, bow pen, bow pencil, bow dividers, and bone center.

FIG. 2.21. A large-bow set, in case. It contains large- and small-bow compasses with attachments, dividers, ruling pen, and beam compass.

The student should mark all his instruments and materials plainly with his initials or name as soon as they have been purchased and approved.

2.21. ADDITIONAL INSTRUMENTS. The instruments and materials described in this chapter are all that are needed for ordinary practice and are, with the exception of such supplies as paper, pencils, ink, and erasers, what a draftsman is as a rule expected to take with him into a drafting room.

There are many other special instruments and devices that are not necessary in ordinary work but with which the draftsman should be familiar, as they may be convenient in special cases and are often found as a part of drafting-room equipment. Consult manufacturers' catalogues.

2.22. THE USE OF INSTRUMENTS. In beginning to use drawing instruments, it is important to learn to handle them cor-

FIG. 2.22. A special case. This case is adaptable to many combinations by removing fillers.

rectly. Carefully read the instructions and observe strictly all details of technique.

Facility will come with continued practice, but it is essential to adhere to good form from the outset. Bad form in drawing can be traced in every instance to the formation of bad habits in the early stages of learning. Once formed, these habits are difficult to overcome.

It is best to make a few drawings solely to become familiar with the handling and feel of the instruments so that later, in working a drawing problem, you will not lose time because of faulty manipulation. Practice accurate penciling first, and do not attempt inking until you have become really proficient in penciling. With practice, the correct, skillful use of drawing instruments will become a subconscious habit.

For competence in drawing, *accuracy* and *speed* are essential, and in commercial work neither is worth much without the other. It is well to learn as a beginner that a *good* drawing can be made as quickly as a *poor* one. Erasing is expensive and most of it can be avoided. The draftsman of course erases occasionally, and a student must learn to make corrections, but in beginning to use instruments, strive for sheets without blemish or inaccuracy.

2.23.   PREPARATION FOR DRAWING.   The drawing table should be set so that the light comes from the left, and it should be adjusted to a convenient height, that is, 36 to 40 in., for use while sitting on a standard drafting stool or while standing. There is more freedom in drawing standing, especially when working on large drawings. The board, for use in this manner, should be inclined at a slope of about 1 to 8. Since it is more

tiring to draw standing, many modern drafting rooms use tables so made that the board can be used in an almost vertical position and can be raised or lowered so that the draftsman can use a lower stool with swivel seat and backrest, thus working with comfort and even greater freedom than when an almost horizontal board is used.

The instruments should be placed within easy reach, on the table or on a special tray or stand beside the table. The table, board, and instruments should be wiped with a dustcloth before starting to draw.

2.24.   THE PENCIL AND ITS USE.   The grade of pencil must be selected carefully, with reference to the surface of the paper as well as to the line quality desired. For a pencil layout on detail paper of good texture, a pencil as hard as 5H or 6H may be used, while for finished pencil drawings on the same paper, 2H, 3H, or 4H pencils give the blacker line needed. For finished pencil drawings or tracings on vellum, softer pencils, H to 3H, are employed to get printable lines. The F pencil is much used for technical sketching, and the H is popular for lettering. In every case the pencil must be hard enough not to blur or smudge but not so hard as to cut grooves in the paper under reasonable pressure.

To sharpen a pencil, cut away the wood from the unlettered end with a penknife or mechanical sharpener, as shown in Fig. 2.23 *A,* and then sharpen the lead to make a long, conic point, as at (*B*), by twirling the pencil as the lead is rubbed with long even strokes against the sandpaper pad or file or placed in a special lead sharpener.

A flat or wedge point will not wear

REMOVE WOOD

MAKE POINT ON SANDPAPER
PAD OR FILE

A

B

C

WEDGE POINT FOR STRAIGHT LINES

FIG. 2.23. Sharpening the pencil. Wood is removed first, then the point is made with sandpaper or a file or special lead sharpener. For semiautomatic pencils, adjust the lead to the proper length and make the point with sandpaper or a file.

away in use so fast as a conic point, and on that account some prefer it for straight-line work. The long, wedge point illustrated at (*C*) is made by first sharpening, as at (*A*), then making the two long cuts on opposite sides, as shown, then flattening the lead on the sandpaper pad or file, and finishing by touching the corners to make the wedge point narrower than the diameter of the lead.

Have the sandpaper pad within easy reach, and *keep the pencils sharp*. Some hang the pad or file on a cord attached to the drawing table. The professional draftsman sharpens his pencil every few minutes. After sharpening the lead, wipe off excess graphite dust before using the pencil. Form the habit of sharpening the lead as often as you might dip a writing pen into the inkwell. Most commercial and many college drafting rooms are equipped with Dexter or other pencil sharpeners to save time.

Not only must pencil lines be clean and sharp, but for pencil drawings and tracings to be blueprinted, it is absolutely necessary that all the lines of each kind be uniform, firm, and opaque. This means a careful choice of pencils and the proper use of them. The attempt to make a dark line with too hard a pencil results in cutting deep grooves in the paper. Hold the pencil firmly, yet with

as much ease and freedom as possible.

Keep an even constant pressure on the pencil, and when using a conic point, rotate the pencil as the line is drawn so as to keep both the line and pencil sharp. Use a draftsman's brush or soft cloth occasionally to dust off excess graphite from the drawing.

Too much emphasis cannot be given to the importance of clean, careful, accurate penciling. Never entertain the thought that poor penciling can be corrected in tracing.

2.25. PLACING THE PAPER. Since the T-square blade is more rigid near the head than toward the outer end, the paper, if much smaller than the size of the board, should be placed close to the left edge of the board (within an inch or so) with its lower edge several inches from the bottom of the board. With the T square against the left edge of the board, square the top of the paper; hold it in this position, slipping the T square down from the edge, and put a thumbtack in each upper corner, pushing it in up to the head so that the head aids in holding the paper. Then move the T square down over the paper to smooth out possible wrinkles, and put thumbtacks in the other two corners. Drafting tape may be used instead of thumbtacks.

SLIDE TO POSITION

ADJUST CAREFULLY

HOLD IN POSITION
AS LINE IS DRAWN

FIG. 2.24. Manipulating the T square. The head must be firmly against the straight left edge of the board.

2.26. USE OF THE T SQUARE. The T square and the triangles have straight edges and are used for drawing straight lines. Horizontal lines are drawn with the T square, which is used with its head against the left edge of the drawing board and manipulated as follows: Holding the head of the tool, as shown in Fig. 2.24A, slide it along the edge of the board to a spot very near the position desired. Then, for closer adjustment, change your hold either to that shown at (*B*), in which the thumb remains on top of the T-square head and the other fingers press against the underside of the board, or, as is more usual, to that shown at (*C*), in which the fingers remain on the T square and the thumb is placed on the board.

Figure 2.25 shows the position of the hand and pencil for drawing horizontal lines. Note that the pencil is inclined in the direction the line is drawn, that is, toward the right, and also slightly away from the body so that the pencil point is as close as possible to the T-square blade.

In drawing lines, take great care to keep them accurately parallel to the guiding edge of the T square. The pencil should be held lightly, but close against the edge, and the angle should not vary during the progress of the line. Horizontal lines should always be drawn from left to right. A T-square blade can be tested for straightness by drawing a sharp line through two points and then turning the square over and with the same edge drawing another line through the points, as shown in Fig. 2.26.

2.27. USE OF THE TRIANGLES. Vertical lines are drawn with the triangle, which is set against the T square with the perpendicular edge nearest the head of the square and thus toward the light (Fig. 2.27). These lines are always drawn upward, from bottom to top.

In drawing vertical lines, the T square is held in position against the left edge of the board by the thumb and little finger of the left hand while the other fingers of this hand adjust and hold the triangle. You can be sure that the T square is in contact with the board when you hear the little double click as the two come together, and slight pressure of the thumb and little finger toward the right will maintain the position. As the line is drawn, pressure of all the fingers against the board will hold the T square and triangle firmly in position.

As in using the T square, care must be taken to keep the line accurately parallel

FIG. 2.25. Drawing a horizontal line. Hold the T square with the left hand; draw the line from left to right; incline the pencil in the direction of stroke, so that the pencil "slides" over the paper.

FIG. 2.26. To test a T square. Turn the T square upside down; draw the line; turn it right side up and align it with the original line; draw the second line and compare it with the first.

FIG. 2.27. Drawing a vertical line. With the T square and triangle in position, draw the line from bottom to top —always away from the body.

to the guiding edge. Note the position of the pencil in Fig. 2.27.

In both penciling and inking, the triangles must always be used in contact with a guiding straightedge. To ensure accuracy, never work to the extreme corner of a triangle; to avoid having to do so, keep the T square below the lower end of the line to be drawn.

With the T square against the edge of the board, lines at 45° are drawn with the standard 45° triangle, and lines at 30° and 60° with the 30-60° triangle, as shown in Fig. 2.28. With vertical and horizontal lines included, lines at increments of 45° are drawn with the 45° triangle as at (*B*), and lines at 30° increments with the 30-60° triangle as at (*A*). The two triangles are used in combination for angles of 15, 75, 105°, etc. (Fig.

FIG. 2.28. To draw angles of 30°, 45°, 60°. Multiples of 30° are drawn with the 30-60° triangle, multiples of 45° with the 45° triangle.

FIG. 2.29. To draw angles of 15° and 75°. Angles in increments of 15° are obtained with the two triangles in combination.

FIG. 2.30. To draw parallel lines. With the T square as a base, the triangle is aligned and then moved to the required position.

2.29). Thus any multiple of 15° is drawn directly; and a circle is divided with the 45° triangle into 8 parts, with the 30-60° triangle into 12 parts, and with both into 24 parts.

To Draw One Line Parallel to Another (Fig. 2.30). Adjust to the given line a triangle held against a straightedge, hold the guiding edge in position, and slide the triangle on it to the required position.

To Draw a Perpendicular to Any Line (Fig. 2.31). Place a triangle with one edge against the T square (or another triangle), and move the two until the hypotenuse of the triangle is coincident with the line, as at (*A*); hold the T square in position and turn the triangle,

FIG. 2.31. To draw perpendicular lines. With the T square as a base and the triangle in position *A*, the triangle is aligned, then rotated and moved to perpendicular position; for position *B*, the triangle is only moved.

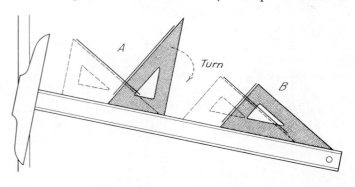

as shown, until its other side is against the T square; the hypotenuse will then be perpendicular to the original line. Move the triangle to the required position. A quicker method is to set the triangle with its hypotenuse against the guiding edge, fit one side to the line, slide the triangle to the required point, and draw the perpendicular, as shown at (*B*).

Never attempt to draw a perpendicular to a line with only one triangle by placing one leg of the triangle along the line.

Through internal strains, triangles sometimes lose their accuracy. They may be tested by drawing a perpendicular and then reversing the triangle, as shown in Fig. 2.32.

2.28. THE LEFT-HANDED DRAFTSMAN. If you are left-handed, reverse the T square and triangles left for right as compared with the regular right-handed position. Use the head of the T square along the right edge of the board, and draw horizontal lines from right to left. Place the triangle with its vertical edge to the right, and draw vertical lines from bottom to top. The drawing table should be placed with the light coming from the right.

2.29. USE OF THE SCALE. Scale technique is governed largely by the requirements of accuracy and speed. Before a line can be drawn, its relative position must be found by scaling, and the speed with which scale measurement can be made will greatly affect the total drawing time.

Precise layouts and developments, made to scale for the workmen, must be very accurately drawn, at the expense of speed; conversely, drawings with figured dimensions need not be quite so carefully scaled, and better speed may be attained.

To make a measurement, place the scale on the drawing where the distance is to be laid off, align the scale in the direction of the measurement, and make a *light* short dash with a sharp pencil at the proper graduation mark (Fig. 2.33). In layout work where extreme accuracy is required, a "pricker," or needle point set in a wood handle, may be substituted for the pencil, and a *small* hole pricked into the paper in place of the pencil mark. It is best to start with the "zero" of the scale when setting off lengths or when measuring distances. In using an

open-divided scale, inches (or fractions) are accounted for in one direction from the zero graduation while feet (or units) are recorded in the opposite direction.

Measurements should not be made on a drawing by taking distances off the scale with dividers, as this method is time-consuming and not more accurate than the regular methods.

To avoid cumulative errors, successive measurements on the same line should, if possible, be made without shifting the scale. In representing objects that are larger than can be drawn to their natural or full size, it is necessary to reduce the size of the drawing in some regular proportion, and for this purpose one of the standard mechanical engineer's, civil engineer's, or architect's scales is used. Standard scales are given in Fig. 2.34.

The first reduction is to *half size,* or to the scale of 6″ = 1′-0″. In other words, ½ in. on the drawing represents a distance of 1 in. on the object. Stated in terms used for the architect's scales, a

FIG. 2.32. To test a triangle for right angle. Draw a line with the triangle in each position; twice the error is produced.

FIG. 2.33. Making a measurement. Place the scale in position; the distance is marked on paper by short, light *lines.*

SCALES

MECHANICAL ENGINEER'S

1″ = 1″ (full size)	½″ = 1″ (½ size)
¼″ = 1″ (¼ size)	⅛″ = 1″ (⅛ size)

ARCHITECT'S OR MECHANICAL ENGINEER'S

12″ = 1′-0″ (full size)	1″ = 1′-0″ (1/12 size)	¼″ = 1′-0″ (1/48 size)
6″ = 1′-0″ (½ size)	¾″ = 1′-0″ (1/16 size)	3/16″ = 1′-0″ (1/64 size)
3″ = 1′-0″ (¼ size)	½″ = 1′-0″ (1/24 size)	⅛″ = 1′-0″ (1/96 size)
1½″ = 1′-0″ (⅛ size)	⅜″ = 1′-0″ (1/32 size)	3/32″ = 1′-0″ (1/128 size)

CIVIL ENGINEER'S

10, 20, 30, 40, 50, 60, or 80 divisions to the inch representing feet, 10 ft, 100 ft, rods, miles, or any other necessary unit

FIG. 2.34. Standard scales. Special scales are available. See manufacturers' catalogues.

distance of 6 in. on the drawing represents 1 ft on the object. This scale is used even if the object is only slightly larger than could be drawn full size. If this reduction is not sufficient, the drawing is made to *quarter size,* or to the scale of $3'' = 1'\text{-}0''$. If the quarter-size scale is too large, the next reduction is *eighth size,* or $1\frac{1}{2}'' = 1'\text{-}0''$, the smallest proportion usually supplied on standard mechanical engineer's scales, but the architect's scales are used down to $\frac{3}{32}'' = 1'\text{-}0''$, as shown by the listings in Fig. 2.34.

In stating the scale used on a drawing, the information should be given in accordance with the scale used to make the drawing. If a standard mechanical engineer's scale is employed, the statement may read that the scale is (1) *full size,* (2) *half size,* (3) *quarter size,* or (4) *eighth size.* These scales may also be given as (1) $1'' = 1''$, (2) $\frac{1}{2}'' = 1''$, (3) $\frac{1}{4}'' = 1''$, or (4) $\frac{1}{8}'' = 1''$. If a standard architect's scale is used, the statement is given in terms of inches to the foot. Examples are (1) $3'' = 1'\text{-}0''$, (2) $1\frac{1}{2}'' = 1'\text{-}0''$, or (3) $1'' = 1'\text{-}0''$. In stating the scale, the first figure always refers to the drawing and the second to the object. Thus $3'' = 1'\text{-}0''$ means that 3 in. on the *drawing* represents 1 ft on the *object.*

Drawings to odd proportions, such as $9'' = 1'\text{-}0''$, $4'' = 1'\text{-}0''$, $5'' = 1'\text{-}0''$, are used only in rare cases when drawings are made for reduction and the conditions of size demand a special scale.

The terms "scale" and "size" have different meanings: The scale $\frac{1}{4}'' = 1'\text{-}0''$ is the usual one for ordinary house plans and is often called by architects the "quarter scale." This term should not be confused with the term "quarter size," as the former means $\frac{1}{4}$ in. to 1 ft and the latter $\frac{1}{4}$ in. to 1 in.

The size of a circle is generally stated by giving its diameter, while to draw it the radius is necessary. Two scales are usually supplied together on the same body, for example, half and quarter size. Therefore, in drawing to half size, it is often convenient to lay off the amount of the diameter with the quarter-size scale and use this distance as the radius.

Small pieces are often made "double size," and very small mechanisms, such as watch parts, are drawn to greatly enlarged sizes: 10 to 1, 20 to 1, 40 to 1, and 50 to 1, using special enlarging scales.

For plotting and map drawing, the civil engineer's scales of decimal parts, with 10, 20, 30, 40, 50, 60, and 80 divisions to the inch, are used. These scales are not used for machine or structural work but in certain aircraft drawings.

The important thing in drawing to scale is to think and speak of each dimension in its full size and not in the reduced (or enlarged) size it happens to be on the paper. This practice prevents confusion between *actual* and *represented* size.

2.30. READING THE SCALE. Reading the standard mechanical engineer's scales is rather simple, because the scale is plainly marked in inches, and the smaller graduations are easily recognized as the regular divisions of the inch into $\frac{1}{2}$, $\frac{1}{4}$, $\frac{1}{8}$, and $\frac{1}{16}$. Thus the scales for half size, quarter size, and eighth size are employed in exactly the same manner as a full-size scale.

The architect's scales, being open divided and to stated reductions, such as $3'' = 1'\text{-}0''$, may require some study by the beginner in order to prevent confusion and mistakes. As an example, consider the scale of 3″ = 1′-0″. This is the first reduction scale of the usual triangular scale; on it the distance of 3 in. is divided into 12 equal parts, and each of these is subdivided into eighths. This distance should be thought of not as 3 in. but as a foot divided into inches and eighths of an inch. Notice that the divisions start with the *zero* on the inside, the inches of the divided foot running to the *left* and the open divisions of feet to the *right,* so that dimensions given in feet and in inches may be read directly, as 1′-0½″ (Fig. 2.35). On the other end will be found the scale of 1½″ = 1′-0″, or eighth size, with the distance of 1½ in. divided on the right of the zero into 12 parts and subdivided into quarter inches, with the foot divisions to the left of the zero coinciding with the marks of the 3-in. scale. Note again that in reading a distance in feet and inches, for example, the 2′-7⅛″ distance in Fig. 2.35, feet are determined to the left of the zero and inches to the right of it. The other scales, such as ¾″ = 1′-0″ and ¼″ = 1′-0″, are divided in a similar way, the only difference being in the value of the smallest graduations. The scale of ³⁄₃₂″ = 1′-0″, for example, can be read only to the nearest 2 in.

2.31. "LAYING OUT" THE SHEET. The paper is usually cut somewhat larger than the desired size of the drawing and trimmed to size after the work is finished. Suppose the finished size is to be 11 by 17 in. with a ½-in. border inside. Lay the scale down on the paper close to the lower edge and measure 17 in., marking the distance with the pencil; at the same time mark ½ in. inside at each end for the border line. Use a short dash forming a continuation of the division line on the scale in laying off a dimension. Do not bore a hole with the pencil. Near the left edge mark 11- and ½-in. borderline points. Through these four marks on the left edge, draw horizontal lines with the T square; and through the points on the lower edge, draw vertical lines, using the triangle against the T square.

2.32. USE OF DIVIDERS. Dividers are used for transferring measurements and for dividing lines into any number of equal parts. Facility in their use is essential, and quick and absolute control of their manipulation must be gained. The instrument should be opened with one hand by pinching the chamfer with the thumb and second finger. This will throw it into correct position with the thumb and forefinger outside the legs and the second and third fingers inside, with the head resting just above the second joint of the forefinger (Fig. 2.36). It is thus under perfect control, with the

FIG. 2.36. Handling the dividers. The instrument is opened and adjusted with one hand.

FIG. 2.37. Bisecting a line. Half is estimated; then the dividers are readjusted by estimating half the original error.

FIG. 2.38. Adjusting the needle point of a large compass. The point is adjusted to the pen; the pen is then replaced by the pencil leg and the pencil adjusted to the point.

FIG. 2.39. Adjusting the pencil lead. The length is adjusted so that the instrument will be vertically centered.

thumb and forefinger to close it and the other two to open it. Practice this motion until you can adjust the dividers to the smallest fraction. In coming down to small divisions, the second and third fingers must be gradually slipped out from between the legs as they are closed down upon them. Notice that the little finger is not used in manipulating the dividers.

2.33. TO DIVIDE A LINE BY TRIAL. In bisecting a line, the dividers are opened at a guess to roughly half the length. This distance is stepped off on the line, holding the instrument by the handle with the thumb and forefinger. If the division is short, the leg should be thrown out to half the remainder (estimated by eye), without removing the other leg from the paper, and the line spaced again with this new setting (Fig. 2.37). If the result does not come out exactly, the operation can be repeated. With a little experience, a line can be divided rapidly in this way. Similarly, a line, either straight or curved, can be divided into any number of equal parts, say, five, by estimating the first division, stepping this lightly along the line, with the dividers held vertically by the handle, turning the instrument first in one direction and then in the other. If the last division falls

short, one-fifth of the remainder should be added by opening the dividers, keeping one point on the paper. If the last division is over, one-fifth of the excess should be taken off and the line respaced. If it is found difficult to make this small adjustment accurately with the fingers, the hairspring may be used. You will find the bow spacers more convenient than the dividers for small or numerous divisions. Avoid pricking unsightly holes in the paper. The position of a small prick point may be preserved, if necessary, by drawing a small circle around it with the pencil.

2.34. USE OF THE COMPASSES. The compasses have the same general shape as the dividers and are manipulated in a similar way. First of all, the needle should be permanently adjusted. Insert the pen in place of the pencil leg, turn the needle with the shoulder point out, and set it a trifle longer than the pen, as in Fig. 2.38; replace the pencil leg, sharpen the lead to a long bevel, as in Fig. 2.39, and adjust it to the needle point. All this is done so that the needle point will be in perfect position for using the pen; the pencil, which must be sharpened frequently, can be adjusted each time to mate in length with the needle point.

To Draw a Circle. Set the compass on

FIG. 2.40. Setting the compass to radius size. Speed and accuracy are obtained by adjusting directly on the scale.

FIG. 2.41. Guiding the needle point. For accuracy of placement, guide with the little finger.

FIG. 2.42. Starting a circle. The compass is inclined in the direction of the stroke.

FIG. 2.43. Completing a circle. The stroke is completed by twisting the knurled handle in the fingers.

FIG. 2.44. Drawing a large circle. Knuckle joints are bent to make the legs perpendicular to the paper.

FIG. 2.45. Use of the lengthening bar. The joints must be bent to bring the legs perpendicular. Usually two hands are used because the handle is off center.

the scale, as shown in Fig. 2.40, and adjust it to the radius needed; then place the needle point at the center on the drawing, guiding it with the left hand (Fig. 2.41). Raise the fingers to the handle and draw the circle in one sweep, rolling the handle with the thumb and forefinger, inclining the compass slightly in the direction of the line (Fig. 2.42).

The position of the fingers after the rotation is shown in Fig. 2.43. The pencil line can be brightened, if necessary, by making additional turns. Circles up to perhaps 3 in. in diameter can be drawn with the legs of the compass straight, but for larger sizes, both the needle-point leg and the pencil or pen leg should be bent at the knuckle joints so as to be perpendicular to the paper (Fig. 2.44).

The 6-in. compass may be used in this way for circles up to perhaps 10 in. in diameter; larger circles are made by using the lengthening bar, as illustrated in Fig. 2.45, or the beam compass (Fig. 2.18). In drawing concentric circles, the *smallest* should always be drawn first, before the center hole has become worn.

The bow instruments are used for small circles, particularly when a number are to be made of the same diameter. To avoid wear (on side-wheel instruments), the pressure of the spring against the nut can be relieved in changing the setting by holding the points in the left hand and spinning the nut in or out with the finger. Small adjustments should be made with one hand with the needle point in position on the paper (Fig. 2.46).

FIG. 2.46. Adjusting a bow instrument. One hand only is needed. Center-wheel bows are held similarly.

FIG. 2.47. Correct shape of pen nibs. A nicely uniform elliptical shape is best.

FIG. 2.48. Incorrect shape of pen nibs. This point is much too sharp. Ink will not flow well.

FIG. 2.49. Incorrect shape of pen nibs. This point is too flat. Ink will blob at the beginning and end of the line.

FIG. 2.50. Shape of worn pen nibs. This point needs sharpening to the shape of Fig. 2.47.

When several concentric circles are drawn, time may be saved by marking off the several radii on the paper from the scale and then setting the compass to each mark as the circles are made. In some cases it may be advantageous to measure and mark the radius on the paper instead of setting the compass directly on the scale. This method must be used whenever the radius is greater than the length of the scale.

When *extreme accuracy* is required, the compass is set, a light circle is drawn on the paper, and the diameter is checked with the scale; if the size is not satisfactory, the compass is adjusted and the operation is repeated until the size needed is obtained.

2.35.   THE RULING PEN.   The ruling pen is for inking straight lines and noncircular curves. Several types are illustrated in Fig. 2.19. The important feature is the shape of the blades; they should have a well-designed ink space between them, and their points should be rounded (actually elliptical in form) equally, as in Fig. 2.47. If pointed, as in Fig. 2.48, the ink will arch up as shown and will be provokingly hard to start. If rounded to a blunt point, as in Fig. 2.49, the ink will flow too freely, forming blobs and overruns at the ends of the lines. Pens in constant use become dull and worn, as illustrated in Fig. 2.50. It is easy to tell whether a pen is dull by looking for the reflection of light that travels from the side and over the end of the point when the pen is turned in the hand. If the reflection can be seen all the way, the pen is too dull. A pen in poor condition is an abomination, but a well-sharpened one is a delight to use. Every draftsman should be able to keep his pens in fine condition.

High-grade pens usually come from the makers well sharpened. Cheaper ones often need sharpening before they can be used.

2.36.   TO SHARPEN A PEN.   The best stone for the purpose is a hard Arkansas knife piece. It is well to soak a new stone in oil for several days before using. The ordinary carpenter's oilstone is too coarse for drawing instruments.

The nibs must first be brought to the correct shape, as in Fig. 2.47. Screw the nibs together until they touch and, holding the pen as in drawing a line, draw it back and forth on the stone, starting the stroke with the handle at 30° or less with the stone and swinging it up past the perpendicular as the line across the stone progresses. This will bring the nibs to exactly the same shape and length, leaving them very dull. Then open them slightly, and sharpen each blade in turn, on the outside only, until the bright spot on the end has just disappeared. Hold the pen, as in Fig. 2.51, at a small angle with the stone and rub it back and forth with a slight oscillating or rocking motion to conform to the shape of the blade. A stone 3 or 4 in. long held in the left hand with the thumb and fingers gives better control than one laid on the table. Silicon carbide cloth or paper can be substituted for the stone, and for a fine job, crocus cloth may be used for finishing. A pocket magnifying glass may be helpful in examining the points. The blades should not be sharp enough to cut the paper when tested by drawing a line across it without ink. If oversharpened, the blades should again be brought to touch and a line swung very lightly across the stone as in the first operation. When tested with ink, the pen should be capable of drawing clean sharp lines down to the finest hairline. If these finest lines are ragged or broken, the pen is not

FIG. 2.51. Sharpening a pen. After bringing the point to the shape of Fig. 2.47, work down the sides by a rocking motion to conform to blade contour.

FIG. 2.52. Correct position of ruling pen. The pen is inclined in the direction of the stroke but held perpendicular to the paper, as in Fig. 2.53.

perfectly sharpened. It should not be necessary to touch the inside of the blades unless a burr has been formed, which might occur if the metal is very soft, the stone too coarse, or the pressure too heavy. To remove such a burr, or wire edge, draw a strip of detail paper between the nibs, or open the pen wide and lay the entire inner surface of the blade flat on the stone and move it with a very light touch.

2.37. USE OF THE RULING PEN. The ruling pen is always used in connection with a guiding edge—T square, triangle, or curve. The T square and triangle should be held in the same positions as for penciling.

To fill the pen, take it to the bottle and touch the quill filler between the nibs. Be careful not to get any ink on the outside of the blades. If the newer plastic squeeze bottle is used, place the small spout against the sides of the nibs and carefully squeeze a drop of ink *between* the nibs. Not more than ¾₆ to ¼ in. of ink should be put in; otherwise the weight of the ink will cause it to drop out in a blot. The pen should be held in the fingertips, as illustrated in Fig. 2.52, with the thumb and second finger against the sides of the nibs and the handle rest-ing on the forefinger. Observe this hold carefully, as the tendency will be to bend the second finger to the position used when a pencil or writing pen is held. The position illustrated aids in keeping the pen at the proper angle and the nibs aligned with the ruling edge.

The pen should be held against the straightedge or guide with the blades parallel to it, the screw on the outside and the handle inclined slightly to the right and always kept in a plane passing through the line and perpendicular to the paper. The pen is thus directed by the upper edge of the guide, as illustrated in actual size in Fig. 2.53. If the pen point is thrown out from the perpendicular, it will run on one blade and make a line that is ragged on one side. If the pen is turned in from the perpendicular, the ink is likely to run under the edge of the guide and cause a blot.

A line is drawn with a steady, even arm movement, the tips of the third and fourth fingers resting on, and sliding along, the straightedge, keeping the angle of inclination constant. Just before the end of the line is reached, the two guiding fingers on the straightedge should be stopped and, without stopping the motion of the pen, the line finished with a finger movement. Short lines are

FIG. 2.53. Correct pen position. Even though the pen is inclined in the direction of the stroke, both nibs must touch the paper equally.

FIG. 2.54. Inking over a pencil line. The line must be *centered* over the original layout line.

FIG. 2.55. Correct and incorrect tangents. Lines must be the width of one line at tangent point.

FIG. 2.56. The alphabet of lines for pencil drawings.

drawn with this finger movement alone. When the end of the line is reached, the pen is lifted quickly and the straightedge moved away from the line. The pressure on the paper should be light but sufficient to give a clean-cut line, and it will vary with the kind of paper and the sharpness of the pen. The pressure against the T square, however, should be only enough to guide the direction.

If the ink refuses to flow, it may be because it has dried in the extreme point of the pen. If pinching the blades slightly or touching the pen on the finger does not start it, the pen should immediately be wiped out and fresh ink supplied.

Pens must be wiped clean after using.

In inking on either paper or cloth, the full lines will be much wider than the pencil lines. You must be careful to have the center of the ink line cover the pencil line, as illustrated in Fig. 2.54.

Instructions in regard to the ruling pen apply also to the compass. The compass should be slightly inclined in the direction of the line and both nibs of the pen kept on the paper, bending the knuckle joints, if necessary, to effect this.

It is a universal rule in inking that *circles and circle arcs must be inked first.* It is much easier to connect a straight line

FINISHED PENCIL DRAWING OR TRACING

VISIBLE OUTLINE (FULL LINE)

HIDDEN OUTLINE (DASHED LINE)

CENTER LINE

EXTENSION LINE

DIMENSION LINE

CUTTING PLANE

SECTION LINING

ADJACENT PARTS, ALTERNATE POSITION OR REPEAT LINE

SHORT BREAK

LONG BREAK

to a curve than a curve to a straight line.

2.38.   **TANGENTS.**   It should be noted particularly that two lines are tangent to each other when the center lines of the lines are tangent and not simply when the lines touch each other; thus at the point of tangency, the width will be equal to the width of a single line (Fig. 2.55). Before inking tangent lines, the point of tangency should be marked in pencil. For an arc tangent to a straight line, this point will be on a line through the center of the arc and perpendicular to the straight line, and for two circle arcs it will be on the line joining their

centers, as described in paragraphs 3.5 to 3.16.

2.39.   **THE "ALPHABET OF LINES."**   As the basis of drawing is the line, a set of conventional symbols covering all the lines needed for different purposes may properly be called an alphabet of lines. Figures 2.56 and 2.57 show the alphabet of lines adopted by the ASA as applied to the following:

1. Drawings made directly or traced in pencil on tracing paper or pencil cloth, from which blueprints or other reproductions are to be made (Fig. 2.56).

2. Tracings in ink on tracing cloth or

FIG. 2.57.   The alphabet of lines for inked drawings.

INKED   DRAWING   OR   TRACING

VISIBLE OUTLINE (FULL LINE)

HIDDEN OUTLINE (DASHED LINE)

CENTER LINE

EXTENSION LINE

DIMENSION LINE

CUTTING PLANE

SECTION LINING

ADJACENT PARTS, ALTERNATE POSITION OR REPEAT LINE

SHORT BREAK

LONG BREAK

1-250 TH (.004) INCH

1-200 TH (.005)

1-150 TH (.0067)

1-100 TH (.010)

1-80 TH (.0125)

1-60 TH (.0167)

1-50 TH (.020)

1-40 TH (.025)

1-30 TH (.033)

1-20 TH (.050)

1-16 TH (.0625)

FIG. 2.58. Line gage. Draw a line on the paper to be used and apply it here to determine the width.

FIG. 2.59. Faulty ink lines. The difficulty is indicated in each case.

tracing paper and inked drawings on white paper for display or photoreproductions (Fig. 2.57).

The ASA recommends three widths of lines for finished drawings: *thick* for visible outlines and cutting-plane and short-break lines; *medium* for hidden outlines; and *thin* for section, center, extension, dimension, long-break, adjacent-part, alternate-position, and repeat lines. The actual widths of the three weights of lines, on average drawings, should be about as in Figs. 2.56 and 2.57. A convenient line gage is given in Fig. 2.58. If applied to Fig. 2.57, this gage would show the heavy lines in ink to be between $\frac{1}{30}$ and $\frac{1}{40}$ in., the medium lines $\frac{1}{60}$ in., and the fine lines $\frac{1}{100}$ in. in width. To use the line gage, draw a line about 1½ in. long in pencil or ink on a piece of the drawing paper and apply it alongside the gage. By this method a good comparison can be made. Note that the standard lines for pencil drawings are somewhat thinner than for inked drawings, the thick line being about $\frac{1}{60}$ in., medium about $\frac{1}{80}$ in. and thin between $\frac{1}{100}$ and $\frac{1}{150}$ in. Study Figs. 2.56 and 2.57 carefully and try to make your drawings conform to these standard lines. Professional appearance depends to a great extent upon the line weights used. Line widths for layout drawings are *thin* throughout because the watchword here is accuracy. Layout drawings are often traced in pencil or ink to the weights given in Figs. 2.56 and 2.57 and are then *finished* drawings.

2.40. LINE PRACTICE. After reading the preceding paragraphs, take a blank sheet of paper and practice making straight lines and circles in all the forms —full, dashed, etc.—shown in Figs. 2.56 and 2.57. Include starting and stopping lines, with special attention to tangents and corners.

In pencil, try to get all the lines uniform in width and color for each type. Circle arcs and straight lines should match exactly at tangent points.

In ink, proceed as for pencil practice and pay particular attention to the weight of lines and to the spacing of dashed lines and center lines.

If the inked lines appear imperfect in any way, ascertain the reason immediately. It may be the fault of the pen, the ink, the paper, or the draftsman; the probabilities are greatly in favor of the last if the faults resemble those in Fig. 2.59, which illustrates the characteristic appearance of several kinds of poor line. The correction in each case will suggest itself.

2.41. USE OF THE FRENCH CURVE. The french curve is a guiding edge for noncircular curves. When sufficient points have been determined, it is best to sketch in the line lightly in pencil, freehand and without losing the points, until it is clean, smooth, continuous, and satisfactory to the eye. Then apply the curve to

Pen pressed against T square too hard

Pen sloped away from T square

Pen too close to edge, ink ran under

Ink on outside of blade, ran under

Pen blades not kept parallel to T square

T square (or triangle) slipped into wet line

Not enough ink to finish line

it, selecting a part that will fit a portion of the line most nearly and seeing to it, particularly, that the curve is so placed that the direction in which its curvature increases is the direction in which the curvature of the line increases (Fig. 2.60). In drawing the part of the line matched by the curve, *always* stop a little short of the distance in which the guide and the line seem to coincide. After drawing this portion, shift the curve to find another place that will coincide with the continuation of the line. In shifting the curve, take care to preserve smoothness and continuity and to avoid breaks or cusps. Do this by seeing that in its successive positions the curve is always adjusted so that it coincides for a short distance with the part of the line already drawn. Thus at each junction the tangents will coincide.

If the curved line is symmetrical about an axis, marks locating this axis, after it has been matched accurately on one side, may be made in pencil on the curve and the curve then reversed. In such a case take exceptional care to avoid a "hump" at the joint.

It is often better to stop a line short of the axis on each side and close the gap afterward with another setting of the curve.

When using the curve in inking, the pen should be held perpendicular and the blades kept parallel to the edge. The inking of curves is excellent practice.

Sometimes, particularly at sharp turns, a combination of circle arcs and curves may be used: In inking a long, narrow ellipse, for example, the sharp curves may be inked by selecting a center on the major diameter by trial, drawing as much arc as will practically coincide with the ends of the ellipse, and then finishing the ellipse with the curve.

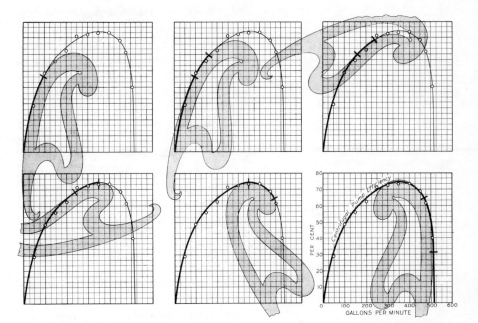

The experienced draftsman will sometimes ink a curve that cannot be matched accurately by varying the distance of the pen point from the ruling edge as the line progresses.

2.42. ERASING. The erasing of pencil lines and ink lines is a necessary technique to learn. When changing some detail, a designer, working freely but lightly, uses a soft pencil eraser so as not to damage the finish of the paper. Heavier lines are best removed with a Ruby pencil eraser. If the paper has been grooved by the line, it may be rubbed over with a burnisher or even with the back of the thumbnail. In erasing an ink line, hold the paper down firmly and rub lightly and patiently, with a Ruby pencil eraser, first along the line and then across it, until the ink is removed. A triangle slipped under the paper or cloth gives a good backing surface.

When an erasure is made close to

FIG. 2.60. Use of the french curve. The changing curvature of line and curve must match.

other lines, select an opening of the best shape on the erasing shield (Fig. 2.3*D*) and rub through it, holding the shield down firmly, first seeing that both of its sides are clean. Wipe the eraser crumbs off the paper with a dustcloth or brush. Never scratch out a line or blot with a knife or razor blade, and use so-called ink erasers sparingly, if at all. A skilled draftsman sometimes uses a sharp blade to trim a thickened spot or overrunning end on a line.

For extensive erasing, an electric erasing machine is a great convenience. Several successful models are on the market.

2.43. CAUTIONS IN THE USE OF INSTRUMENTS.   To complete this discussion of instruments, here are a few points worth noting:

NEVER use the scale as a ruler for drawing lines.

NEVER draw horizontal lines with the lower edge of the T square.

NEVER use the lower edge of the T square as a horizontal base for the triangles.

NEVER cut paper with a knife and the edge of the T square as a guide.

NEVER use the T square as a hammer.

NEVER put either end of a pencil into the mouth.

NEVER work with a dull pencil.

NEVER sharpen a pencil over the drawing board.

NEVER jab the dividers into the drawing board.

NEVER oil the joints of compasses.

NEVER use the dividers as reamers, pincers, or picks.

NEVER use a blotter on inked lines.

NEVER screw the pen adjustment past the contact point of the nibs.

NEVER leave the ink bottle uncorked.

NEVER hold the pen over the drawing while filling.

NEVER put into the drawing-ink bottle a writing pen that has been used in ordinary writing ink.

NEVER try to use the same thumbtack holes in either paper or board when putting paper down a second time.

NEVER scrub a drawing all over with an eraser after finishing. It takes the life out of the lines.

NEVER begin work without wiping off the table and instruments.

NEVER put instruments away without cleaning them. This applies with particular force to pens.

NEVER put bow instruments away without opening to relieve the spring.

NEVER work on a table cluttered with unneeded instruments or equipment.

NEVER fold a drawing or tracing.

2.44. EXERCISES IN THE USE OF INSTRUMENTS.   The following problems can be used as progressive exercises for practice in using the instruments. Do them as finished pencil drawings or in pencil layout to be inked. Line work should conform to that given in the alphabet of lines (Figs. 2.56 and 2.57).

The problems in Chap. 3 afford excellent additional practice in accurate penciling.

PROBLEMS

GROUP 1. STRAIGHT LINES

2.1.1. An exercise for the T square, triangle, and scale. Through the center of the space draw a horizontal and a vertical line. Measuring on these lines as diameters, lay off a 4-in. square. Along the lower side and upper half of the left side measure ½-in. spaces with the scale. Draw all horizontal lines with the T square and all vertical lines with the T square and triangle.

2.1.2. An interlacement. For T square, triangle, and dividers. Draw a 4-in. square. Divide the left side and lower side into seven equal parts with dividers. Draw horizontal and vertical lines across the square through these points. Erase the parts not needed.

2.1.3. A street-paving intersection. For 45° triangle and scale. An exercise in starting and stopping short lines. Draw a 4-in. square. Draw its diagonals with 45° triangle. With the scale, lay off ½-in. spaces along the diagonals from their intersection. With 45° triangle, complete the figure, finishing one quarter at a time.

2.1.4. A square pattern. For 45° triangle, dividers, and scale. Draw a 4-in. square and divide its sides into three equal parts with

dividers. With 45° triangle, draw diagonal lines connecting these points. Measure ⅜ in. on each side of these lines, and finish the pattern as shown.

2.1.5. An acoustic pattern. For 45° triangle, T square, and scale. Draw two intersecting 45° diagonals 4 in. long, to form a field. With the scale lay off ½-in. spaces from their intersection. Add the narrow border ³⁄₁₆ in. wide. Add a second border ½ in. wide. The length of the border blocks is projected from the corners of the field blocks.

2.1.6. Five cards. Visible and hidden lines. Five cards 1¾ by 3 in. are arranged with the bottom card in the center, the other four overlapping each other and placed so that their outside edges form a 4-in. square. Hidden lines indicate edges covered.

2.1.7. A Maltese cross. For T square, spacers, and 45° and 30-60° triangles. Draw a 4-in. square and a 1⅜-in. square. From the corners of the inner square, draw lines to the outer square at 15° and 75°, with the two triangles in combination. Mark points with spacers ¼ in. inside each line of this outside cross, and complete the figure with triangles in combination.

PROB. 2.1.1.

PROB. 2.1.2.

PROB. 2.1.3.

PROB. 2.1.4.

PROB. 2.1.5.

PROB. 2.1.6.

PROB. 2.1.7.

GROUP 2. STRAIGHT LINES AND CIRCLES

2.2.1. Insigne. For T square, triangles, scale, and compasses. Draw the 45° diagonals and the vertical and horizontal center lines of a 4-in. square. With compass, draw a ¾-in.-diameter construction circle, a 2¾-in. circle, and a 3¼-in. circle. Complete the design by adding a square and pointed star as shown.

2.2.2. A six-point star. For compass and 30-60° triangle. Draw a 4-in. construction circle and inscribe the six-point star with the T square and 30-60° triangle. Accomplish this with four successive changes of position of the triangle.

2.2.3. A stamping. For T square, 30-60° triangle, and compasses. In a 4-in. circle draw six diameters 30° apart. Draw a 3-in. con-struction circle to locate the centers of ⁵⁄₁₆-in.-radius circle arcs. Complete the stamping with perpendiculars to the six diameters as shown.

2.2.4. Aircraft insigne. This device is a white star with a red center on a blue background. Draw a 4-in. circle and a 1¼-in. circle. Divide the large circle into five equal parts with the dividers and construct the star by connecting alternate points as shown. Red is indicated by vertical lines and blue by horizontal lines. Space these by eye approximately ¹⁄₁₆-in. apart.

2.2.5. A 24-point star. For T square and tri-angles in combination. In a 4-in. circle draw 12 diameters 15° apart, using T square and triangles singly and in combination. With the same combinations, finish the figure as shown.

PROB. 2.2.1.

PROB. 2.2.2.   **PROB. 2.2.3.**

PROB. 2.2.4.   **PROB. 2.2.5.**

GROUP 3. CIRCLES AND TANGENTS

2.3.1. Concentric circles. For compass (legs straight) and scale. Draw a horizontal line through the center of a space. On it mark off radii for eight concentric circles ¼ in. apart. In drawing concentric circles, always draw the smallest first.

2.3.2. A four-centered spiral. For accurate tangents. Draw a ⅛-in. square and extend its sides as shown. With the upper right corner as center, draw quadrants with ⅛- and ¼-in. radii. Continue with quadrants from each cor-ner in order until four turns have been drawn.

2.3.3. A loop ornament. For bow compass.

Draw a 2-in. square, about center of space. Di-vide *AE* into four ¼-in. spaces with scale. With bow pencil and centers *A, B, C,* and *D,* draw four semicircles with ¼-in. radius, and so on. Complete the figure by drawing the horizontal and vertical tangents as shown.

2.3.4. A rectilinear chart. For french curve. Draw a 4-in. field with ½-in. coordinate divi-sions. Plot points at the intersections shown, and through them sketch a smooth curve very lightly in pencil. Finish by marking each point with a ¹⁄₁₆-in. circle and drawing a smooth line with the french curve.

PROB. 2.3.1.

PROB. 2.3.2.   **PROB. 2.3.3.**

PROB. 2.3.4.

GROUP 4.   SCALES

2.4.1.   Scale practice.

(*a*) Measure lines *A* to *G* to the following scales: *A*, full size; *B*, ½ size; *C*, 3″ = 1′-0″; *D*, 1″ = 1′-0″; *E*, ¾″ = 1′-0″; *F*, ¼″ = 1′-0″; *G*, ³⁄₁₆″ = 1′-0″.

(*b*) Lay off distances on lines *H* to *N* as follows: *H*, 3³⁄₁₆″, full size; *I*, 7″, ½ size; *J*, 2′-6″, 1½″ = 1′-0″; *K*, 7′-5½″, ½″ = 1′-0″; *L*,

10′-11″, ⅜″ = 1′-0″; *M*, 28′-4″, ⅛″ = 1′-0″; *N*, 40′-10″, ³⁄₃₂″ = 1′-0″.

(*c*) For engineer's scale. Lay off distances on lines *H* to *N* as follows: *H*, 3.2″, full size; *I*, 27′-0″, 1″ = 10′-0″; *J*, 66′-0″, 1″ = 20′-0″; *K*, 105′-0″, 1″ = 30′-0″; *L*, 156′-0″, 1″ = 40′-0″; *M*, 183′-0″, 1″ = 50′-0″; *N*, 214′-0″, 1″ = 60′-0″.

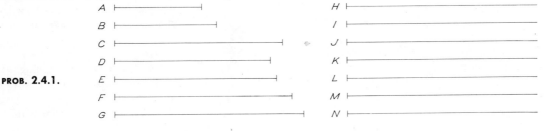

PROB. 2.4.1.

GROUP 5.   COMBINATIONS

2.5.1.   A telephone dial plate. Draw double size.

2.5.2.   A film-reel stamping. Draw to scale of 6″ = 1′-0″.

2.5.3.   Box cover. Make a one-view drawing for rectangular stamping 3 by 4 in., corners rounded with ½-in. radius. Four holes, one in each corner, ³⁄₁₆-in. diameter, 3 and 2 in. center to center, for fasteners. Rectangular hole in center, ⅜ by 1 in., with 1-in. side parallel to 4-in. side. Two slots ¼ in. wide, 2 in. long with semicircular ends, located midway between center and 4-in. edges, with 2-in. side parallel to 4-in. side and centered between 3-in. edges.

2.5.4.   Spacer. Make a one-view drawing for circular stamping 4 in. OD (outside diameter), 2 in. ID (inside diameter). Six ¼-in.-diameter holes equally spaced on 3-in.-diameter circle, with two holes on vertical center line. Two semicircular notches 180° apart made with ⅜-in. radius centered at intersections of horizontal center line and 4-in.-OD circle.

2.5.5.   Blank for wheel. Make a one-view drawing for stamping 5 in. OD; center hole ½ in. in diameter; eight spokes ⅜ in. wide connecting 1½-in.-diameter center portion with ½-in. rim. Eight ¼-in.-diameter holes with centers at intersection of center lines of spokes and 4½-in. circle; ⅛-in. fillets throughout to break sharp corners.

PROB. 2.5.1.   A telephone dial plate.

PROB. 2.5.2.   A film-reel stamping.

PROB. 2.5.7. Fixture base.

PROB. 2.5.8. Gage plate.

2.5.6. Cover plate. Make a one-view drawing for rectangular stamping 3 by 4 in., corners beveled ½-in. each way. Four holes, one in each corner, ¼-in. diameter, 3 and 2 in. center to center, for fasteners. Rectangular hole in center, ½ by 1 in. with 1-in. side parallel to 4-in. side. Two holes, ¾-in. diameter, located midway between the slot and short side of rectangle on center line through slot.

2.5.7. Drawing of fixture base. Full size. Drill sizes specify the diameter (see Glossary).

2.5.8. Drawing of gage plate. Scale, twice size. Drill sizes specify the diameter (see Glossary).

2.5.9. Drawing of milling fixture plate. Scale, twice size. Drill size specifies diameter (see Glossary).

2.5.10. Drawing of dial shaft. Use decimal scale and draw 10 times size.

2.5.11. Drawing of inner toggle for temperature control. Use decimal scale and draw 10 times size.

2.5.12. Drawing of mounting surface—O control. Scale, twice size.

2.5.13. Drawing of mounting leg—O control. Scale, full size.

2.5.14. Drawing of cooling fin and tube support. Full size.

2.5.15. Drawing of cone, sphere, and cylinder combinations. Scale, half size.

2.5.16. Drawing of cone-and-ball check. Scale, four times size.

PROB. 2.5.10. Dial shaft.

PROB. 2.5.9. Milling fixture plate.

PROB. 2.5.11. Inner toggle for temperature control.

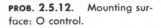

PROB. 2.5.12. Mounting surface: O control.

PROB. 2.5.13. Mounting leg: O control.

PROB. 2.5.14. Cooling fin and tube support.

PROB. 2.5.15. Cone, sphere, and cylinder combinations.

PROB. 2.5.16. Cone and ball check.

3

Applied Geometry

3.1. Strict interpretation of constructional geometry allows use of only the compass and an instrument for drawing straight lines, and with these the geometer, following mathematical theory, accomplishes his solutions. In engineering drawing the principles of geometry are employed constantly, but instruments are not limited to the basic two as T square, triangles, scales, curves, etc., are used to make constructions with speed and accuracy. Since there is continual application of geometric principles, the methods given in this chapter should be mastered thoroughly. It is assumed that students using this book understand the elements of plane geometry and will be able to apply their knowledge.

The constructions given here afford excellent practice in the use of instruments. Remember that the results you obtain will be only as accurate as your skill makes them. Take care in measuring and in drawing so that your work will be accurate and professional in appearance.

For easy reference, the various geometric figures are given in Fig. 3.101 at the end of this chapter.

This chapter is divided, for convenience and logical arrangement, into four parts: Line Relationships and Connections, which represent the bulk of the geometry needed in everyday work; Geometry of Straight-line Figures; Geometry of Curved Lines; and Constructions for Lofting and Large Layouts.

FIG. 3.1. To draw a line through two points. Use the pencil as a pivot and align the triangle or T square with the second point.

FIG. 3.2. To draw a line through two points (*alternate method*). Carefully align the triangle or T square with the points, and draw the required line.

FIG. 3.3. To draw a line parallel to another. Align a triangle with the given line *AB* using a base as shown; move it to position through the given point *P* and draw the required line.

FIG. 3.4. To draw a line parallel to and a given distance from a line. Space the distance with circle arc *R;* then align a triangle on a base as shown, move to position tangent to the circle arc, and draw the required line.

LINE RELATIONSHIPS AND CONNECTIONS

3.2.   TO DRAW STRAIGHT LINES (FIGS. 3.1 AND 3.2).   Straight lines are drawn by using the straight edge of the T square or one of the triangles. For short lines a triangle is more convenient. Observe the directions for technique in paragraphs 3.2, 3.3, and 3.4.

To draw a straight line through two points (Fig. 3.1), place the point of the pencil at *Q* and bring the triangle (or T square) against the point of the pencil. Then, using this point as a pivot, swing the triangle until its edge is in alignment with point *P,* and draw the line.

To draw a straight line through two points, *alternate method* (Fig. 3.2), align the triangle or T square with points *P* and *Q,* and draw the line.

3.3   TO DRAW PARALLEL LINES (FIGS. 3.3 AND 3.4).   Parallel lines may be required in any position. Parallel horizontals or verticals are most common. Horizontals are drawn with T square alone, verticals with T square and triangle. The general cases (odd angles) are shown in Figs. 3.3 and 3.4.

To draw a straight line through a point, parallel to another line (Fig. 3.3), adjust a triangle to the given line *AB,* with a second triangle as a base. Slide the aligned triangle to its position at point *P* and draw the required line.

To draw a straight line at a given distance from and parallel to another line (Fig. 3.4), draw an arc with the given distance *R* as radius and any point on the given line *AB* as center. Then adjust a triangle to line *AB,* with a second triangle as a base. Slide the aligned triangle to position tangent to the circle arc and draw the required line.

3.4.   TO DRAW PERPENDICULAR LINES (FIGS. 3.5 AND 3.6).   Perpendiculars occur frequently as horizontal-to-vertical (Fig. 3.5) but also often in other positions (Fig. 3.6). Note that the construction of a perpendicular utilizes the 90° angle of a triangle.

To erect a perpendicular to a given straight line (*when the given line is horizontal, Fig. 3.5*), place a triangle on the T square as shown and draw the required perpendicular.

To erect a perpendicular to a given straight line (*general position, Fig. 3.6*), set a triangle with its hypotenuse against a guiding edge and adjust one side to the given line. Then slide the triangle so that the second side is in the position of the perpendicular and draw the required line.

3.5.   TANGENTS (FIGS. 3.7 TO 3.20).   A *tangent* to a curve is a line, either straight

FIG. 3.5. To draw a line perpendicular to another (when the *given line* is *horizontal*). Place the triangle on the T square and draw the required line.

FIG. 3.6. To draw a line perpendicular to another (general position). Align a triangle with the given line as shown; slide it (on another triangle as a base) to position of perpendicular and draw the required line.

or curved, that passes through two points on the curve infinitely close together. One of the most frequent geometric operations in drafting is the drawing of tangents to circle arcs and the drawing of circle arcs tangent to straight lines or other circles. These should be constructed accurately, and on pencil drawings that are to be inked or traced the points of tangency should be located by short cross marks to show the stopping points for the ink lines. The method of finding these points is indicated in the following constructions. Note in all the following tangent constructions that the location of tangent points is based on one of these geometric facts: (1) the tangent point of a straight line and circle will lie at the intersection of a perpendicular to the straight line that passes through the circle center, and (2) the tangent point of two circles will lie on the circumferences of both circles and on a straight line connecting the circle centers. See Fig. 3.7.

3.6. TANGENT POINTS (FIG. 3.7).
To find the point of tangency for line AB and a circle with center D, draw DC perpendicular to line AB. Point C is the tangent point.

To find the tangent point for two circles (Fig. 3.7) with centers at D and E, draw DE, joining the centers. Point P is the tangent point.

3.7. TO DRAW A CIRCLE OF GIVEN SIZE TANGENT TO A LINE AND PASSING THROUGH A POINT (FIG. 3.8).
Draw a line AB, the given radius distance R away from and parallel to the given line. Using the given point S as center, cut line AB at O with the given radius. O is the center of the circle. Note that there are two possible positions for the circle.

3.8. TO DRAW A CIRCLE TANGENT TO A LINE AT A POINT AND PASSING THROUGH A SECOND POINT (FIG. 3.9).
Connect the two points P and S and draw the perpendicular bisector AB (see paragraph 3.38). Draw a perpendicular to the given line at P. The point where this perpendicular intersects the line AB is the center O of the required circle.

3.9. TO DRAW A TANGENT TO A CIRCLE AT A POINT ON THE CIRCLE (FIG. 3.10).
Given the arc ACB, draw a tangent at the point C. Arrange a triangle in combination with the T square (or another triangle) so that its hypotenuse passes through center O and point C. Holding the T square firmly in place, turn the triangle about its square corner and move it until the hypotenuse passes through C. The required tangent then lies along the hypotenuse.

3.10. TO DRAW A TANGENT TO A CIRCLE FROM A POINT OUTSIDE (FIG. 3.11).
Given the arc ACB and point P, arrange a triangle in combination with another triangle (or T square) so that one side passes through point P and is tangent to the circle arc. Then slide the triangle until the right-angle side passes through

FIG. 3.7. Tangent points. The tangent point of a straight line and circle is on the perpendicular from the circle center. The tangent point of two circles is on a line connecting their centers.

FIG. 3.8. A circle tangent to a line and passing through a point. The circle center must be equidistant from the line and the point.

FIG. 3.9. A circle tangent to a line at a point and passing through a second point. The circle center is at the intersection of the bisector of the chord connecting the points and the perpendicular from the point on the line tangent.

FIG. 3.11. A tangent to a circle from a point outside. The line is drawn by alignment through the point and tangent to the circle; the tangent point is then located on the perpendicular from the circle center.

FIG. 3.10. A tangent at a point on a circle. The tangent line must be perpendicular to the line from the point to the center of the circl

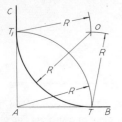

FIG. 3.12. An arc tangent at right-angle corner. The arc center must be equidistant from both lines.

FIG. 3.13. An arc tangent to two straight lines. The arc center must be equidistant from both straight lines.

the center of the circle and mark lightly the tangent point C. Bring the triangle back to its original position and draw the tangent line.

3.11. TO DRAW A CIRCLE ARC OF GIVEN RADIUS TANGENT TO TWO LINES AT RIGHT ANGLES TO EACH OTHER (FIG. 3.12). Draw an arc of radius R, with center at corner A, cutting the lines AB and AC at T and T_1. Then with T and T_1 as centers and with the same radius R, draw arcs intersecting at O, the center of the required arc.

3.12. TO DRAW AN ARC OF GIVEN RADIUS TANGENT TO TWO STRAIGHT LINES (FIG. 3.13). Given the lines AB and CD, set the compass to radius R, and at any convenient point on the given lines draw the arcs R and R_1. With the method of Fig. 3.4, draw parallels to the given lines through the limits of the arcs. These parallels are the loci of the centers of all circles of radius R tangent to lines AB and CD, and their intersection at point O will be the center of the required arc. Find the tangent points by erecting perpendiculars, as in Fig. 3.11, to the given lines through the center O. The figure above shows the method for an obtuse angle, below for an acute angle.

3.13. TO DRAW A TANGENT TO TWO CIRCLES (FIG. 3.14, OPEN BELT). Arrange a triangle in combination with a T square or triangle so that one side is in the tangent position. Move to positions 2 and 3, marking lightly the tangent points T_1 and T_2. Return to the original position and draw the tangent line. Repeat for the other side.

3.14. TO DRAW A TANGENT TO TWO CIRCLES (FIG. 3.15, CROSSED BELT). Arrange a triangle in combination with a T square or triangle so that one side is in the tangent position. Move to positions 2 and 3, marking lightly the tangent points T_1 and T_2. Return to the original position and draw the tangent line. Repeat for the other side.

3.15. TO DRAW A CIRCLE OF RADIUS R TANGENT TO A GIVEN CIRCLE AND A STRAIGHT LINE (FIG. 3.16). Let AB be the given line and R_1 the radius of the given circle. Draw a line CD parallel to AB at a distance R from it. With O as center and radius $R + R_1$, swing an arc intersecting CD at X, the desired center. The tangent point for AB will be on a perpendicular to AB from X; the tangent point for the two circles will be on a line joining their centers X and O.

FIG. 3.14. Tangents to two circles (open belt). Tangent lines are drawn by alignment with both circles. Tangent points lie on perpendicular lines from circle centers.

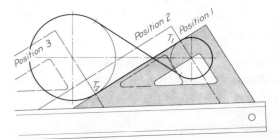

FIG. 3.15. Tangents to two circles (crossed belt). Tangent lines are drawn by alignment with both circles. Tangent points lie on perpendicular lines from circle centers.

FIG. 3.16. An arc tangent to a straight line and a circle. The arc center must be equidistant from the line and the circle.

FIG. 3.17. An arc tangent to two circles. The arc center must be equidistant from both circles.

FIG. 3.18. An ogee curve. It is made of circle arcs tangent to each other and to straight lines.

3.16. TO DRAW A CIRCLE OF RADIUS R TANGENT TO TWO GIVEN CIRCLES.

First Case (*Fig. 3.17, Left*). The centers of the given circles are outside the required circle. Let R_1 and R_2 be the radii of the given circles and O and P their centers. With O as center and radius $R + R_1$, describe an arc. With P as center and radius $R + R_2$, swing another arc intersecting the first arc at Q, which is the center sought. Mark the tangent points in line with OQ and QP.

Second Case (*Fig. 3.17, Right*). The centers of the given circles are inside the required circle. With O and P as centers and radii $R - R_1$ and $R - R_2$, describe arcs intersecting at the required center Q.

3.17. TO DRAW A REVERSE, OR OGEE, CURVE (FIG. 3.18).

Given two parallel lines AB and CD, join B and C by a straight line. Erect perpendiculars at B and C. Any arcs tangent to lines AB and CD at B and C must have their centers on these perpendiculars. On the line BC assume point E, the point through which it is desired that the curve shall pass. Bisect BE and EC by perpendiculars. Any arc to pass through B and E must have its center somewhere on the perpendicular from the middle point. The intersection, therefore, of these perpendicular bisectors with the first two perpendiculars will be the centers for arcs BE and EC. This line might be the center line for

a curved road or pipe. The construction may be checked by drawing the line of centers, which *must* pass through E. Figure 3.19 illustrates the principle of reverse-curve construction in various combinations.

3.18. TO DRAW A REVERSE CURVE TANGENT TO TWO LINES AND TO A THIRD SECANT LINE AT A GIVEN POINT (FIG. 3.20).

Given two lines AB and CD cut by the line EF at points E and F, draw a perpendicular JH to EF through a given point P on EF. With E as center and radius EP, intersect CD at G. Draw a perpendicular from G intersecting JH at H. With F as center and radius FP, intersect AB at K. Draw a perpendicular to AB from K intersecting JH at J. H and J will be the centers for arcs tangent to the three lines.

FIG. 3.20. Reverse curve tangent to three lines. Note that the arc centers must lie on a line perpendicular to the tangent line at the point of tangency.

FIG. 3.19. Ogee applications. Note that the circle arcs are tangent on a line connecting the centers.

FIG. 3.22. To bisect a line (with T square and triangle). Equal angles locate one point on the perpendicular bisector.

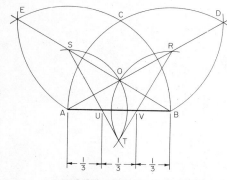

FIG. 3.23. To trisect a line (with compass). Construction is based on the geometry of an equilateral triangle.

FIG. 3.24. To trisect a line (with T square and triangle). Third points are located by 30° and 60° angles.

GEOMETRY OF STRAIGHT-LINE FIGURES

3.19.   TO BISECT A LINE (FIG. 3.21).

With Compass.   From the two ends of the line, swing arcs of the same radius, greater than one-half the length of the line, and draw a line through the arc intersections. This line bisects the given line and is also the *perpendicular* bisector. Many geometric problems depend upon this construction.

With T Square and Triangles (Fig. 3.22). At two points, A and B, on the line, draw lines AC and BC at equal angles with AB. A perpendicular CD to AB then cuts AB at D, the midpoint, and CD is the perpendicular bisector of AB.

3.20.   TO TRISECT A LINE.   Trisection of

a line is not nearly so often needed as bisection, but will occasionally be required.

With Compasses and Straightedge (Fig. 3.23).   On given line AB and with radius AB, draw two arcs of somewhat more than quarter circles, using A and B as centers. These arcs will intersect at C. Using the same radius AB and with C as center cut the first arcs at D and E. Then draw DA and EB, which intersect at O. Using OA (or OB) as radius and A and B as centers, cut AD and BE at R and S. Using AB as radius and R and S as centers, draw arcs to intersect at T and draw RT and ST, which will intersect

AB at third points U and V. You will recognize, upon analysis, that this construction is based on the geometry of an equilateral triangle inscribed in a circle, where the diameter of the circle is equal to one side of the triangle.

With T Square and Triangles (Fig. 3.24). The above construction can be accomplished with less detail by using a 30-60° triangle to obtain the needed angles. From A and B draw lines at 30° to intersect at C. Then at 60° to AB draw lines from C that intersect AB at U and V, the third points.

3.21.   TO DIVIDE A LINE INTO 2, 3, 4, 6, 8, 9, 12, OR 16 PARTS (FIGS. 3.25 AND 3.26).   Divisions into successive halves,

2, 4, 8, etc., are the most common. The principle of Fig. 3.22 can easily be applied to accomplish the division. As shown in Fig. 3.25, equal angles from A and B locate C, and the perpendicular from C to AB then gives the mid-point. Successive operations will give 4, 8, 16, etc., parts.

The principles of bisection (Fig. 3.22) and trisection (Fig. 3.24) can be combined to get 6, 9, or 12 parts. As indicated in Fig. 3.26, lines at 30° to AB from A and B locate C, and lines at 60° to AB from C locate D and E, the third points. Then 30° lines from A and D will bisect AD at F, giving sixth divisions; or trisecting by the principle of Fig. 3.24 as from D and E, giving G and H, will pro-

FIG. 3.25. To divide a line into 2, 4, 8, or 16 parts. Equal angles locate a point for bisection.

FIG. 3.26. To divide a line into 3, 6, 9, or 12 parts. The 30-60° triangle is used to obtain third points.

FIG. 3.27. To divide a line. Equal divisions on any line *BC* are transferred to *AB* by parallels to *AC*.

FIG. 3.28. To divide a line. Scale divisions are transferred to given line *AB*.

FIG. 3.29. To divide a line. Scale divisions divide (in this case) the vertical space.

FIG. 3.30. Angle by tangent. The proportion of *Y* to *X* is obtained from a table of natural tangents.

duce ninth points; or as from *E* and *B*, the half point located at *J*, and again the half points of *EJ* and *BJ* located at *K* and *L*, give twelfth divisions of *AB*.

3.22. TO DIVIDE A LINE INTO ANY NUMBER OF PARTS. *First Method (Fig. 3.27).* To divide a line *AB* into, say, five equal parts, draw any line *BC* of indefinite length. On it measure, or step off, five divisions of convenient length. Connect the last point with *A*, and using two triangles as shown in Fig. 3.3, draw lines through the points parallel to *CA* intersecting *AB*.

Second Method (Figs. 3.28 and 3.29). Draw a perpendicular *AC* from *A*. Then place a scale so that five convenient equal divisions are included between *B* and the perpendicular, as in Fig. 3.28. With a triangle and T square draw perpendiculars through the points marked, dividing the line *AB* as required. Figure 3.29 illustrates an application in laying off stair risers. This method can be used for dividing a line into any series of proportional parts.

3.23. TO LAY OUT A GIVEN ANGLE. *Tangent Method (Fig. 3.30).* The trigonometric tangent of an angle of a triangle is the ratio of the length of the side opposite the angle divided by the length of the adjacent side. Thus, tan $A = Y/X$, or $X \tan A = Y$. To lay out a given angle, obtain the value of the tangent from a table of natural tangents (see the Appendix), assume any convenient distance X, and multiply X by the tangent to get distance Y. Note that the angle between the sides X and Y must be a right angle.

3.24. TO LAY OUT A GIVEN ANGLE. *Chordal Method (Fig. 3.31).* If the length of a chord is known for an arc of given radius and included angle, the angle can be accurately laid out. Given an angle in degrees, to lay out the angle, obtain the chord length for a 1-in. circle arc from the table in the Appendix. Select any convenient arc length *R* and multiply the chord length for a 1-in. arc by this distance, thus obtaining the chord length *C* for the radius distance selected. Lay out the chord length on the arc with compass or dividers and complete the sides of the angle.

The chord length for an angle can be had from a sine table by taking the sine of one-half the given angle and multiplying by two.

3.25. TO LAY OUT AN ANGLE OF 45° (FIG. 3.32). Angles of 45° occur often, and are normally drawn with the 45° triangle. However, for large constructions or when great accuracy is needed, the method of equal legs is valuable (tangent 45° = 1.0). With any distance *AB* on the given line, with center *B* and radius *AB* draw more than a quarter circle. Erect a perpendicular at *B* (to *AB*) which intersects the arc at point *C*. Then *CA* makes 45° with *AB*.

3.26. TO LAY OUT ANGLES OF 30°, 60°, 90°, 120°, ETC. (FIG. 3.33). As with 45° angles, angles in multiples of 30° may

FIG. 3.31. Angle by chord. The proportion of *C* to *R* is obtained from a table of chords.

FIG. 3.32. To lay out a 45° angle. The two legs, *AB* and *BC*, are equal and perpendicular.

FIG. 3.33. To construct angles in multiples of 30°. Chords equal to the radius will divide a circle into six equal parts.

FIG. 3.34. To bisect an angle. Equal arcs from *A* and *B* locate *C* on the bisector.

FIG. 3.35. To divide an angle into equal parts. Equal divisions (chords) are stepped off on an arc of the angle.

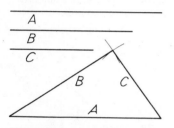

FIG. 3.36. To construct a triangle. The legs are laid off with a compass.

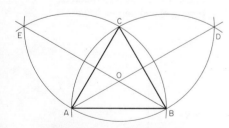

FIG. 3.37. To locate the geometric center of an equilateral triangle. Perpendicular bisectors of the sides intersect at the center.

also be needed for large constructions or when great accuracy is required. On a given line, with any convenient radius *AB*, swing an arc with *A* as center. With the same radius and *B* as center cut the original arc at *C*. The included angle *CAB* is 60° and by bisection (equal arcs from *C* and *B* to locate *E*) 30° is obtained at *CAE* and *EAB*. For 120°, *AB* laid off again from *C* to *D* gives *DAB* as 120°, and by bisecting *DAC,* 90° is given at *FAB*.

3.27. TO BISECT AN ANGLE (FIG. 3.34). Given angle *SOR*, using any convenient radius shorter than *OR* or *OS*, swing an arc with *O* as center, locating *A* and *B*. Then with the same radius or another radius longer than one-half the distance from *A* to *B*, swing arcs with *A* and *B* as centers, locating *C*. The bisector is *CO*. With repeated bisection, the angle can be divided into 4, 8, 16, 32, 64, etc., parts.

3.28. TO DIVIDE AN ANGLE (FIG. 3.35). Sometimes an angle must be divided into some number of parts, say 3, 5, 6, 7, or 9, that cannot be obtained by bisection. It is possible to trisect an angle by employing a movable scale, but this method is more complicated and not as accurate as dividing an arc with the dividers and is of no use for odd parts such as 5 and 7.

To divide an angle into, for example, 5 parts (Fig. 3.35), draw any arc across the angle as shown, and use the bow dividers to divide the arc into equal parts. Lines through these points to the apex are the required divisions.

3.29. TO CONSTRUCT A TRIANGLE HAVING GIVEN THE THREE SIDES (FIG. 3.36). Given the lengths *A*, *B*, and *C*. Draw one side *A* in the desired position. With its ends as centers and radii *B* and *C*, draw two intersecting arcs as shown. This construction is used extensively in developments by triangulation.

3.30. TO LOCATE THE GEOMETRIC CENTER OF AN EQUILATERAL TRIANGLE (FIG. 3.37). With *A* and *B* as centers and radius *AB*, draw arcs as shown. These will intersect at *C*, the third corner. With center *C* and radius *AB* cut the original arcs at *D* and *E*. Then *D* and *E* intersect at *O*, the geometric center.

3.31. TO TRANSFER A POLYGON TO A NEW BASE. *By Triangulation (Fig. 3.38).* Given polygon *ABCDEF* and a new position of base *A'B'*, consider each point as the vertex of a triangle whose base is *AB*. With centers *A'* and *B'* and radii *AC* and *BC*, describe intersecting arcs locating the point *C'*. Similarly, with radii *AD* and *BD* locate *D'*. Connect *B'C'* and *C'D'* and continue the operation always using *A* and *B* as centers.

Box or Offset Method (Fig. 3.39). Enclose the polygon in a rectangular "box." Draw the box on the new base and locate the points *ABCEF* on this box. Then set point *D* by rectangular coordinates as shown.

FIG. 3.38. To transfer a polygon: by triangulation. All corners are located by triangles having a common base.

FIG. 3.39. To transfer a polygon: by "boxing." Each corner is located by its position on a rectangle.

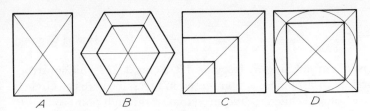

FIG. 3.40. Uses of the diagonal. The diagonals will locate the center of any regular or symmetrical geometric shape that has an even number of sides.

FIG. 3.41. A hexagon. Arcs equal to the radius locate all points. (Corner distance *AB* is known.)

FIG. 3.42. A hexagon. The 30-60° triangle gives construction for all points. (Corner distance *AB* is known.)

FIG. 3.43. A hexagon. Tangents drawn with the 30-60° triangle locate all points. (Across-flats distance is known.)

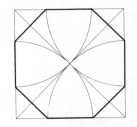

FIG. 3.44. To inscribe a regular pentagon in a circle. Arc construction locates one side; others are stepped off.

FIG. 3.45. To inscribe a regular octagon in a square. Arcs from the corners of the enclosing square locate all points.

3.32. USES OF THE DIAGONAL. The diagonal is used in many ways to simplify construction and save drafting time. Figure 3.40 illustrates the diagonal used at (*A*) for locating the center of a rectangle, at (*B*) for enlarging or reducing a geometric shape, at (*C*) for producing similar figures having the same base, and at (*D*) for drawing inscribed or circumscribed figures.

3.33. TO CONSTRUCT A REGULAR HEXAGON, GIVEN THE DISTANCE ACROSS CORNERS. *First Method* (*Fig. 3.41*). Draw a circle with *AB* as a diameter. With the same radius and *A* and *B* as centers, draw arcs intersecting the circle and connect the points.

Second Method (*without Compass*). Draw lines with the 30-60° triangle in the order shown in Fig. 3.42.

GIVEN THE DISTANCE ACROSS FLATS. The distance across flats is the diameter of the inscribed circle. Draw this circle, and with the 30-60° triangle draw tangents to it as in Fig. 3.43.

3.34. TO INSCRIBE A REGULAR PENTAGON IN A CIRCLE (FIG. 3.44). Draw a diameter *AB* and a radius *OC* perpendicular to it. Bisect *OB*. With this point *D* as center and radius *DC*, draw arc *CE*. With center *C* and radius *CE*, draw arc *EF*. *CF* is a side of the pentagon. Step off this distance around the circle with dividers.

3.35. TO INSCRIBE A REGULAR OCTAGON IN A SQUARE (FIG. 3.45). Draw the diagonals of the square. With the corners of the square as centers and a radius of half the diagonal, draw arcs intersecting the sides and connect these points.

3.36. TO CONSTRUCT A REGULAR POLYGON, GIVEN ONE SIDE (FIG. 3.46). Let the polygon have seven sides. With the side *AB* as radius and *A* as center, draw a semicircle and divide it into seven equal parts with dividers. Through the second division from the left draw radial line *A-2*. Through points *3, 4, 5,* and *6* extend radial lines as shown. With *AB* as radius and *B* as center, cut line *A-6* at *C*. With *C* as center and the same radius, cut *A-5* at *D,* and so on at *E* and *F*. Connect the points *or*, after *A-2* is found, draw the circumscribing circle. Another method is to guess at *CF* and divide the circle by trial; this is more common than the geometric method because the intersections of arcs are sometimes difficult.

GEOMETRY OF CURVED LINES

3.37. DEFINITIONS. A *curved line* is generated by a point moving in a constantly changing direction, according to some mathematical or graphic law. Curved lines are classified as single-curved or double-curved.

FIG. 3.46. To construct a regular polygon. Given one side, a polygon of any number of sides can be drawn by this method.

A *single-curved line* is a curved line having all points of the line in a plane. Single-curved lines are often called "plane curves."

A *double-curved line* is a curved line having no four consecutive points in the same plane. Double-curved lines are also known as "space curves."

We have defined (paragraph 3.5) a *tangent* to a curved line as a line, either straight or curved, that passes through two points on the curve that are infinitely close together. Note that this definition of tangency places the tangent in the plane of the curve for single-curved lines and in an instantaneous plane of the curve for double-curved lines.

A *normal* is a line (or plane) perpendicular to a tangent line of a curve at the point of tangency. A normal to a single-curved line will be a line in the plane of the curve and perpendicular to a straight line connecting two consecutive points on the curve.

3.38. ARC AND CIRCLE CENTERS (FIGS. 3.47 TO 3.50).

The center of any arc must lie on the perpendicular bisector of any and all chords of the arc. Thus, in Fig. 3.47, through two points *O* and *P*, an infinite number of arcs may be drawn but all will have centers such as *R* and *S* which lie on the perpendicular

bisector *AB* of chord *OP*. This construction is used in Fig. 3.9 where the circle is required to pass through points *S* and *P*.

Using the above principle, only one circle can be drawn through three points, as illustrated in Fig. 3.48. The center must lie on the perpendicular bisectors of both chords, *AB* and *BC*. Incidentally, the center will also lie on the perpendicular bisector of chord *AC*. This construction can be used as a check on accuracy.

Any diameter of a circle and a third point on the circumference, connected to form a triangle, will produce two chords of the circle that are perpendicular to each other. Therefore, the center of a circle may be found, as in Fig. 3.49, by selecting any two points such as *A* and *B*, drawing the perpendicular chords *AC* and *BD* and then the two diameters *CB* and *DA*, which cross at center *O*. Note in Fig. 3.50 that all chords connecting the diameter *AB*— *AD* and *DB*, *AC* and *CB*, *AE* and *EB*, *AF* and *FB*—form a right angle between the chords.

3.39. TO INSCRIBE A CIRCLE IN AN EQUILATERAL TRIANGLE (FIG. 3.51).

With center *A* and radius *AB*, draw an arc as shown. With *B* and *C* as centers and radius *AB*, cut this arc at *D* and *E*. Then *EC* and *DB* intersect at *O*, the geometric center, and the radius of the subscribing circle is *OG* and/or *OF*.

3.40. TO INSCRIBE AN EQUILATERAL TRIANGLE IN A CIRCLE (FIG. 3.52).

Using the radius of the circle and starting at *A*, the known point of orientation, step off distances *AB*, *BC*, *CD*, and *DE*. The equilateral triangle is *ACE*. Note that six chords equal in length to the radius will give six equally spaced points on the circumference.

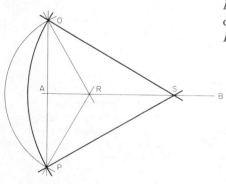

Application of circles and arcs

FIG. 3.47. Arc centers. The center of any arc lies on the perpendicular bisector of any chord of the arc.

FIG. 3.48. Circle through three points. Perpendicular bisectors of chords locate the center.

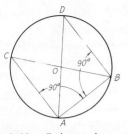

FIG. 3.49. To locate the center of a circle. Perpendicular chords to chord *AB* produce diameters *BC* and *AD*.

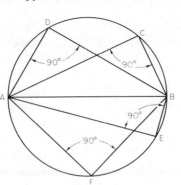

FIG. 3.50. Chords connecting a diameter. Chords from a point, connected to a diameter, form a right angle between the chords.

FIG. 3.51. To inscribe a circle in an equilateral triangle. Construction (to get perpendicular bisectors of two sides) locates the circle center.

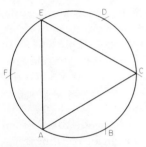

FIG. 3.52. To inscribe an equilateral triangle in a circle. By stepping off the radius twice, corners are located. Compare with Fig. 3.41.

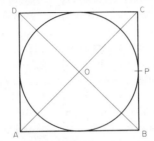

FIG. 3.53. To inscribe a circle in a square. Diagonals locate the circle center.

FIG. 3.54. To inscribe a square in a circle. The perpendicular bisector of one diameter locates the two corners to be found.

FIG. 3.55. To draw a circle on a regular polygon. Perpendicular bisectors of two sides locate the center.

FIG. 3.56. To approximate the length of an arc. See footnote[1] for accuracy.

3.41. TO INSCRIBE A CIRCLE IN A SQUARE (FIG. 3.53). Given the circle *ABCD*, draw diagonals *AC* and *BD*, which intersect at point *O*, the center. *OP* is the radius of the circle.

3.42. TO INSCRIBE A SQUARE IN A CIRCLE (FIG. 3.54). From *A*, the known point of orientation, draw diameter *AC* and then erect *BD*, the perpendicular bisector of *AC*. The square is *ABCD*.

3.43. TO SCRIBE A CIRCLE IN OR ON A REGULAR POLYGON (FIG. 3.55). Draw perpendicular bisectors of any two sides, for example *PO* and *SO* of *AB* and *CD*, giving *O*, the center. The inner circle radius is *OF* or *OG* and the external circle radius is *OA*, *OB*, etc.

3.44. TO LAY OFF ON A STRAIGHT LINE THE APPROXIMATE LENGTH OF A CIRCLE ARC (FIG. 3.56). Given the arc *AB*. At *A* draw the tangent *AD* and the chord produced, *BA*. Lay off *AC* equal to half the chord *AB*. With center *C* and radius *CB*, draw an arc intersecting *AD* at *D*; then *AD* will be equal in length to arc *AB* (very nearly).[1] If the given arc is between 45° and 90°, a closer approximation will result by making *AC* equal to the chord of half the arc instead of half the chord of the arc.

The usual way of rectifying an arc is to set the dividers to a space small

[1] In this (Professor Rankine's) solution, the error varies as the fourth power of the subtended angle. For 60° the line will be 1/900 part short, while at 30° it will be only 1/14,400 part short.

FIG. 3.57. To approximate the length of an arc. The sum of short chords closely approaches the arc length.

FIG. 3.58. To lay off, on an arc, a specified distance. See footnote[1] for accuracy.

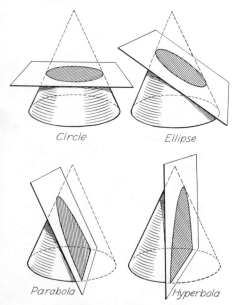

Circle   *Ellipse*

Parabola   *Hyperbola*

FIG. 3.59. The conic sections. Four plane curves are produced by "cutting" a cone.

Application of the ellipse (intersection)

enough to be practically equal in length to a corresponding part of the arc. Starting at *B*, step along the arc to the point nearest *A* and without lifting the dividers step off the same number of spaces on the tangent, as shown in Fig. 3.57.

3.45. TO LAY OFF ON A GIVEN CIRCLE THE APPROXIMATE LENGTH OF A STRAIGHT LINE (FIG. 3.58). Given the line *AB* tangent to the circle at *A*. Lay off *AC* equal to one-fourth *AB*. With *C* as center and radius *CB*, draw an arc intersecting the circle at *D*. The line *AD* is equal in length to *AB* (very nearly).[1] If arc *AD* is greater than 60°, solve for one-half *AB*.

3.46. PLANE CURVES: THE CONIC SECTIONS. In cutting a right-circular cone (a cone of revolution) by planes at different angles, we obtain four curves called "conic sections" (Fig. 3.59). These are the *circle,* cut by a plane perpendicular to the axis; the *ellipse,* cut by a plane making a greater angle with the axis than do the elements; the *parabola,* cut by a plane making the same angle with the axis as do the elements; the *hyperbola,* cut by a plane making a smaller angle than do the elements.

3.47. THE ELLIPSE: MAJOR AND MINOR DIAMETERS (FIG. 3.60). An ellipse is the plane curve generated by a point moving so that the sum of its distances from two fixed points (F_1 and F_2), called

"focuses," is a constant equal to the major axis,[2] or *major diameter, AB.*

The minor axis, or *minor diameter, DE,* is the line through the center perpendicular to the major diameter. The focuses may be determined by cutting the major diameter with an arc having its center at an end of the minor diameter and a radius equal to one-half the major diameter.

Aside from the circle, the ellipse is met with in practice much more often than any of the other conics, so it is important to be able to construct it readily. Several methods are given for its construction, both as a true ellipse and as an approximate curve made by circle arcs. In the great majority of cases when this curve is required, its major and minor diameters are known.

The mathematical equation of an ellipse with the origin of rectilinear coordinates at the center of the ellipse is $x^2/a^2 + y^2/b^2 = 1$, where a is the intercept on the X axis and b is the intercept on the Y axis.

3.48. THE ELLIPSE: CONJUGATE DIAMETERS (FIG. 3.61). Any line through the center of an ellipse may serve as *one of*

[2] "Major axis" and "minor axis" are the traditional terms. However, because of the confusion between these and the mathematical X and Y axes and the central axis (axis of rotation), the terms "major diameter" and "minor diameter" will be used in this discussion.

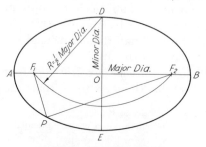

FIG. 3.60. The ellipse: major and minor diameters. These are perpendicular to each other.

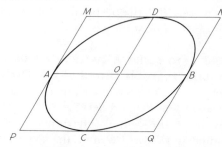

FIG. 3.61. The ellipse: conjugate diameters. Each is parallel to the tangent at the end of the other.

FIG. 3.62. Determination of major and minor diameters from conjugate diameters. Curve is given.

FIG. 3.63. Determination of major and minor diameters from conjugate diameters. Curve is not given.

FIG. 3.64. An ellipse by trammel (first method). Points on the curve are plotted.

FIG. 3.65. An ellipse by trammel (second method). Points on the curve are plotted.

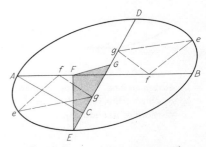

FIG. 3.66. An ellipse by triangle trammel (conjugate diameters). Points are plotted at the apex of the triangle.

a pair of conjugate diameters. Each of a pair of conjugate diameters is always parallel to the tangents to the curve at the extremities of the other. For example, *AB* and *CD* are a pair of conjugate diameters. *AB* is parallel to the tangents *MN* and *PQ;* and *CD* is parallel to the tangents *MP* and *NQ.* Also, each of a pair of conjugate diameters bisects all the chords parallel to the other. A given ellipse may have an unlimited number of pairs of conjugate diameters.

To Determine the Major and Minor Diameters, Given the Ellipse and a Pair of Conjugate Diameters. First Method (Fig. 3.62). The conjugate diameters are *CN* and *JG.* With center *O* and radius *OJ,* draw a semicircle intersecting the ellipse at *P.* The major and minor diameters will be parallel to the chords *GP* and *JP,* respectively.

Second Method: When the Curve Is Not Given (Fig. 3.63). The conjugate diameters *CN* and *JG* are given. With center *O* and radius *OJ,* describe a circle and draw the diameter *QR* at right angles to *JG.* Bisect the angle *QCR.* The major diameter will be parallel to this bisector and equal in length to *CR* + *CQ.* The length of the minor diameter will be *CR* − *CQ.*

3.49. ELLIPSE CONSTRUCTION: PIN-AND-STRING METHOD. This well-known method, sometimes called the "gar-

dener's ellipse," is often used for large work and is based on the definition of the ellipse. Drive pins at the points *D*, F_1, and F_2 (Fig. 3.60), and tie an inelastic thread or cord tightly around the three pins. If the pin *D* is removed and a marking point moved in the loop, keeping the cord taut, it will describe a true ellipse.

3.50. ELLIPSE CONSTRUCTION: TRAMMEL METHOD FOR MAJOR AND MINOR DIAMETERS. *First Method (Fig. 3.64).* On the straight edge of a strip of paper, thin cardboard, or sheet of celluloid, mark the distance *ao* equal to one-half the major diameter and *do* equal to one-half the minor diameter. If the strip is moved, keeping *a* on the minor diameter and *d* on the major diameter, *o* will give points on the ellipse. This method is convenient as no construction is required, but for accurate results great care must be taken to keep the points *a* and *d* exactly on the major and minor diameters.

Second Method (Fig. 3.65). On a strip —as used in the first method—mark the distance *do* equal to one-half the minor diameter and *oa* equal to one-half the major diameter. If this strip is moved, keeping *a* on the minor diameter and *d* on the major diameter, *o* will give points on the ellipse. This arrangement is preferred where the ratio between the major and minor diameters is small.

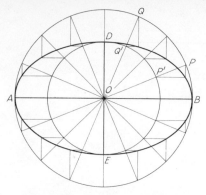

FIG. 3.67. An ellipse by concentric-circle method. Major- and minor-diameter circles and construction give points on the curve.

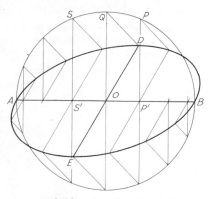

FIG. 3.68. An ellipse by circle method (conjugate diameters). After first construction, parallels plot points on the curve.

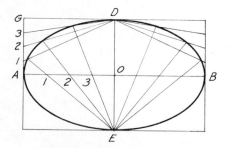

FIG. 3.69. An ellipse by parallelogram method. Points are plotted by construction through equal divisions of AO and AG.

3.51. ELLIPSE CONSTRUCTION: TRIANGLE TRAMMEL FOR CONJUGATE DIAMETERS (FIG. 3.66). The conjugate diameters AB and DE are given. Erect the perpendicular AC to the diameter ED and lay off distance AC from E to locate point G. Erect the perpendicular EF to the diameter AB. Transfer to a piece of paper, thin cardboard, or sheet of celluloid, and cut out the triangle EFG. If this triangle is moved, keeping f on AB and g on ED, e will give points on the ellipse. Extreme care must be taken to keep points f and g on the conjugate diameters.

3.52. ELLIPSE CONSTRUCTION: CONCENTRIC-CIRCLE METHOD FOR MAJOR AND MINOR DIAMETERS (FIG. 3.67). This is perhaps the most accurate method for determining points on the curve. On the two principal diameters, which intersect at O, describe circles. From a number of points on the outer circle, as P and Q, draw radii OP, OQ, etc., intersecting the inner circle at P', Q', etc. From P and Q draw lines parallel to OD, and from P' and Q' draw lines parallel to OB. The intersection of the lines through P and P' gives one point on the ellipse, the intersection of the lines through Q and Q' another point, and so on. For accuracy, the points should be taken closer

together toward the major diameter. The process may be repeated in each of the four quadrants and the curve sketched in lightly freehand; or one quadrant only may be constructed and repeated in the remaining three by marking the french curve.

3.53. ELLIPSE CONSTRUCTION: CIRCLE METHOD FOR CONJUGATE DIAMETERS (FIG. 3.68). The conjugate diameters AB and DE are given. On the conjugate diameter AB, describe a circle; then from a number of points, as P, Q, and S, draw perpendiculars as PP', QO, and SS' to the diameter AB. From S and P, etc., draw lines parallel to QD, and from S' and P' draw lines parallel to OD. The intersection of the lines through P and P' gives one point on the ellipse, the intersection of the lines through S and S' another point, and so on.

3.54. ELLIPSE CONSTRUCTION: PARALLELOGRAM METHOD (FIGS. 3.69 AND 3.70). This method can be used either with the major and minor diameters or with any pair of conjugate diameters. On the given diameters construct a parallelogram. Divide AO into any number of equal parts and AG into the same number of equal parts, numbering points

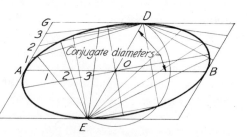

FIG. 3.70. An ellipse by parallelogram method (conjugate diameters). The constructive method of Fig. 3.69 is used, but here applied to conjugate diameters.

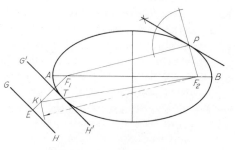

FIG. 3.71. Tangents to an ellipse at a point and parallel to a given line. Focuses are used in construction.

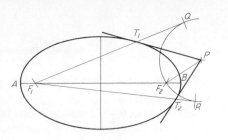

FIG. 3.72. Tangents to an ellipse from an outside point. Tangent points T_1 and T_2 are accurately located.

FIG. 3.73. Tangent and normal to an ellipse. The concentric-circle method is used.

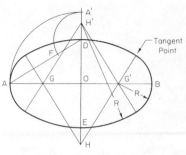

FIG. 3.74. A four-centered approximate ellipse. Four tangent circle arcs give elliptical shape.

from A. Through these points draw lines from D and E, as shown. Their intersections will be points on the curve.

3.55. TO DRAW A TANGENT TO AN EL-LIPSE.

At a Given Point on the Curve (Fig. 3.71). Draw lines from the given point P to the focuses. The line bisecting the exterior angle of these focal radii is the required tangent.

Parallel to a Given Line (Fig. 3.71). Draw F_1E perpendicular to the given line GH. With F_2 as center and radius AB, draw an arc cutting F_1E at K. The line F_1K cuts the ellipse at the required point of tangency T, and the required tangent passes through T parallel to GH.

From a Point Outside (Fig. 3.72). Find the focuses F_1 and F_2. With the given point P and radius PF_2, draw the arc RF_2Q. With F_1 as center and radius AB, strike an arc cutting this arc at Q and R. Connect QF_1 and RF_1. The intersections of these lines with the ellipse at T_1 and T_2 will be the tangent points of tangents to the ellipse from P.

Concentric-circle Method (Fig. 3.73). When the ellipse has been constructed by the concentric-circle method (Fig. 3.67), a tangent at any point H can be drawn by dropping a perpendicular to AB from the point to the outer circle at K and drawing the auxiliary tangent KL to the outer circle, cutting the major diameter at L. From L draw the required tangent LH.

3.56. TO DRAW A NORMAL TO AN ELLIPSE (FIG. 3.73).

From point P on the curve, project a parallel to the minor diameter to intersect the major diameter circle at Q. Draw OQ extended to intersect (at N) an arc with center at O and radius $AO + OE$. NP is the required normal.

Or, normals may be drawn perpendicular to the tangents of Figs. 3.71 and 3.72.

3.57. TO DRAW A FOUR-CENTERED AP-PROXIMATE ELLIPSE (FIG. 3.74).

Join A and D. Lay off DF equal to $AO - DO$. This is done graphically as indicated on the figure by swinging A around to A' with O as center where now DO from OA' is DA', the required distance. With D as center, an arc from A' to the diagonal AD locates F. Bisect AF by a perpendicular crossing AO at G and intersecting DE produced (if necessary) at H. Make OG' equal to OG, and OH' equal to OH. Then G, G', H, and H' will be centers for four tangent circle arcs forming a curve *approximating* the shape of an ellipse.

Another method is shown in Fig. 3.75. This should be used only when the minor diameter is at least two-thirds the length of the major diameter.

3.58. TO DRAW AN EIGHT-CENTERED AP-PROXIMATE ELLIPSE (FIG. 3.76).

When a closer approximation is desired, the eight-centered ellipse, the upper half of which is known in masonry as the "five-

OF and $OG = AB - DE$
OH and $OI = \frac{3}{4} OG$

FIG. 3.75. A four-centered approximate ellipse. This method works best when major and minor diameters are nearly equal.

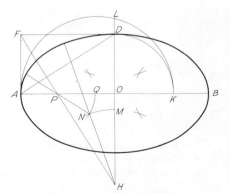

FIG. 3.76. An eight-centered approximate ellipse. This gives a much better approximation than the four-center methods but requires more construction.

Application of the parabola

FIG. 3.77.   A curve constructed with circle arcs. Note that lines through pairs of centers locate the tangent points of arcs.

FIG. 3.78.   A parabola. Points on the curve are equidistant from the focus F and directrix AB.

centered arch," may be constructed. Draw the rectangle $AFDO$. Draw the diagonal AD and a line from F perpendicular to it, intersecting the extension of the minor diameter at H. Lay off OK equal to OD, and, on AK as a diameter, draw a semicircle intersecting the extension of the minor diameter at L. Make OM equal to LD. With center H and radius HM, draw the arc MN. From A, along AB, lay off AQ equal to OL. With P as center and radius PQ, draw an arc intersecting MN at N; then P, N, and H are centers for one-quarter of the eight-centered approximate ellipse.

It should be noted that an ellipse changes its radius of curvature at every successive point and that these approximations are therefore not ellipses, but simply curves of the same general shape and, incidentally, not nearly so pleasing in appearance.

3.59.   TO DRAW ANY NONCIRCULAR CURVE (FIG. 3.77).   This may be approximated by drawing tangent circle arcs: Select a center by trial, draw as much of an arc as will practically coincide with the curve, and then, changing the center and radius, draw the next portion, remembering always that *if arcs are to be*

tangent, their centers must lie on the common normal at the point of tangency.

Curves are sometimes inked in this way in preference to using irregular curves.

3.60.   THE PARABOLA.   The parabola is a plane curve generated by a point so moving that its distance from a fixed point, called the "focus," is always equal to its distance from a straight line, called the "directrix." Among its practical applications are searchlights, parabolic reflectors, some loud-speakers, road sections, and certain bridge arches.

The mathematical equation for a parabola with the origin of rectilinear coordinates at the intercept of the curve with the X axis and the focus on the axis is $y^2 = 2\,px$, where p is twice the distance from the origin to the focus.

To draw a parabola when the focus F and the directrix AB are given (Fig. 3.78), draw the axis through F perpendicular to AB. Through any point D on the axis, draw a line parallel to AB. With the distance DO as radius and F as center, draw an arc intersecting the line, thus locating a point P on the curve. Repeat the operation as many times as needed.

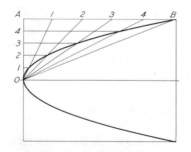

FIG. 3.79.   A parabola by parallelogram method. Points are plotted by lines through equal-numbered divisions of OA and AB.

FIG. 3.80.   A parabola by offset method. Offsets are proportionate to squares of divisions of OA.

To Draw a Tangent at Any Point P. Draw *PQ* parallel to the axis and bisect the angle *FPQ*.

3.61. PARABOLA CONSTRUCTION: PARALLELOGRAM METHOD.

Usually when a parabola is required, the dimensions of the enclosing rectangle, that is, the width and depth of the parabola (or span and rise), are given, as in Fig. 3.79. Divide *OA* and *AB* into the same number of equal parts. From the divisions on *AB*, draw lines converging at *O*. From the divisions on *OA,* draw lines parallel to the axis. The intersections of these with the lines from the corresponding divisions on *AB* will be points on the curve.

3.62. PARABOLA CONSTRUCTION: OFFSET METHOD (FIG. 3.80).

Given the enclosing rectangle, the parabola can be plotted by computing the offsets from the line *OA*. These offsets vary in length as the square of their distances from *O*. Thus if *OA* is divided into four parts, *DD'* will be ¹⁄₁₆ of *AA'; CC',* since it is twice as far from *O* as *DD',* will be ⁴⁄₁₆ of *AA';* and *BB',* ⁹⁄₁₆. If *OA* had been divided into five parts, the relations would be ¹⁄₂₅, ⁴⁄₂₅, ⁹⁄₂₅, and ¹⁶⁄₂₅, the denominator in each case being the square of the number of divisions. This method is the one generally used by civil engineers in drawing parabolic arches.

3.63. PARABOLA CONSTRUCTION: PARABOLIC ENVELOPE (FIG. 3.81).

This method of drawing a pleasing curve is often used in machine design. Divide *OA* and *OB* into the same number of equal parts. Number the divisions from *O* and *B* and connect the corresponding numbers. The tangent curve will be a portion of a parabola—but a parabola whose axis is not parallel to either ordinate.

3.64. THE HYPERBOLA.

The hyperbola is a plane curve generated by a point moving so that the difference of its distances from two fixed points, called the "focuses," is a constant. (Compare this definition with that of the ellipse.)

The mathematical equation for a hyperbola with the center at the origin of rectilinear coordinates and the focuses on the *X* axis is $x^2/a^2 - y^2/b^2 = 1$, where *a* is the distance from the center to the *X* intercept and *b* is the corresponding *Y* value of the asymptotes, lines that the tangents to the curve meet at infinity.

To Draw a Hyperbola When the Focuses F_1 and F_2 and the Transverse Axis AB (Constant Difference) Are Given (Fig. 3.82). With F_1 and F_2 as centers and any radius greater than F_1B, as F_1P, draw arcs. With the same centers and any radius $F_1P - AB$, strike arcs intersecting these arcs, giving points on the curve.

To Draw a Tangent at Any Point P. Bisect the angle F_1PF_2.

3.65. EQUILATERAL HYPERBOLA.

The case of the hyperbola of commonest practical interest to the engineer is the equilateral, or rectangular, hyperbola referred to its asymptotes. With it, the law $PV = c$, connecting the varying pressure and volume of a portion of steam or gas, can be graphically presented.

To Draw an Equilateral Hyperbola (Fig. 3.83). Let *OA* and *OB* be the asymptotes of the curve and *P* any point on it (this might be the point of cutoff on an indicator diagram). Draw *PC* and *PD.* Mark any points 1, 2, 3, etc., on *PC*, and through these points draw a system of lines parallel to *OA* and a second system through the same points converging at *O*. From the intersections of the lines of the second system with *PD* extended,

FIG. 3.81. A parabola by envelope method. The curve is drawn tangent to straight-line construction.

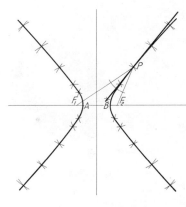

Application of the hyperbola (intersection)

FIG. 3.82. A hyperbola. From any point, the difference in distance to the focuses is a constant.

FIG. 3.83. An equilateral hyperbola. The asymptotes are perpendicular to each other.

Formation of a cycloid

Application of the involute

draw perpendiculars to *OA*. The intersections of these perpendiculars with the corresponding lines of the first system give points on the curve.

3.66. CYCLOID CURVES. A cycloid is the curve generated by the motion of a point on the circumference of a circle rolled in a plane along a straight line. If the circle is rolled on the outside of another circle, the curve generated is called an "epicycloid"; if rolled on the inside, it is called a "hypocycloid." These curves are used in drawing the cycloid system of gear teeth.

The mathematical equation for a cycloid (parametric form) is $x = r\theta - r \sin \theta$, $y = r - r \cos \theta$, where r is the radius of a moving point and θ is the turned angle about the center from zero position.

To Draw a Cycloid (Fig. 3.84). Divide the rolling circle into a convenient number of parts (say, eight), and, using these divisions, lay off on the tangent *AB* the rectified length of the circumference. Draw through *C* the line of centers *CD*, and project the division points up to this line by perpendiculars to *AB*. Using these points as centers, draw circles representing different positions of the rolling circle, and project, in order, the division points of the original circle across to

these circles. The intersections thus determined will be points on the curve. The epicycloid and hypocycloid are drawn similarly, as illustrated in Fig. 3.85.

3.67. THE INVOLUTE. An involute is the spiral curve traced by a point on a taut cord unwinding from around a polygon or circle. Thus the involute of any polygon can be drawn by extending its sides, as in Fig. 3.86, and, with the corners of the polygon as successive centers, drawing arcs terminating on the extended sides.

The equation of the involute of a circle (parametric form) is $x = r (\sin \theta - \theta \cos \theta)$, $y = r (\cos \theta + \theta \sin \theta)$, where r is the radius of the circle and θ is the turned angle for the tangent point.

In drawing a spiral in design, as for example of bent ironwork, the easiest way is to draw it as the involute of a square.

A circle may be conceived of as a polygon of an infinite number of sides. Thus to draw the involute of a circle (Fig. 3.87), divide it into a convenient number of parts, draw tangents at these points, lay off on these tangents the rectified lengths of the arcs from the point of tangency to the starting point, and con-

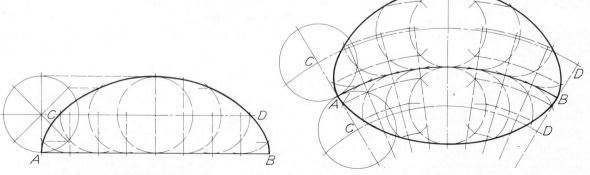

FIG. 3.84. A cycloid. A point on the circumference of a rolling wheel describes this curve.

FIG. 3.85. An epicycloid and hypocycloid. Both are formed by a circle rolling on another circle.

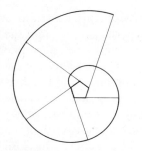

FIG. 3.86.   An involute of a pentagon. A point on a cord unwound from the pentagon describes this curve.

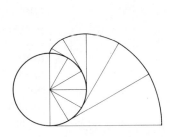

FIG. 3.87.   An involute of a circle. As a taut cord is unwound from the circle, it forms a series of tangents to the circle.

FIG. 3.88.   The spiral of Archimedes. This curve increases uniformly in distance from the center as rotation (angular velocity) is constant.

nect the points by a smooth curve. The involute of the circle is the basis for the involute system of spur gearing.

3.68.   THE SPIRAL OF ARCHIMEDES.   The spiral of Archimedes is the plane curve generated by a point moving uniformly along a straight line while the line revolves about a fixed point with uniform angular velocity.

To Draw a Spiral of Archimedes That Makes One Turn in a Given Circle (Fig. 3.88).   Divide the circle into a number of equal parts, drawing the radii and numbering them. Divide the radius 0-8 into the same number of equal parts, numbering from the center. With 0 as center, draw concentric arcs intersecting the radii of corresponding numbers, and draw a smooth curve through these intersections. The Archimedean spiral is the curve of the heart cam used for converting uniform rotary motion into uniform reciprocal motion.

The mathematical equation is $p = a\theta$ (polar form).

3.69.   OTHER PLANE CURVES.   The foregoing paragraphs discuss common plane curves that occur frequently in scientific work. Other curves, whenever needed, can be found in any good textbook of analytic geometry and calculus. Typical of the curves that may be met with are the catenary, cardioid, sine curve, cosine curve, logarithmic spiral, reciprocal (hyperbolic) spiral, parabolic spiral, logarithmic curve, exponential curve, and curves of velocity and acceleration.

3.70.   DOUBLE-CURVED LINES.   The scarcity of geometric double-curved lines, by comparison with the numerous single-curved lines, is surprising. There are only two double-curved lines, the cylindrical and the conic helix, much used in engineering work. Double-curved lines will, however, often occur as the lines of intersection between two curved solids or surfaces. These lines are not geometric but are double-curved lines of general form.

3.71.   THE HELIX.   The helix is a space curve generated by a point moving uniformly along a straight line while the line revolves uniformly about another line as an axis. If the moving line is parallel to the axis, it will generate a cylinder. The word "helix" alone always

Application of the helix

FIG. 3.89. The cylindrical helix and its development. Any point moves at a constant rate both around and along the axis.

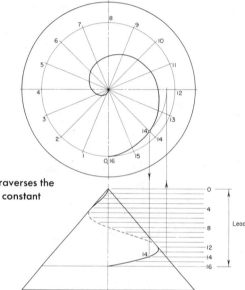

FIG. 3.90. The conic helix. A point traverses the surface of the cone while moving at a constant rate both around and along the axis.

FIG. 3.91. Parallel lines. Two points determine the parallel.

FIG. 3.92. Parallel lines. The parallel is drawn tangent to a pair of arcs.

tour elements. Divide this lead into a number of equal parts (say, 12) and the circle of the front view into the same number. Number the divisions on the top view starting at point 1 and the divisions on the front view starting at the front view of point 1. When the generating point has moved one-twelfth of the distance around the cylinder, it has also advanced one-twelfth of the lead; when halfway around the cylinder, it will have advanced one-half the lead. Thus points on the top view of the helix can be found by projecting the front views of the elements, which are points on the circular front view of the helix, to intersect lines drawn across from the corresponding divisions of the lead. If the cylinder is developed, the helix will appear on the development as a straight line inclined to the base at an angle, called the "helix angle," whose tangent is $L/\pi D$, where L is the lead and D the diameter.

3.73. TO DRAW A CONIC HELIX (FIG. 3.90). First make two views of the right-circular cone (see Chap. 5) on which the helix will be generated. Then lay out uniform angular divisions in the view showing the end view of the axis (in Fig. 3.90, the top view) and divide the lead into the same number of parts. Points can now be plotted on the curve. Each plotted point will lie on a circle cut from the cone by a plane dividing the lead and will also lie on the angular-division line. Thus, for example, to plot point 14, draw the circle diameter obtained from the front view, as shown in the top view. Point 14 in the top view then lies at the intersection of this circle and radial-division line 14. Then locate the front view by projection from the top view to plane 14 in the front view.

means a cylindrical helix. If the moving line intersects the axis at an angle less than 90°, it will generate a cone, and the curve made by the point moving on it will be a "conic helix." The distance parallel to the axis through which the point advances in one revolution is called the "lead." When the angle becomes 90°, the helix degenerates into the Archimedean spiral.

3.72. TO DRAW A CYLINDRICAL HELIX (FIG. 3.89). Draw the two views of the cylinder (see Chap. 5), and then measure the lead along one of the con-

CONSTRUCTIONS FOR LOFTING AND LARGE LAYOUTS

3.74. There are cases when the regular drafting instruments are impractical, either because of size limitations or when extreme accuracy is necessary. The geometric methods for common cases of parallelism, perpendicularity, and tangency are given in the following paragraphs.

3.75. TO DRAW A LINE THROUGH A POINT AND PARALLEL TO A GIVEN LINE (FIG. 3.91). With the given point P as center and a radius of sufficient length, draw an arc CE intersecting the given line AB at C. With C as center and the same radius, draw the arc PD. With C as center and radius DP, draw an arc intersecting CE at E. Then EP is the required line.

3.76. TO DRAW A LINE PARALLEL TO ANOTHER AT A GIVEN DISTANCE. *For Straight Lines (Fig. 3.92).* With the given distance as radius and two points on the given line as centers (as far apart as convenient), draw two arcs. A line tangent to these arcs will be the required line.

For Curved Lines (Fig. 3.93). Draw a series of arcs with centers along the line. Draw tangents to these arcs with a french curve (see Fig. 2.60).

3.77. TO ERECT A PERPENDICULAR FROM A POINT TO A GIVEN STRAIGHT LINE (FIG. 3.94). With point P as center and any convenient radius R_1, draw a circle arc intersecting the given line at A and B. With any convenient radius R_2 and with centers at A and B, draw intersecting arcs locating Q. The required perpendicular is PQ, with S the intersection of the perpendicular and the given line.

3.78. TO ERECT A PERPENDICULAR FROM A POINT ON A GIVEN STRAIGHT LINE. *First Method (Fig. 3.95).* With point P on the line as center and any convenient radius R_1, draw circle arcs to locate points A and B equidistant from P. With any convenient radius R_2 longer than R_1 and with centers at A and B, draw intersecting arcs locating Q. PQ is the required perpendicular.

Second Method (Fig. 3.96). With any convenient center C and radius CP, draw somewhat more than a semicircle from the intersection of the circle arc with the given line at A. Draw AC extended to meet the circle arc at Q. PQ is the required perpendicular.

3.79. TO DRAW A TANGENT TO A CIRCLE AT A POINT ON THE CIRCLE (FIG. 3.97). Given the arc ACB and to draw a tangent at point C, draw the extended diameter CD and locate point M. Then with any convenient radius R_1, locate point P equidistant from C and M. With P as center and the same radius R_1, draw somewhat more than a semicircle and draw the line MPQ. The line QC is a tangent to the circle at point C.

FIG. 3.93.   Curved parallel lines. The curves are drawn tangent to circle arcs.

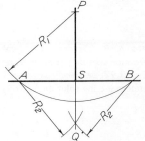

FIG. 3.94.   A perpendicular from a point outside. Equal radii determine the perpendicular.

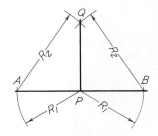

FIG. 3.95.   A perpendicular from a point on a line. Equal radii determine a point on the perpendicular.

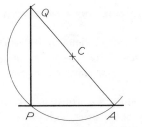

FIG. 3.96.   A perpendicular from a point on a line. Geometrically, perpendicular chords of a circle produce this solution.

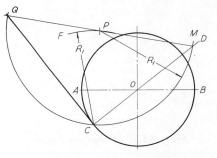

FIG. 3.97.   To draw a tangent at a point on a circle. This solution sets up two right-angle chords of a circle. One chord passes through the center of the given circle.

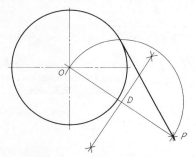

FIG. 3.98. To draw a tangent from an outside point. Here, as in Fig. 3.97, perpendicular chords determine the solution.

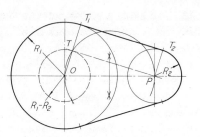

FIG. 3.99. Tangent lines (open belt). The difference in radius of the two circles is the geometric basis. Then perpendicular chords are used.

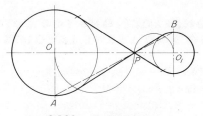

FIG. 3.100. Tangent lines (crossed belt). A duplicate of Fig. 3.99, except for position of the tangent lines.

3.80. TO DRAW A TANGENT TO A CIRCLE FROM A POINT OUTSIDE (FIG. 3.98). Connect the point P with the center of the circle O. Then draw the perpendicular bisector of OP, and with the intersection at D as center, draw a semicircle. Its intersection with the given circle is the point of tangency. Draw the tangent line from P.

3.81. TO DRAW A TANGENT TO TWO CIRCLES. *First Case: Open Belt* (*Fig. 3.99*). At center O draw a circle with radius $R_1 - R_2$. From P draw a tangent to this circle by the method of Fig. 3.98. Extend OT to T_1, and draw PT_2 parallel to OT_1. Join T_1 and T_2, giving the required tangent.

Second Case: Crossed Belt (*Fig. 3.100*). Draw OA and O_1B perpendicular to OO_1. From P, where AB crosses OO_1, locate tangents as in Fig. 3.98.

PROBLEMS

To be of value both as drawing exercises and as solutions, geometric problems must be worked accurately. Keep your pencil sharp, and use comparatively light lines. Locate a point by two intersecting lines; indicate the length of a line by short dashes across it.

GROUP 1.   LINES AND PLANE FIGURES

3.1.1. Near the center of the working space, draw a horizontal line 4½ in. long. Divide it into seven equal parts by the method of Fig. 3.27.

3.1.2. Draw a vertical line 1 in. from the left edge of the space and 3⅞ in. long. Divide it into parts proportional to 1, 3, 5, and 7.

3.1.3. Construct a polygon as shown in the problem illustration, drawing the horizontal line AK (of indefinite length) ⅜ in. above the bottom of the space. From A draw and measure AB. Proceed in the same way for the remaining sides. The angles can be obtained by proper combinations of the two triangles (see Figs. 2.28 and 2.29).

3.1.4. Draw a line AK making an angle of 15° with the horizontal. With this line as base, transfer the polygon of Prob. 3.1.3.

3.1.5. Draw a regular hexagon having a distance across corners of 4 in.

3.1.6. Draw a regular hexagon, distance across flats 3⅜ in.

3.1.7. Draw a regular dodecagon, distance across flats 3⅜ in.

$AB = 1\frac{5}{16}$ $EF = \frac{11}{16}$
$BC = 2\frac{1}{16}$ $FG = \frac{7}{8}$
$CD = \frac{3}{4}$ $GH = 1\frac{3}{4}$
$DE = 1\frac{1}{4}$ $HJ = 1\frac{13}{16}$
$JK = 1\frac{3}{8}$ (check)

PROB. 3.1.3. Irregular polygon.

FIG. 3.101. Geometric shapes. These plane figures, solids, and surfaces should be studied and remembered.

PROB. 3.2.1.   Offset swivel plate.

PROB. 3.2.4.   Bracket.

74

Applied Geometry

GROUP 2.   PROBLEMS IN ACCURATE JOINING OF TANGENT LINES

3.2.1.   Draw the offset swivel plate.

3.2.2.   Draw two lines AB and AC making an included angle of 30°. Locate point P, 4 in. from A and ½ in. from line AB. Draw two circle arcs centered at point P, one tangent to line AB, the other to AC. Then draw two lines tangent to the opposite sides of the arcs and passing through point A. Locate all tangent points by construction.

3.2.3.   Construct an ogee curve joining two parallel lines AB and CD as in Fig. 3.18, making $X = 4$ in., $Y = 2½$ in., and $BE = 3$ in. Consider this as the center line for a rod 1¼ in. in diameter, and draw the rod.

3.2.4.   Make contour view of the bracket. In the upper ogee curve, the radii R_1 and R_2 are equal. In the lower one, R_3 is twice R_4.

3.2.5.   Draw an arc of a circle having a radius of $3\frac{13}{16}$ in., with its center ½ in. from the top of the space and 1¼ in. from the left

edge. Find the length of an arc of 60° by construction; compute the length arithmetically, and check the result.

3.2.6.   Front view of washer. Draw half size.

3.2.7.   Front view of shim. Draw full size.

3.2.8.   Front view of rod guide. Draw full size.

3.2.9.   Front view of a star knob. Radius of circumscribing circle, 2⅜ in. Diameter of hub, 2½ in. Diameter of hole, ¾ in. Radius at points, ⅜ in. Radius of fillets, ⅜ in. Mark tangent points in pencil.

3.2.10.   Front view of sprocket. *OD*, 4¼ in. Pitch diameter, 4 in. Root diameter, 3¼ in. Bore, 1¼ in. Thickness of tooth at the pitch line is ⁹⁄₁₆ in. Splines, ¼ in. wide by ⅛ in. deep. Mark tangent points in pencil. See Glossary for terms.

3.2.11.   Front view of a fan. Draw full size.

3.2.12.   Front view of a level plate. Draw full size.

PROB. 3.2.6.   Washer.

PROB. 3.2.7.   Shim.

PROB. 3.2.8.   Rod guide.

PROB. 3.2.9.   Star knob.

PROB. 3.2.10.   Sprocket.

PROB. 3.2.11.
Fan.

PROB. 3.2.12. Level plate.

3.2.13. Front view of an eyelet. Draw full size.

3.2.14. Front view of a stamping. Draw full size.

3.2.15. Front view of spline lock. Draw full size.

3.2.16. Front view of gage cover plate. Draw full size.

3.2.17. Drawing of heater tube. Draw twice size.

PROB. 3.2.13. Eyelet.

3.2.18. Drawing of exhaust-port contour. Draw twice size.

3.2.19. Drawing of toggle spring for leaf switch. Use decimal scale and draw 20 times size.

3.2.20. Drawing of pulley shaft. Draw full size.

PROB. 3.2.14. Stamping.

PROB. 3.2.15. Spline lock.

PROB. 3.2.16. Gage cover plate.

Scale Detail

PROB. 3.2.17. Heater tube.

$\frac{1}{4}$ Drill, 4 Holes

PROB. 3.2.18. Exhaust-port contour.

DETERMINE

PROB. 3.2.19. Toggle spring for leaf switch.

PROB. 3.2.20. Pulley shaft.

PROB. 3.2.21. Cam for type A control.

PROB. 3.3.24. Front view of cam.

PROB. 3.3.25. Front view of fan base.

3.2.21. Drawing of cam for type A control. Plot cam contour from the polar coordinates given. Use decimal scale and draw five times size.

GROUP 3. PLANE CURVES

3.3.1. The conjugate diameters of an ellipse measure 3 and 4 in., the angle between them being 60°. Construct the major and minor diameters of this ellipse and draw the ellipse.

3.3.2. Using the pin-and-string method, draw an ellipse having a major diameter of 6 in. and a minor diameter of 4¼ in.

3.3.3. Using the trammel method, draw an ellipse having a major diameter of 4½ in. and a minor diameter of 3 in.

3.3.4. Using the trammel method, draw an ellipse having a major diameter of 4½ in. and a minor diameter of 4 in.

3.3.5. Using the concentric-circle method, draw an ellipse having a major diameter of 4⅜ in. and a minor diameter of 1½ in.

3.3.6. Draw an ellipse on a major diameter of 4 in. One point on the ellipse is 1½ in. to the left of the minor diameter and ⅞ in. above the major diameter.

3.3.7. Draw an ellipse having a minor diameter of 2³⁄₁₆ in. and a distance of 3¼ in. between focuses. Draw a tangent at a point 1⅜ in. to the right of the minor diameter.

3.3.8. Draw an ellipse whose major diameter is 4 in. A tangent to the ellipse intersects the minor diameter 1¾ in. from the center, at an angle of 60°.

3.3.9. Draw a five-centered arch with a span of 5 in. and a rise of 2 in.

3.3.10. Draw an ellipse having conjugate diameters of 4¾ in. and 2¾ in., making an angle of 75° with each other. Determine the major and minor diameters.

3.3.11. Draw the major and minor diameters for an ellipse having a pair of conjugate diameters 60° apart, one horizontal and 6¼ in. long, the other 3¼ in. long.

3.3.12. Using the circle method, draw an ellipse having a pair of conjugate diameters, one making 15° with the horizontal and 6 in. long, the other making 60° with the first diameter and 2½ in. long.

3.3.13. Using the triangle-trammel method, draw an ellipse having a pair of conjugate diameters 60° apart, one horizontal and 6 in. long, the other 4 in. long.

3.3.14. Using the triangle-trammel method, draw an ellipse having a pair of conjugate diameters 45° apart, one making 15° with the horizontal and 6 in. long, the other 3 in. long.

3.3.15. Draw a parabola, axis vertical, in a rectangle 4 by 2 in.

3.3.16. Draw a parabolic arch, with 6-in. span and a 2½-in. rise, by the offset method, dividing the half span into eight equal parts.

3.3.17. Draw an equilateral hyperbola passing through a point P, ½ in. from OB and 2½ in. from OA. (Reference letters correspond to Fig. 3.83.)

3.3.18. Draw two turns of the involute of a pentagon whose circumscribed circle is ½ in. in diameter.

3.3.19. Draw one-half turn of the involute of a circle 3¼ in. in diameter whose center is 1 in. from the left edge of the space. Compute the length of the last tangent and compare with the measured length.

3.3.20. Draw a spiral of Archimedes making one turn in a circle 4 in. in diameter.

3.3.21. Draw the cycloid formed by a rolling circle 2 in. in diameter. Use 12 divisions.

Quarter ellipse
Major axis 24"
Minor axis 6"

PROB. **3.3.26.** Front view of trip lever.

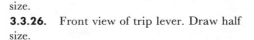

30°

3/4 Drill

Semi-ellipse
Major axis 8"
Minor axis 3"

1 3/4 R

1/2 R

3/4 R

1/2 Drill

1 R 2

2 1/4

4 3/4

9 1/4

3.3.22. Draw the epicycloid formed by a 2-in.-diameter circle rolling on a 15-in.-diameter directing circle. Use 12 divisions.

3.3.23. Draw the hypocycloid formed by a 2-in.-diameter circle rolling inside a 15-in.-diameter directing circle. Use 12 divisions.

3.3.24. Front view of cam. Draw full size.

3.3.25. Front view of fan base. Draw full size.

3.3.26. Front view of trip lever. Draw half size.

GROUP 4. PROBLEMS FOR SLIDE RULE AND MATHEMATICAL TABLES

3.4.1. Find the altitude of an equilateral triangle, each side of which is 4 in.

3.4.2. Find the value of one-third of an angle of 231°4'2".

3.4.3. A tank is 31 in. in diameter and 4 ft 7½ in. long. Find the capacity in liters.

3.4.4. A 4-in.-diameter cold-rolled steel bar is 96 cm long. What is the weight in pounds? In grams?

3.4.5. A circle of 12⅝-in. diameter used as a target for optical devices is to be compared in area with a lens of 80 mm diameter. What percentage is the lens area to the target area?

3.4.6. A guided missile is fired, hits a target 841 miles away, and during flight rises to a height of 91 miles. What are these distances in kilometers?

3.4.7. Find one side of a square whose equivalent area is a circle of 6⅝-in. diameter. Answer in centimeters.

3.4.8. An ellipse has a major axis of 14 in. and a minor axis of 8½ in. How far from the geometric center is each focus? What is the equivalent distance in centimeters?

3.4.9. A certain pressure is recorded by a column of water 2 ft 4½ in. high. What is the equivalent pressure in inches of mercury?

3.4.10. Find the area of a tract of land designated by a traverse that is an equilateral triangle each side of which is 228 ft 4 in. long. Answer in square miles. Also calculate the area in square kilometers.

3.4.11. A square is inscribed in a circle of 4-in. diameter. What is the area of the square?

3.4.12. An equilateral triangle is inscribed in a circle of 9⅜-in. diameter. What is the sum of the sides of the triangle? What is the circumference of the circle? What is the area of the triangle and of the circle?

3.4.13. A round copper bar 2 in. in diameter and 4 ft long is to be balanced in weight by a cube of aluminum. What is the size of the cube?

3.4.14. If a 2-in. round bar of steel 2 ft 6 in. long is to be replaced by a bar of bakelite, what will be the difference in weight?

3.4.15. A circular opening 6 in. in diameter is to be replaced by a number of openings 0.70 cm in diameter. How many openings must be used in order to give an equivalent area?

3.4.16. A 3⅛-in. cube of aluminum is to be replaced by steel. What is the percentage difference in weight?

3.4.17. A vertical water tank 4 ft 0 in. square holds 980 gallons. What is the pressure, per square inch, on the bottom of the water tank?

PC. NO.	NAME	MAT.	QUAN.	NOTES
101	Valve	Bro.	1	
102	Valve Ring	Comp.	1	Purchased

4

Lettering

4.1. Graphic representation of the shape of a part, machine, or structure gives one aspect of the information needed for its construction. To this must be added, to complete the description, figured dimensions, notes on material and finish, and a descriptive title—all lettered, freehand, in a style that is perfectly legible, uniform, and capable of rapid execution. As far as the appearance of a drawing is concerned, the lettering is the most important part. But the usefulness of a drawing, too, can be ruined by lettering done ignorantly or carelessly, because illegible figures are apt to cause mistakes in the work.

In a broad sense, lettering is a branch of design. Students of lettering fall into two general classes: those who will use letters and words to convey information on drawings, and those who will use lettering in applied design, for example, art students, artists, and craftsmen. The first group is concerned mainly with legibility and speed, the second with beauty of form and composition. In our study of engineering graphics we are concerned only with the problems of the first group. The engineering student takes up lettering as an early part of his work in drawing and continues its practice throughout his course, becoming more and more skillful and proficient.

4.2. SINGLE-STROKE LETTERING. By far the greatest amount of lettering on drawings is done in a rapid single-stroke letter, either vertical or inclined, and every engineer must have absolute command of these styles. The ability to letter well can be acquired only by continued and careful practice, but it can be acquired by anyone with normal muscular control of his fingers who will practice faithfully and intelligently and take the trouble to observe carefully the shapes of the letters, the sequence of strokes in making them, and the rules for their composition. It is not a matter of artistic talent or even of dexterity in handwriting. Many persons who write poorly letter very well.

The term "single-stroke," or "one-stroke," does not mean that the entire letter is made without lifting the pencil or pen but that the width of the stroke of the pencil or pen is the width of the stem of the letter.

4.3. GENERAL PROPORTIONS.

There is no standard for the proportions of letters, but there are certain fundamental points in design and certain characteristics of individual letters that must be learned by study and observation before composition into words and sentences should be attempted. Not only do the widths of letters in any alphabet vary, from *I*, the narrowest, to *W*, the widest, but different alphabets vary as a whole. Styles narrow in their proportion of width to height are called "**COMPRESSED**," or "**CONDENSED**," and are used when space is limited. Styles wider than the normal are called "**EXTENDED**."

The proportion of the thickness of stem to the height varies widely, ranging from ⅓ to ½₀. Letters with heavy stems are called "**BOLDFACE**," or "**BLACK-FACE**," those with thin stems "LIGHT-FACE."

4.4. THE RULE OF STABILITY.

In the construction of letters, the well-known optical illusion in which a horizontal line drawn across the middle of a rectangle appears to be below the middle must be provided for. In order to give the appearance of stability, such letters as *B, E, K, S, X,* and *Z* and the figures *3* and *8* must be drawn smaller at the top than at the bottom. To see the effect of this illusion, turn a printed page upside down and notice the appearance of the letters mentioned.

4.5. GUIDE LINES.

Always draw light guide lines for both tops and bottoms of letters, using a sharp pencil. Figure 4.1 shows a method of laying off a number of equally spaced lines. Draw the first base line; then set the bow spacers to the distance wanted between base lines and step off the required number of base lines. Above the last line mark the desired height of the letters. With the same setting, step down from this upper point, thus obtaining points for the top of each line of letters.

The Braddock-Rowe triangle (Fig. 4.2*A*) and the Ames lettering instrument (Fig. 4.2*B*) are convenient devices for spacing lines of letters. In using these instruments, a sharp pencil is inserted in the proper row of countersunk holes, and the instrument, guided by a T-square blade, is drawn back and forth by the pencil, as indicated by Fig. 4.3. The holes are grouped for capitals and lower case, the numbers indicating the height of capitals in thirty-seconds of an inch; thus no. 6 spacing of the instrument means that the capitals will be ⁶⁄₃₂, or ³⁄₁₆, in. high.

4.6. LETTERING IN PENCIL.

Good technique is as essential in lettering as in

FIG. 4.1. To space guide lines. Bow dividers are spaced for the distance between base lines; this distance stepped off from capital and base lines locates successive lines of lettering.

FIG. 4.2. (*A*) Braddock-Rowe triangle. Numbered sets of holes locate capital, waist (see Fig. 4.18), and base lines of successive lines of lettering. (*B*) Ames lettering instrument. A center disk, adjusted to letter-height number, gives equal spaces or 2:3 and 3:5 waist-line proportion for successive lines of lettering.

FIG. 4.3. Using the Ames lettering instrument. Lines are drawn as the pencil moves the instrument along the T square (or triangle).

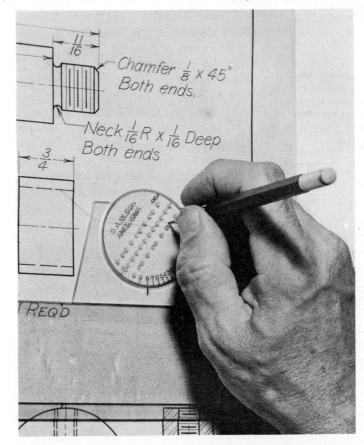

drawing. The quality of the lettering is important whether it appears on finished work to be reproduced by one of the printing processes or as part of a pencil drawing to be inked. In the first case, the penciling must be clean, firm, and opaque; in the second, it may be lighter. The lettering pencil should be selected carefully by trial on the paper. In one instance, the same grade may be chosen as that used for the drawing; in another, a grade or two softer may be preferred. Sharpen the pencil to a long, conic point, and then round the lead slightly on the end so that it is not so sharp as a point used for drawing.

The first requirement in lettering is the correct holding of the pencil or pen.

FIG. 4.4. Vertical strokes. These are made entirely by finger movement.

FIG. 4.5. Horizontal strokes. These are made by pivoting the whole hand at the wrist; fingers move slightly to keep the stroke perfectly horizontal.

FIG. 4.6. The *I-H-T* group. Note the direction of fundamental horizontal and vertical strokes.

FIG. 4.7. The *L-E-F* group. Note the successive order of strokes.

Figure 4.4 shows the pencil held comfortably with the thumb, forefinger, and second finger on alternate flat sides and the third and fourth fingers on the paper. Vertical, slanting, and curved strokes are drawn with a steady, even, *finger* movement; horizontal strokes are made similarly but with some pivoting of the hand at the wrist (Fig. 4.5). Exert pressure that is firm and uniform but not so heavy as to cut grooves in the paper. To keep the point symmetrical, form the habit of rotating the pencil after every few strokes.

4.7. SINGLE-STROKE VERTICAL CAPITALS. The vertical, single-stroke, commercial Gothic letter is a standard for titles, reference letters, etc. As for the proportion of width to height, the general rule is that the smaller the letters are, the more extended they should be in width. A low extended letter is more legible than a high compressed one and at the same time makes a better appearance.

For proficiency in lettering it is essential to learn the form and peculiarity of each of the letters. Although lettering must be based on a careful regard for the fundamental letter forms, this is not to say that it will be without character. Individuality in lettering is often nearly as marked as in handwriting.

4.8. ORDER OF STROKES. In the following figures an alphabet of slightly extended vertical capitals has been arranged in family groups. Study the shape of each letter, with the order and direc-

tion of the strokes forming it, and practice it until its form and construction are perfectly familiar. Practice it first in pencil to large size, perhaps ⅜ in. high, then to smaller size, and finally directly in ink.

To bring out the proportions of widths to heights and the subtleties in the shapes of the letters, they are shown against a square background with its sides divided into sixths. Several of the letters in this alphabet, such as *A* and *T,* fill the square; that is, they are as wide as they are high. Others, such as *H* and *D,* are approximately five spaces wide, or their width is five-sixths of their height. *These proportions must be learned visually* so well that letters of various heights can be drawn in correct proportion without hesitation.

The I-H-T Group (Fig. 4.6). The letter *I* is the foundation stroke. You may find it difficult to keep the stems vertical. If so, draw direction lines lightly an inch or so apart to aid the eye. The *H* is nearly square (five-sixths wide), and in accordance with the rule of stability, the crossbar is just above the center. The top of the *T* is drawn first to the full width of the square, and the stem is started accurately as its middle point.

The L-E-F Group (Fig. 4.7). The *L* is made in two strokes. The first two strokes of the *E* are the same as for the *L;* the third, or upper, stroke is slightly shorter than the lower; and the last stroke is two-thirds as long as the lower and just above the middle. *F* has the same proportions as *E.*

The N-Z-X-Y Group (Fig. 4.8). The

FIG. 4.8. The *N-Z-X-Y* group. Note that *Z* and *X* are smaller at the top than at the bottom, in accordance with the rule of stability.

FIG. 4.9. The *V-A-K* group. The horizontal of *A* is one-third from the bottom; the second and third strokes of *K* are perpendicular to each other.

FIG. 4.10.   The *M-W* group. *M* is one-twelfth wider than it is high; *W* is one-third wider than it is high.

FIG. 4.11.   The *O-Q-C-G* group. All are based on the circle.

FIG. 4.12.   The *D-U-J* group. These are made with combinations of straight and curved strokes.

FIG. 4.13.   The *P-R-B* group. Note the rule of stability with regard to *R* and *B*.

FIG. 4.14.   The *S-8-3* group. A perfect *S* and *3* can be completed to a perfect *8*.

FIG. 4.15.   The *0-6-9* group. The width is five-sixth of the height.

FIG. 4.16.   The *2-5-7-&* group. Note the rule of stability. The width is five-sixth of the height.

parallel sides of *N* are generally drawn first, but some prefer to make the strokes in consecutive order. *Z* and *X* are both started inside the width of the square on top and run to full width at the bottom. This throws the crossing point of the *X* slightly above the center. The junction of the *Y* strokes is at the center.

The V-A-K Group (Fig. 4.9).   *V* is the same width as *A*, the full breadth of the square. The *A* bridge is one-third up from the bottom. The second stroke of *K* strikes the stem one-third up from the bottom; the third stroke branches from it in a direction starting from the top of the stem.

The M-W Group (Fig. 4.10).   These are the widest letters. *M* may be made in consecutive strokes or by drawing the two vertical strokes first, as with the *N*. *W* is formed of two narrow *V*'s, each two-thirds of the square in width. Note that with all the pointed letters the width at the point is the width of the stroke.

The O-Q-C-G Group (Fig. 4.11).   In this extended alphabet the letters of the *O* family are made as full circles. The *O* is made in two strokes, the left side a longer arc than the right, as the right side is harder to draw. Make the kern of the *Q* straight. A large-size *C* and *G* can be made more accurately with an extra stroke at the top, whereas in smaller letters the curve is made in one stroke (Fig. 4.19). Note that the bar on the *G* is halfway up and does not extend past the vertical stroke.

The D-U-J Group (Fig. 4.12).   The top and bottom strokes of *D* must be horizontal. Failure to observe this is a common fault with beginners. In large letters *U* is formed by two parallel strokes, to which the bottom stroke is added; in smaller letters, it may be made in two strokes curved to meet at the bottom. *J* has the same construction as *U*, with the first stroke omitted.

The P-R-B Group (Fig. 4.13).   With *P*, *R*, and *B*, the number of strokes depends upon the size of the letter. For large letters the horizontal lines are started and the curves added, but for smaller letters only one stroke for each lobe is needed. The middle lines of *P* and *R* are on the center line; that of *B* observes the rule of stability.

The S-8-3 Group (Fig. 4.14).   The *S*, *8*, and *3* are closely related in form, and the rule of stability must be observed carefully. For a large *S*, three strokes are used; for a smaller one, two strokes; and for a very small size, one stroke only is best. The *8* may be made on the *S* construction in three strokes, or in "head and body" in four strokes. A perfect *3* can be finished into an *8*.

The 0-6-9 Group (Fig. 4.15).   The cipher is an ellipse five-sixths the width of the letter *O*. The backbones of the *6* and *9* have the same curve as the cipher, and the lobes are slightly less than two-thirds the height of the figure.

The 2-5-7-& Group (Fig. 4.16).   The secret in making the *2* lies in getting the

FIG. 4.17. Fractions. The total height of a fraction is twice that of the integer.

FIG. 4.18. Basic forms for lower-case letters. For standard letters, the waist-line height is two-thirds of capital height; capital line and drop line are therefore one-third above and one-third below the body of the letter.

reverse curve to cross the center of the space. The bottom of *2* and the tops of *5* and *7* should be horizontal straight lines. The second stroke of *7* terminates directly below the middle of the top stroke. Its stiffness is relieved by curving it slightly at the lower end. The ampersand (&) is made in three strokes for large letters and two for smaller ones and must be carefully balanced.

The Fraction Group (Fig. 4.17). Fractions are always made with horizontal bar. Integers are the same height as capitals. The total fraction height is best made twice the height of the integer. The numerator and denominator will be about three-fourths the height of the integer. Be careful to leave a clear space above and below the horizontal bar. Guide lines for fractions are easily obtained with lettering instruments by using the set of uniformly spaced holes or by drawing the integer height above and below the center, the position of the horizontal bar.

4.9. VERTICAL LOWER-CASE LETTERS. The single-stroke, vertical lower-case letter is not commonly used on machine drawings but is used extensively in map drawing. It is the standard letter for hypsography in government topographic drawing. The bodies are made two-thirds the height of the capitals with the ascenders extending to the capital line and the descenders dropping the same distance below. The basic form of the letter is the combination of a circle and a straight line (Fig. 4.18). The alphabet, with some alternate shapes, is shown in Fig. 4.19, which also gives the capitals in alphabetic order.

4.10. SINGLE-STROKE INCLINED CAPITALS. Many draftsmen use the inclined, or slant, letter in preference to the upright. The order and direction of strokes are the same as in the vertical form.

After ruling the guide lines, draw slanting "direction lines" across the lettering area to aid the eye in keeping the slope uniform. These lines may be drawn with a special lettering triangle of about $67\frac{1}{2}°$, or the slope of 2 to 5 may be fixed on the paper by marking two units on a horizontal line and five on a vertical line and using T square and triangle as shown in Fig. 4.20. The Braddock-Rowe

FIG. 4.19. Single-stroke vertical capitals and lower case. Note the alternate strokes for small-size capitals and the alternate shapes for lower-case *a, g,* and *y.*

triangle and the Ames instrument (Figs. 4.2*A* and *B*) both provide for the drawing of slope lines. The form taken by the rounded letters when inclined is illustrated in Fig. 4.21, which shows that curves are sharp in all upper right-hand and lower left-hand corners and flattened in the other two corners. Take particular care with the letters that have sloping sides, such as *A*, *V*, and *W*. The sloping sides of these letters must be drawn so that they appear to balance about a slope guide line passing through each vertex, as in Fig. 4.22. The alphabet is given in Fig. 4.23. Study the shape of each letter carefully.

Professional appearance in lettering is due to three things: (1) keeping to a uniform slope, (2) having the letters full and well shaped, and (3) keeping them close together. The beginner invariably cramps the individual letters and spaces them too far apart.

4.11. SINGLE-STROKE, INCLINED LOWER-CASE LETTERS.

The inclined lower-case letters (Fig. 4.23) have bodies two-thirds the height of the capitals with the ascenders extending to the capital line and the descenders dropping the same distance below the base line. Among older engineers, particularly civil engineers, this letter is generally known as the "Reinhardt letter," in honor of Charles W. Reinhardt, who first systematized its construction. It is legible and effective and, after its swing has been mastered, can be made rapidly. The lower-case letter is suitable for notes and statements on drawings because it is much more easily read than all capitals, since we read words by the word shapes, and it can be done much faster.

All the letters of the Reinhardt alphabet are based on two elements, the

FIG. 4.20. Slope guide lines. The standard slope angle of 67½° (see Figs. 4.2*A* and *B*) can be approximated by a slope of 2 to 5.

FIG. 4.21. Form of curved-stroke inclined capitals. The basic shape is elliptical.

FIG. 4.22. Form of straight-stroke inclined capitals. The "center line" must be a slope line.

FIG. 4.23. Single-stroke inclined capitals and lower case. Note the alternate strokes for small-size capitals and the alternate shapes for lower case *a*, *g*, and *y*.

FIG. 4.24. The straight-line inclined lower-case letters. Note that the center lines of the letters follow the slope angle.

ijkltvwxyz

aβabdfgpq

FIG. 4.25. The loop letters. Note the graceful combination of elliptical body, ascenders, and descenders.

ceeos

FIG. 4.26. The ellipse letters. Their formation is basically elliptical.

hmnruy

FIG. 4.27. The hook letters. They are combinations of ellipses and straight lines.

straight line and the ellipse, and have no unnecessary hooks or appendages. They may be divided into four groups, as shown in Figs. 4.24 to 4.27. The dots of *i* and *j* and the top of the *t* are on the "*t* line," halfway between the waist line and the capital line. The loop letters are made with an ellipse whose long axis is inclined about 45° in combination with a straight line. In lettering rapidly, the ellipse tends to assume a pumpkin-seed form; guard against this.

The *c, e,* and *o* are based on an ellipse of the shape of the capitals but not inclined quite so much as the loop-letter ellipse. In rapid small work, the *o* is often made in one stroke, as are the *e, v,* and *w.* The *s* is similar to the capital but, except in letters more than ⅛ in. high, is made in one stroke. In the hook-letter group, note particularly the shape of the hook.

The single-stroke letter may, if necessary, be much compressed and still be clear and legible (Fig. 4.28). It is also used sometimes in extended form.

COMPRESSED LETTERS ARE USED when space is limited. Either vertical or inclined styles may be compressed.

EXTENDED LETTERS OF A given height are more legible

FIG. 4.28. Compressed and extended letters. Normal width has *O* the same in width as in height and the other letters in proportion. Wider than high for *O* is extended, narrower compressed.

4.12. FOR LEFT-HANDERS ONLY. The order and direction of strokes in the preceding alphabets have been designed for right-handed persons. The principal reason that left-handers sometimes find lettering difficult is that whereas the right-hander progresses away from the body, the left-hander progresses toward the body; consequently his pencil and hand partially hide the work he has done, making it harder to join strokes and to preserve uniformity. Also, in the case of inclined lettering, the slope direction, instead of running toward his eye, runs off into space to the left of his body, making this style so much harder for him that he is strongly advised to *use vertical letters exclusively.*

For the natural left-hander, whose writing position is the same as a right-hander except reversed left for right, a change in the sequence of strokes of some of the letters will obviate part of the difficulty caused by interference with the line of sight. Figure 4.29 gives an analyzed alphabet with an alternate for some letters. In *E* the top bar is made before the bottom bar, and *M* is drawn from left to right to avoid having strokes hidden by the pencil or pen. Horizontal portions of curves are easier to make from right to left; hence the starting points for *O, Q, C, G,* and *U* differ from the standard right-hand stroking. *S* is the perfect letter for the left-hander and is best made in a single smooth stroke. The figures *6* and *9* are difficult and require extra practice. In the lower-case letters *a, d, g,* and *q,* it is better to draw the straight line before the curve even though it makes spacing a little harder.

The hook-wrist left-handed writer, who pushes his strokes from top to bottom, finds vertical lettering more difficult than does the natural left-hander.

In Fig. 4.29, where alternate strokes are given for some of the letters, the hook-wrist writer will probably find the second stroking easier than the first. Some prefer to reverse *all* the strokes, drawing vertical strokes from bottom to top and horizontal strokes from right to left.

By way of encouragement it may be said that many left-handed draftsmen letter beautifully.

4.13. COMPOSITION. Composition in lettering has to do with the selection, arrangement, and spacing of appropriate styles and sizes of letters. On engineering drawings the selection of the style is practically limited to vertical or inclined single-stroke lettering, so composition here means arrangement into pleasing and legible form. After the shapes and strokes of the individual letters have been learned, the entire practice should be on composition into words and sentences, since proper spacing of letters and words does more for the appearance of a block of lettering than the forms of the letters themselves. Letters in words are not spaced at a uniform distance from each other but are arranged so that the areas of white space (the irregular backgrounds between the letters) are approximately equal, making the spacing *appear* approximately uniform. Figure 4.30 illustrates these background shapes. Each letter is spaced with reference to its shape and the shape of the letter preceding it. Thus adjacent letters with straight sides would be spaced farther apart than those with curved sides. Sometimes combinations such as *LT* or *AV* may even overlap. Definite rules for spacing are not successful; it is a matter for the draftsman's judgment and sense of design. Figure 4.31 illustrates word composition. The sizes of letters to use in

FIG. 4.29. Strokes for left-handers. Several alternate strokes are given. Choose the one that is most effective for you.

any particular case can be determined better by sketching them lightly than by judging from the guide lines alone. A finished line of letters always looks larger than the guide lines indicate. Avoid the use of a coarse pen for small sizes and one that makes thin wiry lines for large sizes. When capitals and small capitals are used, the height of the small capitals should be about four-fifths that of the capitals.

In spacing words, a good principle is to leave the space that would be taken by an assumed letter *I* connecting the two words into one, as in Fig. 4.32. The

FIG. 4.30. Background areas. Equal areas between letters produce spacing that is visually uniform.

COMPOSITION IN LETTERING
REQUIRES CAREFUL SPACING, NOT ONLY
OF LETTERS BUT OF WORDS AND LINES

FIG. 4.31. Word composition. Careful spacing of letters and words and the proper emphasis of size and weight are important.

WORDSISPACEDIBYISKETCHINGIANIIIBETWEEN
WORDS SPACED BY SKETCHING AN I BETWEEN

FIG. 4.32. Word spacing. Space words so that they read naturally and do not run together (too close) or appear as separate units (too far apart).

FIG. 4.33. Shapes in symmetrical composition. Design for clarity and emphasis.

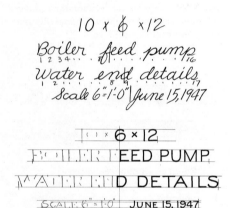

FIG. 4.34. Title composition. Sketch lightly; then when satisfactory, complete.

space would never be more than the height of the letters.

The clear distance between lines may vary from ½ to 1½ times the height of the letter but for the sake of appearance should not be exactly the same as the letter height. The instruments in Figs. 4.2 and 4.3 provide spacing that is two-thirds of the letter height. Paragraphs should always be indented.

4.14. TITLES. The most important problem in lettering composition is the design of titles. Every drawing has a descriptive title that is either all hand-lettered or filled in on a printed form. It gives necessary information concerning the drawing, and the information that is needed will vary with the different kinds of drawings (see paragraph 13.15 on working-drawing titles).

The usual form of lettered title is the *symmetrical title,* which is balanced or "justified" on a vertical center line and designed with an elliptical or oval outline. Sometimes the wording necessitates a pyramid or inverted-pyramid ("bag") form. Figure 4.33 illustrates several shapes in which titles can be composed. The lower right-hand corner of the sheet is, from long custom and because of convenience in filing, the usual location for the title, and in laying out a drawing, this corner is reserved for it. The space allowed is a matter of judgment and depends on the size and purpose of the

drawing. On an 11- by 17-in. working drawing, the title may be about 3 in. long.

4.15 TO DRAW A TITLE. When the wording has been determined, write out the arrangement on a separate piece of paper as in Fig. 4.34 (or, better, typewrite it). Count the letters, including the word spaces, and make a mark across the middle letter or space of each line. The lines must be displayed for prominence according to their relative importance as judged from the point of view of the persons who will use the drawing. Titles are usually made in all capitals. Draw the base line for the most important line of the title and mark on it the approximate length desired. To get the letter height, divide this length by the number of letters in the line, and draw the capital line. Start at the center line, and sketch lightly the last half of the line, drawing only enough of the letters to show the space each will occupy. Lay off the length of this right half on the other side, and sketch that half, working forward or backward. When this line is satisfactory in size and spacing, draw the remainder in the same way. Study the effect, shift letters or lines if necessary, and complete in pencil. Use punctuation marks only for abbreviations.

Scratch-paper Methods. Sketch each line of the title separately on a piece of scratch paper, using guide lines of determined height. Find the middle point of each of these lines, fold the paper along the base line of the letters, fit the middle point to the center line on the drawing, and draw the final letters directly below the sketches. *Or* draw the letters along the edge of the scratch paper, using the upper or lower edge as

LEONARDT 516 F: 506 F
HUNT 512: ESTERBROOK 968
Esterbrook 1000   Spencerian No.1
Gillott 404: Gillott 303

For very fine lines Gillott 170 and 290 or Esterbrook 356 and 355

FIG. 4.35. Pen strokes, full size. These are used principally for average-size lettering on working drawings.

one of the guide lines. *Or* letter the title on scratch paper, cut it apart and adjust until satisfactory, and then trace it.

4.16 **NOTES AND FILLED-IN TITLES.** By far the principal use of lettering on engineering drawings occurs on working drawings, where the dimensions, explanatory notes, record of drawing changes, and title supplement the graphic description of the object represented. The style varies between industries and even within industries, but the trend is toward the use of capital letters exclusively. Most draftsmen are able to letter in capital letters with greater readability and fewer mistakes than in lower case. However, for some structural drawings and others where space may be at a premium, lower case is used.

On any working drawing the accuracy of the information conveyed is paramount. For this reason it is important to make the shapes of the letters precisely correct with no personal flourishes, embellishments, or peculiarities. For example, a poorly made *3* may be read as an *8* or vice versa. A poorly made *5* may be misconstrued as a *6*. Strive for a smooth, professional appearance with, above all, perfect readability. The problems of Group 5 at the end of this chapter give practice in the lettering of notes. For added practice and greater experience in the form and style of standard notes, copy some of the information from the working drawings in Chap. 13.

4.17. **LETTERING PENS.** There are many steel writing pens that are adaptable to or made especially for lettering. The size of the strokes of a few popular ones is shown in full size in Fig. 4.35. Several special pens made in sets of graded sizes

have been designed for single-stroke lettering; among them are those illustrated in Fig. 4.36. These are particularly useful for large work. The ink-holding reservoir of the Henry tank pen (Fig. 4.37) assists materially in maintaining uniform weight of line. A similar device can be made by bending a brass strip from a paper fastener, a piece of annealed watch spring, or—perhaps best —a strip cut from a piece of shim brass into the shape shown in Fig. 4.38 and inserting it in the penholder so that the curved end just touches the pen nib.

To remove the oil film, always wet a new pen and wipe it thoroughly before using. A lettering pen well broken in by use is worth much more than a new one. It should be kept with care and never lent. A pen that has been dipped into writing ink should never be put into drawing ink. When in use, a pen should be wiped clean frequently with a cloth penwiper.

4.18. **USING THE PEN.** Use a penholder with cork grip (the small size) and set the pen in it firmly. Many prefer to ink a pen with the quill filler, touching the quill to the underside of the pen point, rather than dipping the pen in the ink bottle. If the pen is dipped, the surplus ink should be shaken back into the bottle or the pen touched against the neck of the bottle as it is withdrawn. Lettering with too much ink on the pen is responsible for results of the kind shown in Fig. 4.39.

In lettering, the penholder is held in the fingers firmly but without pinching, in the position shown in Fig. 4.40. The strokes of the letters are made with a steady, even motion and a slight, uniform pressure on the paper that will not spread the nibs of the pen.

FIG. 4.36. Barch-Payzant, Speedball, Edco, and Leroy pens. These are used principally for displays, large titles, and number blocks.

FIG. 4.37. Henry tank pen. The reservoir is designed to prevent spreading of the nibs.

FIG. 4.38. Ink holder. This helps to avoid heavy flow of ink when the pen is full.

EHMNWTZ

FIG. 4.39. Too much ink. Fill the pen sparingly and often.

FIG. 4.40. Holding the pen. Note that the thumb, forefinger, and second finger make a three-point support.

4.19. OTHER LETTERING STYLES. This chapter has been devoted entirely to the commercial Gothic letter because this style predominates in all types of commercial drawings. However, other letter styles are used extensively on architectural drawings and on maps, in design and for display, and for decorative letters on commercial products. Some traditional letter styles are illustrated and their uses described in the Appendix.

PROBLEMS

GROUP 1. SINGLE-STROKE VERTICAL CAPITALS

4.1.1. Large letters in pencil for careful study of the shapes of the individual letters. Starting 9/16 in. from the top border, draw guide lines for five lines of ⅜-in. letters. Draw each of the straight-line letters *I, H, T, L, E, F, N, Z, Y, V, A, M, W,* and *X,* four times in pencil only, studying carefully Figs. 4.6 to 4.10. The illustration is a full-size reproduction of a corner of this exercise.

4.1.2. Same as Prob. 4.1.1 for the curved-line letters *O, Q, C, G, D, U, J, B, P, R,* and *S.* Study Figs. 4.11 to 4.14.

4.1.3. Same as Prob. 4.1.1 for the figures *3, 8, 6, 9, 2, 5, ½, ¾, ⅜, 7/16,* and 9/32. Study Figs. 4.14 to 4.17.

4.1.4. Composition. Same layout as for Prob. 4.1.1. Read paragraph 4.13 on composition; then letter the following five lines in pencil: (*a*) WORD COMPOSITION, (*b*) TOPOGRAPHIC SURVEY, (*c*) TOOLS AND EQUIPMENT, (*d*) BRONZE BUSHING, (*e*) JACK-RAFTER DETAIL.

4.1.5. Quarter-inch vertical letters in pencil and ink. Starting ¼ in. from the top, draw guide lines for nine lines of ¼-in. letters. In the group order given, draw each letter four times in pencil and then four times directly in ink, as shown in the illustration.

4.1.6. Composition. Make a three-line design of the quotation from Benjamin Lamme on the Lamme medals: "THE ENGINEER VIEWS HOPEFULLY THE HITHERTO UNATTAINABLE."

4.1.7. One-eighth-inch vertical letters. Starting ¼ in. from the top, draw guide lines for 18 lines of ⅛-in. letters. Make each letter and numeral eight times directly in ink. Fill the remaining lines with a portion of paragraph 4.13 on composition.

4.1.8. Composition. Letter the following definition: "Engineering is the art and science of directing and controlling the forces and utilizing the materials of nature for the benefit of man. All engineering involves the organization of human effort to attain these ends. It also involves an appraisal of the social and economic benefits of these activities."

PROB. 4.1.1.

PROB. 4.1.5.

GROUP 2. SINGLE-STROKE INCLINED CAPITALS

4.2.1 to 4.2.8. Same spacing and specifications as for Group 1, Probs. 4.1.1 to 4.1.8, but for inclined letters. Study paragraph 4.10 and Figs. 4.20 to 4.23.

GROUP 3.   SINGLE-STROKE INCLINED LOWER CASE

4.3.1. Large letters in pencil for use with ⅜-in. capitals. The bodies are ¼ in., the ascenders ⅛ in. above, and the descenders ⅛ in. below. Starting ⅜ in. from the top, draw guide lines for seven lines of letters. This can be done quickly by spacing ⅛ in. uniformly down the sheet and bracketing capital and base lines. Make each letter of the alphabet four times in pencil only. Study Figs. 4.23 to 4.27.

4.3.2. Lower case for 3/16-in. capitals. Starting ½ in. from the top, draw capital, waist, and base lines for 13 lines of letters (Braddock or Ames no. 6 spacing). Make each letter six times in pencil and then six times in ink.

4.3.3. Composition. Same spacing as Prob. 4.3.2. Letter the opening paragraph of this chapter.

4.3.4. Letter paragraph 4.4.

GROUP 4.   TITLES

4.4.1. Design a title for the assembly drawing of a rear axle, drawn to the scale of 6 in. = 1 ft, as made by the Chevrolet Motor Co., Detroit. The number of the drawing is C82746. Space allowed is 3 by 5 in.

4.4.2. Design a title for the front elevation of a powerhouse, drawn to ¼-in. scale by Burton Grant, Architect, for the Citizens Power and Light Company of Punxsutawney, Pennsylvania.

GROUP 5.   NOTES

4.5.1 to 4.5.3. Vertical capitals. Copy each note in no. 6 (Ames or Braddock) spacing; then in no. 4 spacing.

4.5.4 to 4.5.6. Inclined capitals. Copy in no. 5 or no. 4 spacing.

4.5.7 to 4.5.9. Vertical lower case. Copy in no. 5 spacing.

4.5.10 to 4.5.12. Inclined lower case. Copy in no. 4 spacing.

4.5.13. For extra practice, select any of Probs. 4.5.1 to 4.5.12 and letter in a chosen style and size.

PAINT WITH METALLIC SEALER AND TWO COATS LACQUER AS PER CLIENT COLOR ORDER.

PROB. 4.5.1.

THIS PRINT IS AMERICAN THIRD-ANGLE PROJECTION

PROB. 4.5.2.

TO BE REMOVED AFTER MACHINING AND BEFORE ASSEMBLY.

PROB. 4.5.3.

THIS HOLE IN PIECE NO. 821 ONLY. REMOVE BURR ON UPPER SIDE.

PROB. 4.5.6.

CUTOFF BURR MUST NOT PROJECT BEYOND THIS SURFACE.

PROB. 4.5.4.

ALTERNATE MATERIAL:

1ST. RED BRASS 85 % CU.

2ND. COMM. BRASS 90 % CU.

3RD. COMM. BRASS 95 % CU.

PROB. 4.5.5.

Pivot point for high pressure bellows.

PROB. 4.5.9.

Flatten ear on this side to make piece No. 51367. See detail.

PROB. 4.5.7.

Deburring slot must be centered on 0.625 hole within ± 0.001.

PROB. 4.5.8.

Material: #19 Ga (0.024) C R Steel. Temper to Rockwell B-40 to 65.

PROB. 4.5.10.

This length varies from 0.245 to 0.627. See table (A) below.

PROB. 4.5.11.

Extrude to 0.082 ± .002 Dia. 3-56 Class 2 tap.

PROB. 4.5.12.

5

Orthographic Drawing and Sketching

THEORY

5.1. The previous chapters have been preparatory to the real subject of drawing as a language. Typically, engineers design and develop machines and structures and direct their construction. Furthermore, to design and then *communicate* every detail to manufacturing groups, descriptions must be prepared that show every aspect of the *shape* and *size* of each part and of the complete machine or structure. Because of this necessity, drawing is the fundamental method of communication. Only as a supplement, for notes and specifications, is the word language used.

In this chapter and Chap. 6 we are concerned with the methods of describing shape. Chapter 11 discusses size description.

Shape is described by projection, that is, by the process of causing an image to be formed by rays of sight taken in a particular direction from an object to a picture plane.[1] Methods of projection vary according to the direction in which the rays of sight are taken to the plane. When the rays are perpendicular to the plane, the projective method is *orthographic*. If the rays are at an angle to the plane, the projective method is called *oblique*. Rays taken to a particular station point result in *perspective*

---

[1] Only in *projective geometry*, a highly theoretical graphic subject, are surfaces other than a plane used.

projection. By the methods of perspective the object is represented as it would appear to the eye.

Projective theory is the basis of background information necessary for shape representation. In engineering drawing, two fundamental methods of *shape representation* are used:

(1) *Orthographic views,* consisting of a set of two or more separate views of an object taken from different directions, generally at right angles to each other and arranged relative to each other in a definite way. Each of the views shows the shape of the object for a particular view direction and collectively the views describe the object completely. Orthographic projection *only* is used.

(2) *Pictorial views,* in which the object is oriented behind and projected upon a single plane. Either orthographic, oblique, or perspective projection is used.

Since orthographic views provide a means of describing the *exact shape* of any material object, they are used for the great bulk of engineering work.

5.2. THEORY OF ORTHOGRAPHIC PROJECTION.   Let us suppose that a transparent plane has been set up between an object and the station point of an observer's eye (Fig. 5.1). The intersection of this plane with the rays formed by lines of sight from the eye to all points of the object would give a picture that is practically the same as the image formed in the eye of the observer. This is perspective projection.

If the observer would then walk backward from the station point until he reached a theoretically *infinite* distance, the rays formed by lines of sight from his eye to the object would grow longer and finally become infinite in length, parallel to each other, and perpendicular to the picture plane. The image so formed on the picture plane is what is known as "orthographic projection." See Fig. 5.2.

5.3.   DEFINITION.   Basically, orthographic[2] projection could be defined as

[2] Literally, "right writing."

FIG. 5.1. Perspective projection. The rays of projection converge at a station point from which the object is observed. Rays intersect a picture plane and produce a projection of the object.

FIG. 5.2. Orthographic projection. The station point is at infinity, making the rays parallel to each other. The rays are perpendicular to the picture plane.

FIG. 5.3. The frontal plane of projection. This produces the front view of the object.

FIG. 5.4. The frontal and horizontal planes of projection. Projection on the horizontal plane produces the top view of the object. Frontal and horizontal planes are perpendicular to each other.

FIG. 5.5. The horizontal plane rotated into the same plane as the frontal plane. This makes it possible to draw two views of the object on a plane, the drawing paper.

any single projection made by dropping perpendiculars to a plane. However, it has been accepted through long usage to mean the combination of two or more such views, hence the following definition: *Orthographic projection is the method of representing the exact shape of an object by dropping perpendiculars from two or more sides of the object to planes, generally at right angles to each other; collectively, the views on these planes describe the object completely.* (The term "orthogonal"[3] is sometimes used for this system of drawing.)

5.4. ORTHOGRAPHIC VIEWS. The rays from the picture plane to infinity may be discarded and the picture, or "view," thought of as being found by extending perpendiculars to the plane from all points of the object, as in Fig. 5.3. This picture, or projection on a frontal plane, shows the shape of the object when viewed from the front, but it does not tell the shape or distance from front to rear. Accordingly, more than one projection is required to describe the object.

In addition to the frontal plane, imagine another transparent plane placed horizontally above the object, as in Fig. 5.4. The projection on this plane, found by extending perpendiculars to it

[3] Meaning right-angled.

from the object, will give the appearance of the object as if viewed from directly above and will show the distance from front to rear. If this horizontal plane is now rotated into coincidence with the frontal plane, as in Fig. 5.5, the two views of the object will be in the same plane, as if on a sheet of paper. Now imagine a third plane, perpendicular to the first two (Fig. 5.6). This plane is called a "profile plane," and a third view can be projected on it. This view shows the shape of the object when viewed from the side and the distance from bottom to top and front to rear. The horizontal and profile planes are shown rotated into the same plane as the frontal plane (again thought of as the plane of the drawing paper) in Fig. 5.7. Thus related in the same plane, they give correctly the three-dimensional shape of the object.

In orthographic projection the picture planes are called "planes of projection;" and the perpendiculars, "projecting lines" or "projectors."

In looking at these theoretical projections, or views, do not think of the views as flat surfaces on the transparent planes, but try to imagine that you are looking *through* the transparent planes at the object itself.

FIG. 5.6. The three planes of projection: frontal, horizontal, and profile. Each is perpendicular to the other two.

FIG. 5.7. The horizontal and profile planes rotated into the same plane as the frontal plane. This makes it possible to draw three views of the object on a plane, the drawing paper.

FIG. 5.8. "The transparent box." This encloses the object with another frontal plane behind, another horizontal plane below, and another profile plane to the left of the object.

FIG. 5.9. The transparent box as it opens and all planes rotate to the plane of the frontal plane. Note that horizontal and profile planes are hinged to the frontal plane and that the "rear-view" plane is hinged to the left profile plane.

FIG. 5.10. The relative position of the six views. Study this figure carefully in conjunction with Figs. 5.8 and 5.9 to fix all relationships. (The dashed lines are explained in paragraph 5.12.)

FIG. 5.11. Top, front, and right-side views. This is the most common combination. Note that the top view is directly above and in projection (alignment) with the front view; and that the right-side view is to the right of and in projection with the front view. Observe also that *two* (and remember *which two*) space dimensions of height, width, and depth are represented in each view.

5.5. THE SIX PRINCIPAL VIEWS. Considering the matter further, we find that the object can be entirely surrounded by a set of six planes, each at right angles to the four adjacent to it, as in Fig. 5.8. On these planes, views can be obtained of the object as it is seen from the top, front, right side, left side, bottom, and rear.

Think now of the six sides, or planes, of the box as being opened up, as in Fig. 5.9, into one plane, the plane of the paper. The front is already in the plane of the paper, and the other sides are, as it were, hinged and rotated into position as shown. The projection on the frontal plane is the *front view, vertical projection,* or *front elevation;* that on the horizontal plane, the *top view, horizontal projection,* or *plan;* that on the side, or "profile," plane, the *side view, profile projection, side elevation,* or sometimes *end view* or *end elevation.* By reversing the direction of sight, a *bottom view* is obtained instead of a *top view,* or a *rear view* instead of a *front view.* In comparatively rare cases a bottom view or rear view or both may be required to show some detail of shape or construction. Figure 5.10 shows the relative position of the six views as set by the ASA. In actual work there is rarely an occasion when all six principal views are needed on one drawing, but no matter how many are required, their positions relative to one another are given in Fig. 5.10 (except as noted in paragraph 5.7). All these views are principal views. Each of the six views shows two of the three dimensions of height, width, and depth.

5.6. COMBINATION OF VIEWS. The most usual combination selected from the six possible views consists of the *top, front,* and *right-side* views, as shown in Fig.

FIG. 5.12.   Top, front, and left-side views. Note that the left-side view is drawn to the left of and in projection with the front view. The left-side view is preferred only when, because of the shape of the object, representation is clearer with the left-side view than with the right-side view.

FIG. 5.13.   Front, bottom, and right-side views. The bottom view is used instead of the top view only when its use gives clearer representation.

FIG. 5.14.   Top, front, left-side, and rear views. The rear view is added *only* when some detail on the rear of the object is important and representation can be improved by its use.

5.11, which, in this case, best describes the shape of the given block. Sometimes the left-side view helps to describe an object more clearly than the right-side view. Figure 5.12 shows the arrangement of *top, front,* and *left-side* views for the same block. In this case the right-side view would be preferred, as it shows no hidden edges (see paragraph 5.12 on hidden features). Note that the *side view of the front face of the object is adjacent to the front view* and that the side view of any point will be the same distance from the front surface as is its distance from the front surface on the top view. The combination of *front, right-side,* and *bottom* views is shown in Fig. 5.13 and of *front, top, left-side,* and *rear* views in Fig. 5.14.

5.7.   "ALTERNATE-POSITION" VIEWS. The top of the enclosing transparent box may be thought of as in a fixed position with the front, rear, and sides hinged, as in Fig. 5.15, thus bringing the sides in line with the top view and the rear view above the top view, Fig. 5.16. This

FIG. 5.15.   The transparent box opening for alternate-position views. Note that frontal and profile planes are hinged to the horizontal plane.

FIG. 5.16.   Alternate-position views. Study this figure carefully in conjunction with Fig. 5.15.

FIG. 5.17. Right-side view in alternate position. Note the saving in paper area (compared with regular position) for this broad, flat object. Compare with Fig. 5.11.

FIG. 5.18. Rear view in alternate position. This method is preferable when no left-side view is needed. Compare with Fig. 5.14.

alternate-position arrangement is of occasional use to save space on the paper in drawing a broad, flat object (Fig. 5.17). The alternate position for the rear view may be used if this arrangement makes the drawing easier to read (Fig. 5.18).

5.8. THE THREE SPACE DIMENSIONS. As all material objects, from single pieces to complicated structures, have distinct limits and are measurable by three space dimensions,[4] it is desirable for drawing purposes to define these dimensions and to fix their direction.

Height is the difference in elevation between any two points, measured as the perpendicular distance between a pair of horizontal planes that contain the points, as shown in Fig. 5.19. Edges of the object may or may not correspond with the height dimensions. Edge *AB* corresponds with the height dimension, while edge *CD* does not, but the space heights of *A* and *C* are the same, as are *B* and *D*. Height is always measured in a vertical direction and has

[4] *Space dimensions* and *dimensions of the object* should not be confused. The primary function of orthographic projection is to show the shape of the object. Size is not established until the figured dimensions and/or the scale are placed on the drawing. Space dimensions are *only* the measure of three-dimensional space.

FIG. 5.19. Definition of height. This is the difference in elevation between two points.

no relationship whatever to the shape of the object.

Width is the positional distance left to right between any two points measured as the perpendicular distance between a pair of profile planes containing the points. In Fig. 5.20 the relative width between points *E* and *G* on the left and *H* and *F* on the right of an object is shown by the dimension marked "width." The object edge *EF* is parallel to the width direction and corresponds with the width dimension, but edge *GH* slopes downward from *G* to *H*, so this actual edge of the object is longer than the width separating points *G* and *H*.

Depth[5] is the positional distance front to rear between any two points measured as the perpendicular distance between two frontal planes containing the points. Figure 5.21 shows two frontal planes, one at the front of the object containing points *J* and *L*, the other at the rear containing points *K* and *M*. The relative depth separating the front and rear of the object is the perpendicular distance between the planes as shown.

Any point can be located in space by giving its height, width, and depth relative to some other known point. Figure 5.22 shows a cube with four identified corners *A, B, C,* and *D*. Assuming that

[5] As in the civil engineering sense.

FIG. 5.20. Definition of width. This is the difference from left to right between two points.

FIG. 5.21. Definition of depth. This is the difference from front to rear between two points.

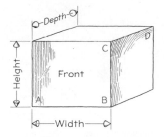

FIG. 5.22. Location of points in space. Height, width, and depth must be designated.

FIG. 5.23. The relationship between space directions and the planes of projection. View directions are perpendicular to their planes of projection. Height is parallel to frontal and profile planes, width is parallel to frontal and horizontal planes, and depth is parallel to horizontal and profile planes.

the plane containing points *A* and *B* is the front of the object, height, width, and depth would be as marked. Assuming also that point *A* is fixed in space, point *B* could be located from point *A* by giving the width dimension, including the statement that height and depth measurements are zero. *C* could be located from *A* by giving width, height, and zero depth. *D* could be located from *A* by giving width, height, and depth measurements.

5.9. THE RELATIONSHIP OF PLANES, VIEW DIRECTIONS, AND SPACE DIMENSIONS.
As explained in paragraphs 5.4 and 5.5, the object to be drawn may be thought of as surrounded by transparent planes upon which the actual views are projected. The three space dimensions—height, width, and depth—and the planes of projection are unchangeably oriented and connected with each other and with the view directions (Fig. 5.23). Each of the planes of projection is perpendicular, respectively, to its own view direction. Thus the frontal plane is perpendicular to the front-view direction, the horizontal plane is perpendicular to the top-view direction, and the profile plane is perpendicular to the side-view direction. The two space measurements for a view are parallel to the plane of

that view and perpendicular to the view direction. Therefore height and width are parallel to the frontal plane and perpendicular to the front-view direction; width and depth are parallel to the horizontal plane and perpendicular to the top-view direction; height and depth are parallel to the profile plane and perpendicular to the side-view direction. Note that the three planes of projection are *mutually* perpendicular, as are the three space measurements and the three view directions. Carefully study the views in Figs. 5.11 to 5.17 and note the space dimensions marked on each figure.

5.10. CLASSIFICATION OF SURFACES AND LINES.
Any object, depending upon its shape and space position, may or may not have some surfaces parallel or perpendicular to the planes of projection.

Surfaces are classified according to their space relationship with the planes of projection (Fig. 5.24). *Horizontal, frontal,* and *profile* surfaces are shown at (*A*). When a surface is inclined to two of the planes of projection (but perpendicular to the third), as at (*B*), the surface is said to be *auxiliary* or *inclined*. If the surface is at an angle to all three planes, as at (*C*), the term *oblique* or *skew* is used.

A—Horizontal, frontal, and profile surfaces

B—One auxiliary surface

C—One oblique surface

FIG. 5.24. Classification of surface positions.

Lines inclined by object shape	Lines inclined by object position	A horizontal line
A frontal line	A profile line	A horizontal-frontal line
A horizontal-profile line	A frontal-profile line	An oblique line

FIG. 5.25. Classification of line positions.

Intersection of two surfaces

Edge view of surface
Surface Limit

LEGEND
• Edge view of surface   ○ Intersection of two surfaces
△ Surface Limit

FIG. 5.26. What a line indicates.

The edges (represented by lines) bounding a surface may, because of the shape or position of the object, also be in a simple position or inclined to the planes of projection. A line in, or parallel to, a plane of projection takes its name from the plane. Thus a *horizontal line* is a line in a horizontal, a *frontal line* is a line in a frontal plane, and a *profile line* is a line in a profile

plane. When a line is parallel to two planes, the line takes the name of both planes, as *horizontal-frontal, horizontal-profile,* or *frontal-profile.* A line not parallel to any plane of projection is called an *oblique* or *skew line.* Figure 5.25 shows various positions of lines.

An edge appears in true length when it is parallel to the plane of projection, as a point when it is perpendicular to the plane, and shorter than true length when it is inclined to the plane. Similarly, a surface appears in true shape when it is parallel to the plane of projection, as a line when it is perpendicular to the plane, and foreshortened when it is inclined to the plane. As an example, Fig. 5.24*A* shows an object with its faces parallel to the planes of projection; top, front, and right-side surfaces are shown in true shape; and the object edges appear either in true length or as points. The inclined surface of the object at (*B*) does not show in true shape in any of the views but appears as an edge in the front view. The front and rear edges of the inclined surface are in true length in the front view and foreshortened in the top and side views. The top and bottom edges of the inclined surface appear in true length in top and side views and as

Definite corners join dashes

Arc dash starts at tangent point

Drilled hole

No space - beginning of line

Space here - continuation of line

No space - beginning of line

FIG. 5.27. Dashed-line technique. Note especially that a dashed line begins with a space when it continues in the same direction as a full line.

points in the front view. The oblique (skew) surface of the object at (*C*) does not show in true shape in any of the views, but each of the bounding edges shows in true length in one view and is foreshortened in the other two views.

5.11. REPRESENTATION OF LINES. Although uniform in appearance, the lines on a drawing may indicate three different types of directional change on the object. An *edge* view is a line showing the edge of a receding surface that is perpendicular to the plane of projection. An *intersection* is a line formed by the meeting of two surfaces when either one surface is parallel and one at an angle or both are at an angle to the plane of projection. A *surface limit* is a line that indicates the reversal of direction of a curved surface (or the series of points of reversal on a warped surface). Figure 5.26 illustrates the different line meanings, and these are further explained in paragraph 5.45.

5.12. HIDDEN FEATURES. To describe an object completely, a drawing should contain lines representing all the edges, intersections, and surface limits of the object. *In any view there will be some parts of the object that cannot be seen from the position of the observer, as they will be covered by portions of the object closer to the observer's eye.* The edges, intersections, and surface limits of these hidden parts are indicated by a discontinuous line called a *dashed line.*[6] See the alphabet of lines

[6] The line indicating hidden features has been traditionally known as a "dotted" line. However, in this treatise the term "dashed" line will be used because it accurately describes the appearance of the line. The term "hidden line," also sometimes used, is completely inaccurate because there are no *lines* on the object, and the line indicating hidden features *is* visible on the drawing.

(Figs. 2.56 and 2.57). In Fig. 5.27 the drilled hole[7] that is visible in the right-side view is hidden in the top and front views, and therefore it is indicated in these views by a dashed line showing the hole and the shape as left by the drill point. The milled slot (see Glossary) is visible in the front and side views but is hidden in the top view.

The beginner must pay particular attention to the execution of these dashed lines. If carelessly drawn, they ruin the appearance of a drawing and make it harder to read. Dashed lines are drawn lighter than full lines, of short dashes uniform in length with the space between them very short, about one-fourth the length of the dash. It is important that they start and stop correctly. A dashed line always starts with a dash except when the dash would form a continuation of a full line; in that case a space is left, as shown in Fig. 5.27. Dashes always meet at corners. An arc must start with a dash at the tangent point except when the dash would form a continuation of a straight or curved full line. The number of dashes used in a tangent arc should be carefully judged to maintain a uniform appearance (Fig. 5.28). Study carefully all dashed lines in Figs. 5.27 and 5.29.

[7] See Glossary and Index.

FIG. 5.28. Dashed arcs, actual size.

Space here – continuation of line

Space here – continuation of line

No space – beginning of line

FIG. 5.29. Dashed lines and arcs. Study this figure in conjunction with Figs. 5.27 and 5.28.

FIG. 5.30. Coincident-line study. Coincident lines are caused by the existence of features of identical size or position, one behind the other.

FIG. 5.31. Projection studies. Study each picture and the accompanying orthographic views and note the projection of all features.

5.13. CENTER LINES. In general, the first lines drawn in the layout of an engineering drawing are the center lines, which are the axes of symmetry for all symmetrical views or portions of views: (1) Every part with an axis, such as a cylinder or a cone, will have the axis drawn as a center line before the part is drawn. (2) Every circle will have its center at the intersection of two mutually perpendicular center lines.

The standard symbol for center lines on finished drawings is a fine line made up of alternate long and short dashes, as shown in the alphabet of lines (Figs. 2.56 and 2.57). Center lines are always extended slightly beyond the outline of the view or portion of the view to which they apply. They form the skeleton construction of the drawing; the important measurements are made and dimensions given to and from these lines. Study the center lines in Probs. 5.5.1 to 5.5.21.

5.14. PRECEDENCE OF LINES. In any view there is likely to be a coincidence of lines. Hidden portions of the object may project to coincide with visible portions. Center lines may occur where there is a visible or hidden outline of some part of the object.

Since the physical features of the object must be represented, full and dashed lines take precedence over all other lines. Since the visible outline is more prominent by space position, full lines take precedence over dashed lines. A full line could cover a dashed line, but a dashed line could not cover a full line. It is evident also that a dashed line could not occur as one of the boundary lines of a view.

When a center line and cutting-plane (explained in Chap. 8) line coincide, the one that is more important for the readability of the drawing takes precedence over the other.

Break lines (explained in Chap. 8) should be placed so that they do not spoil the readability of the over-all view.

Dimension and extension lines must always be placed so as not to coincide with other lines of the drawing.

The following list gives the order of precedence of lines:

1. Full line
2. Dashed line
3. Center line or cutting-plane line
4. Break lines
5. Dimension and extension lines
6. Crosshatch lines

Note the coincident lines in Fig. 5.30.

5.15. EXERCISES IN PROJECTION. The principal task in learning orthographic projection is to become thoroughly familiar with the theory and then to practice this theory by translating from a picture of the object to the orthographic views. Figures 5.31 and 5.32 contain a variety of objects shown by a pictorial sketch and translated into orthographic views. Study the objects and note (1) how the object is oriented in space, (2) why the orthographic views given were chosen, (3) the projection of visible features, (4) the projection of hidden features, and (5) center lines.

FIG. 5.32. Projection studies. Study each picture and the accompanying orthographic views and note the projection of all features.

FIG. 5.33. Object orientation. Use the simplest position. It will give the clearest possible representation and be the easiest to draw.

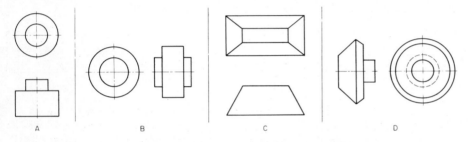

FIG. 5.34. Two-view drawings. These are sufficient for any object having a third view identical with or similar to one of the two views given.

FIG. 5.35. Geometric shapes combined. Even the most complicated objects can be analyzed as combined geometric shapes.

and facility in the use of instruments (Chap. 2), a knowledge of applied geometry (Chap. 3), and fluency in lettering (Chap. 4). In writing the graphic language, a topic we will now take up, always pay careful attention to accuracy and neatness.

5.17. OBJECT ORIENTATION. An object can, of course, be drawn in any of several possible positions. *The simplest position should be used*, with the object oriented so that the principal faces are perpendicular to the sight directions for the views and parallel to the planes of projection, as shown in Fig. 5.33. Any other position of the object, with its faces at some angle to the planes of projection, would complicate the drawing, foreshorten the object faces, and make the drawing difficult to make and to read.

5.18. SELECTION OF VIEWS. In practical work it is important to choose the combination of views that will describe the shape of an object in the best and most economical way. Often only two views are necessary. For example, a cylindrical shape, if on a vertical axis, would require only a front and top view; if on a horizontal axis, only a front and side view. Conic and pyramidal shapes can also be described in two views. Figure 5.34 illustrates two-view drawings. Some shapes will need more than the three regular views for adequate description.

Objects can be thought of as being made up of combinations of simple geometric solids, principally cylinders and rectangular prisms, and the views necessary to describe any object would be determined by the directions from which it would have to be viewed to see the characteristic contour shapes of

WRITING THE GRAPHIC LANGUAGE

5.16. The major objective of a student of the graphic language is to learn orthographic drawing. In addition to an understanding of the theory of orthographic projection, several aspects of drawing are necessary preliminaries to its study. These have been discussed in the preceding chapters and include skill these parts. Figure 5.35, for example, is made up of several prisms and cylinders. If each of these simple shapes is described and its relation to the others is shown, the object will be fully represented. In the majority of cases the three regular views—top, front, and side—are sufficient to do this.

Sometimes two views are proposed as sufficient for an object on the assumption that the contour in the third direction is of the shape that would naturally be expected. In Fig. 5.36, for example, the figure at (A) would be assumed to have a uniform cross section and be a square prism. But the two views *might* be the top and front views of a wedge, as shown in three views at (B). Two views of an object, as drawn at (C), do not describe the piece at all. The object at (A) might be assumed to be square in section, but it could as easily be round, triangular, quarter-round, or of another shape, which should have been indicated by a side view. Sketch several different front views for each top view, Fig. 5.37 A to C.

With the object preferably in its functioning position and *with its principal surfaces parallel to the planes of projection,* visualize the object, mentally picturing the orthographic views one at a time to decide on the best combination. In Fig. 5.38, the arrows show the direction of observation for the six principal views of an object, and indicate the mental process of the person making the selection. He notes that the front view would show the two horizontal holes as well as the width and height of the piece, that a top view is needed to show the contour of the vertical cylinder, and that the cutout corner calls for a side view to show its shape. He notes further that the right-side view would show this

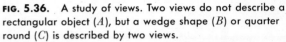

Two views do not describe the object

FIG. 5.36. A study of views. Two views do not describe a rectangular object (A), but a wedge shape (B) or quarter round (C) is described by two views.

cut in full lines, while the left-side view would give it in dashed lines. He observes also that neither a bottom view nor a rear view would be of any value in describing this object. Thus he has correctly chosen the front, top, and right-side views as the best combination for describing this piece. As a rule, the side view containing the fewer dashed lines is preferred. If the side views do not differ in this respect, the right-side view is preferred in standard practice.

In inventive and design work, any simple object should be visualized mentally and the view selected without a picture sketch. In complicated work, a pictorial or orthographic sketch may be used to advantage, but it should not be necessary, in any case, to sketch all possible views in order to make a selection.

FIG. 5.37. Top views given. One view does not describe an object unless some additional explanation is given. Sketch several front views for (A), (B), and (C).

FIG. 5.38. Selection of views. A view must be drawn in each direction (top, front, side) needed to conclusively designate every feature of the object, but unnecessary views must *not* be drawn.

FIG. 5.39. Selection-of-view study. Determine in each case (*A* to *K*) why the views shown are the best choice.

FIG. 5.40. Spacing the views on the paper. This is done graphically. Study the text carefully while referring to this figure and go through the steps by laying out the given object on a standard 11- × 17-in. sheet.

Study the drawings in Fig. 5.39 and determine why the views given were chosen.

5.19. DRAWING SIZES. Standard sizes for sheets of drawing paper, based on multiples of 8½ by 11 in. and 9 by 12 in., are specified for drawings by the ASA. Trimmed sizes of drawing paper and cloth, with recommended border and title dimensions, are given in Fig. 13.8.

5.20. SPACING THE VIEWS. View spacing is necessary so that the drawing will be balanced within the space provided. A little preliminary measuring, is necessary to locate the views. The following example describes the procedure: Suppose the piece illustrated in Fig. 5.40 is to be drawn full size on an 11- by 17-in. sheet. With an end-title strip, the working space inside the border will be 10½ by 15 in. The front view will require $7\frac{11}{16}$ in., and the side view 2¼ in. This leaves $5\frac{1}{16}$ in. to be distributed between the views and at the ends.

This preliminary planning need not be to exact dimensions, that is, small fractional values, such as $\frac{15}{64}$ in. or $3\frac{1}{32}$ in., can be adjusted to ¼ and 1 in., respectively, to speed up the planning. In this case the $7\frac{11}{16}$-in. dimension can be adjusted to 7¾ in.

Locate the views graphically and quickly by measuring with your scale along the bottom border line. Starting at the lower right corner, lay off first 2¼ in. and then 7¾ in. The distance between views can now be decided upon. It is chosen by eye to separate the views without crowding, yet placing them sufficiently close together so that the drawing will read easily (in this case 1½ in.). Measure the distance; half the remain-

FIG. 5.41. Projection of lines. Carry all views along together. The greatest mistake possible is to try to complete one view before starting another.

FIG. 5.42. Making a horizontal projection. This is the simplest operation in drawing. The T square provides *all* horizontal lines.

FIG. 5.43. Making a vertical projection. The 90° angle of a triangle with one leg on the horizontal T square produces the vertical.

ing distance to the left corner is the starting point of the front view. For the vertical location: the front view is 4 in. high, and the top view 2¼ in. deep. Starting at the upper left corner, lay off first 2¼ in. and then 4 in.; judge the distance between views (in this case 1 in.), and lay it off; then a point marked at less than half the remaining space will locate the front view, allowing more space at the bottom than at the top for appearance.

Block out lightly the spaces for the views, and study the over-all arrangement, because changes can easily be made at this stage. If it is satisfactory, select reference lines in each view from which the space measurements of height, width, and depth that appear in the view can be measured. The reference line may be an edge or a center line through some dominant feature, as indicated on Fig. 5.40 by the center lines in the top and side views and the medium-weight lines in all the views. The directions for height, width, and depth measurements for the views are also shown.

5.21. PROJECTING THE VIEWS. After laying out the views locate and draw the various features of the object. In doing this, carry the views *along together,* that is, *do not* attempt to complete one view before proceeding to another. Draw first the most characteristic view of a feature and then project it and draw it in the

other views before going on to a second feature. As an example, the vertical hole of Fig. 5.41 should be drawn first in the top view, and then the dashed lines representing the limiting elements or portions should be projected and drawn in the front and side views.

In some cases, one view cannot be completed before a feature has been located and drawn in another view. Study the pictorial drawing in Fig. 5.41, and note from the orthographic views that the horizontal slot must be drawn on the front view before the edge *AB* on the slanting surface can be found in the top view.

Projections (horizontal) between the front and side views are made by employing the T square to draw the required horizontal line (or to locate a required point), as illustrated in Fig. 5.42.

Projections (vertical) between the front and top views are made by using the T square and a triangle as illustrated in Fig. 5.43.

Projections between the top and side views cannot be projected directly but must be measured and transferred or found by special construction. In carrying the top and side views along together, it is usual to transfer the depth measurement from one to the other with dividers, as in Fig. 5.44*A,* or with a scale, as at (*B*). Another method, used for an irregular figure, is to "miter" the points around,

A

B

FIG. 5.44. Transferring depth measurements. Depth cannot be projected. Transfer the necessary distances with dividers, as at (*A*), or with scale, as at (*B*).

FIG. 5.45. Projecting depth measurements. A "miter line" at 45°, with horizontal and vertical projectors, transfers the depth from top to side view (or vice versa).

FIG. 5.46. Projections of surfaces bounded by linear edges. Depth measurements cannot be projected directly with T square and triangle. They must be transferred.

using a 45° line drawn through the point of intersection of the top and side views of the front face, extended as shown in Fig. 5.45. The method of Fig. 5.45, however, requires more time and care than the methods of Fig. 5.44 and is, therefore, not recommended.

5.22. PROJECTIONS OF SURFACES BOUNDED BY LINEAR EDGES. In drawing projections of inclined surfaces, in some cases the corners of the bounding edges may be used, and in other cases the bounding edges themselves may be projected. In illustration of these methods Fig. 5.46A shows a vertical hexagonal hole that is laid out from specifications in the top view. Then the front view is drawn by projecting from the six corners of the hexagon and drawing the four dashed lines to complete the front view. To get the side view, a horizontal projection is made from each corner on the front view to the side view, thus locating the height of the points needed on the side view. Then measurements D_1, D_2, and D_3 taken from the top view and transferred to the side view locate all six corners in the side view. The view is completed by connecting these corners and drawing the three vertical dashed lines. The object in Fig. 5.46B shows a horizontal slot running out on an inclined surface. In the front view the

true width and height of this slot is laid out from specifications. The projection to the side view is a simple horizontal projection for the dashed line, indicating the top surface of the slot. To get the top view, the width is projected from the front view and then the position of the runout line is measured (distance D_1) and transferred to the top view.

In summary, it may be stated that, if a line appears at some angle on a view, its two ends must be projected; if a line appears parallel to its path of projection, the complete line can be projected.

5.23. PROJECTIONS OF AN ELLIPTICAL BOUNDARY. The intersection of a cylindrical hole (or cylinder) with a slanting (inclined or skew) surface, as shown in Fig. 5.47, will be an ellipse, and some projections of this elliptical edge will appear as another ellipse. The projection can be made as shown in Fig. 5.47A by assuming a number of points on the circular view and projecting them to the edge view (front) and then to an adjacent view (side). Thus points 1 to 4 are located in the top view and projected to the front view, and the projectors are then drawn to the side view. Measurements of depth taken from the top view (as D_1) will locate the points in the side view. Draw a smooth curve through the points, using a french curve.

FIG. 5.47. Projection of an elliptical boundary. Points on the curve are projected to determine the curve (A), or the curve is determined by major and minor diameters (B).

For an ellipse on an inclined surface, the projection can also be made by establishing the major and minor diameters of the ellipse, as shown in Fig. 5.47B. A pair of diameters positioned so as to give the largest and smallest extent of the curve will give the required major and minor diameters. Thus, AB will project to the side view as the smaller, or minor, diameter $A_S B_S$, and CD will project as the larger, or major, diameter $C_S D_S$. The ellipse can then be drawn by one of the methods of paragraphs 3.50, 3.52, and 3.54.

If the surface intersected by the cylinder is skew, as shown in Fig. 5.48, a pair of perpendicular diameters located in the circular view will give a pair of conjugate diameters in an adjacent view. Therefore, $A_T B_T$ and $C_T D_T$ projected to the front view will give conjugate diameters, which can be employed as explained in paragraphs 3.51, 3.53, and 3.54 to draw the required ellipse.

In projecting the axes, they can be extended to the straight-line boundary of the skew surface. Thus the line 1–2 located in the front view and intersected by projection of $A_T B_T$ from the top view locates $A_F B_F$. Similarly, lines 3–4 and 5–6 at the ends of the axis CD locate $C_F D_F$.

5.24.   PROJECTIONS OF A CURVED BOUNDARY.   Any nongeometric curve (or a geometric curve not having established axes) must be projected by locating points on the curve. If the surface is in an inclined position, as in Fig. 5.49A, points may be assumed on the curve laid out from data (assumed in this case to be the top view) and projected first to the edge view (front) and then to an adjacent view (side). Measurements,

such as 1, 2, etc., from the top view transferred to the side view complete the projection. A smooth curve is then drawn through the points.

If the surface is skew, as in Fig. 5.49B, elements of the skew surface, such as 1'-1, 2'-2, etc., located in an adjacent view (by drawing the elements parallel to some known line of the skew surface, such as AB) make it possible to project points on the curve 1, 2, etc., to the adjacent view, as shown.

5.25.   PROJECTIONS BY IDENTIFYING CORNERS.   In projecting orthographic views or in comparing the views with a picture, it is helpful in some cases to letter (or number) the corners of the object and, with these identifying marks, to letter the corresponding points on each of the views, as in Fig. 5.50. Hidden points

FIG. 5.48.   Projection of an elliptical boundary by employing conjugate diameters. Refer to paragraph 3.53 and Fig. 3.68.

FIG. 5.49.   Projection of a curved boundary. Points are plotted and a smooth curve is drawn through them.

FIG. 5.50.   Identified corners. Each corner is lettered (or numbered) as an aid in making projections.

FIG. 5.51. Projection study. Number the corners of the orthographic views to correspond with the numbers on the picture.

FIG. 5.52. Stages in penciling. (A) block out the views; (B) locate center lines; (C) start details, drawing arcs first; (D) draw dominant details; (E) finish. See text for explanation.

directly behind visible points are lettered to the right of the letter of the visible point, and in this figure, they have been further differentiated by the use of "phantom," or dotted, letters. Study Fig. 5.51, and number or letter the corners of the three views to correspond with the pictorial view.

5.26.   ORDER OF DRAWING.   The order of working is important, as speed and accuracy depend largely upon the methods used in laying down lines. Avoid duplications of the same measurement and keep to a minimum changing from one instrument to another. Naturally, *all* measurements cannot be made with the scale at one time or *all* circles and arcs drawn without laying down the compass, but as much work as possible should be done with one instrument before shifting to another. An orderly placement of working tools on the drawing table will save time when changing instruments. The usual order of working is shown in Fig. 5.52.

1.   Decide what combination of views will best describe the object. A freehand sketch will aid in choosing the views and in planning the general arrangement of the sheet.

2.   Decide what scale to use, and by calculation or measurement find a suitable standard sheet size; or pick one of the standard drawing-sheet sizes and find a suitable scale.

3.   Space the views on the sheet, as described in paragraph 5.20.

4.   Lay off the principal dimensions, and then block in the views with light, sharp, accurate outline and center lines. Draw center lines for the axes of all symmetrical views or parts of views. Every cylindrical part will have a center line—the projection of the axis of the piece. Every circle will have two center lines intersecting at its center.

5.   Draw in the details of the part, beginning with the dominant characteristic shape and progressing to the minor details, such as fillets and rounds. Carry the different views along together, projecting a characteristic shape, as shown in one view to the other views, instead of finishing one view before starting another. Use a minimum of construction and draw the lines to finished weight, if possible, as the views are carried along. *Do not make the drawing lightly and then "heavy" the lines later.*

6.   Lay out and letter the title.

7.   Check the drawing carefully.

5.27.   ORDER OF TRACING.   If the drawing is to be traced in ink as an exercise in the use of instruments or for a finished orthographic drawing without dimensions, the order of working is as follows:

1.   Place the pencil drawing to be traced on the drawing board, carefully align it with the T square, and put thumbtacks in the two upper corners. Then place the tracing paper or cloth (dull side up) over the drawing. Holding the cloth in position, lift the tacks one at a time and replace them to hold both sheets. Then put tacks in the two lower corners.

2. To remove any oily film, prepare the surface of the cloth or paper by dusting it lightly with prepared pounce or soft white chalk. *Then wipe the surface perfecty clean with a soft cloth.*

3. Carefully set the pen of the compass to the correct line width, and ink all full-line circles and circle arcs, beginning with the smallest. Correct line weights are given in Fig. 2.57.

4. Ink dashed circles and arcs in the same order as full-line circles.

5. Carefully set the ruling pen to draw a line exactly the same width as the line in the full-line circles. The best way to match the straight lines to the circles is to draw with the compass and ruling pen outside the trim line of the sheet or on another sheet of the same kind of paper and adjust the ruling pen until the lines match.

6. Ink irregular curved lines.

7. Ink straight full lines in this order: horizontal (begin at the top of the sheet and work down), vertical (from the left side of the sheet to right), and inclined (uppermost first).

8. Ink straight dashed lines in the same order. Be careful to match these lines with the lines in the dashed circles.

9. Ink center lines.

10. Crosshatch all areas representing cut surfaces.

11. Draw pencil guide lines and letter the title.

12. Ink the border.

13. Check the tracing for errors and omissions.

5.28. ORTHOGRAPHIC FREEHAND DRAWING.
Facility in making freehand orthographic drawings is an essential part of the equipment of every engineer, and since ability in sketching presupposes some mastery of other skills (as we have seen in Chaps. 1 to 4), practice should be started early. Although full proficiency in freehand drawing is synonymous with mastery of the graphic language and is gained only after acquiring a background of knowledge and skill in drawing with instruments, sketching is an excellent method for learning the fundamentals of orthographic projection and can be used by the beginner even before he has had much practice with instruments. In training, as in professional work, time can be saved by working freehand instead of with instruments, as with this method more problems can be solved in an allotted amount of time.

Although some experienced teachers advocate the making of freehand sketches before practice in the use of instruments, some knowledge of the use of instruments and especially of applied geometry is a great help because the essentials of line tangents, connections, and intersections as well as the basic geometry of the part should be well defined on a freehand drawing. Drawing freehand is, of course, an excellent exercise in accuracy of observation. Figure 5.53 is an example of a good freehand drawing.

FIG. 5.53. A freehand drawing. Note the "roughness" of lines as compared with instrument work, but that all features are concise and readable.

FIG. 5.54. Different pencil grades, using medium pressure on paper of medium texture.

FIG. 5.55. Different pencil grades, using firm pressure on paper of medium texture.

5.29. LINE QUALITY FOR FREEHAND WORK. Freehand drawings are made on a wide variety of papers, ranging from inexpensive notebook or writing grades to the finer drawing and tracing papers and even pencil cloth. The surface texture— smooth, medium, or rough—combined with the grade of pencil and pressure used will govern the final result. If a bold rough effect is wanted for a scheming or idea sketch, a soft pencil and possibly rough paper would be employed. For a working sketch or for representation of an object with much small or intricate detail, a harder pencil and smoother paper would help to produce the necessary line quality.

Figure 5.54 is a photograph (reproduced about half size) showing lines made with pencils of various grades with medium pressure on paper of medium texture. Note that the 6B pencil gives a rather wide and rough line. As the hardness increases from 5B to 4B, etc., up to 2H, the line becomes progressively narrower and lighter in color. This does not mean that a wide line cannot be made with a fairly hard pencil, but with ordinary sharpening and with uniform pressure the softer grades wear down much faster than the harder grades. Unless a soft pencil such as 6B, 5B, or 4B is

sharpened after each short stroke, fine lines are impossible. Also, the harder grades such as F, H, and 2H, once sharpened, will hold their point for some time, and fairly fine lines can be obtained without much attention to the point. With ordinary pressure and normal use the soft grades give bold rough results, and the harder grades give light smooth lines.

5.30. RANGE OF PENCIL GRADES. The 6B grade is the softest pencil made and gives black, rough lines. With normal pressure, the line erases easily but is likely to leave a slight smear. The 6B, 5B, and 4B pencils should be used when a rather rough line is wanted, for example, for scheming or idea sketches, architectural renderings, and illustrations. The range from 3B to HB, inclusive, is usually employed for engineering sketches on medium-textured paper. For example, a sketch of a machine part with a normal amount of small detail can be made effectively with a 2B or B pencil. The smoothness and easy response to variations in pressure make these grades stand out as the preferred grades for a wide variety of work. However, for more critical work where there is much detail and also where the smear-

FIG. 5.56. Different pencil grades, using firm pressure on smooth paper.

FIG. 5.57. Different pencil grades, using firm pressure on rough paper.

ing of the soft grades is objectionable, the grades from F to 2H are used. For a sketch on fairly smooth paper, F or H are quite satisfactory. Grades harder than 2H are rarely used for freehand work. Incidentally, a fine pencil for ordinary writing is the 2B grade.

5.31. SHARPENING THE PENCIL. The pencil should be sharpened to a fairly long, conic point, as explained in paragraph 2.23. However, for freehand work a point not quite so sharp as for instrument drawing gives the desired line width without too much pressure. If after sharpening in the regular way the point is too fine, it can be rounded off slightly on a piece of scratch paper before use on the drawing.

5.32. PENCIL PRESSURE AND PAPER TEXTURE. The pencil grade, pressure, and paper texture all have an effect on the final result. Figure 5.54 shows the various pencil grades with medium pressure on paper of medium texture. To mark the difference in line quality obtainable by increasing the pressure, Fig. 5.55 shows the same paper but with firm pressure on the pencil. Note that the lines in Fig. 5.55 are much blacker than those in Fig. 5.54. The line quality of

Fig. 5.55 is about right for most engineering sketches. The rather firm opaque lines are preferred to the type in Fig. 5.54, especially if reproductions, either photographic or by transparency process, are to be made from the sketch.

To show the difference in line quality produced by paper texture, Fig. 5.56 shows the same firm pressure used in Fig. 5.55, but this time on smooth paper. In Fig. 5.57 the same pressure has been used on rough paper. Figure 5.58 is given to aid in comparing the effect of pressure and texture. On the left is the medium pressure on medium-textured paper; at (A), (B), and (C) firm pressure

FIG. 5.58. Comparison of different pencil pressures and paper surfaces. Medium pressure on medium paper—left column. Firm pressure on medium paper at (A), on smooth at (B), and on rough at (C).

FIG. 5.59. A freehand drawing on plain paper. This drawing was made by an expert of long experience. More "roughness" or "waviness" of lines is permissible on freehand than on instrument drawings, but care should be taken to keep all details concise and readable.

FIG. 5.60. A freehand drawing on coordinate tracing paper. The coordinates, on the back of the paper, aid greatly in making projections, in keeping the right proportions, and in drawing straight and accurate lines.

has been used but at (*A*) on medium-, at (*B*) on smooth-, and at (*C*) on rough-textured paper.

5.33. KINDS OF PAPER. *Plain and Coordinate.* Sketches are made for many purposes and under a variety of circumstances, and as a result on a number of different paper types and surfaces. A field engineer in reporting information to the central office may include a sketch made on notebook paper or a standard letterhead. On the other hand, a sketch made in the home office may be as important as any instrument drawing and for this reason may be made on good-quality drawing or tracing paper and filed and preserved with other drawings in a set. Figure 5.59 is an example of a sketch made on plain paper, which might be the letterhead paper of the field engineer or a piece of fine drawing or tracing paper. The principal difficulty in using plain paper is that proportions and projections must be estimated by eye. A good sketch on plain paper requires better-than-average ability and experience. Use of some variety of coordinate paper is a great aid in producing good results. There are many kinds of paper and coordinate divisions available, from smooth to medium texture and coordinate divisions of ⅛ or ¹⁄₁₀ to ½ in., printed on tracing paper or various weights of drawing paper. Usually one coordinate size on tracing paper and another (or the same) on drawing paper will supply the needs of an engineering office. Figure 5.60 is an example of a sketch on paper with coordinate divisions of ⅛ in. Figure 5.61 has divisions of ¼ in. Figure 5.62 is a sketch made on ¼-in. coordinate paper, actual size.

FIG. 5.61. A freehand drawing on coordinate notebook paper. Coordinates are ¼ in. apart.

FIG. 5.63. Sketching a vertical line. Draw downward with finger movement, overlapping the strokes for long lines.

FIG. 5.64. Sketching a horizontal line. Draw from left to right with wrist pivot for short lines and forearm movement for long lines. Overlap strokes if necessary.

The paper type, tracing or regular, is another factor to be considered. Reproduction by any of the transparency methods demands the use of tracing paper. If coordinate paper is used, it may be desirable to obtain prints on which the coordinate divisions do not show. Figure 5.60 is an example of a sketch on tracing paper with the coordinate divisions printed on the back of the paper in faint purplish-blue ink. Since the divisions are on the back, erasures and corrections can be made without erasing the coordinate divisions. Normally the divisions will not reproduce, so prints give the appearance of a sketch made on plain paper. Figure 5.61 is a sketch on standard, three-hole notebook paper with ¼-in. divisions in pale blue ink.

The use of coordinate paper is a great aid in freehand drawing, and speeds up the work considerably. Projections are much easier to make on it than on plain paper, and to transfer distances from top to side view, the divisions can be counted.

5.34. TECHNIQUE. The pencil is held with freedom and not close to the point. Vertical lines are drawn downward with a finger movement in a series of overlapping strokes, the hand somewhat in the position of Fig. 5.63. Horizontal lines are drawn with the hand shifted to the position of Fig. 5.64, using a wrist motion for short lines and a forearm motion for longer ones. In drawing any straight line between two points, *keep your eyes on the point to which the line is to go rather than on the point of the pencil.* Do not try to draw the whole length of a line in a single stroke. It may be helpful to draw a very light line first, as in

FIG. 5.65. Technique of sketching lines. (*A*) set direction with a *light* construction line; (*B*) first stroke; (*C*) complete line with a series of overlapping strokes.

FIG. 5.66. Sketching a horizontal line. Draw from left to right.

Fig. 5.65*A,* and then to sketch the finished line, correcting the direction of the light line and bringing the line to final width and blackness by using strokes of convenient length, as at (*B*). The finished line is shown at (*C*). Do not be disturbed by any nervous waviness. Accuracy of direction is more important than smoothness of line.

5.35. STRAIGHT LINES. Horizontal lines are drawn from left to right as in Fig. 5.66, vertical lines from top to bottom as in Fig. 5.67.

Inclined lines running downward from right to left (Fig. 5.68) are drawn with approximately the same movement as vertical lines, but the paper may be turned and the line drawn as a vertical (Fig. 5.69).

Inclined lines running downward from left to right (Fig. 5.70) are the hardest to draw because the hand is in a somewhat awkward position; for this reason, the paper should be turned and the line drawn as a horizontal, as in Fig. 5.71.

The sketch paper can easily be turned

in any direction to facilitate drawing the lines because there is no necessity to fasten the paper to a drawing-table top. The paper may, of course, be taped to a drawing board or attached to a clip board.

It is legitimate in freehand drawing to make long vertical or horizontal lines using the little finger as a guide along the edge of the pad or clip board. The three important things about a straight line are that it (1) be essentially straight, (2) be the right length, and (3) go in the right direction.

5.36 CIRCLES. Circles can be drawn by marking the radius on each side of the center lines. A more accurate method is to draw two diagonals in addition to the center lines and mark points equidistant from the center of the eight radii; at these points, draw short arcs perpendicular to the radii, and then complete the circle as shown in Fig. 5.72. A modification is to use a slip of paper as a trammel. Large circles can be done smoothly, after a little practice, by using the third or fourth finger as a

FIG. 5.67. Sketching a vertical line. Draw from top to bottom.

FIG. 5.68. Sketching an inclined line sloping downward from right to left. This line may be drawn in either direction, whichever is more convenient by personal preference.

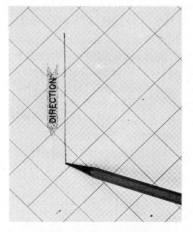

FIG. 5.69. Turning the paper to sketch an inclined line as a vertical line. This is often a great help because of the awkward position of the inclined line. An alternate turn is to the position of Fig. 5.71.

FIG. 5.70. Sketching an inclined line sloping downward from left to right. This is the most awkward position of any line. The paper should be turned as in Fig. 5.71 to aid in obtaining a smooth, accurate line.

FIG. 5.71. Paper turned to sketch an inclined line as a horizontal line. This should be done especially for the type of line shown in Fig. 5.70.

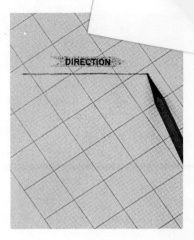

pivot, holding the pencil stationary and rotating the paper under it, or by holding two pencils and using one as a pivot about which to rotate the paper. Another way of drawing a circle is to sketch it in its circumscribing square.

5.37. PROJECTION. In making an orthographic sketch, remember and apply the principles of projection and applied geometry. Sketches are *not* made to scale but are made to show fair proportions of objects sketched. It is legitimate, however, when coordinate paper is used, to count the spaces or rulings as a means of proportioning the views and as an aid in making projections. Take particular care to have the various details of the views in good projection from view to view. It is an inexcusable mistake to have a detail sketched to a different size on one view from that on another.

When working on plain paper, projections between the top and front views or between the front and side views are easily made by simply "sighting" between the views or using *very* light construction lines, as in Fig. 5.73. Projections between the top and

FIG. 5.72. Method of drawing freehand circles. (A) draw center lines; (B) draw diagonals; (C) space points on the circle with *light,* short lines (by eye); (D) correct and begin filling in; (E) finish.

A   B   C   D   E

side views are laid off by judging the distance by eye, by measuring the distance by holding the finger at the correct distance from the end of the pencil and transferring to the view, or by marking the distance on a small piece of paper and transferring to the view. Note in Fig. 5.73 that distances A, B, and others could be transferred from the top to the side view by the methods just mentioned.

Even though freehand lines are somewhat "wavy" and not so accurate in position as ruled lines, a good freehand drawing should present the same clean appearance as a good instrument drawing.

FIG. 5.73. Freehand projections. Judge the projections by eye (aided by coordinate lines if lined paper is used). Judge the measurements (A and B) by eye; or measure the distances with a pencil or by marking on a strip of paper.

5.38. METHOD. Practice in orthographic freehand drawing should be started by drawing the three views of a number of simple pieces, developing the technique and the ability to "write" the orthographic language, while exercising the constructive imagination in visualizing the object by looking at the three projections. Observe the following order of working:

1. Study the pictorial sketch and decide what combination of views will best describe the shape of the piece.

2. Block in the views, as in Fig. 5.74*A*, using a very light stroke of a soft pencil (2B, B, HB, or F) and spacing the views so as to give a well-balanced appearance to the drawing.

3. Build up the detail in each view, carrying the three views along together as at (*B*).

4. Brighten the outline of each view with bold strokes as at (*C*).

5. Brighten the detail with bold strokes, thus completing the full lines of the sketch as at (*D*).

6. Sketch in all dashed lines, using a stroke of medium weight and making them lighter than the full lines, as at (*E*), thus completing the shape description of the object.

7. Check the drawing carefully. Then cover the pictorial sketch and visualize the object from the three views.

After drawing a number of simple pieces freehand, try more complicated problems such as Probs. 5.2.9 to 5.2.37. Faintly ruled coordinate paper (illustrated in Fig. 5.60) may be used if desired.

5.39 SHOP PROCESSES. Shop processes are properly a part of dimensioning and specification for working drawings and in this text are given in Chap. 10, preceding dimensioning and tolerancing, screw threads and fasteners, and working drawings. However, in order to read the pictorial drawings (problems) to be drawn in orthographic projection, some knowledge of processing fundamentals is necessary. Therefore, Chap. 10, Drawings and the Shop, should be studied, especially for a knowledge of hole processing (drilling, reaming, etc.) and for information on fillets, rounds, finished surfaces, and methods of part manufacture. Consult the Glossary for unfamiliar terms.

5.40. DIMENSIONING SYSTEMS. For the same reasons given in the previous paragraph, some knowledge of dimensioning systems is necessary at this time. Basically, two methods are used: fractional and decimal. These are explained in Chap. 11, paragraph 11.12. Note especially that a decimally dimensioned part is laid out with a decimal scale.

FIG. 5.74. Stages in making an orthographic freehand drawing. (*A*) block in view spaces; (*B*) locate principal features with light lines; (*C*), (*D*), and (*E*) finish progressively to final weight, working from dominant to smaller details.

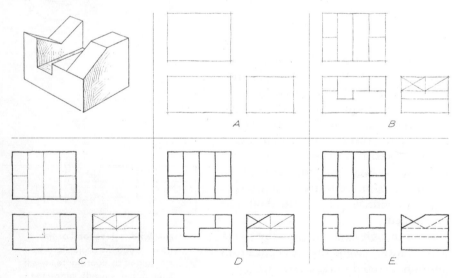

READING THE GRAPHIC LANGUAGE

5.41. ORTHOGRAPHIC READING. The engineer must be able to *read* and *write* the orthographic language. The necessity of learning to read is absolute because everyone connected with technical industry must be able to read a drawing without hesitation or concede technical illiteracy.

Reading the orthographic language is a mental process; a drawing is not read aloud. To describe even a simple object with words is almost impossible. Reading proficiency develops with experience, as similar conditions and shapes occur so often that a person in the field gradually acquires a background of knowledge that enables him to visualize readily the shapes shown. Experienced readers read quickly because they can draw upon their knowledge and recognize familiar shapes and combinations without hesitation. However, reading a drawing should always be done carefully and deliberately, as a whole drawing cannot be read at a glance any more than a whole page of print.

5.42. PREREQUISITES AND DEFINITION. Before attempting to read a drawing, familiarize yourself with the principles of orthographic projection, as explained in paragraphs 5.1 to 5.14. Keep constantly in mind the arrangement of views and their projection, the space measurements of height, width, and depth, what each line represents, etc.

Visualization is the medium through which the shape information on a drawing is translated to give the reader an understanding of the object represented. The *ability to visualize* is often thought to be a "gift" that some people possess and others do not. This, however, is not true. Any person of reasonable intelligence has a visual memory, as can be seen from his ability to recall and describe scenes at home, actions at sporting events, and even details of acting and facial expression in a play or motion picture.

The ability to visualize a shape shown on a drawing is almost completely governed by a person's knowledge of the principles of orthographic projection. The common adage that "the best way to learn to read a drawing is to learn how to make one" is quite correct, because in learning to make a drawing you are forced to study and apply the principles of orthographic projection.

Reading a drawing can be defined as *the process of recognizing and applying the principles of orthographic projection to interpret the shape of an object from the orthographic views.*

5.43. METHOD OF READING. A drawing is read by visualizing units or details one at a time from the orthographic projection and mentally orienting and combining these details to interpret the whole object finally. The form taken in this visualization, however, may not be the same for all readers or for all drawings. Reading is primarily a reversal of the process of making drawings; and inasmuch as drawings are usually first made from a picture of the object, the beginner often attempts to carry the reversal too completely back to the pictorial. The result is that the orthographic views of an object like those shown in Fig. 5.75 are translated to the accompanying picture, with the thought of the object as positioned in space or

FIG. 5.75. Orthographic views and picture. Simple objects can be visualized in pictorial form but for complex objects this is difficult.

FIG. 5.76. Views to be read. Compare this drawing with Fig. 5.77.

FIG. 5.77. Views to be read. Compare this drawing with Fig. 5.76.

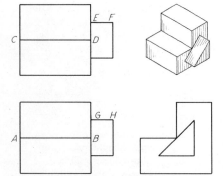

FIG. 5.78. The meaning of lines. *AB, CD,* and *EF* represent the edge views of surfaces. *GH* represents an edge. Study carefully, reading *all* views.

placed on a table or similar surface. Another will need only to recognize in the drawing the geometry of the solid, which in the case of Fig. 5.75 would be a rectangular prism so high, so wide, and so deep with a hole passing vertically through the center of it. This second reader will have read the views just as completely as the first but with much less mental effort.

To most, it is a mental impossibility (and surely unnecessary) to translate more than the simplest set of orthographic views into a complete pictorial form that can be pictured in its entirety. Actually, the reader goes through a routine pattern of procedure (listed in paragraph 5.44). Much of this is done subconsciously. For example, consider the object in Fig. 5.76. A visible circle is seen in the top view. Memory of previous projection experience indicates that this must be a hole or the end of a cylinder. The eyes rapidly shift back and forth from the top view to the front view, aligning features of the same size ("in projection"), with the mind assuming the several possibilities and finally accepting the fact that, because of the dashed lines and their extent in the front view, the circle represents a hole that extends through the prism. Following a similar pattern of analysis, the reader will find that Fig. 5.77 represents a rectangular prism surmounted by a cylinder. This thinking is done so rapidly that the reader is scarcely aware of the steps and processes involved.

The foregoing is the usual method of reading; but how does the beginner develop this ability?

First, as stated in paragraph 5.42, he must have a reasonable knowledge of the principles of orthographic projection.

Second, as described in paragraphs 5.45 and 5.46 he must acquire a complete understanding of the principles behind the meaning of lines, areas, etc., and the mental process involved in interpreting them, as these principles are applied in reading.

There is very little additional learning required. Careful study of all these items plus practice will develop the ability and confidence needed.

5.44. PROCEDURE FOR READING. The actual steps in reading are not always identical because of the wide variety of subject matter (drawings). Nevertheless, the following outline gives the basic procedure and will serve as a guide:

First, orient yourself with the views given.

Second, obtain a general idea of the over-all shape of the object. Think of each view as the object itself, visualizing yourself in front, above, and at the side, as is done in making the views. Study the dominant features and their relation to one another.

Third, start reading the simpler individual features, beginning with the most dominant and progressing to the subordinate. Look for familiar shapes or conditions that your memory retains from previous experience. Read all views of these familiar features to note the extent of holes, thickness of ribs and lugs, etc.

Fourth, read the unfamiliar or complicated features. Remember that every point, line, surface, and solid appears in every view and that you must find the projection of every detail in the given views to learn the shape.

Fifth, as the reading proceeds, note the relationship between the various portions or elements of the object. Such items as the number and spacing of holes, placement of ribs, tangency of surfaces, and the proportions of hubs, etc., should be noted and remembered.

Sixth, reread any detail or relationship not clear at the first reading.

5.45. THE MEANING OF LINES. As explained in paragraph 5.11, a line on a drawing indicates (1) the *edge of a surface,* (2) an *intersection of two surfaces,* or (3) a *surface limit.* Because a line on a view may mean any one of these three conditions, the corresponding part of another view must be consulted to determine the meaning. For example, the meaning of line *AB* on the front view of Fig. 5.78 cannot be determined until the side view is consulted. The line is then found to be the edge view of the horizontal surface of the cutout corner. Similarly, line *CD* on the top view cannot be fully understood without consulting the side view, where it is identified as the edge view of the vertical surface of the cutout corner. Lines *EF* on the top view and *GH* on the front view are identical in appearance. However, the side view shows that line *EF* represents the edge view of the rear surface of the triangular block and that line *GH* is the intersection of the front and rear surfaces of the triangular block.

The top and front views of the objects shown in Figs. 5.78 and 5.79 are identical. Nevertheless, lines *AB* and *CD* in Fig. 5.79 do not represent what they represent in Fig. 5.78 but are in Fig. 5.79 the intersection of two surfaces. Also, lines *EF* and *GH* in Fig. 5.79 are identical in appearance with those in Fig. 5.78, but in Fig. 5.79 they represent the surface limits of the circular boss.

From Figs. 5.78 and 5.79 it is readily seen that a drawing cannot be read by looking at a single view. Two views are not always enough to describe an object completely, and when three or more views are given, all must be consulted to be sure that the shape has been read correctly. To illustrate with Fig. 5.80, the front and top views show what appears to be a rectangular projection on the front of the object, but the side view shows this projection to be quarter-round. Similarly, in the front and side views the rear portion of the object appears to be a rectangular prism, but the top view shows that the two vertical rear edges are rounded.

A shape cannot be assumed from one or two views—*all the views must be read carefully.*

The several *lines* representing one feature must be read in all the views. As an exercise in reading the lines on an orthographic drawing, find *all* the lines representing the hole, triangular prism, slot, and cutoff corner in Fig. 5.81.

5.46. THE MEANING OF AREAS. The term "area" as used here means the contour limits of a surface or combination of tangent surfaces as seen in the different orthographic views. To illustrate, an area of a view as shown in

FIG. 5.79. The meaning of lines. *AB* and *CD* represent the intersection of two surfaces. *EF* and *GH* represent a curved-surface limit. Compare this drawing carefully with Fig. 5.78.

FIG. 5.80. Read all views. Read each feature by looking at all three views; then school yourself to remember all features.

FIG. 5.81. Read all views, features, and lines. This drawing is more complex than Fig. 5.80. Read all features in all views, by reading all lines, then school yourself to remember all features.

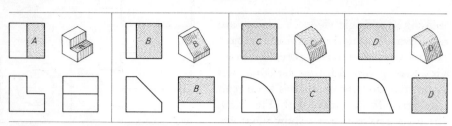

A–Surface in true shape   B–Surface foreshortened   C–Curved surface   D–Tangent surfaces

FIG. 5.82. The meaning of areas. Two views must be read to determine what an area means. Compare *A* with *B* and *C* with *D*.

FIG. 5.83. Oblique surface. This will appear as an area in all three principal views.

FIG. 5.84. Oblique surface. Note that area *A*, representing this surface, appears in all views as an area of similar shape formed by lines connected in the same order.

FIG. 5.85. Auxiliary surface. Note that the surface appears as an edge in the front view and as an area of similar shape in top and side views.

FIG. 5.86. Adjacent areas. *A*, *B*, *C*, and *D* all lie in different planes.

Fig. 5.82 may represent (1) a surface in true shape as at *A*, (2) a foreshortened surface as at *B*, (3) a curved surface as at *C*, or (4) a combination of tangent surfaces as at *D*.

When a surface is in an oblique position, as surface *E* of Fig. 5.83, it will appear as an area in all principal views of the surface. A study of the surfaces in Figs. 5.82, 5.83, and others will establish with the force of a rule that *a plane surface, whether it is positioned in a horizontal, frontal, profile, or an inclined or skew position, will always appear in a principal orthographic view as a line or an area.* Principal views that show a skew surface as an area in more than one view will always show it in like shape. As an example, surface *A* of Fig. 5.84 appears as a triangular area in all the principal views; the length of the edges and the angles between the edges may change, but all views show the area with the same number of sides. It should be noted that a plane surface bounded by a certain number of sides can never

appear to have more or fewer sides except when the surface appears as an edge. Moreover, the sides in any view will always connect in the same sequence. For example, in Fig. 5.85 the front view shows surface *B* as an edge; the top and side views show the surface as an area having a similar shape, the same number of sides, and with the corners in the same sequence.

5.47.   ADJACENT AREAS. No two adjacent areas can lie in the same plane. It is simple logic that, if two adjacent areas *did* lie in the same plane, there would be no boundary between the areas, and therefore, orthographically, the two adjacent areas would not exist. As an illustration, note that in Fig. 5.86 areas *A*, *B*, *C*, and *D* are shown in the front and side views to lie in different planes.

Further proof of these principles is given by Fig. 5.87, in which two top views are shown. By analysis of the projection between top and front views, it is seen that areas *G* and *H* shown in the top views must lie in planes *G* and *H*, respectively, shown in the front view. Also, by projection, it is seen that area *J* of top view *A* must lie in plane *H* and that area *K* must lie in plane *G*. Because areas *H* and *J* lie in plane *H*, and areas *G* and *K* lie in plane *G*, the cor-

FIG. 5.87. Adjacent areas. Read all areas and note that *B* is the correct top view.

FIG. 5.88. Reading hidden areas. Read all views and note that areas *A*, *B*, and *C* do not represent three different surfaces.

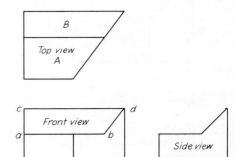

FIG. 5.89. Reading lines and areas. Read this drawing to determine how areas *A* and *B* of the top view are represented in the front and side views.

rect top view, therefore, is top view *B*.

Hidden areas may sometimes be confusing to read because the areas may overlap or even coincide with each other. For example, areas *A*, *B*, and *C* in Fig. 5.88 are not separate areas because they are all formed by the slot on the rear of the object. The apparent separation into separate areas is caused by the dashed lines from the rectangular hole, which is not connected with the slot in any way.

5.48. READING LINES AND AREAS. The foregoing principles regarding the meaning of lines and areas must be used to analyze any given set of views by correlating a surface appearing in one view as a line or an area with its representation in the other views, in which it may appear as a line or an area. Study, for example, Fig. 5.89, first orienting yourself with the given views. From their arrangement, the views are evidently top, front, and right-side. An over-all inspection of the views does not reveal a familiar geometric shape, such as a hole or boss, so an analysis of the surfaces is necessary. Beginning with the trapezoidal area *A* in the top view and

then moving to the front view, note that a similar-shaped area of the same width is not shown; therefore, the front view of area *A* must appear as an edge, the line *ab*. Next, consider area *B* in the top view. It is shown as a trapezoidal area (four sides) the full width of the view. Again, going to the front view for a mating area or line, the area *abcd* is of similar shape and has the same number of sides with the corners in projection. Area *abcd*, therefore, satisfies the requirements of orthographic projection and is the front view of area *B*. The side view should be checked along with the other views to see if it agrees. Proceed in this way with additional areas, correlating them one with another and visualizing the shape of the complete object.

Memory and experience aid materially in reading any given drawing. However, every new set of views must be approached with an open mind because sometimes a shape that looks like a previously known condition will crowd the correct interpretation from the mind of the reader. For example, area *E* in Fig. 5.90 is in a vertical position. The front view in Fig. 5.91 is identical with the

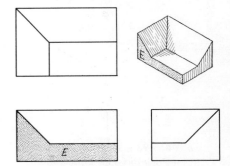

FIG. 5.90. Identical areas may have different meanings. Compare area *E* with area *F* of Fig. 5.91.

FIG. 5.91. Identical areas may have different meanings. Compare area *F* with area *E* of Fig. 5.90.

FIG. 5.92. Identification of corners. This helps to determine mating lines and areas in the views.

FIG. 5.93. Pictorial axes (isometric). This is the "framework" for sketching in isometric. See Fig. 5.94.

front view in Fig. 5.90, but in Fig. 5.91 the surface F is inclined to the rear and is not vertical.

5.49. READING CORNERS AND EDGES. The corners and edges of areas may be numbered or lettered to identify them in making additional views or as an aid in reading some complicated shape. If there are no coincident conditions, the corners and edges are easily named by projection; that is, the top view is directly over the front view, and the side view lies on a horizontal projector to the front view. When coincident conditions are present, it may be necessary to coordinate a point with an adjacent point as shown in Fig. 5.92. Corner c in the front view (c_F) may be in projection with c_T at any one of the three positions marked 1, 2, 3. However, the point c is one end of an edge dc, and the front view of c must therefore be at position 2. An experienced reader could probably make the above observations without marking the points, but a beginner can in many cases gain much valuable experience by marking corners and edges, especially if the object he is studying has an unusual combination of surfaces.

5.50. LEARNING TO READ BY SKETCHING. A drawing is interpreted by mentally understanding the shape of the object represented. You can prove that you have read and understood a drawing by making the object in wood or metal, by modeling it in clay, or by making a pictorial sketch of it. Sketching is the usual method. Before attempting to make a pictorial sketch, make a preliminary study of the method of procedure. Pictorial sketching may be based on a skeleton of three axes, one vertical and two at 30°,[8] representing three mutually perpendicular lines (Fig. 5.93). On these axes are marked the proportionate width, depth, and height of any rectangular figure. Circles are drawn in their circumscribing squares.

Study the views given in Fig. 5.94, following the procedure outlined in paragraph 5.44. Then with a soft pencil (F) and notebook paper make a *very light* pictorial construction sketch of the object, estimating its height, width, and depth and laying the distances off on the axes as at (A); sketch the rectangular box that would enclose the piece, or the

[8] Isometric position. Oblique or other pictorial methods may also be used. See Chap. 6 for pictorial methods.

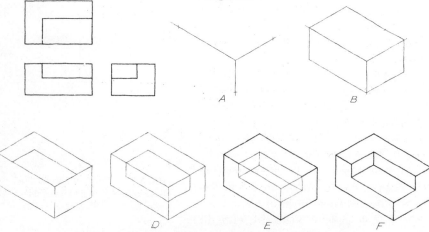

FIG. 5.94. Stages in making a pictorial sketch. (A) draw axes; (B) block in the enclosing shape; (C) and (D) draw outline of detail on top, front, and side; (E) and (F) finish by completing surfaces represented on the orthographic drawing.

FIG. 5.95. A drawing to be read. This is the object modeled in Fig. 5.96.

block from which it could be cut (*B*). On the top face of this box sketch lightly the lines that occur on the top view of the orthographic drawing (*C*). Note that some of the lines in top views may not be in the top plane. Next sketch lightly the lines of the front view on the front face of the box or block, and if a side view is given, outline it similarly (*D*). Now begin to cut the figure from the block, strengthening the visible edges and adding the lines of intersection where faces of the object meet (*E*). Omit edges that do not appear as visible lines unless they are necessary to describe the piece. Finish the sketch, checking back to the three-view drawing. The construction lines need not be erased unless they confuse the sketch.

5.51. PICTORIAL DRAWING AND SKETCHING. The foregoing discussion of pictorial sketching should suffice as a guide for making rough sketches as an aid in reading a drawing. However, many experienced teachers like to correlate orthographic drawing, sketching, and reading, with pictorial drawing (which we will take up in Chap. 6). This is found helpful not only because it gives the student valuable training in understanding all methods of graphic expression but also because the making of a pictorial drawing from an othographic drawing forces the student to read the orthographic drawing.

5.52. LEARNING TO READ BY MODELING. Modeling the object in clay or modeling wax is another interesting, and effective aid in learning to read a drawing. It is done in much the same way as reading by pictorial sketching. Some shapes are easily modeled by cutting out from the enclosing block; others, by first

FIG. 5.96. Stages in modeling. (*A*) score details on top, front, and side; then make cuts at (*B*), (*C*), (*D*), and (*E*) to finish as at (*F*).

analyzing and dividing the object into its basic geometric shapes and then combining these shapes.

Starting with a rectangular block of clay, perhaps 1 in. square and 2 in. long, read Fig. 5.95 by cutting the figure from the solid. With the point of the knife or a scriber, scribe lightly the lines of the three views on the three corresponding faces of the block (Fig. 5.96*A*). The first cut could be as shown at (*B*) and the second as at (*C*). Successive cuts are indicated at (*D*) and (*E*), and the finished model is shown at (*F*).

Figure 5.97 illustrates the type of

FIG. 5.97. A built-up model. Separate pieces (*A*) are combined to make the finished model (*B*).

FIG. 5.98. Shape breakdown for volume and weight calculations. Each feature of the object is analyzed individually.

BREAKDOWN

DECIMAL EQUIVALENTS			
1/2	0.5	1/16	0.0625
1/4	0.25	3/16	0.1875
3/4	0.75	5/16	0.3125
		7/16	0.4375
1/8	0.125	9/16	0.5625
3/8	0.375	11/16	0.6875
5/8	0.625	13/16	0.8125
7/8	0.875	15/16	0.9375

BEARING REST		MATERIAL		WT. — LB. PER CU. IN.	
PART	DIMENSIONS			PLUS VOLUME	MINUS VOLUME
A					
B					
C					
D					
E					
F					
G					
H					
			TOTALS		

WEIGHT PER CUBIC INCH	TOTAL NET VOLUME IN CUBIC INCHES	
GRAY CAST IRON 0.260 LB		
TOBIN BRONZE 0.304 LB	WEIGHT IN POUNDS	
CAST STEEL 0.282 LB		

model that can be made by building up the geometric shapes of which the object is composed.

5.53. CALCULATION OF VOLUME AS AN AID IN READING.

To calculate the volume of an object, it must be broken down into its simple geometric elements and the shape of each element must be carefully analyzed before beginning computation. Thus the calculation of volume is primarily an exercise in reading a drawing. Before the computations are completed, the object has usually been visualized, but the mathematical record of the volume of each portion and the correct total volume and weight are proof that the drawing has been read and understood.

The procedure closely follows the usual steps in reading a drawing. Figure 5.98 illustrates the method.

1. Study the orthographic drawing and pick out the principal masses (A, B, and C on the breakdown and in the pictorial drawing). Pay no attention in the beginning to holes, rounds, etc., but study each principal over-all shape and its relation to the other masses of the object. Record the dimensions of each of these principal portions and indicate plus volume by placing a check mark in the plus-volume column.

2. Examine each principal mass and find the secondary masses (D and E) that must be added to or subtracted from the principal portions. Bosses, lugs, etc., must be added; cutout portions, holes, etc., subtracted. Record the dimensions of these secondary masses, being careful to indicate plus or minus volume.

3. Further limit the object to its actual shape by locating smaller details, such as holes, fillets, rounds, etc. (parts F, G, and H). Record the dimensions of these parts.

4. Compute the volume of each portion. This may be done by longhand multiplication or, more conveniently, with a slide rule. Record each volume in the proper column, plus or minus. When all unit volumes are completed, find the net volume by subtracting total minus volume from total plus volume.

5. Multiply net volume by the weight per cubic inch of metal to compute the total weight.

The calculations are simplified if all fractional dimensions are converted to decimal form. When a slide rule is used, fractions *must* be converted to decimals. A partial conversion table is given in Fig. 5.98 and a more complete one in the Appendix.

Complete volume and weight calculation not only gives training in recognition of the fundamental geometric portions of an object but also serves to teach neat and concise working methods in the recording of engineering data.

5.54. EXERCISES IN READING. Figures 5.99 and 5.100 contain a number of three-view drawings of block shapes

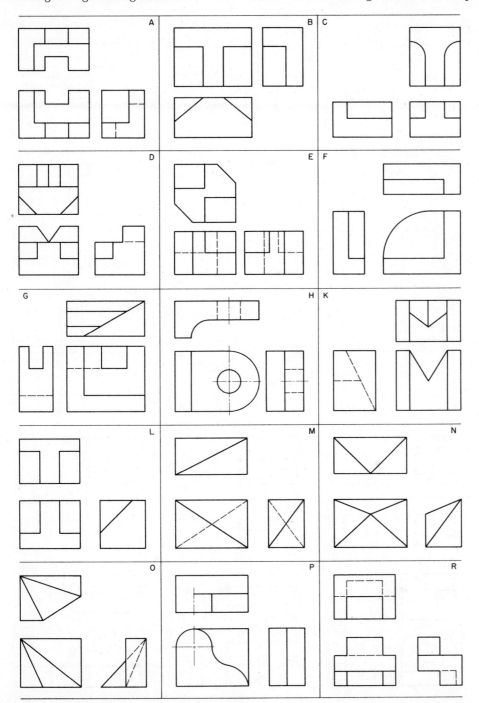

FIG. 5.99. Reading exercises. Read each drawing, (A) to (R). Make pictorial sketches or models if necessary for understanding.

made for exercises in reading orthographic projection and translating into pictorial sketches or models. Proceed as described in the previous paragraphs, making sketches not less than 4 in. overall. Check each sketch to be sure that all

FIG. 5.100. Reading exercises. Read each drawing, (A) to (R). Make pictorial sketches or models if necessary for understanding.

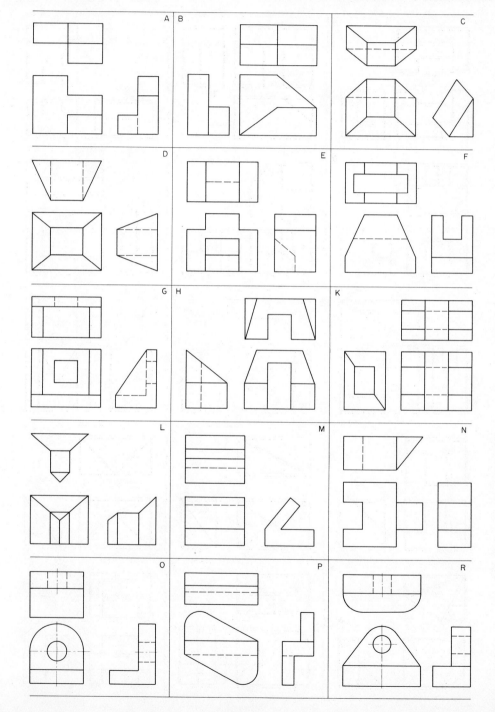

intersections are shown and that the original three-view drawing could be made from the sketch. In each drawing in Fig. 5.101 some lines have been intentionally omitted. Read the drawings and supply the missing lines.

FIG. 5.101. Missing-line exercises. Read each drawing, (A) to (R), and sketch the lines missing on the views. Check carefully. Use a model or sketch, if necessary, as an aid in locating all lines.

PROBLEMS

For practice in orthographic freehand drawing, select problems from the following group.

GROUP 1.   FREEHAND PROJECTIONS FROM PICTORIAL VIEWS

The figures for Probs. 5.1.1 to 5.1.16 contain a number of pictorial sketches of pieces of various shapes which are to be translated into three-view orthographic freehand drawings. Make the drawings of fairly large size, the front view, say, 2 to 2½ in. in length, and estimate the proportions of the different parts by eye or from the proportionate marks shown but without measuring. The problems are graduated in difficulty for selection depending on ability and experience.

Problem 5.1.16 gives a series that can be used for advanced work in freehand drawing or that can be used later on, by adding dimensions, as dimensioning studies or freehand working-drawing problems.

PROB. 5.1.1.

PROB. 5.1.2.

PROB. 5.1.3.

PROB. 5.1.4.

PROB. 5.1.5.

PROB. 5.1.6.

A

B

C

D

PROB. 5.1.7.

A

B

C

D

PROB. 5.1.8.

A

B

C

D

PROB. 5.1.9.

A

B

C

D

PROB. 5.1.10.

A

B

C

D

PROB. 5.1.11.

A

B

C

D

PROB. 5.1.12.

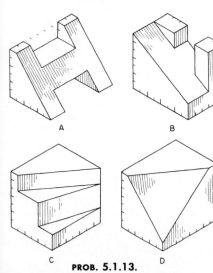

A

B

C

D

PROB. 5.1.13.

A

B

C

D

PROB. 5.1.14.

A

B

C

D

PROB. 5.1.15.

PROB. 5.1.16.   Pieces to be drawn freehand in orthographic projection.

Select problems from the following groups for practice in projection drawing. Most of the problems are intended to be drawn with instruments but will give valuable training done freehand, on plain or coordinate paper.

The groups are as follows:

2. Projections from pictorial views
3. Special scales, decimal sizes, projections from photo drawings, references to Appendix material
4. Views to be supplied, freehand
5. Views to be supplied
6. Views to be changed
7. Drawing from memory
8. Volume and weight calculations with slide rule

GROUP 2. PROJECTIONS FROM PICTORIAL VIEWS

5.2.1. Draw the top, front, and right-side views of the beam support.

5.2.2. Draw the top, front, and right-side views of the vee rest.

5.2.3. Draw three views of the saddle bracket.

5.2.4. Draw three views of the wedge block.

5.2.5. Draw three views of the slotted wedge.

5.2.6. Draw three views of the pivot block.

5.2.7. Draw three views of the inclined support.

5.2.8. Draw three views of the corner stop.

5.2.9. Draw three views of the switch base.

PROB. 5.2.1. Beam support.

PROB. 5.2.2. Vee rest.

PROB. 5.2.3. Saddle bracket.

PROB. 5.2.4. Wedge block.

PROB. 5.2.5. Slotted wedge.

PROB. 5.2.6. Pivot block.

PROB. 5.2.9. Switch base.

PROB. 5.2.7. Inclined support.

PROB. 5.2.8. Corner stop.

5.2.10. Draw three views of the adjusting bracket.

5.2.11. Draw three views of the guide base.

5.2.12. Draw three views of the bearing rest.

5.2.13. Draw three views of the swivel yoke.

5.2.14. Draw three views of the truss bearing.

5.2.15. Draw three views of the sliding-pin hanger.

5.2.16. Draw two views of the wire thimble.

5.2.17. Draw three views of the hanger jaw.

5.2.18. Draw three views of the adjustable jaw.

PROB. 5.2.10. Adjusting bracket.

PROB. 5.2.11. Guide base.

PROB. 5.2.12. Bearing rest.

PROB. 5.2.13. Swivel yoke.

PROB. 5.2.14. Truss bearing.

PROB. 5.2.15. Sliding-pin hanger.

PROB. 5.2.16. Wire thimble.

PROB. 5.2.17. Hanger jaw.

PROB. 5.2.18. Adjustable jaw.

5.2.19. Draw two views of the shifter fork.

5.2.20. Draw three views of the mounting bracket.

5.2.21. Draw three views of the hinged bearing.

5.2.22. Draw two views of the clamp lever.

5.2.23. Draw three views of the bedplate stop.

5.2.24. Draw top, front, and partial side views of the spanner bracket.

5.2.25. Draw two views of the sliding stop.

5.2.26. Draw three views of the clamp bracket.

5.2.27. Draw three views of the tube hanger.

PROB. 5.2.19. Shifter fork.

PROB. 5.2.20. Mounting bracket.

PROB. 5.2.21. Hinged bearing.

PROB. 5.2.22. Clamp lever.

PROB. 5.2.23. Bedplate stop.

PROB. 5.2.24. Spanner bracket.

PROB. 5.2.25. Sliding stop.

PROB. 5.2.26. Clamp bracket.

PROB. 5.2.27. Tube hanger.

5.2.28.   Draw three views of the gage holder.
5.2.29.   Draw three views of the shaft guide.
5.2.30.   Draw three views of the clamp block.
5.2.31.   Draw three views of the offset yoke.
5.2.32.   Draw three views of the angle connector.

5.2.33.   Draw three views of the buckstay clamp.
5.2.34.   Draw three views of the stop base.
5.2.35.   Draw three views of the sliding buttress.
5.2.36.   Draw two views of the end plate.

PROB. 5.2.28.   Gage holder.

PROB. 5.2.29.   Shaft guide.

PROB. 5.2.30.   Clamp block.

PROB. 5.2.31.   Offset yoke.

PROB. 5.2.32.   Angle connector.

PROB. 5.2.33.   Buckstay clamp.

PROB. 5.2.34.   Stop base.

PROB. 5.2.35.   Sliding buttress.

PROB. 5.2.36.   End plate.

5.2.37.   Draw three views of the plastic switch base.

5.2.38.   Draw two views of the pawl hook.

5.2.39.   Draw three views of the step-pulley frame.

PROB. 5.2.39.   Step-pulley frame.

PROB. 5.2.37.   Switch base.

PROB. 5.2.38.   Pawl hook.

GROUP 3. **SPECIAL SCALES, DECIMAL SIZES, PROJECTIONS FROM PHOTO DRAWINGS, REFERENCES TO APPENDIX MATERIAL**

The problems in this group (5.3.1 to 5.3.16) will give practice in the use of a decimal scale for layout. The projections from the photo drawings of Chap. 13 are given here to not only serve as problem material, but to acquaint the student with this form of pictorial representation. Details of photo-drawing methods are given in Chap. 22.

5.3.1.   Draw top, front, and right-side views.

5.3.2.   Draw top, front, and right-side views.

5.3.3.   Draw top, front, and right-side views.

Wood-screw and bolt sizes are given in the Appendix.

PROB. 5.3.1.   Motor mount.

PROB. 5.3.2.   Assembly-jig base.

PROB. 5.3.3.   Cargo-hoist tie-down.

PROB. 5.3.4.   Aileron tab-rod servo fitting.

PROB. 5.3.5.   Cover bracket.

PROB. 5.3.8.   Control crank.

5.3.4.   Draw top, front, and left-side views.
5.3.5.   Draw top, front, and right-side views.
Bend radii and setbacks are 0.10 in.
5.3.6.   Draw top, front, and right-side views.
Screw and bolt sizes are given in the Appendix. Clearance over bolt and screw diameters are necessary in dimensioning but not in drawing the views.
5.3.7.   Draw top, front, left-side, and right-side views. Show only *necessary* hidden detail. The 0.44D hole extends through the piece. The limit-dimensioned holes (.75 $\frac{+0.005}{-0.002}$ and

PROB. 5.3.6.   Seat-latch support.

PROB. 5.3.9.   Transformer mounting.

5.3.11.   Draw two views of the conveyor link, Prob. 13.6.1.
5.3.12.   Draw necessary views of lift-strut pivot, Prob. 13.6.3.
5.3.13.   Draw necessary views of hydrocylinder support (right- and left-hand), Prob. 13.6.2.
5.3.14.   Draw necessary views of length-

$\frac{.86}{.89}$) are given here as an introduction to precise methods, which will be presented in detail later. Regardless of their dimensional accuracy, features are drawn to their basic size with no more scaled accuracy than for other less accurate features.
5.3.8.   Draw top and front views. See Prob. 5.3.7 for comment on limit-dimensioned holes.
5.3.9.   Draw top, front, and left-side views. Bolts should have clearance. Undimensioned radii are ¼R.
5.3.10.   Draw top and front views. See Prob. 5.3.7 for comment on limit-dimensioned holes.

PROB. 5.3.7.   Latch bracket.

PROB. 5.3.10.   Stabalizer link.

adjuster tube, Prob. 13.6.4. See Chap. 12 for thread symbol.
5.3.15.   Draw necessary views of third terminal, Prob. 13.6.6.
5.3.16.   Select a part from the conveyor link assembly, Prob. 13.6.7, and make an orthographic drawing.

GROUP 4. VIEWS TO BE SUPPLIED FREEHAND

These problems (5.4.1 to 5.4.3) will give valu-able training in reading orthographic views, as well as further practice in applying the princi-ples of orthographic projection.

Study the meaning of lines, areas, and adjacent areas. Corners or edges of the object may be numbered or lettered to aid in the reading or to aid later in the projection.

A pictorial sketch may be used, if desired, as an aid in reading the views. This sketch may be made before the views are drawn and com-pleted or at any time during the making of the drawing. For some of the simpler objects, a clay model may be of assistance.

After the views given have been read and drawn, project the third view or complete the views as specified in each case.

Remember that every line representing an edge view of a surface, an intersection of two surfaces, or a surface limit will have a mating projection in the other views. Be careful to represent all hidden features and pay atten-tion to the precedence of lines.

The figures in this group contain a num-ber of objects with two views drawn and the third to be supplied. In addition to helping to develop the ability to draw freehand this exercise will give valuable practice in read-ing. These problems may be worked directly in the book or on plain or coordinate paper.

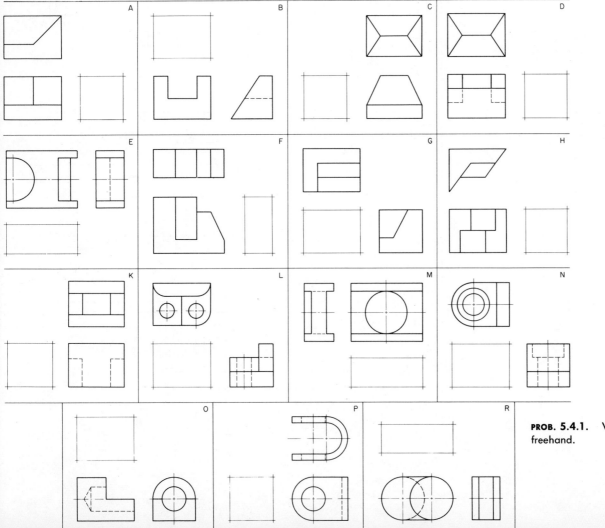

PROB. 5.4.1. Views to be supplied freehand.

PROB. 5.4.2. Views to be supplied freehand.

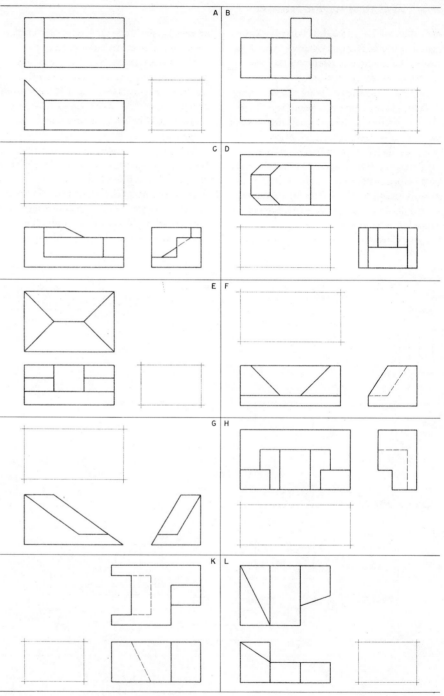

PROB. 5.4.3. Views to be supplied freehand.

GROUP 5.   VIEWS TO BE SUPPLIED

5.5.1.   Draw the views given, completing the top view from information given on the front and side views. Carry the views along together.

5.5.2.   Given top and front views of the block, add side view. See that dashed lines start and stop correctly.

5.5.3.   Given front and right-side views, add top view.

5.5.4.   Given front and right-side views, add top view.

5.5.5.   Given front and top views, add right-side view.

5.5.6.   Given top and front views, add right-side view.

5.5.7.   Complete the three views given.

5.5.8.   Given front and left-side views, add top view.

5.5.9.   Given front and right-side views, add top view.

PROB. 5.5.1.   Projection study.

PROB. 5.5.2.   Projection study.

PROB. 5.5.5.   Rabbeting-plane guide.

PROB. 5.5.4.   Bit-point forming die.

PROB. 5.5.7.   Projection study.

PROB. 5.5.8.   Burner-support key.

PROB. 5.5.3.   Projection study.

PROB. 5.5.6.   Wedge block.

PROB. 5.5.9.   Abutment block.

5.5.10. Given front and top views, add right-side view.

5.5.11. Assume this to be the right-hand part. Draw three views of the left-hand part.

5.5.12. Given front and top views, add side view.

5.5.13. Given front and top views, add side view.

5.5.14. Given top and front views, add left-side view.

5.5.15. Given front and top views, add side view.

PROB. 5.5.10. Sliding port.

PROB. 5.5.11. Bumper support and post cap.

PROB. 5.5.12. Anchor bracket.

PROB. 5.5.13. Entrance head.

PROB. 5.5.14. Yoked link.

PROB. 5.5.15. Rubber-mounting bracket.

PROB. 5.5.16. Crosshead.

5.5.16. Given front and top views, add side view.

5.5.17. Given front and top views, add side view.

5.5.18. Given top and front views, add side view.

5.5.19. Given top and front views, add left-side view.

5.5.20. Given top and front views, add side view.

5.5.21. Given front and top views, add side view.

PROB. 5.5.17. Tool holder.

PROB. 5.5.18. Lock plate.

PROB. 5.5.19. Bevel-gear mounting.

PROB. 5.5.20. Cylinder support.

PROB. 5.5.21. Rod yoke.

GROUP 6. VIEWS TO BE CHANGED

These problems (5.6.1 to 5.6.6) are given to develop the ability to visualize the actual piece in space and from this mental picture to draw the required views as they would appear if the object were looked at in the directions specified.

In addition to providing training in reading orthographic views and in orthographic projection, these problems are valuable exercises in developing drawing technique. Note that all the problems given are castings containing the usual features found on such parts, that is, fillets, rounds runouts, etc., on the unfinished surfaces. Note also that sharp corners are formed by the intersection of an unfinished and finished surface or by two finished surfaces. After finishing one of these problems, check the drawing carefully to make sure that all details of construction have been represented correctly.

5.6.1. Given front and top views, new front, top, and side views are required, turning the block so that the back becomes the front and the top the bottom. The rib contour is straight.

5.6.2. Given front, left-side, and bottom views, draw front, top, and right-side views.
5.6.3. Given front, right-side, and bottom views, draw front, top, and left-side views.

PROB. 5.6.1. Sliding block.

PROB. 5.6.2. Plunger bracket.

PROB. 5.6.3. Offset bracket.

5.6.4. Given front, right-side, and bottom views, draw new front, top, and right-side views, turning the support so that the back becomes the front.

5.6.5. Given front and left-side views of the left-hand part, draw the right-hand part.

5.6.6. Given front, left-side, and bottom views, draw front, top, and right-side views.

PROB. 5.6.4. Toggle-shaft support.

PROB. 5.6.5. Compound link.

PROB. 5.6.6. Sector bracket.

GROUP 7. DRAWING FROM MEMORY

One of the valuable assets of an engineer is a trained memory for form and proportion. A graphic memory can be developed to a surprising degree in accuracy and power by systematic exercises in drawing from memory. It is well to begin this training as soon as you have a knowledge of orthographic projection.

Select an object not previously used; look at it with concentration for a certain time (from 5 sec to ½ min or more), close the book, and make an accurate orthographic sketch. Check with the original and correct any mistakes or omissions. Follow with several different figures. The next day, allow a 2-sec view of one of the objects, and repeat the orthographic views of the previous day.

GROUP 8. VOLUME AND WEIGHT CALCULATIONS WITH SLIDE RULE

In calculating the weight of a piece from a drawing, the object is broken up into the geometric solids (prisms, cylinders, pyramids, or cones) of which it is composed. The volume of each of these shapes is calculated and the individual volumes are added, or subtracted, to find the total volume. The total volume multiplied by the weight of the material per unit of volume gives the weight of the object.

A table of weights of materials is given in the Appendix.

5.8.1. Find the weight of the cast-iron anchor bracket, Prob. 5.5.12.
5.8.2. Find the weight of the cast-iron bracket, Prob. 5.5.15.
5.8.3. Find the weight of the wrought-iron tool holder, Prob. 5.5.17.
5.8.4. Find the weight of the cast-steel cylinder support, Prob. 5.5.20.
5.8.5. Find the weight of the malleable-iron sliding block, Prob. 5.6.1.

6

Pictorial Drawing and Sketching

6.1. In discussing the theory of projection in Chap. 5, we noted that in perspective projection (Fig. 5.1) the object is represented as it appears to the eye. However, its lines cannot be measured directly for accurate description of the object; and in orthographic projection the object is shown, in two or more views, as it really is in form and dimensions but interpretation requires experience to visualize the object from the views. To provide a system of drawing that represents the object pictorially and in such a way that its principal lines can be measured directly, several forms of one-plane conventional or projectional picture methods have been devised in which the third dimension is taken care of either by turning the object so that its three dimensions are visible or by employing oblique projection. A knowledge of these picture methods and of perspective projection is extremely desirable as they can all be used to great advantage.

Mechanical or structural details not clear in orthographic views can be drawn pictorially or illustrated by supplementary pictorial views. Pictorial views are used advantageously in technical illustrations, Patent Office drawings, layouts, piping plans, and the like. Pictorial methods are useful also in making freehand sketches, and this is one of the most important reasons for learning them.

FIG. 6.1. Pictorial methods.

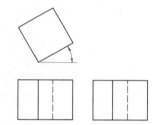

FIG. 6.2. The object face is parallel to the picture plane. One face only is seen in the front view.

FIG. 6.3. The object is rotated about a vertical axis. Two faces are seen.

FIG. 6.4. The object is rotated about both a vertical and a profile axis. Three faces are seen.

6.2. PICTORIAL METHODS. There are three main divisions of pictorial drawing: (1) axonometric, with its divisions into trimetric, dimetric, and isometric; (2) oblique, with several variations; and (3) perspective. These methods are illustrated in Fig. 6.1.

The trimetric form gives an effect more pleasing to the eye than the other axonometric and oblique methods and allows almost unlimited freedom in orienting the object, but is difficult to draw. With the dimetric method the result is less pleasing and there is less freedom in orienting the object, but execution is easier than with trimetric. The isometric method gives a result less pleasing than dimetric or trimetric, but it is easier to draw and has the distinct advantage that it is easier to dimension. The oblique method is used principally for objects with circular or curved features only on one face or on parallel faces, and for objects of this type the oblique is easy to draw and dimension. Perspective drawing gives a result most pleasing to the eye, but it is of limited usefulness because many lines are unequally foreshortened; isometric and oblique are the forms most commonly used.

6.3. AXONOMETRIC PROJECTION. Axonometric projection is theoretically orthographic projection in which only one plane is used, the object being turned so that three faces show. Imagine a transparent vertical plane with a cube behind it, one face of the cube being par-

allel to the plane. The projection on the plane, that is, the front view of the cube, will be a square (Fig. 6.2). Rotate the cube about a vertical axis through any angle less than 90°, and the front view will now show two faces, both foreshortened (Fig. 6.3). From this position, tilt the cube forward (rotation axis perpendicular to profile) any amount less than 90°. Three faces will now be visible on the front view (Fig. 6.4). There can be an infinite number of axonometric positions, depending upon the angles through which the cube is rotated. Only a few of these positions are ever used for drawing. The simplest is the isometric (equal-measure) position, in which the three faces are foreshortened equally.

6.4. ISOMETRIC PROJECTION. If the cube in Fig. 6.5*A* is rotated about a vertical axis through 45°, as shown at (*B*), and then tilted forward, as at (*C*), until the edge *RU* is foreshortened equally with *RS* and *RT,* the front view of the cube in this position is said to be an "isometric projection." (The cube has been tilted forward until the body diagonal through *R* is perpendicular to the front plane. This makes the top face slope approximately 35°16′.[1]) The projections

---

[1] The only difference between rotation and auxiliary projection is that in the former the object is moved and in the latter the plane is moved or the observer is considered to have changed his viewing position. Thus an auxiliary view on a plane perpendicular to a body diagonal of the cube in position (*B*) would be an isometric projection, as illustrated by the dotted view.

of the three mutually perpendicular edges *RS, RT,* and *RU* meeting at the front corner *R* make equal angles, 120°, with each other and are called "isometric axes." Since the projections of parallel lines are parallel, the projections of the other edges of the cube will be, respectively, parallel to these axes. Any line parallel to an edge of the cube, whose projection is thus parallel to an isometric axis, is called an "isometric line." The planes of the faces of the cube and all planes parallel to them are called "isometric planes."

The isometric axes *RS, RT,* and *RU* are all foreshortened equally because they are at the same angle to the picture plane.

6.5. ISOMETRIC DRAWING.

In nearly all practical use of the isometric system, this foreshortening of the lines is disregarded, and *their full lengths are laid off on the axes,* as explained in paragraph 6.6. This gives a figure of exactly the same shape but larger in the proportion of 1.23 to 1, linear, or in optical effect 1.23^3 to 1.00^3 (Fig. 6.6). Except when drawn beside the same piece in orthographic projection, the effect of increased size is usually of no consequence, and since the advantage of measuring the lines directly is of great convenience, isometric drawing is used almost exclusively rather than isometric projection.

In isometric projection the isometric lines have been foreshortened to approximately $8\frac{1}{100}$ of their length, and an isometric scale to this proportion can be made graphically as shown in Fig. 6.7 if it is necessary to make an isometric projection by the method of isometric drawing.

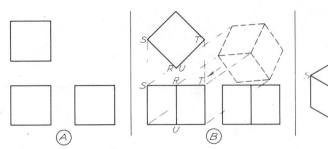

FIG. 6.8. Isometric axes, first position. The starting point is the upper front corner.

6.6. TO MAKE AN ISOMETRIC DRAWING.

If the object is rectangular (Fig. 6.8), start with a point representing a front corner, shown at (*A*) with heavy lines, and draw from it the three isometric axes 120° apart, one vertical (*B*), the other two with the 30° triangle. On these three lines measure the height, width, and depth of the object, as indicated at (*C*); through the points so determined draw lines parallel to the axes, completing the figure. When drawing in isometric, remember the direction of the three principal isometric planes. Hidden lines are omitted except when they are needed to describe the piece.

It is often convenient to build up an isometric drawing from the lower front corner as illustrated in Fig. 6.9, starting from axes in what may be called the "second position." The location of the starting corner is again shown by heavy lines at (*A*), (*B*), and (*C*).

6.7. NONISOMETRIC LINES.

Edges whose projections or drawings are not parallel to one of the isometric axes are called "nonisometric lines." The one impor-

FIG. 6.5. The isometric cube. Rotated from position (*A*) to (*B*) then to (*C*), the three perpendicular edges are now equally foreshortened.

FIG. 6.6. (*A*) isometric projection; (*B*) isometric drawing.

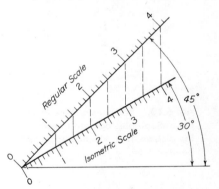

FIG. 6.7. To make an isometric scale.

FIG. 6.9. Isometric axes, second position. The starting point is the lower front corner.

FIG. 6.10. Box construction. Points on the orthographic box are transferred to the pictorial box. Identical scale must be used.

tant rule is that *measurements can be made only on the drawings of isometric lines;* conversely, measurements *cannot* be made on the drawings of *nonisometric* lines. For example, the diagonals of the face of a cube are nonisometric lines; although equal in length, their isometric drawings will not be at all of equal length on the isometric drawing of the cube. Compare the length of the diagonals on the cube in Fig. 6.6. Since a nonisometric line does not appear in the isometric drawing in its true length, the isometric view of each end of the line must be located and the isometric view of the line found by joining these two points. In Fig. 6.9, *A* and *C,* line *AB* is a nonisometric edge whose true length cannot be measured on the isometric drawing. However, the vertical distances above the base to points *A* and *B* are parallel to the vertical isometric axis. These lines can, therefore, be laid off, as shown at (*C*), to give the isometric view of line *AB.*

6.8. NONISOMETRIC LINES: BOXING METHOD. When an object contains many nonisometric lines, it is drawn by the "boxing method" or the "offset method." When the boxing method is used, the object is enclosed in a rectangular box, which is drawn around it in orthographic projection. The box is then drawn in isometric and the object located in it by its points of contact, as in Figs. 6.10 and 6.12. It should be noted that the isometric views of lines that are parallel on the object are parallel. This knowledge can often be used to save a large amount of construction, as well as to test for accuracy. Figure 6.10 might be drawn by putting the top face into isometric and drawing vertical lines equal in length to the edges downward from each corner. It is not always necessary to enclose the whole object in a rectangular "crate." The pyramid (Fig. 6.11) would have its base enclosed in a rectangle and the apex located by erecting a vertical axis from the center.

The object shown in Fig. 6.12 is composed almost entirely of nonisometric lines. In such cases the isometric drawing cannot be made without first making the orthographic views necessary for boxing. In general, the boxing method is adapted to objects that have the nonisometric lines in isometric planes.

FIG. 6.11. Semibox construction. Points on the base are transferred by boxing. The altitude is located by a vertical from the base center. Identical scale must be used.

FIG. 6.12. Box construction. Points on, and offsets from, the orthographic box are transferred to the pictorial box. Identical scale must be used.

6.9. NONISOMETRIC LINES: OFFSET METHOD.

When an object is made up of planes at different angles, it is better to locate the ends of the edges by the offset method rather than by boxing. When the offset method is used, perpendiculars are extended from each point to an isometric reference plane. These perpendiculars, which are isometric lines, are located on the drawing by isometric coordinates, the dimensions being taken from the orthographic views. In Fig. 6.13, line AB is used as a base line and measurements are made from it as shown, first to locate points on the base; then verticals from these points locate e, f, and g. Figure 6.14 is another example of offset construction. Here a vertical plane is used as a reference plane. Note that, as in Fig. 6.13, the *base* of the offset is located first; then the offset distance is measured.

6.10. ANGLES IN ISOMETRIC.

The three isometric axes, referred back to the isometric cube, are mutually perpendicular but in an isometric drawing appear at 120° to each other. For this reason, angles specified in degrees do not appear in their true size on an isometric drawing and must be laid off by coordinates that will be parallel to the isometric axes. Thus if an orthographic drawing has edges specified by angular dimensions, as in Fig. 6.15A, *a view to the same scale as the isometric drawing* is made as at (B); from this view the coordinate dimensions a, b, and c are transferred with dividers or scale to the isometric drawing.

6.11. CURVES IN ISOMETRIC.

For the reasons given in paragraphs 6.7 and 6.10, a circle or any other curve will not show in its true shape when drawn in isometric. A circle on any isometric plane will be an ellipse, and a curve will be shown as the isometric projection of the true curve.

Any curve can be drawn by plotting points on it from isometric reference lines (coordinates) that are parallel to the isometric axes, as shown in Fig. 6.16. A circle plotted in this way is shown in Fig. 6.17. Note that in both these figures coordinates a and b are parallel to the isometric axes and the coordinate distances must be obtained from an orthographic view drawn to the same scale as the isometric.

6.12. ISOMETRIC CIRCLES.

Circles occur so frequently that they are usually drawn by a four-centered approximation, which is sufficiently accurate for ordinary work. Geometrically, the center for any arc tangent to a straight line lies on a *perpendicular from the point of tangency*

FIG. 6.14. Offset construction. All points are located on a plane or by offsets from the plane. Identical scale must be used.

FIG. 6.15. Angles in isometric. These must be laid out by offsets from an orthographic view to the same scale.

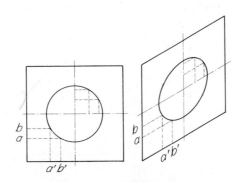

FIG. 6.17. Isometric circle, points plotted. Points are transferred from the orthographic view to the pictorial by offsets. Identical scale must be used.

FIG. 6.16. Curves in isometric. Points are transferred from the orthographic view to the pictorial by offsets. Identical scale must be used.

FIG. 6.18. ·Isometric circles, four-centered method. The ellipse is approximated by circle arcs.

FIG. 6.19. Locating and laying out a hole in isometric. Locate the center, draw the enclosing isometric square, and then draw the circle by the method of Fig. 6.18.

FIG. 6.20. Isometric quarter circles. The radius center lies on perpendiculars from tangent points that are the radius distance from the corner.

(Fig. 6.18*A*). In isometric, if perpendiculars are drawn from the middle point of each side of the circumscribing square, the intersections of these perpendiculars will be centers for arcs tangent to two sides (*B*). Two of these intersections will evidently fall at the corners *A* and *C* of the isometric square, as the perpendiculars are altitudes of equilateral triangles. Thus the construction at (*B*) to (*D*) can be made by simply drawing 60° lines (horizontals also at *C* and *D*) from the corners *A* and *C* and then drawing arcs with radii *R* and R_1, as shown.

Figure 6.19 shows the method of locating and laying out a hole in isometric from the given orthographic views. First locate and then draw the center lines for the hole by laying out the distances *X* and *Y*, as shown. On these lines construct an isometric square with sides equal to the diameter of the hole by laying out the radius *R* in each direction from the intersection of the center lines. Then use the four-center method, as shown in Fig. 6.18. Should the piece be thin enough, a portion of the back

side of the hole will be visible. To determine this, drop the thickness *T* back on an isometric line and swing the large radius R_1 of the isometric circle with this point as center. If the arc thus drawn comes within the boundary of the isometric circle, that portion of the back will be visible. In extra-thin pieces, portions of the small arcs R_2 might be visible. This would be determined the same way.

If a true ellipse is plotted by the method of paragraph 6.11 in the same square, it will be a little longer and narrower and of much more pleasing shape than this four-center approximation, but in most drawings the difference is not sufficient to warrant the extra expenditure of time required in execution.

The isometric drawing of a *sphere* is a circle with its diameter equal to the long axis of the ellipse that is inscribed in the isometric square of a great circle of the sphere. It would thus be 1.23/1.00 of the actual diameter (the isometric *projection* of a sphere would be a circle of the actual diameter of the sphere).

6.13. ISOMETRIC CIRCLE ARCS. To draw any circle arc, draw the isometric square of its diameter in the plane of its face, with as much of the four-center construction as is necessary to find

FIG. 6.21. Isometric with reversed axes. The bottom and two sides are shown. Construction methods are the same as for regular position.

6.17. Trimetric Projection

centers for the part of the circle needed, as illustrated in Fig. 6.20. The arc occurring most frequently is the quarter circle. Note that in illustrations (*D*) and (*E*) only two construction lines are needed to find the center of a quarter circle in an isometric plane. Measure the true radius *R* of the circle from the corner on the two isometric lines as shown, and draw *actual* perpendiculars from these points. Their intersection will be the required center for radius R_1 or R_2 of the isometric quadrant. (*F*) illustrates the construction for the two vertical isometric planes.

6.14. REVERSED ISOMETRIC. It is often desirable to show the lower face of an object by tilting it *back* instead of *forward,* thus reversing the usual position so as to show the underside. The construction is the same as when the top is shown, but the directions of the principal isometric planes must be kept clearly in mind. Figure 6.21 shows the reference cube and the position of the axes, as well as the application of reversed-isometric construction to circle arcs. A practical use of this construction is in the representation of such architectural features as are naturally viewed from below. Figure 6.22 is an example of this use.

Sometimes a piece is shown to better advantage with the main axis horizontal, as in Fig. 6.23.

6.15. ISOMETRIC SECTIONS. Isometric drawings are, from their pictorial nature, usually outside views, but sometimes a sectional view (see Chap. 8) is used to good advantage to show a detail of shape or interior construction. The cutting planes are taken as isometric planes, and the section lining is done in the di-

FIG. 6.22. An architectural detail on reversed axes.

rection that gives the best effect; this is, in almost all cases, the direction of the long diagonal of a square drawn on the surface. As a general rule, a half section is made by outlining the figure in full and then cutting out the front quarter, as in Fig. 6.24; for a full section, the cut face is drawn first and then the part of the object behind it is added (Fig. 6.25).

6.16. DIMETRIC PROJECTION. The reference cube can be rotated into any number of positions in which two edges are equally foreshortened, and the direction of axes and ratio of foreshortening for any one of these positions might be taken as the basis for a system of dimetric drawing. A simple dimetric position is one with the ratios 1 to 1 to ½. In this position the tangents of the angles are ⅛ and ⅞, making the angles approximately 7° and 41°. Figure 6.26 shows a drawing in this system. Dimetric is seldom used because of the difficulty of drawing circles in this projection.

6.17. TRIMETRIC PROJECTION. Any position in which all three axes are unequally foreshortened is called "trimetric." Compared with isometric and dimetric, distortion is reduced in trimetric projection, and even this effect can be lessened with some positions. However, because it is slower to execute

FIG. 6.23. Isometric with the main axis horizontal. It is used when the object looks more natural in this position.

FIG. 6.24. Isometric half section. One-fourth of the object is removed to reveal interior construction.

FIG. 6.25. Isometric full section. Half of object is removed to reveal object shape.

FIG. 6.26. Dimetric drawing. It is used principally for rectangular objects.

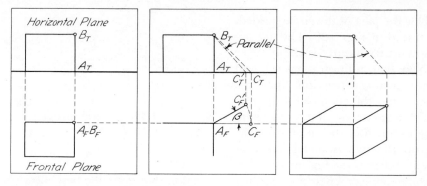

FIG. 6.27. Oblique projection. Projectors are at an oblique angle to the picture plane.

FIG. 6.28. Various oblique positions. (*A*) up, to the right at 30°; (*B*) up, to the right at 45°; (*C*) up, to the left at 45°; (*D*) down, to the right at 30°; (*E*) down, to the left at 30°.

than isometric or dimetric, it is seldom used except when done by projection. Axonometric projection from orthographic views is given in paragraph 6.26.

6.18. OBLIQUE PROJECTION. When the projectors make an angle other than 90° with the picture plane, the resulting projection is called "oblique." The name "cavalier projection" is given to the special and most used type of oblique projection in which the projectors make an angle of 45° with the plane of projection. Cavalier projection is often called by the general name "oblique projection," or "oblique drawing." The principle is as follows: Imagine a vertical plane with a rectangular block behind it, having its long edges parallel to the plane. Assume a system of parallel projecting lines in any direction making an angle of 45° with the picture plane (they could be parallel to any one of the elements of a 45° cone with its base in the picture plane). Then that face of the block which is parallel to the plane is projected in its true size, and the edges perpendicular to the plane are projected in their true length. Figure 6.27 illustrates the principle. The first panel shows the regular orthographic projection of a rectangular block with its front face in the frontal plane. An oblique projector from the back corner

B is the hypotenuse of a 45° right triangle of which AB is one side and the projection of AB on the plane is the other side. When this triangle is horizontal, the projection on the plane will be AC. If the triangle is rotated about AB through any angle β, C will revolve to C' and $A_F C_F'$ will be the oblique projection of AB.

6.19. TO MAKE AN OBLIQUE DRAWING. Oblique drawing is similar to isometric drawing in that it has three axes that represent three mutually perpendicular edges and upon which measurements can be made. Two of the axes are always at right angles to each other, as they are in a plane parallel to the picture plane. The third, or depth, axis may be at any angle to the horizontal, 30° or 45° being generally used (Fig. 6.28). Oblique drawing is thus more flexible than isometric drawing. To draw a rectangular object (Fig. 6.29) start with a point representing a front corner (*A*) and draw from it the three oblique axes, one vertical, one horizontal, and one at an angle. On these three axes measure the height, width, and depth of the object. In this case the width is made up of the 2½-in. distance and the 1⁵⁄₁₆-in. radius. Locate the center of the arc, and draw it as shown. The center for the arc of the hole in the

FIG. 6.29. Oblique drawing. The front face, parallel to the picture plane, is identical with an orthographic view.

FIG. 6.30. Illustration of the first rule. Note the distortion at (B) and (C).

figure will be at the same point as the center for the outside arc on the front face. The center for the rear arc of the hole will be 1⅛-in. rearward on a depth-axis line through the front center.

6.20. **OBJECT ORIENTATION FOR OBLIQUE.**
Any face parallel to the picture plane will evidently be projected without distortion. In this, oblique projection has an advantage over isometric that is of particular value in representing objects with circular or irregular outline.

The *first rule* for oblique projection is to *place the object with the irregular outline or contour parallel to the picture plane*. Note in Fig. 6.30 the greater distortion at (B) and (C) than at (A).

One of the greatest disadvantages in the use of isometric or oblique drawing is the effect of distortion produced by the lack of convergence in the receding lines—a violation of perspective. In some cases, particularly with large objects, this becomes so painful as practically to preclude the use of these methods. This is perhaps even more noticeable in oblique than in isometric and of course increases with the length of the depth dimension.

Hence the *second rule: preferably, the longest dimension should be parallel to the picture plane.* In Fig. 6.31, (A) is preferable to (B).

In case of conflict between these two rules, *the first always takes precedence,* as the advantage of having the irregular face without distortion is greater than that gained by the second rule, as illustrated in Fig. 6.32. The first rule should be given precedence even with shapes that are not irregular if, in the draftsman's judgment, the distortion can be lessened, as in Fig. 6.33, where (B) is perhaps preferable to (A).

6.21. **STARTING PLANE.** Note that as long as the front of the object is in one plane parallel to the plane of projection, the front face of the oblique projection is *exactly the same as in the orthographic front view.* When the front is made up of more than one plane, take care to preserve the relationship between the planes by selecting one as the starting plane and working from it. In a piece such as the

FIG. 6.31. Illustration of the second rule. Note the exaggerated depth at (B).

FIG. 6.32. Precedence of the first rule. (A), following the first rule, is easier to draw and also shows less distortion than (B).

FIG. 6.33. Choice of position. (B) is preferable to (A).

FIG. 6.34. Offsets from reference plane. Distances forward and rearward are measured from the frontal plane.

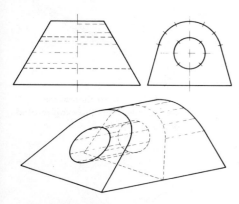

FIG. 6.35. Offsets from right section. Measurements forward and rearward are made from the frontal plane.

FIG. 6.36. Oblique circle construction. Note that the tangent points of arcs must be at the midpoints of the enclosing oblique square.

link in Fig. 6.34, the front bosses can be imagined as cut off on the plane *A-A,* and the front view, that is, the section on *A-A,* drawn as the front of the oblique projection. Then lay off depth axes through the centers *C* and *D,* the distances, for example, *CE* behind and *CF* in front of the plane *A-A.*

When an object has no face perpendicular to its base, it can be drawn in a similar way by cutting a right section and measuring offsets from it, as in Fig. 6.35. This offset method, previously illustrated in the isometric drawings in Figs. 6.13, 6.14, and 6.16, is a rapid and convenient way of drawing almost any figure, and it should be studied carefully.

6.22.   CIRCLES IN OBLIQUE.   When it is necessary to draw circles that lie on oblique faces, they can be drawn as circle arcs, with the compasses, on the same principle as the four-center isometric approximation shown in Fig. 6.18. In isometric it happens that *two of the four intersections of the perpendiculars from the middle points* of the containing square fall at the corner of the square, and advantage is taken of the fact. In oblique, the position of the corresponding points depends on the angle of the depth axis. Figure 6.36 shows three squares in oblique positions at different angles and the construction of their inscribed circles. The important point to remember is that the circle arcs *must* be tangent at the mid-points of the sides of the oblique square.

6.23.   ARCS IN OBLIQUE.   Circle arcs representing rounded corners, etc., are

drawn in oblique by the same method given for isometric arcs in paragraph 6.13. The only difference is that the angle of the sides tangent to the arc will vary according to the angle of the depth axis chosen.

6.24.   CABINET DRAWING.   This is a type of oblique projection in which the parallel projectors make an angle with the picture plane of such a value that distances measured parallel to the depth axis are reduced one-half that of cavalier projection. The appearance of excessive thickness that is so disagreeable in cavalier projection is entirely overcome in cabinet projection. The depth axis may be at any angle with the horizontal but is usually taken at 30° or 45°. The appearance of cavalier and cabinet drawing is shown in Fig. 6.37.

6.25.   OTHER FORMS.   Cabinet drawing is popular because of the easy ratio, but the effect is often too thin. Other oblique drawing ratios, such as 2 to 3 or 3 to 4, may be used with pleasing effect.

6.26.   AXONOMETRIC PROJECTION FROM ORTHOGRAPHIC VIEWS.   In making pictorial drawings of complicated parts, especially whenever curves are plotted, axonometric projection from orthographic views may give an advantage in speed and ease of drawing over axonometric projection made directly from the object. Any position—isometric, dimetric, or trimetric—may be used.

FIG. 6.37.   Oblique (*A*) and cabinet drawing (*B*). Note less exaggeration of depth at (*B*).

The three axes of an axonometric drawing are *three mutually perpendicular edges* in space. If the angle or rotation and the angle of tilt of the object are known or decided upon, the three axes for the pictorial drawing and the location of the orthographic views for projection to the pictorial can easily be found. Figure 6.38 illustrates the procedure. The three orthographic views of a cube are shown at (*G*). The three mutually perpendicular edges *OA*, *OB*, and *OC* will be foreshortened differently when the cube is rotated in space for some axonometric position, but the ends of the axes *A*, *B*, and *C* will always lie on the surface of a sphere whose radius is *OA* = *OB* = *OC*, as illustrated by (*G'*). At any particular angle of tilt of the cube, the axis ends *A* and *B* will describe an ellipse, as shown, if the cube is rotated about the axis *OC*. The axis *OC* will appear foreshortened at *oc'*. Thus for any particular position of the cube in space, representing some desired axonometric position, the axes can be located and their relative amounts of foreshortening found.

Moreover, if a face of the cube is rotated about a *frontal axis perpendicular to the axis that is at right angles to the face*, an orthographic view of the face, in projection with the axonometric view, will result. Thus, the top and right-side views may be located as at (*J*) and projected as at (*K*) to give the axonometric drawing.

The drawings at (*H*), (*J*), and (*K*) illustrate the practical use of the theory of rotation just described. The actual size of the sphere is unimportant, as it is used only to establish the direction of the axes. First, the desired angle of rotation *R* and the angle of tilt *T* are decided upon and laid out as at (*H*). The minor diameter for the ellipse upon which *A*

and *B* will lie is found by projecting vertically from *c* and drawing the circle as shown. *A* and *B* on the major-diameter circle of the ellipse will be at *a* and *b*; on the minor-diameter circle, they will be at a_m and b_m; and they are found in the axonometric position by projecting, as in the concentric-circle ellipse method, to *a'* and *b'*. The foreshortened position of *C* is found by projecting horizontally across from *c* to *c'*.

The top orthographic view of the cube (or object) will be parallel to *oa* and *ob*, and projection from the orthographic view to the axonometric will be vertical (parallel to *aa'* and *bb'*).

FIG. 6.38. Axonometric projection from orthographic views. (*G*) construction to locate axes; (*H*) location of top view; (*J*) location of side view; (*K*) projection.

ORDER OF DRAWING:
1. DRAW CIRCLE OF ANY CONVENIENT RADIUS (IN THIS CASE WITH CENTER ON FRONT OBJECT CORNER EXTENDED).
2. LOCATE P-1 (R=ANGLE OF ROTATION).
3. LOCATE P-2 (T= ANGLE OF TILT).
4. COMPLETE CONSTRUCTION, AS SHOWN, TO LOCATE LINES P-3 AND P 4.

5. LOCATE TOP VIEW WITH A RECEDING EDGE PARALLEL TO P-1.
6. LOCATE RIGHT-SIDE VIEW WITH HORIZONTAL EDGE PARALLEL TO P-3.
7. LOCATE FRONT VIEW WITH HORIZONTAL EDGE PARALLEL TO P-4.
8. DRAW AXONOMETRIC BY PROJECTION FROM ORTHOGRAPHIC VIEWS.

Top View

Front View

Right-Side View

FIG. 6.39. An axonometric drawing by projection from orthographic views. Note the order of drawing and refer back to Fig. 6.38 for details of construction.

FIG. 6.40. Isometric by projection. Top view turned 45° and side view turned 15° locates the views for projection to the isometric.

Projection from an orthographic right-side view would be as shown at (*J*). The right side of the cube, containing axes *OC* and *OB*, is found by projecting from *b'* and *c'*, parallel to *oa'*, to locate *b''* and *c''* on the circle representing the sphere. The sides of the cube (or object) are parallel to *ob''* and *oc''*, as shown at (*J*). Projection from the right-side view to the axonometric view is in the direction of *oa'*, as indicated.

The axonometric drawing is shown projected at (*K*). The dashed lines indicate the actual projectors, and the light solid lines and circles show the necessary construction just described.

One advantage of this method is that the angle of rotation and tilt can be decided upon so that the object will be shown in the best position. Figure 6.39 is an example of an axonometric drawing made by projection from orthographic views. The curved faces are plotted by projecting points as shown.

6.27. ISOMETRIC PROJECTION FROM ORTHOGRAPHIC VIEWS. Isometric is, of course, a special type of axonometric projection in which all three axes are foreshortened equally. The work of finding the axes for isometric projection from orthographic views is reduced if the views are located by angle, as illustrated in Fig. 6.40.

6.28. OBLIQUE PROJECTION FROM ORTHOGRAPHIC VIEWS. In oblique projection the projectors make some oblique angle with the picture plane. The actual angle of the projectors (with horizontal and frontal planes) is not critical, and a variety of angles may be used. The making of an oblique drawing by projection from orthographic views is simple, as illustrated by Fig. 6.41. The picture plane is located, and one face of the object is made coincident with the picture plane. The front view is located at a convenient place on the paper. The angle of the projectors in the top view may be assumed (in this case 45°) and projections made to the picture plane as shown. The angle of the projectors in the front view can then be assumed (in this case 30°). Projection from the front view at the assumed angle and vertically from the picture plane, as shown, will locate the necessary lines and points for the oblique view.

Reversed axes can be obtained by projecting downward from the front view. An axis to the left can be located by changing the direction of the projectors in the top view. Any desired oblique axes can be located by altering the angles (top and front) for the projectors.

6.29. PERSPECTIVE DRAWING. Perspective drawing represents an object as it appears to an observer stationed at a particular position relative to it. The object is seen as the figure resulting when visual rays from the eye to the object are cut by a picture plane. There is a difference between an artist's use of perspective and geometric perspective. The artist often disregards true perspective since he draws the object as he sees it through his creative imagination, while geometric perspective is projected instrumentally on a plane from views or measurements of the object represented. Projected geometric perspective is, theoretically, very similar to the optical system in photography.

In a technical way, perspective is used more in architecture and in illustration than in other fields, but every engineer will find it useful to know the principles of the subject.

6.30. FUNDAMENTAL CONCEPTS.

Imagine an observer standing on the sidewalk of a city street, as in Fig. 6.42, with the picture plane erected between him and the street scene ahead. Visual rays from his eye to the ends of lamppost *A* intercept a distance *aa'* on the picture plane. Similarly, rays from post *B* intercept *bb'*, a smaller distance than *aa'*. This apparent diminution in the size of like objects as the distance from the objects to the eye increases agrees with our everyday experience and is the keynote of perspective drawing. It is evident from the figure that succeeding lampposts will intercept shorter distances on the picture plane than the preceding ones, and that a post at infinity would show only as a point *o* at the level of the observer's eye.

In Fig. 6.43 the plane of the paper is the picture plane, and the intercepts *aa'*, *bb'*, etc., show as the heights of the respective lampposts as they diminish in their projected size and finally disappear

FIG. 6.41.   Oblique by projection. Projection at an angle from the top view to the picture plane and directly from the side view gives the oblique view.

FIG. 6.42.   Theory of perspective illustrated. Rays from the objects to the observer's eye intersect the picture plane.

FIG. 6.43.   The perspective drawing. This is the image formed on the picture plane of Fig. 6.42.

FIG. 6.44. Perspective nomenclature.

FIG. 6.45. Lateral angle of view.

FIG. 6.46. Comparative lateral angles of view. Angles greater than 30° give an unpleasing perspective.

plane perpendicular to the horizontal projection of the line of sight to the object's center of interest. The *horizon line* is the intersection of the horizon plane and picture plane, and the *ground line* is the intersection of the ground plane and picture plane. The *axis of vision* is the line through the station point which is perpendicular to the picture plane. The piercing point of the axis of vision with the picture plane is the *center of vision.*

6.32. SELECTION OF THE STATION POINT. In beginning a perspective drawing, take care in selecting the station point, as an indiscriminate choice may result in a distorted drawing. If the station point is placed to one side of the drawing, the same effect is obtained as when a theater screen is viewed from a position close to the front and well off to one side: heights are seen properly but not horizontal distances. Therefore, *the center of vision should be somewhere near the picture's center of interest.*

Wide angles of view result in a violent convergence of horizontal lines and so should be avoided. The angle of view is the included angle θ between the widest visual rays (Fig. 6.45). Figure 6.46 shows the difference in perspective foreshortening for different lateral angles of view. In general, an angle of about 20° gives the most natural picture.

The station point should be located at the point from which the object is seen to best advantage. For this reason, for large objects such as buildings, the station point is usually taken at a normal standing height of about 5 ft above the ground plane; for small objects, the best

at a point on the horizon. In a similar way the curbings and balustrade appear to converge at the same point *O.* Thus a system of parallel horizontal lines will vanish at a single point on the horizon, and all horizontal planes will vanish on the horizon. Verticals such as the lamp-posts and the edges of the buildings, being parallel to the picture plane, pierce the picture plane at an infinite distance and therefore show as vertical lines in the picture.

6.31. DEFINITIONS AND NOMENCLATURE. Figure 6.44 illustrates perspective theory and names the points, lines, and planes used. An observer in viewing an object selects his *station point* and thereby determines the *horizon plane,* as the horizontal plane is at eye level. This horizon plane is normally above the horizontal *ground plane* upon which the object is assumed to rest. The *picture plane* is usually located between the station point and the object being viewed and is ordinarily a vertical

FIG. 6.47. Elevation angle of view.

representation demands that the top, as well as the lateral surfaces, be seen, and the station point must be elevated accordingly. Figure 6.47 shows the angle of elevation Ω between the horizon plane and the extreme visual ray. By illustrating several different angles of elevation (Ω), Fig. 6.48 shows the effect of elevation of the station point. In general, the best picturization is obtained at an angle of about 20° to 30°.

Accordingly, *the visual rays to the object should be kept within a right-circular cone whose elements make an angle of not more than 15° with the cone axis* (total included angle of 30°).

In choosing the station point, see that its position is always offset to one side and also that it is offset vertically from the exact middle of the object, or a rather stiff and awkward perspective will result. Similarly, in locating the object with reference to the picture plane, avoid having the faces make identical angles with the picture plane, or the same stiffness will appear.

6.33. TO DRAW A PERSPECTIVE.

Perspective projection is based on the theory that visual rays from the object to the eye pierce the picture plane and form an image of the object on the plane. Thus in Fig. 6.49, the image of line YZ is formed by the piercing points y and z of the rays. Several projective methods may be used. The simplest method, basically, but the most laborious to draw is illustrated by the purely orthographic method of Fig. 6.50, in which the top and side views are drawn in orthographic. The picture plane (edge view) and the station point are located in each view. Assuming that the line YZ in Fig. 6.49 is one edge of the L-shaped block in Fig. 6.50, visual rays from Y and Z

FIG. 6.48. Comparative elevation angles of view. Angles greater than 30° give an unpleasing perspective.

50°   40°   30°   20°   10°

FIG. 6.49. Perspective of a line.

will intersect the picture plane in the top view, thus locating the perspective of the points laterally. Similarly, the intersections of the rays in the side view give the perspective heights of Y and Z. Projection from the top and side views of the picture plane gives the perspective of YZ, and a repetition of the process for the other lines will complete the drawing. Note that *any* point such as Y or Z can be located on the perspective, and thus the perspective is actually plotted, by projection, point after point.

FIG. 6.50. Perspective drawing (orthographic method). Points are plotted from the intersection of rays with the picture plane.

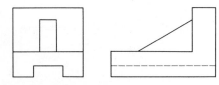

FIG. 6.51. Sliding block. This object is drawn in perspective in Fig. 6.52.

FIG. 6.52. Use of vanishing points and measuring lines. This saves time and extra construction, as compared with the orthographic method used in Fig. 6.50.

6.34. THE USE OF VANISHING POINTS AND MEASURING LINES.

These facilitate the projections. Let it be required to make a perspective of the sliding block in Fig. 6.51. The edge view of the picture plane (plan view) is drawn (Fig. 6.52), and behind it the top view of the object is located and drawn. In this case, one side of the object is oriented at 30° to the picture plane in order to emphasize the L shape more than the end of the block. The station point is located a little to the left of center and far enough in front of the picture plane to give a good angle of view. The ground line is then drawn, and on it is placed the front view of the block from Fig. 6.51. The height of the station point is then decided—in this case, well above the block so that the top surfaces will be seen—and the horizon line is drawn at the station-point height.

To avoid the labor of redrawing the top and front views in the positions just described, the views can be cut from the orthographic drawing, oriented in position, and fastened with tacks or tape.

The *vanishing point* for any horizontal line can be found by drawing a visual ray from the station point *parallel* to the horizontal line and finding the piercing point of this visual ray with the picture plane. Thus, in Fig. 6.52, the line *SP* to *R* is parallel to the edge *AB* of the object, and *R* is the piercing point. Point *R* is then projected to the horizon line, locating *VR*, the vanishing point for *AB* and all edges parallel to *AB*. The vanishing point *VL* for *AC* and edges parallel to *AC* is found similarly, as shown.

In visualizing the location of a vanishing point, imagine that the edge, for example, *AB*, is moved to the right along the ground, still making the same angle with the picture plane; the intercept of *AB* will become less and less until, when *A* is in coincidence with *R*, the intercept will be zero. *R* then must be the top view of the vanishing point for all lines parallel to *AB*.

Point *A* lies in both the picture plane and the ground plane and will therefore be shown in the perspective at *a,* on the ground line, and in direct projection with the top view. The perspective of *AB* is determined by drawing a line from *a* to *VR* (the perspective *direction* of *AB*) and then projecting the intercept *Z* (of the visual rays *SP* to *B*) to the line, thus locating *b*.

All lines behind the picture plane are foreshortened in the picture, and only those lying in the picture plane will appear in their true length. For this reason, *all measurements must be made in the picture plane*. Since *AD* is in the picture plane, it will show in its actual height as *ad*.

A *measuring line* will be needed for any verticals such as *BF* that do not lie in the picture plane. If a vertical is brought forward to the picture plane along some established line, the true height can be measured in the picture plane. If, in Fig. 6.52, *BF* is imagined as moved forward along *ab* until *b* is in coincidence with *a,* the true height can be measured vertically from *a.* This vertical line at *a* is then the measuring line for all heights in the vertical plane containing *a* and *b.* The height of *f* is measured from *a,* and from this height point, a vanishing line is drawn to *VR;* then from *Z* (the piercing point in the picture plane of the visual ray to *F*), *f* can be projected to the perspective.

The measuring line can also be thought of as the intersection of the picture plane with a vertical plane that contains the distance to be found. Thus *ad,* extended, is the measuring line for all heights in surface *ABFEGD.* The triangular rib in Fig. 6.52 is located by continuing surface *HJK* until it intersects the picture plane at *XY,* thereby establishing *xy* as the measuring line for all heights in *HJK.* In the figure, the height of *J* is measured on the measuring line *xy,* and *j* is found as described for *f.*

Note that heights can be measured with a scale on the measuring line or they can be projected from the front view, as indicated in Fig. 6.52.

To Make a Perspective Drawing

1. Draw the top view (edge of the picture plane).

2. Orient the object relative to the picture plane so that the object will appear to advantage, and draw the top view of the object.

3. Select a station point that will best show the shape of the object.

4. Draw the horizon and ground line.

5. Find the top view of the vanishing points for the principal horizontal edges by drawing lines parallel to the edges, through the station point, and to the picture plane.

6. Project from the top views of the vanishing points to the horizon line,

FIG. 6.53. Planes parallel to the picture plane. Compare the position of this object with that of Fig. 6.52.

thus locating the vanishing points for the perspective.

7. Draw the visual rays from the station point to the corners of the object in the top view, locating the piercing point of each ray with the picture plane.

8. Start the picture, building from the ground up and from the nearest corner to the more distant ones.

6.35. PLANES PARALLEL TO THE PICTURE PLANE. Objects with circles or other curves in a vertical plane can be oriented with their curved faces parallel to the picture plane. The curves will then appear in true shape. This method, often called "parallel perspective," is also suitable for interiors and for street vistas and similar scenes where considerable depth is to be represented.

The object in Fig. 6.53 has been

FIG. 6.54. Perspective of a circle. Points are plotted.

ORTHOGRAPHIC

PERSPECTIVE

FIG. 6.55. Graticulation. Points are plotted.

placed so that the planes containing the circular contours are parallel to the picture plane. The horizontal edges parallel to the picture plane will appear horizontal in the picture and will have no vanishing point. Horizontals perpendicular to the picture plane are parallel to the axis of vision and will vanish at the center of vision CV. Except for architectural interiors, the station point is usually located above the object and either to the right or left, yet not so far in any direction as to cause unpleasant distortion. For convenience, one face of the object is usually placed in the picture plane and is therefore not reduced in size in the perspective.

In Fig. 6.53, the end of the hub is in the picture plane; thus the center o is projected from O in the top view, and the circular edges are drawn in their true size. The center line ox is vanished from o to CV. To find the perspective of center line MN, a vertical plane is passed through MN intersecting the picture plane in measuring line gh. A horizontal line from o intersecting gh locates m, and m vanished to CV is the required line.

By using the two center lines from o and m as a framework, the remaining construction is simplified. A ray from the station point to B pierces the picture plane at J, which, projected to mn, locates b. The horizontal line bz is the center line of the front face of the nearer arm, and the intercept IJ gives the perspective radius ab. The circular hole having a radius CB has an intercept PJ, giving cb as the perspective radius. The arc qy has its center on ox at z. On drawing the tangents lq and ky, the face "F" is completed.

The remaining construction for the arms is exactly the same as that for "F."

The centers are moved back on the center lines, and the radii are found from their corresponding intercepts on the picture plane.

6.36. CIRCLES IN PERSPECTIVE. The perspective of a circle is a circle only when its plane is parallel to the picture plane; the circle appears as a straight line when its plane is receding from the station point. In all other positions the circle projects as an ellipse whose major and minor diameters are not readily determinable. The major diameter of the ellipse will be at some odd angle except when a vertical circle has its center on the horizon plane; then the major diameter will be vertical. Also, when a horizontal circle has its center directly above, below, or on the center of vision, the major diameter will be horizontal. It should be noted that in all cases the center of the circle is not coincident with the center of the ellipse representing the circle and that concentric circles are not represented by concentric ellipses. The major and minor diameters of the ellipses for concentric circles are not even parallel except in special cases.

The perspective of a circle can be plotted point by point, but the most rapid solution is had by enclosing the circle in a square, as shown in Fig. 6.54, and plotting points at the tangent points and at the intersections of the diagonals. The eight points thus determined are usually sufficient to give an accurate curve. The square, with its diagonals, is first drawn in the perspective. From the intersection of the diagonals, the vertical and horizontal center lines of the circle are established; where these center lines cross the sides of the square are four points on the curve. In the orthographic view, the measurement X is made, then laid out *in the picture plane* and vanished, crossing the diagonals at four additional points.

Note that the curve is tangent to the lines enclosing it and that the *direction* of the curve is established by these tangent lines; if the lines completing the circumscribing octagon are projected and drawn, the direction of the curve is established at eight points.

6.37. GRATICULATION. The perspectives of irregular curves can be drawn by projecting a sufficient number of points to establish the curve, but if the curve is complicated, the method of graticulation may be used to advantage. A square grid is overlaid on the orthographic view as shown in Fig. 6.55; then the grid is drawn in perspective and the outlines of the curve are transferred by inspection from the orthographic view.

6.38. MEASURING POINTS. It has been shown that all lines lying in the picture plane will be their own perspectives and can be scaled directly on the perspective drawing. The adaptation of this principle has an advantage in laying off a series of measurements, such as a row of pilasters, because it avoids a confusion of intercepts on the picture plane and the inaccuracies due to long projection lines.

In the measuring-points method, a surface, such as the wall between *A* and *B* in Fig. 6.56, is rotated into the picture plane for the purpose of making measurements, as shown at *AB'*. While in the picture plane, the entire surface can be laid out directly to the same scale as the top view; therefore, *ab'* and other horizontal dimensions of the surface are established along the ground line as shown. The counterrotation of the wall

to its actual position on the building and the necessary projections in the perspective are based on the principle that the rotation has been made about a vertical axis and that any point has traveled in a horizontal plane. By drawing, as usual, a line parallel to *BB'*, from the station point to the picture plane, and then projecting to the horizon, the vanishing point *MR* is found. This vanishing point is termed a *measuring point* and may be defined as the vanishing point for lines joining corresponding points of the actual and rotated positions of the face considered. The divisions on *ab'* are therefore vanished to *MR;* where this construction intersects *ab* (the perspective of *AB*), the lateral position of the pilasters, in the perspective, is determined. Heights are scaled on the vertical edge through *a,* as this edge lies in the picture plane. The perspective of the wall between *A* and *B* is completed by the regular methods previously described. For work on the end of the building, the end wall is rotated as indicated, measuring point *ML* is found, and the projections are continued as described for the front wall.

FIG. 6.56. Use of measuring points. An edge of the object is rotated into the picture plane.

Measuring points can be more readily located if the draftsman recognizes that the triangles *ABB'* and *R O SP* are similar. Therefore, a measuring point is as far from its corresponding vanishing point as the station point is from the picture plane, measuring the latter parallel to the face concerned. *MR* can then be found by measuring the distance from the station point to *R* and laying off *RO* equal to the measurement, or by swinging an arc, with *R* as center, from the station point to *O,* as shown. The measuring point *MR* is then projected from *O.*

6.39.   INCLINED LINES.   Any line that is not parallel or perpendicular to either the picture plane or the horizon plane is termed an inclined line. Any line may have a vertical plane passed through it, and if the vanishing line of the plane is found, a line in the plane will vanish at some point on the vanishing line of the plane. Vertical planes will vanish on vertical lines, just as horizontal planes vanish on a horizontal line, the horizon. In Fig. 6.57, the points *a* to *e* have all

been found by regular methods previously described. The vanishing point of the horizontal *ab* is *VR*. The vertical line through *VR* is the vanishing line of the plane of *abc* and all planes *parallel to abc*. This vanishing line is intersected by the extension of *de* at *UR,* thereby determining the vanishing point for *de* and all edges *parallel to de.*

The vanishing point for inclined lines can also be located on the theory that the vanishing point for any line can be determined by moving the line until it appears as a point, while still retaining its original angle with the picture plane. The vanishing point of *de* can therefore be located by drawing a line through the station point parallel to *DE* and finding its piercing point with the picture plane. This is done by laying out *SP T* at the angle *β* to *SP R* and erecting *RT* perpendicular to *SP R*. Then *RT* is the height of the vanishing point *UR* above *VR*.

If measuring points are used for the initial work on the perspective, it will be an advantage to recognize which one of the measuring points was used for determining horizontal measurements in the parallel vertical planes containing the inclined lines; at that measuring point, the angle *β* is laid out, above or below the horizon depending upon whether the lines slope up or down as they go into the distance. Where this construction intersects the vanishing line for the vertical planes containing the inclined lines, the vanishing point is located.

6.40.   INCLINED PLANES.   An inclined plane is any plane not parallel or perpendicular to either the picture plane or the horizon plane. The vanishing line for an inclined plane can be found

FIG. 6.57.   Vanishing point of inclined lines. This simplifies construction when there are many parallel inclined lines.

by locating the vanishing points for any two systems of parallel lines in the inclined plane. To determine the vanishing line of plane *ABCD* in Fig. 6.58, the vanishing point *VL* of the horizontal edges *AD* and *BC* is one point, and the vanishing point *UR* for the inclined edges *AB* and *DC* gives a second point on the vanishing line *VL UR* for plane *ABCD*.

It is often necessary to draw the line of intersection of two inclined planes. The intersection will vanish at the point of intersection of the vanishing lines of both planes. The intersection *J* of the two vanishing lines of the roof planes in Fig. 6.58 is the vanishing point of the line of intersection of the two planes.

6.41. PICTORIAL SKETCHING. The need for the engineer to be trained in freehand sketching was emphasized in Chap. 5, where the discussion referred particularly to sketching in orthographic projection. Before he can be said to have a command of the graphic language, his training in freehand drawing must include also acquiring the ability to sketch *pictorially* with skill and facility.

In designing and inventing, the first ideas come into the mind in pictorial form, and sketches made in this form preserve the ideas as visualized. From this record the preliminary orthographic design sketches are made. A pictorial sketch of an object or of some detail of construction can often be used to explain it to a client or workman who cannot read the orthographic projection intelligently. One of the best ways of reading a working drawing that is difficult to understand is to start a pictorial sketch of it. Usually before the sketch is finished, the orthographic drawing is perfectly clear. Often a pictorial sketch

FIG. 6.58. Vanishing lines for inclined planes and vanishing point for the line of intersection of two inclined planes.

can be made more quickly and serve as a better record than orthographic views of the same piece. A young engineer should not be deterred by any fancied lack of "artistic ability." An engineer's sketch is a record of information, not a work of art. The one requirement is *good proportion.*

6.42. METHODS. Although this is not a complete classification, there may be said to be three pictorial methods of sketching: axonometric, oblique, and perspective. The mechanical construction has been explained in detail.

6.43. PREREQUISITES. It should be clearly understood at the outset that pictorial sketching means the making of a pictorial drawing *freehand.* The same construction that is used for locating points and lines and for drawing circles and arcs with instruments will be used in pictorial sketching. From this standpoint, a knowledge of the constructions already given is necessary before attempting pictorial sketching. Note in Figs. 6.69 to 6.75 that the ellipses representing holes and rounded contours have, before being drawn, been boxed

FIG. 6.59. Choice of axes and object position.

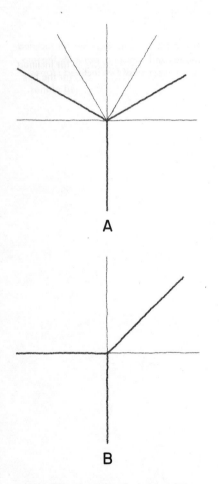

FIG. 6.60. Locating the axes. (*A*) isometric; (*B*) oblique at 45°.

in with construction lines representing the enclosing square in exactly the same manner as for an instrument drawing.

6.44. MATERIALS AND TECHNIQUE. The same materials, pencil grades, etc., used for orthographic freehand drawing, described in Chap. 5, are employed for pictorial sketching. The directions given there for drawing straight lines, circles, and arcs will apply here also.

6.45. PICTORIAL SKETCHING: CHOICE OF TYPE AND DIRECTION OF VIEW. After a clear visualization of the object, the first step is to select the type of pictorial—axonometric, oblique, or perspective—to be used.

Isometric is the simplest axonometric position, and it will serve admirably for representing most objects. Although dimetric or trimetric may be definitely advantageous for an object with some feature that is obscured or misleading in isometric, it is best to try isometric first, especially if there is doubt that another form will be superior. This is principally because proportions are easier to judge in isometric.

Oblique forms (cavalier or cabinet) may be used to advantage for cylindrical objects or for objects with a number of circular features in parallel planes. Nevertheless, a true circle, representing a circular feature parallel to the picture

plane in oblique, is much harder to sketch than an ellipse, representing the same feature in isometric, as the slightest deviation from a circle is evident, while the same deviation in an ellipse is unnoticed. Also, inherently, there is more distortion in the oblique than in axonometric forms. Therefore, especially for the sake of professional appearance, an axonometric form has the advantage.

Perspective is the best form for pictorial sketching because it is free from any distortion. A perspective is not much more difficult to sketch than an axonometric or an oblique, but attention must be paid to the convergence of the lines and to keeping good proportion. However, do not discard axonometric and oblique from consideration. As will be seen in paragraphs 6.46 and 6.47, these forms can be handled as successfully as perspective by some flattening of the axes and by converging the lines properly.

Choose carefully the *direction* in which the object is to be viewed. There are many possibilities. The object may be turned so that any lateral face will be represented on the right or the left side of the pictorial. Orient the object so that the two *principal* faces will show to advantage. Use reversed axes if necessary. Do this by mentally visualizing and turning the object in every possible position in order to arrive at the best representation for all features. Be alert to see that some feature will not be hidden by a portion in front of it. The proper choice of direction is an important factor in pictorial sketching.

Fig. 6.59 illustrates these points. At (*A*) an object is sketched in isometric; all features are clearly represented and the object appears natural in this form. At (*B*) trimetric has been used so that the slot in the lower portion is not obscured by the horizontal middle portion. At (*C*) another trimetric position has been chosen to present the semicircular ear as the definite front face of the object. For further illustration of the possibilities, study the pictorial drawings in Chap. 5.

6.46. SKETCHING THE AXES. After the type of pictorial and the position of the object have been decided upon, the first step in making the sketch is to draw the axes.

In isometric, the three axes should be located as nearly as possible 120° from one another (one vertical and two at 30° with the horizontal). Because no triangles are used in sketching, the angles must be located by judgment. Figure 6.60*A* shows a satisfactory method of judging the position of the lines. First draw a *light* horizontal and vertical and then divide both upper quadrants into thirds. The lines at the top of the lower thirds are then the two axes at 30° to the horizontal, and the third axis is the vertical. This method is simple and accurate because it is easy to estimate equal thirds of a quadrant.

In dimetric, the standard angles are 7° and 41°. For the 7° axis, again referring to Fig. 6.60*A,* draw the bisector of the 30° axis for isometric to get 15°, and then bisect again to get 7½°, which will be quite satisfactory and can be done fairly accurately. For the 41° axis, take the mid-line of the second 30° section, which is 45°, and shade it a little to approximate 41°.

In trimetric, almost any combination representing three mutually perpendicular lines is possible. However, a pronounced distortion will occur if the two transverse axes are more than 30° from

FIG. 6.61. Perspective layout with vanishing points.

the horizontal. Read the cautions in paragraph 6.47.

In oblique, the common angles are 30° and 45° although theoretically any angle is possible. To prevent violent distortion, never make the depth axis greater than 45°. To locate a 45° axis, sketch a vertical and horizontal as in Fig. 6.60*B,* and then sketch the bisector of the quadrant (see oblique positions) where the axis is wanted. For an axis at 30°, proceed as in Fig. 6.60*A* for isometric.

For perspective, as explained in paragraph 6.32, take care to have a reasonable included angle of view; otherwise a violent convergence will occur. In order to prevent difficulty, first locate two vanishing points, as in Fig. 6.61, as widely separated as the paper will allow (attach extra paper with scotch tape if necessary). Then sketch the *bottom* edges of the object (the heavier lines in Fig. 6.61) and on these sketch a rectangular shape, as shown. It will be immediately evident that the arrangement is satisfactory or that the vanishing points must be moved *or* that the base lines must be altered. Remember that the two vanishing points *must* be at the same level, the horizon.

6.47. SKETCHING THE PRINCIPAL LINES. Almost without exception, the first lines sketched should be those that box in the

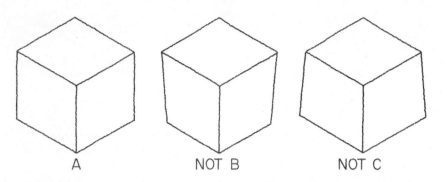

FIG. 6.62. Sketching vertical lines. These must be accurately vertical to define object shape.

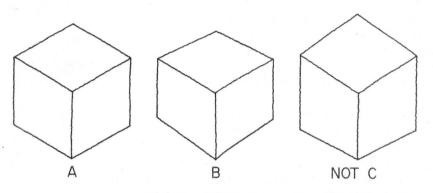

FIG. 6.63. Sketching the receding edges. These must be parallel (*A*); or converging (*B*); *never separating* (*C*).

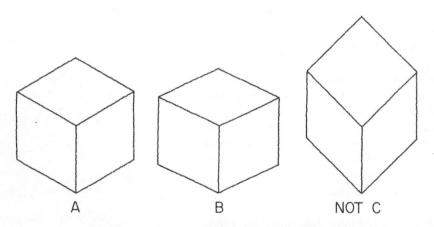

FIG. 6.64. Angle of axes. Isometric position (*A*) or flattened (*B*) gives a natural appearance. Distortion is inherent in steep axes as at (*C*).

whole object, or at least its major portion. These first lines are all-important to the success of the sketch, for mistakes at the outset are difficult to correct later. Observe carefully the following three points:

1. *Verticals must be parallel to the vertical axis.* In Fig. 6.62 a cube is sketched correctly at (*A*). At (*B*) and (*C*) the same cube is sketched but at (*B*) the verticals converge downward and at (*C*), upward. It is evident that (*B*) and (*C*) do not look cubical at all, but like frustums of pyramids. This is proof that verticals *must be kept accurately vertical.* Be critical of the verticals throughout the construction—accurate verticals add a stability and crispness not attained in any other way.

2. *Transverse lines must be parallel or converging.* In Fig. 6.63 a cube is sketched at (*A*) with the transverse lines (receding right and left edges) made accurately parallel. At (*B*) these lines are made to converge as they recede. Note that (*B*) looks more natural than (*A*) because of the effect of perspective foreshortening. The monstrosity at (*C*) is produced by the separating of the receding lines as they recede. In his attempt to get the lines parallel, the beginner often makes a mistake like that at (*C*). Converge the lines deliberately, as in (*B*), to avoid the results of (*C*)!

3. *Axes must be kept flat to avoid distortion.* In Fig. 6.64 an accurate isometric sketch is shown at (*A*). At (*B*) the axes have been flattened to less than 30° with the horizontal. (*B*) possibly looks more natural than (*A*). At (*C*), however, the axes are somewhat more than 30° to the horizontal. Note the definite distortion and awkward appearance of (*C*). Therefore, especially in isometric, but also in other forms, keep the axes at

6.50. Sketching Circular Features

their correct angle or flatter than the normal angle.

The foregoing three points must be kept constantly in mind. Hold your sketch at arm's length often during the work, so that you will see errors that are not so evident in the normal working position. Become critical of your own work and you will soon develop confidence and a good sense of line direction.

6.48. DIVISIONS FOR SYMMETRY. Continually in sketching, centers must be located and divisions of a face must be made into thirds, fourths, fifths, etc. Division into halves to locate a center line is the simplest and most common, and is easily accomplished by judging the mid-point along one of the sides, as indicated on the top face of the rectangular shape in Fig. 6.65. Also shown on this top face are additional divisions into quarters and eighths. Practice this a few times to develop your judgment of equal spacings. It is really quite easy to do.

Division into thirds is a little harder but after short practice is readily done. The left face of Fig. 6.65 shows third divisions and one space divided in half to give a sixth point. The right face of Fig. 6.65 shows division into fifths.

Practice dividing lines or spaces into various equal units. The experience will be valuable in later work.

6.49. USES OF THE DIAGONAL. The two diagonals of a square or rectangle will locate its geometric center, as indicated on the left face of Fig. 6.66. The center is also readily located by drawing two center lines, estimating the middle of the space as shown on the top and right faces of Fig. 6.66.

The diagonals of a rectangular face

FIG. 6.65. Judging equal spaces. This can be done satisfactorily by eye.

FIG. 6.66. Location of centers. Use diagonals or judge the position of center lines.

FIG. 6.67. Use of diagonals for increasing or decreasing rectangular shapes.

can also be used to increase or decrease the rectangle symmetrically about the same center and in proportion as shown on the left face of Fig. 6.67, or with two sides coincident as shown on the right face. To increase or decrease by equal units, the distance (or space) between lines must be judged as explained in paragraph 6.48.

6.50. SKETCHING CIRCULAR FEATURES. A circle in pictorial is an ellipse whose major diameter is always perpendicular to the *rotation axis*. Thus its minor diameter coincides on the drawing with the rotation axis (Fig. 6.68). These facts can be used to advantage when drawing an object principally made up of cylinders on the same axis. Note particularly from the above that *all* circles on horizontal planes are drawn as ellipses *with the major diameter horizontal,* as shown in Fig. 6.69.

Most objects, however, are made up of combinations of rectangular and circular features, and for this reason it is best to draw the enclosing pictorial square for all circular features. Figure 6.70 shows circles on all three axono-

FIG. 6.68. Circles in pictorial. The major diameter of the ellipse is perpendicular to the axis of rotation.

FIG. 6.69. Circular features on horizontal planes. The major diameter of the ellipse is horizontal.

FIG. 6.70. Circles in isometric. Ellipses are tangent to the enclosing isometric squares at the mid-points of the sides.

FIG. 6.71. Boxing construction for circular features. This is necessary to assure correct shape and proportion.

ORTHO.

FIG. 6.72. Proportioning the distances. By dividing one side into units, all other distances are proportioned.

metric planes. Note particularly that the ellipses must be tangent to the sides of the pictorial square at the mid-points of the sides; accordingly, it is best always to draw center lines, also shown. Always sketch the enclosing pictorial square for *all* circular features because by this method the size of the ellipse and the thickness of the cylindrical portion are easily judged. Figure 6.71 illustrates the boxing of circular features. This object would be difficult to sketch without first boxing in the circular portions.

6.51. PROPORTIONING THE DISTANCES. The ability to make divisions into equal units, discussed in paragraph 6.48, is needed in proportioning distances on a sketch. The average object does not have distances that are easily divisible into even *inches, half inches,* etc., but as sketches are *not* made to scale, only to good proportions, great accuracy is not necessary. Also, most objects, dimensioned as they invariably are in various odd distances, are difficult to judge from the standpoint of one distance being ½, ⅓, ¼, etc., of another. Nevertheless, the proportioning can be done easily and quickly by the method we are about to discuss.

Figure 6.72 shows a simple rectangular object, but the distances are not multiples of any simple unit. The best way to proportion this object (and others) is to lay off on *one* axis a distance that is to represent one side of the object. This *sets the size* of the sketch. Then divide this first side into some unit that can be used easily to proportion other distances. At (*A*) the *left* side has been laid off and divided into three parts. Each of these parts now represents *approximately* a half inch. To get the distance for the vertical axis, the last third (at the rear) has been divided in half, and again in half, so that the dimension shown is approximately 1⅛ in. Transfer this distance to the vertical axis (1) by judging by eye, (2) by measuring with the finger on the pencil, or (3) by marking the distance on a piece of scratch paper. The method to be used will suggest itself according to the relative accuracy needed. The right-axis distance is obtained similarly, by first transferring the whole left distance (representing approximately 1½ in.) and then adding two-thirds of the left distance (approx. 1 in.), which gives a total of 2½ in., close enough to the actual 2⅝ in. dimension of the object. Any side may be chosen to start the sketch. At (*B*) the right side has been laid off and divided, this time into five parts so that again each unit is approximately ½ in. The procedure is then similar to that described for (*A*).

Remember that great accuracy is unnecessary. Do not make the proportioning a burden. It is simply a method of getting distances reasonably close to the actual distance and eliminating the need for wild guesses or extra construction on the sketch.

Figure 6.73 shows the method applied to a more complex object. The left axis has been divided into 4 parts. In this case the upper details have been located by projection upward from the left axis divisions, a method that is often used. Note the boxing of circular features, as described in paragraph 6.50. Study this figure carefully, with particular attention to the proportioning and construction.

6.52. STEPS IN MAKING A PICTORIAL SKETCH.

Because a variety of objects are sketched, the order of procedure will not always be the same, but the following will serve as a guide:

A. Visualize the shape and proportions of the object from the orthographic views, a model, or other source.
B. Mentally picture the object in space and decide the pictorial position that will best describe its shape.
C. Decide on the type of pictorial to use —axonometric, oblique, or perspective.
D. Pick a suitable paper size.
E. Then proceed as shown in Fig. 6.74.

FIG. 6.73. Proportioning the distances. After one side is divided into units, distances are projected or transferred.

FIG. 6.74. Steps in making a pictorial sketch. Progressive layout, (1) to (6); finishing, (7) to (9).

FIG. 6.75. An oblique sketch. Note boxing of circular features.

FIG. 6.76. Estimating distances and proportion.

FIG. 6.77. A perspective sketch. The front face of the object is parallel to the picture plane.

FIG. 6.78. A perspective sketch. The object is in an angular position.

The numbers that follow refer to the figure; 1 through 6 shows light construction, 7, 8, and 9 completion to final weight.

1. Sketch the axes.
2. Lay off the proportions of an enclosing rectangular box for the whole object or a principal portion of it.
3. Sketch the enclosing box.
4. Divide one axis for proportioning distances and sketch the most dominant detail of the object.
5. Proportion smaller details by reference to the divided axis and sketch the enclosing boxes, center lines, or outlines.
6. Complete the boxes for circular features. Check to be sure that all features are in good proportion and that there are no errors in representation (see paragraph 6.47). Having worked entirely with light lines, corrections are easily made.
7. Start sketching to the final line width. Begin with the most dominant feature.
8. Sketch the smaller details.
9. Remove construction.

6.53. AXONOMETRIC SKETCHING. The methods presented thus far have been directed toward the making of axonometric sketches because they are the type most used. However, the practices given apply to oblique and perspective sketching, for which additional helps are given in the two paragraphs that follow.

6.54. OBLIQUE SKETCHING. The advantage of oblique projection in preserving one face without distortion is of particular value in sketching, as illustrated by Fig. 6.75. The painful effect of distortion in oblique drawing that is done instrumentally can be greatly lessened in sketching by foreshortening the depth axis to a pleasing proportion. By converging the lines parallel to the depth axis, the effect of perspective is obtained. This converging in axonometric or oblique is sometimes called "fake perspective."

6.55. PERSPECTIVE SKETCHING. A sketch made in perspective gives a better effect than in axonometric or oblique. For constructing a perspective drawing of a proposed structure from its plans and elevations, a knowledge of the principles of perspective drawing is required, but for making a perspective sketch from the object, you can get along by observing the ordinary phenomena of perspective which affect everything we see: the fact that objects appear proportionately smaller as their distance from the eye increases, that parallel lines appear to converge as they recede, and that horizontal lines and planes appear to "vanish" on the horizon.

In perspective sketching from the model, make the drawing simply by observation, estimating the directions and proportionate lengths of lines by sighting and measuring on the pencil held at arm's length and use your knowledge of perspective phenomena as a check. With the drawing board or sketch pad held in a comfortable drawing position perpendicular to the line of sight from the eye to the object, test the direction of a line by holding the pencil at arm's length parallel to the board, rotating the arm until the pencil appears to coincide with the line on the model, and then moving it parallel to this position back to the board. Estimate the apparent lengths of lines in the same way; holding the pencil in a plane perpendicular to the line of sight, mark with the thumb the length of pencil which covers the line of the model, rotate the arm with the thumb held in position until the pencil coincides with another line, and then estimate the proportion of this measurement to the second line (Fig. 6.76).

Make the sketch lightly, with free sketchy lines, and do not erase any lines until the whole sketch has been blocked in. *Do not make the mistake of getting the sketch too small.*

In starting a sketch from the object, set it in a position to give the most advantageous view, and sketch the directions of the principal lines, running them past the limits of the figure toward their vanishing points. Block in the enclosing squares for all circles and circle arcs and proceed with the figure, drawing the main outlines first and adding details later; then brighten the sketch with heavier lines.

The drawing in Fig. 6.77 shows the general appearance of a "one-point" perspective sketch before the construction lines have been erased. Figure 6.78 is an example showing the object turned at an angle to the picture plane.

6.56. PICTORIAL ILLUSTRATION. Pictorial illustration combines any one of the regular pictorial methods with some method of shading or "rendering." In considering a specific problem, decide upon the pictorial form—axonometric, oblique, or perspective—and then choose a method of shading that is suited to the method of reproduction and the general effect desired.

6.57. LIGHT AND SHADE. The conventional position of the light in light-and-shade drawing is the same as that used for orthographic line shading, that is, a position to the left, in front of, and above the object. Any surface or portion of a surface perpendicular to the light direction and directly illuminated by the light would receive the greatest amount of light and be lightest in tone on the drawing; any face not illuminated by the light would be "in shade" and darkest on the drawing. Other surfaces, receiving less light than the "high" light but more than a shade portion, would be intermediate in tone.

An understanding of the simple one-light method of illumination is needed at the outset, as well as some artistic appreciation for the illumination on various surfaces of the object. Figure 6.79 shows a sphere, cylinder, cone, and cube illuminated as described and shaded accordingly. Study the tone values in this illustration.

6.58. SHADE LINES. Shade lines, by their contrast with other lines, add some effect of light and shade to the drawing. These lines used alone, without other shading, give the simplest possible shading method. Usually the best effect is obtained by using heavy lines only for the left vertical and upper horizontal edges of the dark faces (Fig. 6.80). Holes and other circular features are drawn

FIG. 6.79. Light and shade. The light source is from the upper left front.

FIG. 6.80. Outline and shade lines. The side away from the light source is drawn with heavier lines.

FIG. 6.82. Line-tone shading.

FIG. 6.81. Continuous-tone shading.

FIG. 6.83. Line-shading technique in pencil.

FIG. 6.84. Line-shading technique in ink.

with heavy lines on the shade side. Shade lines should be used sparingly as the inclusion of too many heavy lines simply adds weight to the drawing and does not give the best effect.

6.59. PENCIL RENDERING. There are two general methods of pencil shading—continuous tone and line tone. Continuous-tone shading is done with a fairly soft pencil with its point flattened. A medium-rough paper is best for the purpose. Start with a light, over-all tone and then build the middle tones and shade portions gradually. Figure 6.81 is an example. Clean high lights with an eraser.

Line-tone shading requires a little more skill, as the tones are produced by

line spacing and weight. Light lines at wide spacing produce the lightest tone, and heavy lines at close spacing make the darkest shade. Leave high lights perfectly white. Pure black may be used sparingly for deep shade or shadow. Figure 6.82 is an example, drawn with only a light outline.

Complete over-all shading is somewhat heavy, and a lighter, more open treatment is usually desired. To achieve this, leave light portions of the object with little or no shading, and line middle tones and shade sparingly. The few lines used strongly suggest light, shade, and surface finish (Fig. 6.83). There are many variations in this type of rendering.

6.60. PEN-AND-INK RENDERING. Pen-and-ink methods follow the same general pattern as work in pencil, with the exception that no continuous tone is possible. However, there are some variations not ordinarily used in pencil work. Figure 6.84 shows line techniques. As in pencil work, the common and usually the most pleasing method is the partially shaded, suggestive system.

PROBLEMS

The following problems are intended to furnish practice (1) in the various methods of pictorial representation and (2) in reading and translating orthographic projections.

In reading a drawing, remember that a line

on any view always means an edge or a change in direction of the surface of the object and always look at another view to interpret the meaning of the line.

GROUP 1. ISOMETRIC DRAWINGS

PROB. 6.1.1. Jig block.

PROB. 6.1.2. Frustum of pyramid.

PROB. 6.1.3. Hopper.

PROB. 6.1.4. Stop block.

PROB. 6.1.5. Skid mount.

PROB. 6.1.8. Bracket.

PROB. 6.1.12. Wedge block.

PROB. 6.1.15. Dovetail bracket.

PROB. 6.1.6. Guide block.

PROB. 6.1.9. Hinged catch.

PROB. 6.1.10. Bearing.

PROB. 6.1.13. Head attachment.

PROB. 6.1.16. Offset bracket.

PROB. 6.1.7. Dovetail stop.

PROB. 6.1.11. Cross link.

PROB. 6.1.14. Slide stop.

PROB. 6.1.17. Cradle bracket.

PROB. 6.1.18. Dovetail hinge.

PROB. 6.1.19. Cable clip.

PROB. 6.1.20. Strut anchor.

PROB. 6.1.21. Strut swivel.

PROB. 6.1.22. Tie plate.

PROB. 6.1.23. Forming punch.

Reversed axes

PROB. 6.1.24. Springing stone.

Reversed axes

GROUP 2. ISOMETRIC SECTIONS

PROB. 6.2.1. Column base.

$\frac{3}{4}$ Drill, 4 Holes

PROB. 6.2.2. Base plate.

$\frac{7}{8}$ Drill 2 Holes

PROB. 6.2.3. Gland.

PROB. 6.2.4. Squared collar.

PROB. 6.2.5. Blank for gland.

PROB. 6.2.6. Sliding cover.

PROB. 6.2.7. Rod support.

PROB. 6.2.8. Side-beam bracket.

PROB. 6.2.9. Head yoke.

PROB. 6.2.10. Trunnion plate.

PROB. 6.2.11. Section study.

PROB. 6.2.12. Section study.

GROUP 3.   OBLIQUE DRAWINGS

Draw 45° to left

PROB. 6.3.1.   Letter die.

Draw 45° to right
$\frac{3}{4}$ Drill
4 Holes

PROB. 6.3.2.   Guide plate.

Draw 45° to right

PROB. 6.3.3.   Brace base.

Draw half size and 30° to right

PROB. 6.3.4.   Heart cam.

Draw 45° to left

PROB. 6.3.5.   Ratchet wheel.

Draw 30° to left

PROB. 6.3.6.   Slotted link.

Draw 45° to right

PROB. 6.3.7.   Swivel plate.

Draw 45° to right

PROB. 6.3.8.   Slide bracket.

$\frac{5}{8}$ Drill
3 Holes
Draw 45° to right

PROB. 6.3.9.   Jaw bracket.

Draw 45° to left
$\frac{7}{8}$ Drill 2 Holes

PROB. 6.3.10.   Bell crank.

PROB. 6.3.11.   Stop plate.

PROB. 6.3.12.   Hook brace.

PROB. 6.3.13.   Adjusting-rod support.

PROB. 6.3.14.   Link.

PROB. 6.3.15.   Pawl.

Offsets from right section, 30° to right

PROB. 6.3.16.   Culvert model.

Offsets from right section, 30° to right

PROB. 6.3.17.   Slotted guide.

PROB. 6.3.18.   Support bracket.

PROB. 6.3.19.   Port cover.

Draw 30° to right

PROB. 6.4.1. Sliding cone.

GROUP 4. OBLIQUE SECTIONS

6.4.1. Oblique full section of sliding cone.

6.4.1*A.* Oblique half section of sliding cone.

6.4.2. Oblique full section of conveyor-trough end.

6.4.2*A.* Oblique half section of conveyor-trough end.

6.4.3. Oblique full section of ceiling flange.

6.4.3*A.* Oblique half section of ceiling flange.

6.4.4. Oblique full section of hanger flange.

6.4.4*A.* Oblique half section of hanger flange.

6.4.5. Oblique half section of the base plate of Prob. 6.2.2.

6.4.6. Oblique half section of the gland of Prob. 6.2.3.

Draw 30° to right

PROB. 6.4.2. Conveyor-trough end.

Draw 45° to right

PROB. 6.4.3. Ceiling flange.

Draw 45° to right

PROB. 6.4.4. Hanger flange.

GROUP 5. DIMETRIC AND CABINET DRAWING

6.5.1. Make a dimetric drawing of the jig block, Prob. 6.1.1.

6.5.2. Make a dimetric drawing of the guide block, Prob. 6.1.6.

6.5.3. Make a cabinet drawing of the gland, Prob. 6.2.3.

6.5.4. Make a cabinet drawing of the ceiling flange, Prob. 6.4.3.

GROUP 6. PERSPECTIVE DRAWINGS

The following are a variety of different objects to be drawn in perspective. A further selection can be made from the orthographic drawings in other chapters.

6.6.1. Double wedge block.

6.6.2. Notched holder.

6.6.3. Crank.

6.6.4. Corner lug.

6.6.5. House.

6.6.6. Church.

PROB. 6.6.1. Double wedge block.

PROB. 6.6.2. Notched holder.

PROB. 6.6.3. Crank.

PROB. 6.6.4. Corner lug.

PROB. 6.6.5. House.

PROB. 6.6.6. Church.

GROUP 7. PICTORIAL SKETCHING

The following problems are planned to develop skill not only in pictorial sketching but also in reading orthographic drawings. Make the sketches to suitable size on 8½- by 11-in. paper, choosing the most appropriate form of representation—axonometric, oblique, or perspective—with partial, full, or half sections as needed. Small fillets and rounds may be ignored in these problems and shown as sharp corners.

PROB. 6.7.1. Objects to be sketched.

PROB. 6.7.2.   Objects to be sketched.

PROB. 6.7.3.   Objects to be sketched.

PROB. 6.7.4.   Objects to be sketched.

A

B

C

D

E

F

G

H

J

PROB. 6.7.5. Objects to be sketched.

K

L

M

N

O

P

Q

R

GROUP 8. OBLIQUE SKETCHING

Select an object from Group 3 not previously drawn with instruments, and make an oblique sketch.

GROUP 9. PERSPECTIVE SKETCHING

Select an object not previously drawn with instruments, and make a perspective sketch.

GROUP 10. AXONOMETRIC AND OBLIQUE PROJECTION FROM ORTHOGRAPHIC VIEWS

Any of the problems given in this chapter may be used for making axonometric or oblique projections from the orthographic views by first drawing the orthographic views to suitable scale and then employing these views as described in paragraphs 6.26 to 6.28 to obtain the pictorial projection.

GROUP 11. PICTORIAL DRAWINGS FROM MACHINE PARTS

Machine parts, either rough castings and forgings or finished parts, offer valuable practice in making pictorial drawings. Choose pieces to give practice in isometric and oblique drawing. Use the most appropriate form of representation, and employ section and half-section treatments where necessary to give clearer description.

GROUP 12. PICTORIAL WORKING DRAWINGS

Any of the problems in this chapter offer practice in making complete pictorial working drawings. Follow the principles of dimensioning in Chap. 10. The form and placement of the dimension figures are given in paragraph 10.37.

6.12.1 Pictorial working drawing of dovetail stop, Prob. 6.1.7.

6.12.2. Pictorial working drawing of hinged catch, Prob. 6.1.9.

6.12.3. Pictorial working drawing of tie plate, Prob. 6.1.22.

6.12.4. Pictorial working drawing of head yoke, Prob. 6.2.9.

6.12.5. Pictorial working drawing of jaw bracket, Prob. 6.3.9.

6.12.6. Pictorial working drawing of adjusting-rod support, Prob. 6.3.13.

6.12.7. Pictorial working drawing of port cover, Prob. 6.3.19.

6.12.8. Pictorial working drawing of ceiling flange, Prob. 6.4.3.

7

Auxiliaries: Normal and Edge Views

FIG. 7.1. Object faces parallel to the principal projection planes. Top, front, and side views are normal views, respectively, of top, front, and side of the object.

7.1. BASIC CONCEPTS. A plane surface is shown in true shape when the direction of view is perpendicular to the surface; for example, rectangular objects can be placed with their faces parallel to the principal planes of projection and be fully described by the principal views. In Fig. 7.1 the top, front, and right-side views show the true shape, respectively, of the top, front, and right side of the object. Note especially that the planes of projection are *parallel* to the top, front, and right side of the object and that the directions of observation are *perpendicular* to the object faces and to the planes of projection.

Figure 7.2 is a pictorial of Fig. 7.1, given here to aid in visualizing the relationship of object faces, planes of projection, and view directions.

Note in Figs. 7.1 and 7.2 that each view also shows the *edge* of certain surfaces of the object. For example, the front view shows the edge of the top, bottom, and both sides of the object. For a surface to appear as an edge it must be perpendicular to the plane of projection for the view.

Sometimes an object will have one or more *inclined* surfaces whose true shape it is necessary to show, especially if they are irregular in outline. Figure

FIG. 7.2. Pictorial of Fig. 7.1. This is given to aid in visualizing the relationship of principal planes, view directions, and object position.

193

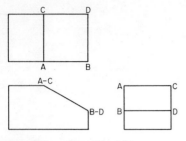

FIG. 7.3. One object face inclined to two principal planes. The inclined face does not appear in its true size and proportions in any view.

FIG. 7.4. Pictorial of Fig. 7.3. A view projected perpendicular to the inclined face will show it in true size and proportions.

FIG. 7.5. Orthographic drawing of the object in Figs. 7.3 and 7.4. The normal view gives the true size and proportions of the inclined face.

7.3 shows an object with one inclined face, *ABDC.* This face is inclined to the horizontal and profile planes and perpendicular to the frontal plane. The face *ABDC* therefore appears as an edge in the front view, but none of the principal views shows the true size and shape of the surface. To show the true size and shape of *ABDC,* a view is needed that has a direction of observation perpendicular to *ABDC* and is projected on a plane parallel to *ABDC,* as shown in Fig. 7.4. This view is known as a *normal* view. The top, front, and side views of Fig. 7.1 are normal views of the top, front, and side surfaces of the object, because they *all* show the true size and shape of a surface by having the direction of observation at right angles to the surface. The dictionary defines a *normal,* in geometry, as "any perpendicular." In graphics, a plane of projection is involved as well as a direction of observation; hence, *a normal view is a projection that has the viewing direction perpendicular to, and made on a plane parallel to, the object face.*

Figure 7.5 is the orthographic counterpart of Fig. 7.4. To get the normal view of surface *ABDC,* a projection is made perpendicular to *ABDC.* This projection is made *from* the view where the surface shows as an edge, in this case, the front view and thus perpendicularity from the surface is seen in true relationship. Extra views such as the normal view of Fig.

7.5 are known as *auxiliary views* to distinguish them from the principal (top, front, side, etc.) views. However, since an auxiliary is made for the purpose of showing the true configuration of a surface, the terms *normal view* or *edge view* state positively what the view is and what it shows.

Detailed instructions for making a normal view of any surface in *any possible position* are given in the paragraphs that follow. Edge views are discussed in paragraph 7.9.

7.2. CLASSIFICATION OF SURFACES. Surfaces may occur in any of the positions shown in Fig. 7.6. At (*A*) all the surfaces are aligned with the principal planes of projection and thus each of the principal views is a normal view. At (*B*) the shaded surface is at an angle to *two* of the principal planes but perpendicular to one plane and is called an *inclined* surface. At (*C*) the shaded surface is at an angle to *all three* principal planes of projection and is known as a *skew,* or *oblique,* surface (that is, one that takes a slanting or oblique course or direction).

7.3. DIRECTIONS OF INCLINED SURFACES. Inclined surfaces may occur anywhere on an object, and because other features of the object must also be represented, the inclined surface may be in any one of the twelve positions shown in Fig. 7.7. The first column, (*B*) to (*E*), shows

NORMAL SURFACES (A)   AN INCLINED SURFACE (B)   A SKEW SURFACE (C)

FIG. 7.6. Classification of surfaces.

surfaces inclined to the front and side so that the surface may be on (*B*) the right front, (*C*) left front, (*D*) left rear, or (*E*) right rear. The second column, (*F*) to (*J*), shows surfaces inclined to the top and side, so that the surface may be on (*F*) the upper right, (*G*) lower right, (*H*) lower left, or (*J*) upper left. The third column, (*K*) to (*N*), shows surfaces inclined to the top and front, so that the surface may be on (*K*) the upper front, (*L*) upper rear, (*M*) lower rear, or (*N*) lower front.

Inclined surfaces occur at *angles* of inclination differing from those shown in Fig. 7.7 but, for general position, no other locations are possible.

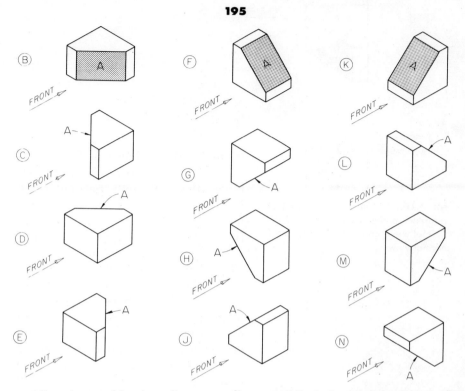

7.4.   THE NORMAL VIEW OF AN INCLINED SURFACE.   No matter what the position of an inclined surface may be, the fundamentals of projecting a normal view of the surface are the same, as will be seen from Figs. 7.8 to 7.21.

Figure 7.8 is the orthographic drawing of the object in position (*B*) of Fig. 7.7. The inclined surface, identified by the letter *A,* is on the right front of the object and shows, in Fig. 7.8, as an *edge* in the top view. Because surface *A* appears as an edge in the top view, the direction of observation for the normal view is established perpendicular to the edge view, as shown. We are looking, in this case, in a horizontal direction, *directly at* surface *A*. Projectors parallel to the viewing direction (also, perpendicular to surface *A*) establish one dimension of the surface needed for the normal view. This is the *horizontal* distance from the left-front vertical edge to the right-rear vertical edge of surface *A*. Figure 7.9*A* shows that the distance *between* the projectors (dimension *P*) is equal to dimension *P* on the object.

All orthographic views have two dimensions, and to complete the normal view of surface *A*, we now need its second dimension. That dimension is, in this case, the vertical distance *Q*, shown at (*B*), which is the vertical height of surface *A* and appears in true length *on the front view* (Fig. 7.8). This distance cannot be projected but must be transferred from the front view to the

FIG. 7.7.   Inclined-surface positions. (*B*) to (*E*) are inclined to front and side; (*F*) to (*J*), to top and side; and (*K*) to (*N*), to front and top.

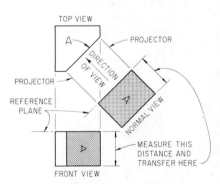

FIG. 7.8.   Normal view of an inclined surface. The object is in position (*B*) of Fig. 7.7.

FIG. 7.9.   Relationship of projectors, reference plane, and surface dimensions.

FIG. 7.10. Relationship of projectors, reference plane, surface dimensions, normal view, and rotated position of normal view.

FIG. 7.11. Normal view of an inclined surface. The object is in position (*C*) of Fig. 7.7.

normal view as shown in Fig. 7.8. In order to facilitate transferring the distance (this will apply particularly in later problems where the surface may not be rectangular), a *reference plane* (Figs. 7.9*B* and 7.10) is established on both the normal view and front view. This reference plane *must* be perpendicular to the distance to be measured and transferred; it is therefore perpendicular to the projectors between the top and front views *and in the front view,* and also perpendicular to the projectors from the top view to the normal view *and in the normal view,* as shown in Fig. 7.8. The reference plane, here, is at the *top edge* of surface *A* in both views. This can be visualized in the normal view by considering the reference plane as a hinge that will rotate the normal view 90° downward to its original position in coincidence with the top view. This is shown pictorially in Fig. 7.10 to aid in visualizing the relationship. It must be understood that the normal view, projected directly out from its original coin-

cidence on the object, occurs in the position first shown in Fig. 7.8. To get the view into coincidence with the plane of the drawing paper, the view is rotated to the position shown in Fig. 7.10. Carefully study Figs. 7.8 to 7.10 and re-read the text to fix all relationships.

The foregoing constitutes all the geometry and projection needed for drawing *any* normal view of an inclined surface. The projection will in some cases be made from a different view and the measurement transferred will be width or depth instead of height, but the fundamental relationships of the views will *be the same in every case.*

Consider the other positions of the object, (*C*) to (*E*), of Fig. 7.7. In every case the inclined surface is similarly oriented in space to that of Fig. 7.8, but turned to a different position. Figure 7.11 (position *C* of Fig. 7.7) has the inclined surface on the left front of the object. As in the first case, the direction of view must be perpendicular to the inclined face, and is seen in true relationship in the top view, where surface *A* appears as an edge. The projectors for the normal view are parallel to the viewing direction and of course perpendicular to surface *A*. The reference plane is established in the normal view perpendicular to the projectors for the normal view and in

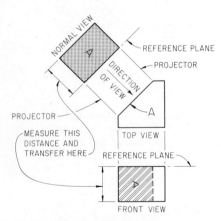

FIG. 7.12. Normal view of an inclined surface. The object is in position (*D*) of Fig. 7.7.

FIG. 7.13. Normal view of an inclined surface. The object is in position (*E*) of Fig. 7.7.

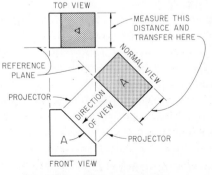

FIG. 7.14. Normal view of an inclined surface. The object is in position (*F*) of Fig. 7.7.

the front view perpendicular to the projectors between top and front views. The measurement of height, transferred from the front view to the normal view, completes the normal view.

Note that the reference plane will *always* appear in the two views that are in projection *with* the view that shows the inclined surface as an edge, and that the reference plane is always perpendicular to the projectors between these pairs of views.

Figure 7.12 shows position (*D*) of Fig. 7.7. This time the inclined surface is at the left rear of the object. Figure 7.13 shows position (*E*) of Fig. 7.7. Read the explanation given for Figs. 7.8, 7.9, and 7.10 while studying these two figures (7.12 and 7.13) and note that the directions given for Figs. 7.8 to 7.10 apply equally well for Figs. 7.12 and 7.13. This shows that the actual position of the inclined surface is simply a variation.

Turning now to the second column of positions (*F* to *J*) of Fig. 7.7, note again that all these positions have the inclined surface at an angle to top and side. Then, looking at Figs. 7.14 to 7.17 inclusive (these are all similar because the inclined surface appears in every case as an edge on the front view), observe that Fig. 7.14 is position (*F*), Fig. 7.15 position (*G*), Fig. 7.16 position (*H*), and 7.17 position (*J*).

The projection of the normal view in Figs. 7.14 to 7.17 is unchanged geometrically and projectively as compared with Figs. 7.8 to 7.13. The *only* difference is that the projectors for the normal view this time emanate from the front view, where the inclined surface appears as an edge. While studying Figs. 7.14 to 7.17, consider again the principles of projection involved and the procedure followed: (1) The direction of observation for the

FIG. 7.15.   Normal view of an inclined surface. The object is in position (*G*) of Fig. 7.7.

normal view is perpendicular to the inclined surface and, on the drawing, perpendicular to the edge view of the surface. (2) The projectors for the normal view are parallel to the viewing direction, perpendicular to the inclined surface and, on the drawing, perpendicular to the edge view of the surface. (3) The projectors (or the spacing between them) determine one dimension of the normal view. (4) The second dimension for the normal view is now needed. (5) The reference plane for making the needed measurement will appear in the normal perpendicular to the projectors between edge view and normal view, and in the principal view (in projection with the edge view) perpendicular to the projectors between edge view and principal view. (6) The measurement perpendicular to the reference plane in the principal view is then transferred to the normal view, perpendicular to the reference plane, thus completing the layout of the normal view.

Figures 7.18 to 7.21 show the inclined surface positions of the third column of Fig. 7.7 (*K* to *N*), in the same order. Note that the projective system is the

FIG. 7.16.   Normal view of an inclined surface. The object is in position (*H*) of Fig. 7.7.

FIG. 7.17.   Normal view of an inclined surface. The object is in position (*J*) of Fig. 7.7.

FIG. 7.18.   Normal view of an inclined surface. The object is in position (*K*) of Fig. 7.7.

FIG. 7.19. Normal view of an inclined surface. The object is in position (*L*) of Fig. 7.7.

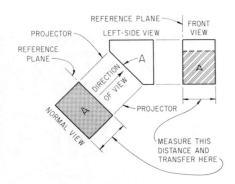

FIG. 7.20. Normal view of an inclined surface. The object is in position (*M*) of Fig. 7.7.

FIG. 7.21. Normal view of an inclined surface. The object is in position (*N*) of Fig. 7.7.

same as before. The only difference now is that the edge view of the inclined surface appears in the *side* view, and because *either* side view *might* be drawn, the projectors from the edge view to the normal view will have to be drawn from whichever side view, right or left, is used. To illustrate this variation, Figs. 7.18 and 7.19 have been drawn with the right-side view and Figs. 7.20 and 7.21 with the left-side view. Note also that the reference plane, with measurements taken from it, will in these cases be in the normal view and the front view, since the front view is the view in *direct* projection with the edge view of the inclined surface.

Study Figs. 7.7 to 7.21 carefully, note the recurrence of certain principles of projection, and study the relationships of views, projectors, directions, and measurements.

7.5. NORMAL VIEWS OF INCLINED SURFACES ON PRACTICAL OBJECTS. So far we have presented only the pertinent principles of projection and the procedure for drawing a normal view, using a rectangular object for illustration. Practical objects are, of course, made up of rec-

tangular, conic, cylindrical, and other shapes, and this is sometimes considered by the uninitiated to be a complication. However, this is not the case; a machine part is often easier to draw than a purely geometric shape because it is more readily visualized.

Figure 7.22 shows a part with a surface inclined to front and side, about in the same position as the inclined surface in Fig. 7.8. At (*A*) the object is shown pictorially, surrounded by the planes of projection, and at (*B*) the projection planes are opened up into the plane of the paper. Note that the reference plane is placed, in this case, at the *base* of the object because this is a natural reference surface. Thus at (*C*) the reference plane is drawn at the base in the front and normal views, and measurements are made *upward* (dimensions *H* and *H'*) to needed points. Note that the top view is the normal view of the reference plane, which appears as an edge in the front and normal views.

Figure 7.23 illustrates the procedure for drawing the normal view of an inclined surface on a machine part. Steps are as follows:

1. Draw the partial top and front

FIG. 7.22. Machine part with surface inclined to front and side. (*A*) planes of projection; (*B*) the planes opened up; (*C*) front, top, and normal views of the inclined surface.

FIG. 7.23. Stages in drawing a machine part with a surface inclined to front and side.

views, as at (B), and locate the view direction by drawing projectors perpendicular to the edge view of the inclined surface, as shown.

2. Locate the reference plane (RP) in the front view. The reference plane may be taken above, below, or through the view, and is chosen for convenience in measuring. In this case it is taken through the natural center line of the front view. The reference plane in the normal view will be perpendicular to the projectors already drawn, and is located at a convenient distance from the top view, as shown at (C).

3. As shown at (D), measure the distance (height) from the reference plane of various points needed, as, for example, H and H_1, and transfer these measurements with dividers or scale to the normal view, measuring from the reference plane in the normal view.

4. Complete the normal view from specifications of the rounds, etc., as shown at (E). Note that any measurement in the front view, made *toward* the top view, is transferred to the *normal view, toward* the top view. Note also that the front view could not be completed without using the normal view.

5. To get the front view of the circular portions, the true shape of which shows only in the normal view as circle arcs, select points in the normal view, project them back to the top view, and then to the front view. On these projectors transfer the heights H_2 and H_3 from the normal view to find the corresponding points in the front view. H_4, H_5, and others will complete the curve in the front view. Note that this procedure is exactly reversed from the operation of measuring from the front view to locate a distance in the normal view.

Figure 7.24 shows an object with *two*

FIG. 7.24. A machine part with surfaces inclined to top and side. (A) planes of projection; (B) the planes opened up; (C) front, top, and normal views of the inclined surfaces.

FIG. 7.25. Stages in drawing a machine part with a surface inclined to top and side.

inclined surfaces. Note that the normal views are only partial views because the base of the object is fully described in top and front views. The reference plane is taken through the center because the object is symmetrical.

Figure 7.25 illustrates the steps in drawing the normal view of a face inclined to top and side:

1. Draw the partial top and front views, as at (B), and locate the view direction by drawing projectors perpendicular to the inclined surface, as shown.

2. Locate the reference plane in the top view. The reference plane may be taken in front of, through, or to the rear of the view but is here located at the rear flat surface of the object because of convenience in measuring. The reference plane in the normal view will be perpendicular to the projectors already drawn, and is located at a convenient distance from the front view, as shown at (C).

3. As shown at (D), measure the distance (depths) from the reference plane (of various points needed), and transfer these measurements with dividers or scale to the normal view, measuring from the reference plane in the normal view. Note that the points are in front of the reference plane in the top view and are therefore measured toward the front in the normal view.

4. From specifications, complete the normal view, as shown at (E).

5. Complete the drawing, as shown at (F). In this case the top view could have been completed before the normal view was drawn. However, it is considered better practice to lay out the

FIG. 7.26. A machine part with a surface inclined to top and front. (A) planes of projection; (B) the planes opened up; (C) front side, and normal views of the inclined surface.

normal view before completing the view that will show the surface foreshortened.

A part might also be drawn with the inclined surface on the lower or upper front or rear. Orientation of this type is shown in Fig. 7.26, where the inclined surface is on the upper front. The steps in drawing an object of this type are given in Fig. 7.27 as follows:

1. Draw the partial front, top, and right-side views, as at (B), and locate the normal view direction by drawing projectors perpendicular to the inclined surface, as shown.

2. Locate the reference plane in the front view. This reference plane is taken at the left side of the object, because both the vertical and inclined portions have a left surface in the same profile plane. The reference plane in the normal view will be perpendicular to the projectors already drawn, and is located at a convenient distance from the right-side view, as shown at (C).

3. As shown at (D), measure the distances (widths) from the reference plane (of various points needed), and transfer these measurements with dividers or scale to the normal view, measuring from the reference plane in the normal view. Note that points to the right of the reference plane in the front view will be measured in a direction *toward* the right-side view in the normal view.

4. From specifications of the surface contour complete the normal view (E).

5. Complete the right-side and front views by projecting and measuring from the normal view. As an example, one intersection of the cut corner is projected to the right-side view and from there to the front view; the other intersection is measured (distance *W*) from the normal view and then laid off in the front view.

7.6. PURPOSES OF NORMAL VIEWS. In practical work the chief reason for using a normal view is to show the true shape of an inclined surface.

In a normal view, the inclined surface will be shown in its true shape, but the other faces of the object appearing in the view will be foreshortened. In practical work these foreshortened parts are usually omitted, as in Fig. 7.28. Views thus drawn are called *partial views*. The exercise of drawing the complete view, however, may aid the student in understanding the subject.

Another important use of a normal view is in the case where a principal view has a part in a foreshortened position which cannot be drawn without first constructing a normal view in its true shape from which the part can be projected back to the principal view. Figure 7.29 illustrates this procedure. Note in this figure that the view direc-

FIG. 7.27. Stages in drawing a machine part with a surface inclined to top and front.

FIG. 7.28. Use of partial views.

FIG. 7.29. Use of the normal view for construction of other views.

FIG. 7.30. Top, front, and right-side views of an irregular part.

FIG. 7.31. Front and two normal views of an irregular part.

tion is set up looking along the semihexagonal slot and perpendicular to the face that is at a right angle to the slot. From the normal view showing the true semihexagonal shape, the side view and then the front view can be completed.

In most cases the normal view cannot be projected from the principal views but *must be drawn from dimensional specifications of the surface shape.*

Another practical example is the flanged 45° elbow of Fig. 7.30, a casting with an irregular inclined face, which not only cannot be shown in true shape in any of the principal views but also is difficult to draw in its foreshortened position. An easier and more practical selection of views for this piece is shown in Fig. 7.31, where normal views looking in directions perpendicular to the inclined faces show the true shape of the surfaces and allow for simplification. This is because each view can be laid out independently from specifications, and there is not even need for a reference plane, measurements, etc.

7.7. NORMAL VIEW OF A LINE. The normal view of a surface shows the true length of *all* lines in the surface. To prove this, go back to Fig. 7.8 and visualize *any* line on surface *A* of the figure. You will find that the line shows in true length in the normal view. Often, however, especially in solving geometric space problems, a line is not a part of a surface, but a separate line located in space by a pair of orthographic views. Any line that is parallel to one of the planes of projection will have a principal view that is the normal view. Thus in Fig. 7.32 where the lines are horizontal (*A*), frontal (*B*), and profile (*C*), the normal views of the lines are at (*A*) the top view, at (*B*) the front view, and at (*C*) the side view.

Often a line is skew to *all* the planes of projection and an extra view is required to give the normal view. To find the normal view of a surface, the direction of observation must be *perpendicular* to the surface; the same direction of observation is needed in finding the normal view of a line—the direction of observation *must* be perpendicular to the line. Thus at (*D*) projectors are drawn in the top view *perpendicular* to the top view of the line. The direction of view is now established perpendicular to the line, since the line could be on a surface, the top view being the *edge* view of the assumed surface. Next, the reference plane will appear perpendicular to the projectors just established for the normal view and will appear again in the front view perpendicular to the projectors between top and front views. Finally, point *A* is *on* the reference plane and on the projector from the top view and is thus located in the normal view. Point *B*, then measured from the reference plane in the front view, transferred to the normal view and laid off

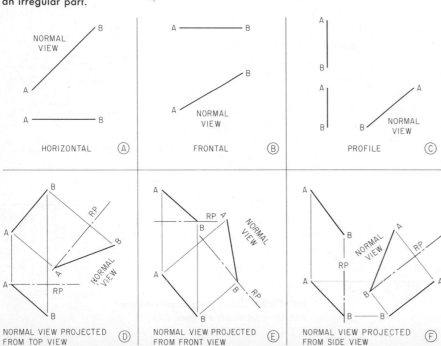

FIG. 7.32. Normal views of lines.

NORMAL VIEW PROJECTED FROM TOP VIEW (D) NORMAL VIEW PROJECTED FROM FRONT VIEW (E) NORMAL VIEW PROJECTED FROM SIDE VIEW (F)

FIG. 7.33. A skew surface. (*A*) relationship to principal views; (*B*) orthographic views.

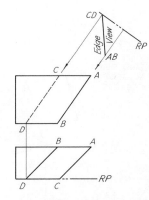

FIG. 7.34. End view of a line. (*A*) horizontal line; (*B*) frontal line; (*C*) profile line.

from the reference plane *on* the projector for point *B*, completes the normal view. A similar normal view can be projected from the front view as at *E*, or from the side view as at *F*. Note in both cases that the projectors for the normal view *must* be perpendicular to the line in the view the normal is projected from.

7.8. SKEW SURFACES. In paragraph 7.2, in the classification of surfaces, the skew surface was described and illustrated. For convenience, Fig. 7.33 again shows this type of surface both pictorially and orthographically. Remember that a skew surface is one that occurs at an angle to *all* the principal planes of projection.

The normal view of a skew surface cannot (without resorting to special projective methods) be projected directly from the principal views, but must be projected from an *edge* view of the surface. Also, the edge view is almost always needed to show other features such as the angle a surface makes with its base. Thus, *two* views are required and we must first learn how to get the edge view.

7.9. EDGE VIEWS OF SKEW SURFACES. The key to determining the direction of observation needed to obtain the edge

view of a surface is to locate a direction that will give the *end view of one line* of the surface. This is easily done if the surface contains a line that is horizontal, frontal, or profile. In Fig. 7.34*A* the line is horizontal and a view made looking in a horizontal direction that is *aligned with the line* will give the end view. Note in Fig. 7.34*A* that points *A* and *B* (the two ends of the line) are both on the same projector and that both lie on the reference plane thus giving coincidence of the two ends of the line in the end view. Also note that the end view must be projected from the normal view of the line, in this case the top view. The end view of a frontal line is shown at (*B*); it is projected from the front (normal) view. The end view of a profile line is shown at (*C*); it is projected from the side (normal) view.

As stated before, the edge view of a surface is made by first obtaining the end view of any line of the surface. In Fig. 7.35 surface *ABDC* is a skew surface (at an angle to *all* principal planes). However, lines *AB* and *DC* are horizontal lines of the surface. Selecting *DC* as the key line, a projector is drawn aligned with *DC* and another projector (parallel) is drawn for *AB*. This establishes the direction of view for the end view of both *DC* and *AB*. The reference

FIG. 7.35. Edge view of a skew surface. Projection is in the direction of the horizontal line *DC*.

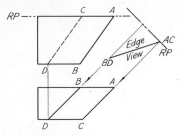

FIG. 7.36. Edge view of a skew surface. Projection is in the direction of frontal line *AC*.

FIG. 7.37. Edge view of a skew surface. The direction of the edge view is located by the horizontal line *AB*.

FIG. 7.38. Normal view of a skew surface. *BCDE* is a skew surface because of the position of the object.

plane for the edge view will appear as an edge perpendicular to these projectors, and will appear again as an edge in the front view perpendicular to the projectors between top and front views. For convenience, the reference plane is placed through points *D* and *C*. Then *D* and *C* both project to the edge view on the same projector and both lie on the reference plane, giving *DC* in the edge view. *A* and *C* both project to the edge view on the same projector. The distance from the reference plane in the front view to points *A* and *C* is measured and transferred to the edge view, thus locating *AC* in the edge view. The line connecting *DC* and *AB* is the edge view of surface *ABDC*.

Figure 7.36 shows the identical surface *ABDC* of Fig. 7.35 but this time the edge view has been obtained by looking along the two frontal lines *AC* and *BD*. The edge view is projected in the direction of *AC* and *BD* from the front view because *AC* and *BD* are

normal in the front view. The reference plane then located in the edge view and top view, and *AC* and *BD* located with reference to it, complete the edge view.

In Fig. 7.37 the surface *ACD* does not contain any horizontal, frontal, or profile line, and so to get an end view of one line of the surface a horizontal, frontal or profile line must be laid out on the surface. A horizontal line has been selected and is drawn at *AB* in the front view and then projected to the top view. This line (*AB*) is then normal in the top view and projectors parallel to it from *AB, C,* and *D* will establish the direction for the edge view of *ACD*. The reference plane is conveniently located through *AB* in front and edge views; then *D* and *C* are measured from the reference plane in the front view and transferred to the edge view. Note that *D* lies *above* the reference plane and *C below* and that they are transferred accordingly to the edge view. To avoid reversing a normal or edge view, remember this simple rule: if a point is on the side of the reference plane *toward* the view projected from in making an edge or normal view (the top view, in this case), the point will be transferred *toward* that same view. As an example of the rule, note in Fig. 7.37 that *D* is on the side *toward* the top view from the reference plane in both front and edge views while *C* is on the side *away* from the reference plane.

7.10. NORMAL VIEWS OF SKEW SURFACES.

A skew surface is produced by an object with an inclined surface that is turned at an angle to the principal planes, as in Fig. 7.38, or by an object with a face at an angle to three object faces, as in Figs. 7.39 and 7.40. Figure 7.38 is easier to visualize, so we will discuss it first.

Surface *BCDE* of Fig. 7.38 is a skew surface. *CB* and *DE* are horizontal lines of the surface. The edge view is obtained by looking in the direction of *CB* and *DE*, as shown in Fig. 7.38 and described in paragraph 7.9.

The normal view is made with the direction of observation perpendicular to the edge view. To draw the normal view, first draw projectors perpendicular to the edge view (Fig. 7.38), establishing the direction for the normal view. As in all earlier examples, the reference plane for the normal view (*RP* No. 2 in Fig. 7.38) is perpendicular to the projectors. The reference plane appears normal in the edge view and appears again as an edge in *any* other view in direct projection with the edge view. In this case therefore, the reference plane shows as an edge in the top view, and is perpendicular to the projectors between top and edge views. To prove this relationship to yourself, note that here the top view, edge view, and normal view have *exactly* the same relationship as the front view, top view, and normal view of Fig. 7.8. Finally, transfer the distance of *B* and *E* from the reference plane (No. 2) in the top view to the normal view, as shown.

Figure 7.39 is similar to 7.38 but this time the object faces are parallel to the principal planes, and surface *BCD* is skew to object faces and principal planes. Again, one line (*BC*) of the skew surface is horizontal and gives the direction for the edge view. In the edge view, *B* and *C* are on the reference plane. Point *D*, measured from reference plane No. 1 in the front view, is transferred to the edge view, as shown. Then, projectors perpendicular to the edge view give the direction for the normal view, and reference plane No. 2 is drawn in normal and top views perpendicular to the

FIG. 7.39.   Normal view of a skew surface. The edge view is projected in the direction of the horizontal line *CB*. The normal view is perpendicular to the edge view.

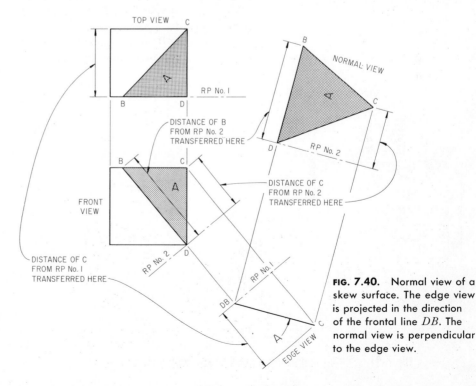

FIG. 7.40.   Normal view of a skew surface. The edge view is projected in the direction of the frontal line *DB*. The normal view is perpendicular to the edge view.

projectors connecting each with the edge view. Finally the distances of *B* and *D* from reference plane No. 2 are transferred to the normal view.

The object of Fig. 7.40 is similar to that of Fig. 7.39 but in Fig. 7.40 the frontal line (*BD*) of surface *BCD* has been used for the direction of the edge view. The edge view is therefore projected from the front view. All other constructions are the same as before and are evident from the figure.

7.11. NORMAL VIEWS OF SKEW SURFACES ON PRACTICAL OBJECTS.

Figure 7.41 illustrates the successive steps in drawing a normal view. The pictorial illustration (*A*) shows a typical object with a skew surface. The line of intersection between the skew portion and the horizontal base is line *AB*. In order to get an edge view of the skew surface, a view may be taken looking in the direction of line *AB*, thus giving an end view of *AB*. Because *AB* is a line of the skew surface, the edge view will result. The reference plane (*RP* No. 1) for this view will be hori-

zontal. The direction of observation for the normal view will be perpendicular to the skew surface. The reference plane (*RP* No. 2) for the normal view will be perpendicular to the edge-view direction and thus perpendicular to edge *AB*, as shown at (*A*).

At (*B*), partial top and front views are shown. The projectors and reference plane for the required edge view are also shown.

At (*C*), the edge view has been drawn. Note that line *AB* appears as a point in the edge view. The angle that the skew surface makes with the base is laid out in this view from specifications.

At (*D*), the normal view is added. The projectors for the view are perpendicular to the edge view. The reference plane is drawn perpendicular to the projectors for the normal view and at a convenient distance from the edge view. The reference plane in the top view is drawn midway between points *A* and *B* in the top view because the skew surface is symmetrical about this reference plane. The normal view is drawn from specifications of the shape. The projection back to the edge view can then be made.

The views thus completed at (*D*) describe the object, but the top and front views may be completed for illustrative purposes or as an exercise in projection. The method is illustrated at (*E*) and (*F*). Any point, say *P*, may be selected and projected back to the edge view. From this view a projector is drawn back to the top view. Then the distance *S* from the normal view is transferred to the reference plane in the top view. A number of points so located will complete the top view of the circular portion, and the straight-line portion can be projected in similar manner. The front view is found by drawing projec-

FIG. 7.41.   Stages in drawing a machine part with a skew surface.

tors to the front view for the points needed, measuring the heights from the reference plane in the edge view, and transferring these distances to the front view. Note that this procedure for completing the top and front views is the same as for drawing the views originally but in reverse order.

7.12.   TERMS OF REFERENCE FOR AUXILIARY VIEWS.

In this text, emphasis is given to the *purpose* for which auxiliary views are made; namely, to show the *edge view* or *normal view* of a surface. This practice is basic to the representation of solid objects, and, fundamentally, an auxiliary view used to depict a surface needs no further identification than the designation *edge view* or *normal view*. However, auxiliaries are named in various ways in other texts on engineering drawing and graphics, and for this reason the following terms of reference are given:

Reference Group 1

Elevation auxiliary or *auxiliary elevation*. Any view made by looking in a horizontal direction but inclined to frontal and profile planes. These are the views illustrated in Fig. 7.7B to E.

Right auxiliary. Any view made by looking from the right side in a frontal direction but inclined to horizontal and profile planes. See Fig. 7.7F and G.

Left auxiliary. Any view made by looking from the left side in a frontal direction but inclined to horizontal and profile planes. See Fig. 7.7H and J.

Front auxiliary. Any view made by looking from the front in a profile direction but inclined to horizontal and frontal planes. See Fig. 7.7K and L.

Rear auxiliary. Any view made by looking from the rear in a profile direc-tion but inclined to horizontal and frontal planes. See Fig. 7.7M and N.

Reference Group 2

Top-adjacent auxiliary. Any auxiliary view projected from the top view. Such auxiliaries are the same as elevation auxiliaries (group 1). See Fig. 7.7B to E.

Front-adjacent auxiliary. Any auxiliary view projected from a front view. Such auxiliaries are the same as right-and-left auxiliaries. See Fig. 7.7F to J.

Side-adjacent auxiliary. Any auxiliary projected from a side view. Such auxil-iaries are the same as front-and-rear auxiliaries. See Fig. 7.7K to N.

Reference Group 3

Oblique view. This is the normal view of a skew (oblique) surface and is pro-jected from an edge view. See Figs. 7.38 to 7.40.

Reference Group 4

Auxiliary-adjacent auxiliary view. This is the normal view of a skew surface, projected from an edge view. See Figs. 7.38 to 7.40.

These terms of reference are used in books on descriptive geometry. How-ever, since the book on descriptive geom-etry you are using with this text may give other terms, the space below is pro-vided for listing them.

_____
_____
_____
_____
_____
_____
_____
_____
_____

PROBLEMS

GROUP 1. NORMAL VIEWS OF INCLINED SURFACES

7.1.1 to 7.1.7. Draw the given views and add the normal view of the inclined surface using the reference plane indicated.

7.1.8. Draw the front view, partial top view, and normal view of the inclined surface.

7.1.9. Draw the partial front view, right-side view, partial top view, and normal view of the inclined surface.

7.1.10. Draw the front view, partial top view, and normal view of the inclined surfaces.

PROB. 7.1.1. Locking wedge.

PROB. 7.1.2. Statue base.

PROB. 7.1.3. Rod slide.

PROB. 7.1.4. Fulcrum.

PROB. 7.1.5. Adjustable pawl.

PROB. 7.1.6. Hexagonal-shaft lock.

PROB. 7.1.7. Molding.

PROB. 7.1.8. Holder.

PROB. 7.1.9. Slotted anchor.

PROB. 7.1.10. Connector strip.

7.1.11. Draw the top view, partial front view, and normal view of the inclined surfaces.

7.1.12. Draw the front view, partial top view, and normal view of the inclined surface.

7.1.13. Draw the front view, partial right-side view, and normal view of the inclined surface. Draw the normal view before completing the front view.

7.1.14. Draw the front view, partial top view, and normal view of the inclined surface.

7.1.15. Draw the front view, partial top view, and normal view of the inclined surface.

7.1.16. Draw the front view, partial top and right-side views, and normal view of the inclined surface.

7.1.17. Draw the front view, partial top and left-side views, and normal view of the inclined surface.

7.1.18 and 7.1.19. Determine what views and partial views will best describe the part. Sketch the proposed views before making the drawing with instruments.

PROB. 7.1.11. Push plate.

PROB. 7.1.12. Bevel washer.

PROB. 7.1.13. Jig angle.

PROB. 7.1.14. Angle clip.

PROB. 7.1.15. Angle swivel.

PROB. 7.1.16. Corner tie.

PROB. 7.1.17. Channel support.

PROB. 7.1.18. Radial swing block.

PROB. 7.1.19. Angle-shaft base.

7.1.20. Draw the front view, partial bottom view, and normal view of the inclined surface.
7.1.21. Draw the front view, partial left-side and bottom views, and normal view of the inclined surface.
7.1.22 and 7.1.23. Determine what views and partial views will best describe the part.
7.1.24. Draw the given front view and add the views necessary to describe the part.
7.1.25. Draw the front view, partial left-side view, and normal view of the inclined surface.

PROB. 7.1.20. Catenary clip.

PROB. 7.1.21. Bevel-gear housing.

PROB. 7.1.22. Slide base.

PROB. 7.1.23. Idler bracket.

PROB. 7.1.24. Corner brace.

PROB. 7.1.25. Spindle support.

7.1.26 and 7.1.27. This pair of similar objects has the upper lug in two different positions. Layouts are for 11- × 17-in. paper. Draw the views and partial views as indicated on the layouts.

7.1.28. Draw the front view; partial top, right-side, and left-side views; and normal view of the inclined surface. Use decimal scale for layout.

7.1.29. Draw the views and partial views that will best describe the part.

PROB. 7.1.26. Spar clip, 90°.

PROB. 7.1.27. Spar clip, 120°.

PROB. 7.1.28. Seat release.

PROB. 7.1.29. Idler link.

GROUP 2.   NORMAL VIEWS OF SKEW SURFACES

7.2.1.   Draw the partial front and top views, edge view showing the contour of the slot, and normal view of the skew surface.

7.2.2.   Draw the partial front and top views, and edge and normal views of the skew surface. Draw the normal view before completing the edge view.

7.2.3.   Draw the partial front and top views, and edge and normal views of the skew surface.

7.2.4.   Draw the views given, omitting the lugs in the top view. Add normal views to describe the lugs.

7.2.5.   Draw the views given, using edge and normal views to obtain the shape of the lugs.

PROB. 7.2.1.   Dovetail clip.

PROB. 7.2.2.   Anchor base.

PROB. 7.2.3.   Adjusting clip.

PROB. 7.2.4.   Bar-strut anchor.

PROB. 7.2.5.   Cable anchor.

7.2.6. Draw the partial top, front, and side views. Add edge and normal views to describe the lugs.

7.2.7. Draw the top and front views and use edge and normal views to describe the slots and skew surfaces. The part is symmetrical about the main axis.

7.2.8. Draw the spar clip, using the layout shown for 11- × 17-in. paper. Note that an edge and two normal views are required.

7.2.9. Draw the views given, using edge and normal views to describe the lugs.

PROB. 7.2.7. Chamfer-tool base.

PROB. 7.2.6. Transverse connection.

PROB. 7.2.8. Spar clip.

PROB. 7.2.9. Crane-masthead collar and cap.

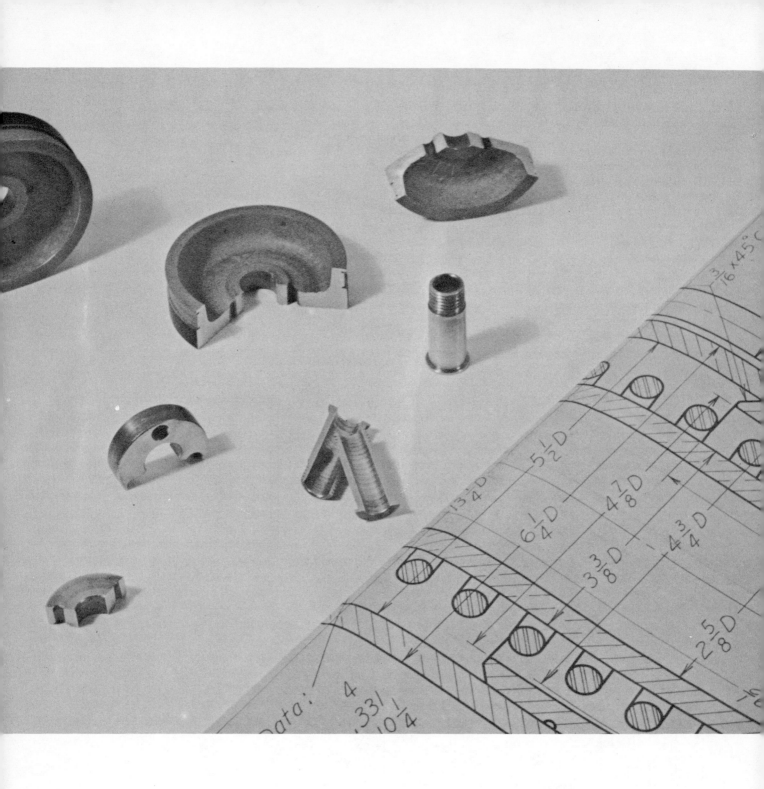

8

Sections and Conventions

8.1. DEFINITION. When the interior of an object is complicated or when the component parts of a machine are drawn assembled, an attempt to show hidden portions by the customary dashed lines in regular orthographic views often results in a confusing network, as shown in Fig. 8.1 at (A), which is difficult to draw and almost impossible to read clearly.

In cases of this kind, to aid in describing the object, one or more views are drawn to show the object as if a portion had been cut away to reveal the interior, as at (B). Also, if some detail of the shape of an object is not clear, a cut taken through the portion and then turned up, or turned up and removed, as at (C), will describe the shape concisely and often eliminate the need for an extra complete view.

Either of these conventions is called a *section*, which is defined as an imaginary cut made through an object to expose the interior or to reveal the shape of a portion. A view in which all or a substantial portion of the view is sectioned is known as a *sectional view*.

For some simple objects where the orthographic, *unsectioned* views can be easily read, sectional views are often preferable because they show clearly and emphasize the solid portions, the voids, and the shape.

215

SEC. C-C

Ⓒ

Ⓐ

FIG. 8.1. Advantage of sectional views. (*A*) orthographic view with hidden edges indicated by dashed lines; (*B*) the same view but made as a section to clarify the shape; (*C*) cross-sectional shape of lug shown by removed section.

Ⓑ

the cutting plane (see alphabet of lines, paragraph 2.39) should be shown. A cutting plane is the imaginary medium used to show the path of cutting an object to make a section. Cutting planes for each kind of section will be discussed in the following paragraphs.

A sectional view must show which portions of the object are solid material and which are spaces. This is done by section lining, sometimes called "cross-hatching," the solid parts with lines, as shown at (*B*) and (*C*). Section-lining practice is given in paragraph 8.11, where codes for materials are also discussed.

8.2. HOW SECTIONS ARE SHOWN. The place from which the section is taken must be identifiable on the drawing, and the solid portions and voids must be distinguished on the sectional view. The place from which the section is taken is in many cases obvious, as it is for the sectional view (*B*) in Fig. 8.1; the section is quite evidently taken through the center (at the center line of the top view). In such cases no further description is needed. If the place from which a section is taken is not obvious, as at (*C*), a *cutting plane,* directional arrows, and identification letters are used to identify it. Whenever there is any doubt of the position where the section is taken,

8.3. TYPES OF SECTIONS. Although the different sections and sectional views have been named for identification and for specifying the type of view required in a drawing, the names are not shown on the drawing for the same reason that a top, front, or side view would not be so labeled—the views are easily interpreted and a workman does not require the name to read the drawing. The names are assigned by the character of the section or the amount of the *view* in section, *not* by the amount of the object removed.

8.4. FULL SECTION. A full section is one in which the cutting plane passes entirely across the object, as in Fig. 8.2, so

FIG. 8.2. Cutting planes for a full section. The plane may cut straight across (*A*) or change direction (*B* and *C*) to pass through features to be shown.

Ⓐ

Ⓑ

Ⓒ

FIG. 8.3. Two cutting planes. The two planes at (*A*) will produce sections (*B*) and (*C*). Each section is considered separately, without reference to what has been removed for the other view.

FIG. 8.4. Full sections. This is the orthographic drawing of the object in Fig. 8.3. The cutting-plane position is obvious for the front-view section and is not identified in the top view. Section *A-A* (side view) has its cutting plane identified because the section might be made elsewhere.

FIG. 8.5. A full section. The cutting plane is offset to pass through both principal features of the object.

that the resulting view is completely "in section." The cutting plane may pass straight through, as at (*A*), or be offset, changing direction forward or backward, to pass through features it would otherwise have missed, as at (*B*) and (*C*). Sometimes *two* views are drawn in section on a pair of cutting planes, as at (*A*) in Fig. 8.3. In such cases each view is considered separately, without reference to what has been removed for another view. Thus (*B*) shows the portion remaining and the cut surface for one sectional view, and (*C*) for the other sectional view. Figure 8.4 is the orthographic drawing of the object, with indication for sectioning, as shown in Fig. 8.3. Both the front and side views are full-sectional views.

Figure 8.5 shows a full section made on an offset cutting plane. Note that the *change in plane direction* is *not* shown on the sectional view, for the cut is purely imaginary and *no edge* is present on the object at this position.

8.5. HALF SECTION. This is a view sometimes used for symmetrical objects in which one half is drawn in section and the other half as a regular exterior view. The cutting plane is imagined to extend halfway across, then forward, as in Fig. 8.6. A half section has the advantage of showing both the interior and exterior

of the object on one view without using dashed lines, as at (*A*) in Fig. 8.7. However, a half section thus made is difficult to dimension without ambiguity, and so, if needed for clarity, dashed lines may be added, as at (*B*).

Note particularly that a *center line* separates the exterior and interior portions on the sectional view. This is for the same reason that the change in plane direction for the offset of the cutting plane of Fig. 8.5 is not shown—no edge exists *on the object* at the center.

8.6. BROKEN-OUT SECTION. Often an interior portion must be shown but a full or half section cannot be used because the cutting plane would remove some feature that must be included. For this condition the cutting plane is ex-

FIG. 8.6. The cutting plane for a half section. The resulting sectional view will be half in section and half an external view.

FIG. 8.7. Half sections. Dashed lines are rarely necessary (*A*), but may be used if needed for clarity or to aid in dimensioning (*B*).

FIG. 8.8. Cutting planes for broken-out sections. The cutting plane extends only slightly beyond the features to be shown in section.

FIG. 8.9. A broken-out section. Note that a standard break line terminates the sectional portion.

FIG. 8.10. The cutting plane for a rotated or a removed section. A slice of negligible thickness is taken.

FIG. 8.11. A rotated section. The section is rotated 90° to bring it into the plane of the view.

FIG. 8.12. A rotated section with broken view. The view is broken thus whenever the view outline interferes with the section.

tended only so far as needed, as illustrated by Fig. 8.8A and B, and then is thought of as "broken out." Figure 8.9 is an example. Note the irregular break line that limits the extent of the section.

8.7. ROTATED SECTION. As indicated in paragraph 8.1, a section may be a slice of negligible thickness used to show a shape that would otherwise be difficult to see or describe. The cutting plane for such a section is shown in Fig. 8.10. If the resulting section is then rotated 90° *onto* the view as in Fig. 8.11, the section is called a rotated section. Whenever the view outline interferes with the section, the view is broken, as in Fig. 8.12.

8.8. REMOVED SECTIONS. These are used for the same purpose as rotated sections, but instead of being drawn *on* the view, they are removed to some adjacent place on the paper, as in Fig. 8.13.

The cutting plane with reference letters should always be indicated unless the place from which the section has

been taken is obvious. Removed sections are used whenever restricted space for the section or the dimensioning of it prevents the use of an ordinary rotated section. When the shape of a piece changes gradually or is not uniform, several sections may be required (Fig. 8.14). It is often an advantage to draw the sections to larger scale than that of the main drawing in order to show dimensions more clearly. Sometimes sections are removed to a separate drawing sheet. When this is done, the section must be carefully shown on the main drawing with cutting plane and identifying letters. Often these identifying letters are made as a fraction in a circle, with the numerator a letter identifying the section and the denominator a number identifying the sheet. The sectional view is then marked with the same letters and numbers. The ASA recommends that, whenever possible, a removed section be drawn in its natural projected position. Note in Fig. 8.14 that this practice is followed.

FIG. 8.13. Removed sections. The cutting planes and the mating sections must be identified.

FIG. 8.14. Removed sections in projection. Identifications of cutting planes and mating sections are not needed.

8.9. AUXILIARY SECTIONS. These are sectional views conforming to all the principles of edge and normal views given in Chap. 7. The section shows the *normal* view of a cutting plane that is in a position on an inclined feature so as to reveal the interior, as shown in Fig. 8.15. The edge view of any perpendicular faces will also be seen in the normal view, as in Fig. 8.15. All types of sections —full, half, broken-out, rotated, and re- moved—are used on auxiliaries. Figure 8.16 shows auxiliary partial sections, which are also properly called removed sections in auxiliary position. Note in Fig. 8.16 that the two sections are nor- mal views of their cutting planes.

8.10. ASSEMBLY SECTIONS. As the name implies, an assembly section is made up of a combination of parts. All the previ-

ously mentioned types of sections may be used to increase the clarity and read- ability of assembly drawings. The cut- ting plane for an assembly section is often offset, as in Fig. 8.17, to reveal the separate parts of a machine or structure.

The purpose of an assembly section is to reveal the interior of a machine or structure so that the separate parts can be clearly shown and identified, but the separate parts do not need to be com- pletely described. Thus only such hidden details as are needed for part identifica- tion or dimensioning are shown. Also, the small amount of clearance between mating or moving parts is not shown be- cause, if shown, the clearance would have to be greatly exaggerated, thus confusing the drawing. Even the clear- ance between a bolt and its hole, which may be as much as $\frac{1}{16}$ in., is rarely

FIG. 8.15. Auxiliary section. The section is a normal view of the cutting plane.

FIG. 8.16. Auxiliary sections (partial). Identifications of the cutting planes and mating sections are necessary.

FIG. 8.17. The cutting plane for an assembly section. It is often offset to pass through features to be shown in the section.

FIG. 8.19. Cutting plane for a sectional view.

FIG. 8.18. A sectional assembly drawing. The sectional views give emphasis to construction and separate parts.

A	B	C	D	E	F	G	H	I	J	K	L	M
$1\frac{3}{16}$	$1\frac{1}{4}$	$1\frac{1}{2}$	$2\frac{1}{4}$	$3\frac{3}{4}$	$2\frac{1}{4}$	$\frac{1}{2}$	$\frac{3}{4}$	$7\frac{3}{4}$	$1\frac{1}{8}$	$5\frac{5}{8}$	$\frac{3}{16}$	$1\frac{1}{4}$
$1\frac{7}{16}$	$1\frac{7}{16}$	$1\frac{3}{4}$	$2\frac{5}{8}$	$4\frac{1}{2}$	$2\frac{5}{8}$	$\frac{1}{2}$	$\frac{13}{16}$	8	$1\frac{1}{4}$	$5\frac{7}{8}$	$\frac{3}{16}$	$1\frac{1}{4}$
$1\frac{11}{16}$	$1\frac{5}{8}$	$2\frac{1}{16}$	3	$5\frac{1}{4}$	3	$\frac{1}{2}$	$\frac{7}{8}$	$8\frac{1}{2}$	$1\frac{1}{4}$	$6\frac{3}{8}$	$\frac{3}{16}$	$1\frac{1}{4}$

FIG. 8.20. A drawing with a sectional view. This is the same object as in Fig. 8.19.

FIG. 8.21. Hidden edges and surfaces not shown. (B) is preferable to (A) because the dashed lines are not necessary for description of the part.

shown. Figure 8.18 is an example of an assembly section in tabular form. The component is similar to that in Fig. 8.17. Note that a half section is used in Fig. 8.18 on both views.

Crosshatching practice for assembly sections is explained in paragraph 8.11.

8.11. DRAWING PRACTICES FOR SECTIONAL VIEWS. In general, the rules of projection are followed in making sectional views. Figure 8.19 shows the picture of a casting intersected by a cutting plane, giving the appearance that the casting has been cut through by the plane *A-A* and the front part removed, exposing the interior. Figure 8.20 shows the drawing of the casting with the front view in section. The edge of the cutting plane is shown in the top view by the cutting-plane symbol, with reference letters and arrows to show the direction in which the view is taken. It must be understood that, in thus removing the nearer portion of the object to make the sectional view, the portion assumed to be removed is not omitted in making other views. Therefore, the top and right-side views of the object in Fig. 8.20 are full and complete, and only in the front view has

part of the object been represented as removed.

The practices recommended by the ASA for inclusion of the cutting-plane symbol, of visible and hidden edges, and for crosshatching are as follows:

The Cutting-plane Symbol. It may be shown on the orthographic view where the cutting plane appears as an edge and may be more completely identified with reference letters along with arrows to show the direction in which the view is taken. The cutting-plane line symbol is shown in the alphabet of lines, Figs. 2.56 and 2.57. Use of the symbol is illustrated in Figs. 8.1 and 8.20. Often when the position of the section is evident, the cutting-plane symbol is omitted (Fig. 8.21). It is not always desirable to show the symbol through its entire length; so in such cases the beginning and ending of the plane is shown, as in sections *A-A* and *B-B* in Prob. 13.3.9. Removed sections usually need the cutting-plane symbol with arrows to show the direction of sight and with letters to name the resulting sectional view (Fig. 8.16).

Unnecessary Hidden Detail. Hidden edges and surfaces are not shown unless they are needed to describe the object. Much confusion may result if all detail behind the cutting plane is drawn. In

Fig. 8.21, (A) shows a sectional view with all the hidden edges and surfaces shown by dashed lines. These lines complicate the view and do not add any information. The view at (B) is preferred because it is simpler, less time-consuming to draw, and more easily read than the view at (A). The holes lie on a circular center line; and where similar details repeat, all may be assumed to be alike.

Necessary Hidden Detail. Hidden edges and surfaces are shown if necessary for the description of the object. In Fig. 8.22 view (A) is inadequate since it does not show the thickness of the lugs. The correct treatment is in view (B), where the lugs are shown by dashed lines.

Visible Detail Shown in Sectional Views. Figure 8.23 shows an object pictorially with the front half removed, thus exposing edges and surfaces behind the cutting plane. At (A) a sectional view of the cut surface only is shown, with the visible elements omitted. This treatment should *never* be used. The view should be drawn as at (B) with the visible edges and surfaces behind the cutting plane included in the sectional view.

Visible Detail Not Shown in Sectional

Views. Sometimes confusion results if all visible detail behind the cutting plane is drawn, and it may be omitted if it does not aid in readability. Omission of detail should be carefully considered and may be justified as time saved in drawing. This applies mainly for assembly drawings, where the function of the drawing is to show how the pieces fit together rather than to give complete information for making the parts. For an example of omitted detail, see Fig. 8.24.

Section Lining. Wherever material has been cut by the section plane, the cut surface is indicated by section lining done with fine lines generally at 45° with the principal lines in the view and spaced uniformly to give an even tint. These lines are spaced entirely by eye except when some form of mechanical section liner is used. The pitch, or distance between lines, is governed by the size of the surface. For ordinary working drawings, it will not be much less than $\frac{1}{16}$ in. and rarely more than $\frac{1}{8}$ in. *Very* small pieces may require a spacing closer than $\frac{1}{16}$ in. Take care in setting the pitch by the first two or three lines, and glance back at the first lines often

FIG. 8.22.   Hidden edges and surfaces shown. (B) *must* be used instead of (A) because the dashed lines are necessary for description of the part.

FIG. 8.23.   Visible edges shown. These are the edges seen behind the plane of the section and must be shown as at (B).

FIG. 8.24.   Omission of detail. Detail behind the plane of the section may be omitted when it does not aid in readability or when it might cause ambiguity.

FIG. 8.25. Crosshatching of adjacent parts. Adjacent parts are crosshatched in opposite directions and/or different spacing, for emphasis. The same piece in different views or in different parts of the same view should be crosshatched with identical spacing and direction (auxiliaries are a possible exception).

FIG. 8.26. Section-line directions for unusual shapes. Avoid crosshatch directions parallel to the view outlines.

FIG. 8.27. Outline sectioning. This saves drafting time on large views or on large drawings.

to see that the pitch does not gradually increase or decrease. Nothing mars the appearance of a drawing more than poor section lining. The alphabet of lines, Figs. 2.56 and 2.57, gives the weight of crosshatch lines.

Two adjacent pieces in an assembly drawing are crosshatched in opposite directions. If three pieces adjoin, one of them may be sectioned at other than 45° (usually 30° or 60°, Fig. 8.25), or all pieces may be crosshatched at 45° by using a different pitch for each piece. If a part is so shaped that 45° sectioning runs parallel, or nearly so, to its principal outlines, another direction should be chosen (Fig. 8.26).

Large surfaces are sometimes sectioned around the edge only, as illustrated in Fig. 8.27.

Very thin sections, as of gaskets, sheet metal, or structural-steel shapes to small scale, may be shown in solid black, with white spaces between the parts where thin pieces are adjacent (Fig. 8.28).

Section lining for the same piece in different views or for the same piece in different parts of the same view should be identical in spacing and direction[1] (Figs. 8.18 and 8.24).

Adjacent pieces are section-lined in opposite directions and are often distinguished more clearly by varying the

---

[1] An exception to this rule is made for the cross-hatching of an auxiliary view in order to avoid crosshatch lines that are parallel or perpendicular, or nearly so, to the outlines of the view.

pitch of the section lines for each piece, using closer spacing for the smaller pieces (Figs. 8.25 and 8.29).

Code for Materials in Section. Symbolic section lining is not commonly used on ordinary working drawings, but in an assembly section it is sometimes useful to show a distinction between materials, and a recognized standard code is an obvious advantage. The ASA symbols for indicating different materials is given in the Appendix. Code section lining is used only as an aid in reading a drawing and is not to be taken as the official specification of the materials. Exact specifications of the material for each piece are always given on the detail drawing.

8.12. CONVENTIONAL PRACTICES. All sections are conventions in that they represent an assumed imaginary cut from which, following the theory of projection rather closely, the sectional views are made. However, the strict rules of projection may be disregarded if by so doing a type of view can be drawn which more accurately depicts the shape of the object. It is impossible to illustrate all the conditions that might occur, but the following discussion shows the principles that are recognized as good practice since observing them results in added clearness and readability.

8.13. PARTS NOT SECTIONED. Many machine elements, such as fasteners, pins, and shafts, have no internal construction and, in addition, are more easily recognized by their exterior views. These parts often lie in the path of the section plane, but if they are sectioned (and crosshatched), they are more difficult to read because their typical identifying features (boltheads, rivet heads,

FIG. 8.28. Thin material in section. This is drawn solid because there is not enough room for crosshatching.

FIG. 8.29. Part of a sectional assembly. Shafts, bolts, nuts, rods, rivets, keys, and the like whose axes occur in the plane of the section are left in full (not sectioned).

FIG. 8.30. Spokes in section. The wheel with spokes (B) is treated as though the cutting plane were in front of the spokes, to avoid misreading the section as a solid web line (A).

chamfers on shafts, etc.) are removed. Thus features of this kind should be left in full view and *not sectioned*. To justify this treatment, the assembly is thought of as being sectioned on a particular plane, with the nonsectioned parts placed in the half holes remaining after the section is made. Figure 8.17 shows a full section made on an offset cutting plane that passes through a bolt, with the bolt in full view. Figure 8.29 shows several nonsectioned parts; it is evident that if the shaft, bolts, nuts, rivets, etc., were sectioned, the drawing would be confusing and difficult to read.

8.14. SPOKES AND ARMS IN SECTION. A basic principle for sectioning circular parts is that any element not continuous (not solid) around the axis of the part should be drawn without crosshatching in order to avoid a misleading effect. For example, consider the two pulleys in Fig. 8.30. Pulley (A) has a solid web connecting the hub and rim. Pulley (B) has four spokes. Even though the cut-

ting plane passes through two of the spokes, the sectional view of (B) must be made without crosshatching the spokes in order to avoid the appearance of a solid web, as in pulley (A).

Other machine elements treated in this manner are teeth of gears and sprockets, vanes and supporting ribs of cylindrical parts, equally spaced lugs, and similar parts.

8.15. RIBS IN SECTION. For reasons identical with those given in paragraph 8.14, when the cutting plane passes longitudinally through the center of a rib or web, as in Fig. 8.31A, the crosshatching is eliminated from the ribs as

FIG. 8.31. Ribs in section. Ribs at (A) are treated as though the cutting plane were in front of them, to avoid misreading the section as a solid (B).

FIG. 8.32. Ribs in section. These are treated as though the cutting plane were in front of the ribs.

FIG. 8.33. Lugs in section. Small lugs (*A*) are treated like spokes (Fig. 8.30) and ribs (Figs. 8.31 and 8.32). Large lugs (*B*) are considered as the solid base of the part.

if the cutting plane were just in front of them or as if they had been temporarily removed and replaced after the section was made. A true sectional view with the ribs crosshatched gives a heavy, misleading effect suggesting a cone shape, as shown at (*B*). The same principle applies to ribs cut longitudinally on rectangular parts (Fig. 8.32). When the cutting plane cuts a rib transversely, that is, at right angles to its length or axis direction (the direction that shows its thickness), it is always crosshatched (Fig. 8.24).

8.16. LUGS IN SECTION. For the same reasons given in paragraphs 8.14 and 8.15, a lug or projecting ear (Fig. 8.33*A*), usually of *rectangular* cross section, is not crosshatched; note that crosshatching either of the lugs would suggest a circular flange. However, the somewhat similar condition at (*B*) should have the projecting ears crosshatched as shown because these ears *are* the base of the part.

8.17. ALTERNATE CROSSHATCHING. In some cases omitting the crosshatching of ribs or similar parts gives an inadequate and sometimes ambiguous treatment. To illustrate, Fig. 8.34*A* shows a full section of an idler pulley. At (*B*) four ribs have been added. Note that the top surfaces of the ribs are flush with the top of the pulley. Without crosshatching, the section at (*B*) is identical with (*A*) and the ribs of (*B*) are not identified at all on the sectional view. A better treatment in this case is to use alternate crosshatching for the ribs, as at (*C*), where half (alternating) the crosshatch lines are carried through the ribs. Note that the line of demarcation between rib and solid portions is a *dashed* line.

8.18. ALIGNED SPOKES AND ARMS. Any part with an odd number (3, 5, 7, etc.) of spokes or ribs will give an unsymmetrical and misleading section if the principles of true projection are strictly adhered to, as illustrated by the drawing of a handwheel in Fig. 8.35. The preferred projection is shown in the second sectional view, where one arm is drawn as if aligned, or in other words, the arm is rotated to the path of the vertical cutting plane and then projected to the side view. Note that neither arm should be sectioned for the reasons given in paragraph 8.14.

This practice of alignment is well justified logically because a part with an

FIG. 8.34. Alternate crosshatching. Section (*B*), with ribs flush at the top, looks like section (*A*), with no ribs. Alternate crosshatching (*C*) identifies the ribs.

odd number of equally spaced elements is just as symmetrical as a part with an even number and, therefore, should be shown by a symmetrical view. Moreover, the symmetrical view shows the true *relationship* of the elements, while the true projection does not.

8.19. ALIGNED RIBS, LUGS, AND HOLES. Ribs, lugs, and holes often occur in odd numbers and following the principles given in paragraph 8.18, should be aligned to show the true relationship of the elements. Figure 8.36 shows several examples of how the cutting plane may pass through a symmetrical object, permitting the removal of a portion of the object so as to better describe the shape. Note how the cutting planes may change direction so as to pass through the holes. In Fig. 8.37, true projection of the ribs would show the pair on the right foreshortened, as at (*A*), suggesting in the sectional view that they would not extend to the outer edge of the base. Here, again, the alignment shown at (*B*) gives a symmetrical section of a symmetrical part and shows the ribs in their true relationship to the basic part. To illustrate further, at (*C*) and (*D*) the lugs and holes are aligned, thus showing the holes at their true radial distance from the axis, and, incidently, eliminating some difficult projections.

In all cases of alignment, the element can be thought of as being swung around to a common cutting plane and then projected to the sectional view. Note at (*C*) that because an offset cutting plane is used, each hole is brought separately into position on a common cutting plane before projection to the sectional view. The cutting plane used here is similar to that of (*D*) in Fig. 8.36.

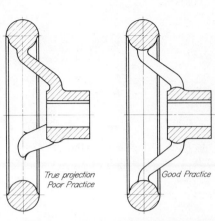

FIG. 8.35. Aligned spokes. True projection is misleading and difficult to draw. Alignment gives a symmetrical section for a symmetrical part.

FIG. 8.36. Cutting planes for alignment of holes.

FIG. 8.37. Aligned ribs, lugs, and holes. True projection of ribs (*A*) is misleading. Alignment (*B*) gives a symmetrical section for a symmetrical part. The same is true for lugs (*C*) and holes (*D*).

FIG. 8.38. Aligned view. This is to avoid drawing in the foreshortened position.

Developed Length

FIG. 8.39. Developed view. This part is drawn as though it were straightened out in one plane.

8.20. ALIGNMENT OF ELEMENTS IN FULL VIEWS. In full views, as well as in sectional views, certain violations of the rules of true projection are recognized as good practice because they add to the clearness of the drawing. For example, if a front view shows a hexagonal bolthead "across corners," the theoretical projection of the side view would be "across flats"; but in a working drawing, boltheads are drawn across corners in both views to show better the shape and the space needed. As another example, the slots of screw heads are always drawn at an angle of 45° in all views so that the closely spaced lines will not be confused with horizontal and vertical center lines.

Lugs or parts cast on for holding purposes and to be machined off are shown by "adjacent-part" lines (Figs 2.56 and 2.57). If such parts are in section, the section lines are dashed. "Alternate-position" lines (Figs. 2.56 and 2.57) are used to indicate the limiting positions of moving parts and to show adjacent parts that aid in locating the position or use of a piece. Note in Figs. 2.56 and

2.57 that the symbol of a long dash and two short dashes, alternating, is used to indicate adjacent parts, alternate positions, and also repeated features.

8.21. ALIGNED AND DEVELOPED VIEWS. Pieces that have elements at an angle to one another, as the lever of Fig. 8.38, may be shown straightened out or aligned in one view. Similarly, bent pieces of the type of Fig. 8.39 should have one view made as a developed view of the *blank* to be punched and formed. Extra metal must be allowed for bends.

8.22. HALF VIEWS. When space is limited, it is allowable to make the top or side view of a symmetrical piece as a half view. If the front is an exterior view, the *front* half of the top or side view would be used, as in Fig. 8.40; but if the front view is a sectional view, the *rear* half would be used, as in Fig. 8.41. Figure 8.42 shows another space-saving combination of a half view with a half section. Examples of half views occur in Probs. 13.3.6 to 13.3.8.

FIG. 8.40. Half view. The front half is drawn when the mating view is external.

FIG. 8.41. Half view. The rear half is drawn when the mating view is a full section.

FIG. 8.42. Half view. The rear half is drawn when mating view is a half section.

FIG. 8.43. Conventional intersections. These are used when there is a small difference as compared with true projection.

8.23. CONVENTIONAL PRACTICES. One statement can be made with the force of a rule: *If anything in clearness can be gained by violating a principle of projection, violate it.* This applies to full as well as sectional views. Permissible violations are not readily apparent to the reader, since when they occur the actual conditions are described in a better and usually simpler form than if they were shown in true projection.

However, some care and judgment must be used in applying conventional treatments. Persons trained in their use ordinarily understand their meaning, but workmen often do not. Some unusual convention may be more confusing than helpful, and result in greater ambiguity than true projection.

There are occasions when the true lines of intersection are of no value as aids in reading and should be ignored. Some typical examples are shown in Fig. 8.43. It must be noted, however, that in certain cases that are similar but where there is a major difference in line position when the true projection is given, as compared with conventional treatment, the true line of intersection should be shown. Compare the treatment of the similar objects in Figs. 8.43

and 8.44. It would not be good practice to conventionalize the intersections on the objects in Fig. 8.44 because the difference between true projection and the convention is too great. To develop your judgment of the use of conventional intersections, carefully study Figs. 8.43 and 8.44 and observe the difference between true projection and conventional treatment in each case.

8.24. FILLETS AND ROUNDS. In designing a casting, never leave sharp internal angles because of the liability of fracture at those points. The radius of the fillet depends on the thickness of the metal and other design conditions. When not dimensioned, it is left to the patternmaker. External angles may be rounded

FIG. 8.44. True intersections. These are used when there is a major difference as compared with conventional treatment.

FIG. 8.45. Conventional fillets, rounds, and runouts. These are **conventionalized intersections.**

FIG. 8.46. Broken view with rotated sections. A broken view saves drawing the whole length of the part.

Rectangular Section

Round Section

Pipe or Tubing

Pipe or Tubing

Wood (Rectangular Section)

Long Break (all materials)

FIG. 8.47. Conventional breaks.

for appearance or comfort, with radii ranging from enough merely to remove the sharp edges to an amount nearly equal to the thickness of the piece. An edge made by the intersection of two unfinished surfaces of a casting should always be "broken" by a very small round. A sharp corner on a drawing indicates that one or both of the intersecting surfaces are machined. Small fillets, rounds, and "runouts" are best put in freehand, both in pencil and ink. Runouts, or "dieouts," as they are sometimes called, are conventional indications of filleted intersections where, theoretically, there would be no line because there is no abrupt change in direction. Figure 8.45 shows some conventional representations of fillets and rounds with runouts of arms and ribs intersecting other surfaces.

8.25. CONVENTIONAL BREAKS. In making the detail of a long bar or piece with a uniform cross section, it is rarely necessary to draw its whole length. It may be shown to a larger and therefore better scale by breaking out a piece, moving the ends together, and giving the true length by a dimension, as in Fig. 8.46. The shape of the cross section is indicated by a rotated section or more often by a semipictorial break line, as in Fig. 8.47.

8.26. CONVENTIONAL SYMBOLS. Engineers and draftsmen use conventional representation to indicate many details, such as screw threads, springs, pipe fittings, and electrical apparatus. These have been standardized by the ASA, whose code for materials in section has already been referred to in paragraph 8.11.

The symbol of two crossed diagonals

FIG. 8.48. Various symbols.

is used for two distinct purposes: (1) to indicate on a shaft the position of finish for a bearing, and (2) to indicate that a certain surface (usually parallel to the picture plane) is flat. These two uses are not apt to be confused (Fig. 8.48).

Because screw threads recur constantly, the designation for them is one of the most important items under conventional symbols. Up to the time of official standardization by the ASA, there were a dozen different thread symbols in use. Now a regular symbol and a simplified one have been adopted for American drawings, and both are understood internationally. The symbols for indicating threads on bolts, screws, and tapped holes are given in Chap. 12.

The conventional symbols mentioned are used principally on machine drawings. Architectural drawing, because of the small scales employed, uses many conventional symbols, and topographic drawing is made up almost entirely of symbols. Electrical *diagrams* are completely symbolic.

PROBLEMS

The following problems can be used for practice in shape description only or, by adding dimensions, in making working drawings.

8.1.1. Draw the top view, and change the front and side views to sectional views as indicated.

8.1.2. Draw the top view, and make the front and two side views in section on cutting planes as indicated. Scale to suit.

8.1.3 to 8.1.5. Given the side view, draw full front and side views in section. Scale to suit.

PROB. 8.1.1. Section study.

PROB. 8.1.2. Section study.

PROB. 8.1.3. Flanged wheel.

PROB. 8.1.4. Step pulley.

PROB. 8.1.5. Double-flanged wheel.

PROB. 8.1.6. Cap.

PROB. 8.1.7. Flanged cap.

PROB. 8.1.10. Ribbed support.

8.1.6 and 8.1.7. Change the right-side view to a full section.

8.1.8 and 8.1.9. Change the right-side view to a full section.

8.1.10. Change the right-side view to a full section.

8.1.11. Change the right-side view to a sectional view as indicated.

8.1.12 and 8.1.13. Change the front view to a full section.

8.1.14 and 8.1.15. Change the front view to a full section.

PROB. 8.1.8. Pump-rod guide.

PROB. 8.1.11. Housing cover.

PROB. 8.1.9. Face plate.

PROB. 8.1.12. Filler block.

PROB. 8.1.13. Filler block.

PROB. 8.1.14. Bumper body.

PROB. 8.1.15. V-belt pulley.

8.1.16 and 8.1.17. Select views that will best describe the piece.

8.1.18. Draw the top view as shown in the illustration and the front view as a full section.

8.1.19. Draw the top view as illustrated and the front view in half section on *A-A*.

8.1.20. Draw the top view as shown, and change the front and side views to sections as indicated.

PROB. 8.1.16. End plate.

PROB. 8.1.17. Piston cap.

PROB. 8.1.18. Pump flange.

PROB. 8.1.19. Brake-rod bracket.

PROB. 8.1.20. Bolted anchor block.

PROB. 8.1.21.   Column collar.

PROB. 8.1.22.   Compound bell-crank.

8.1.21.   Draw the top view and sectional view (or views) to best describe the object.

8.1.22.   Turn the object through 90°, and draw the given front view as the new top view; then make the new front view as section *B-B* and auxiliary section *A-A*. Refer to paragraph 8.9, for instructions on making auxiliary sections. See also Chap. 7 for the method of projection for the auxiliary section. Note in this case that the new top view, front-view section *B-B*, and auxiliary section *A-A* will completely describe the object. However, if desired, the side view may also be drawn, as shown or as an aligned view (described in paragraph 8.21).

PROB. 8.1.23.   Stem support.

8.1.22*A*.   As an alternate for Prob. 8.1.22, draw views as follows: with the object in the position shown, draw the front view as shown, draw the left-side view as section *B-B,* and draw the new top view as an aligned view.

8.1.23.   Draw the top view and front view in section.

8.1.24 and 8.1.25.   Draw the views and add the sectional views indicated.

8.1.26 and 8.1.27.   Draw a view and sectional view to best describe the piece.

8.1.28.   Draw the top view and necessary sectional view (or views) to best describe the object.

8.1.29.   Draw three views, making the side view as a section on *B-B*.

8.1.29*A*.   Draw three views, making the top view as a half section on *A-A*.

PROB. 8.1.24.   Spool base.

PROB. 8.1.25.   Saddle collar.

PROB. 8.1.26. Actuator link.

PROB. 8.1.27. Vibrator-drive bearing support.

Hub to receive shaft with ball bearings.
Bearings are Type R-12, $\frac{3}{4}$ ID, $1\frac{1}{8}$ OD, $\frac{5}{16}$ thick

PROB. 8.1.28. Cover and valve body.

PROB. 8.1.29. Crosshead.

Total Height 4

PROB. 8.1.30. Spindle support.

PROB. 8.1.31. Push rod cap and seal body.

8.1.30. Select views that will best describe the piece.

8.1.31. Draw a half end view and a longitudinal view as full section.

8.1.32. Draw the top view as shown in the figure and new front view in section. Show the shape (right section) of the link with rotated or removed section. The assembly comprises a cast-steel link, two bronze bushings, steel toggle pin, steel collar, steel taper pin, and part of the cast-steel supporting lug.

8.1.33. Draw the front view and longitudinal section. The assembly comprises a cast-iron base, a bronze bushing, a bronze disk, and two steel dowel pins.

PROB. 8.1.32. Link assembly.

PROB. 8.1.33. Step bearing.

PROB. 8.1.34. Pulley-bracket assembly.

8.1.34. Draw two half end views and a longitudinal section. The assembly consists of cast-iron body, two bronze bushings, steel shaft, cast-iron pulley, and steel taper pin.

8.1.35. Make an assembly drawing in section. The bracket is cast iron, the wheel is cast steel, the bushing is bronze, and the pin and taper pin are steel. Scale: full size.

8.1.35A. Make a drawing of the bracket with one view in section. Material is cast iron. Scale: full size.

8.1.35B. Make a drawing of the wheel with

one view in section. Material is cast steel. Scale: full size.

8.1.36. Make an assembly drawing in section. The assembly comprises two cast-iron brackets, two bronze bushings, steel shaft, cast-steel roller, and cast-iron base. The bushings are pressed into the roller, and the shaft is drilled for lubrication. Scale: full size.

8.1.36A. Make a drawing of the roller and bushing assembly that gives one view in section. See Prob. 8.1.36 for materials. Scale: full size.

PROB. 8.1.35. Sliding-door guide.

PROB. 8.1.36. Bell roller-support.

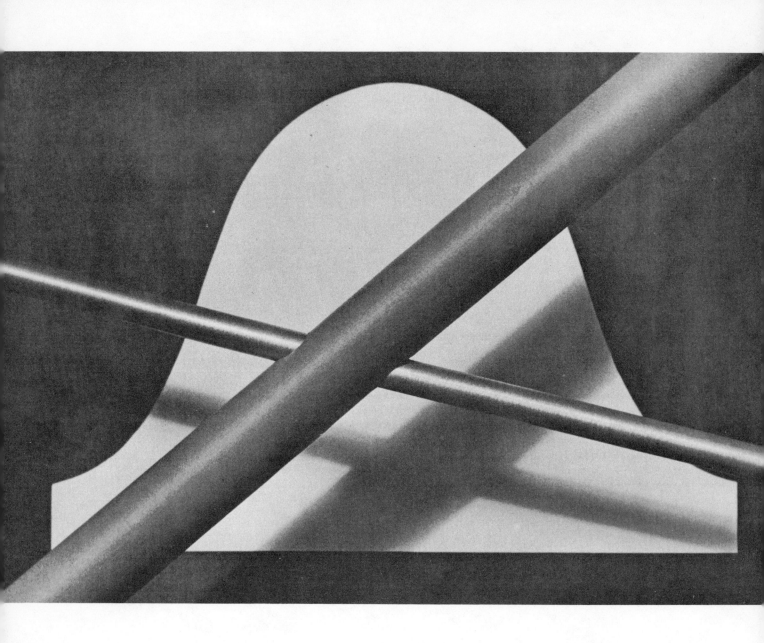

9

Intersections and Developments

9.1. **DEFINITION AND CLASSIFICATIONS.** In making orthographic drawings, there is the repeated necessity to represent the *lines of intersection* between the various surfaces of a wide variety of objects. Nearly every line on a drawing is a line of intersection, generally the intersection of two planes, giving a straight line, or of a cylinder and a plane, giving a circle or an ellipse. The term "intersection of surfaces" refers, however, to the more complicated lines that occur when geometric surfaces such as planes, cylinders, and cones intersect one another. These lines of intersection are shown by one of two basic methods: (1) *conventional intersections,* ordinarily used to represent a fillet, round, or runout,

as explained in paragraph 8.23 and shown in Fig. 8.43, or (2) *plotted intersections,* used when an intersection must be located accurately for purposes of dimensioning or for development of the surfaces. In sheet-metal combinations the intersection *must* be found before the piece can be developed. In this chapter we are concerned solely with the methods of projecting plotted intersections and with the procedures employed in the development of surfaces. *Development* is defined as the unfoldment of a surface to a plane.

Classification of Surfaces. A surface may be considered to be generated by the motion of a line: the generatrix. Surfaces are thus divided into two gen-

237

eral classes: (1) those that can be generated by a moving *straight* line, and (2) those that can be generated by a moving *curved* line. The first are called *ruled surfaces;* the second, *double-curved surfaces.* Any position of the generatrix is called an *element* of the surface.

Ruled surfaces are divided into (*a*) *the plane,* (*b*) *single-curved surfaces,* and (*c*) *warped surfaces.*

The plane is generated by a straight line moving so as to touch two other intersecting or parallel straight lines or a plane curve.

Single-curved surfaces have their elements parallel or intersecting. In this class are the cylinder and the cone and also a third surface, which we shall not consider, known as the "convolute," in which only consecutive elements intersect.

Warped surfaces have no two consecutive elements that are parallel or intersecting. There are a great variety of warped surfaces. The surface of a screw thread and that of an airplane wing are two examples.

Double-curved surfaces are generated by a curved line moving according to some law. The commonest forms are *surfaces of revolution,* made by revolving a curve about an axis in the same plane, such as the sphere, torus or ring, ellipsoid, paraboloid, hyperboloid. Illustrations of various surfaces may be found in Fig. 3.101.

Definitions and Details of Common Surfaces. A *prism* is a polyhedron whose bases or ends are equal parallel polygons and whose lateral faces are parallelograms. A right prism is one whose lateral faces are rectangles; all others are called oblique prisms. The axis of a prism is a straight line connecting the centers of the bases. A truncated prism is that portion of a prism lying between one of its bases and a plane which cuts all its lateral edges.

A *pyramid* is a polyhedron whose base is a polygonal plane and whose other surfaces are triangular planes meeting at a point called the "vertex." The axis is a line passing through the vertex and the mid-point of the base. The altitude is a perpendicular from the vertex to the base. A pyramid is *right* if the altitude coincides with the axis; it is *oblique* if they do not coincide. A truncated pyramid is that portion of a pyramid lying between the base and a cutting plane which cuts all the lateral edges. The frustum of a pyramid is that portion of a pyramid lying between the base and a cutting plane parallel to the base which cuts all the lateral edges.

A *cylinder* is a single-curved surface generated by the motion of a straight-line generatrix remaining parallel to itself and constantly intersecting a curved directrix. The various positions of the generatrix are elements of the surface. It is a *right* cylinder when the elements are perpendicular to the bases, an *oblique* cylinder when they are not. A truncated cylinder is that portion of a cylinder which lies between one of its bases and a cutting plane which cuts all the elements. The axis is the line joining the centers of the bases.

A *cone* is a single-curved surface generated by the movement, along a curved directrix, of a straight-line generatrix, one point of which is fixed. The directrix is the base, and the fixed point is the vertex of the cone. Each position of the generatrix is an element of the surface. The axis is a line connecting the vertex and the center of the base. The altitude is a perpendicular dropped from the vertex to the base. A cone is *right* if the axis and altitude coincide; it is *oblique* if they do not coincide. A truncated cone is that portion of a cone lying between the base and a cutting plane which cuts all the elements. The frustum of a cone is that portion of a cone lying between the base and a cutting plane parallel to the base which cuts all the elements.

9.2. INTERSECTIONS OF PLANE SURFACES.

The intersection of a line and a plane is a *point* common to both. The intersection of two planes is a *line* common to both. After mastering the graphic methods of locating intersections (paragraphs 9.3 to 9.10), apply the principles you have learned to finding the line of intersection between objects made up of plane surfaces (prisms and pyramids, paragraphs 9.11 to 9.13). The method of solution for the intersection of other polyhedrons should follow logically from the examples given.

9.3. INTERSECTION OF A LINE AND A PLANE, BOTH IN PRINCIPAL POSITIONS.

Principal positions of planes are horizontal, frontal, or profile. Principal positions of lines occur when the lines are *not* inclined to any principal plane; thus a line is (1) horizontal-frontal, (2) horizontal profile, or (3) frontal-profile. Therefore, if the line is parallel to, or lies in, the principal plane, no single point of intersection is possible, but in other positions when the line is perpendicular to the plane, a single point exists. To illustrate, Fig. 9.1 shows a rectangular object made up of horizontal, frontal, and profile planes, with an accompanying horizontal-profile line *AB*. Because

the line is parallel to horizontal and profile planes, the line and these planes do not intersect except at infinity. However, the line is perpendicular to frontal planes and there is a single point of intersection, observed in the top view at P_T and in the side view at P_R, where the front of the object appears as an edge. The front view of the intersection is coincident with $A_F B_F$ at P_F because this is the end view of line *AB*.

Thus it is established that *the intersection of a line and plane is a point on the line coincident with the edge view of the plane.* The point of intersection of a line and plane is often called a "piercing point."

9.4. INTERSECTION OF AN INCLINED LINE WITH PLANES IN PRINCIPAL POSITIONS.

Two points of intersection are possible, one with each plane to which the line is not parallel. For example, Fig. 9.2 shows a frontal line *AB* and an object made up of horizontal, frontal, and profile planes. The line will not intersect any frontal plane (except at infinity). The intersection with the (profile) right side is seen at P_T and P_F, where the plane appears as an edge, and is then easily projected to P_R. The intersection with the horizontal bottom is observed at Q_F and Q_R, where the plane appears as an edge, and is projected from Q_F to Q_T.

Observe that line *AB* does not intersect the top or left side of the *object,* but if the top and side planes were extended, a point of intersection would exist.

9.5. INTERSECTION OF A SKEW LINE WITH PLANES IN PRINCIPAL POSITIONS. Theoretically, a skew line (a line inclined to *all* principal planes) will intersect all three principal planes. However, on a *rectangular object,* depending upon the

FIG. 9.1. Intersection of a line and plane. The line is perpendicular to the plane.

FIG. 9.2. Intersection of an inclined line with planes. In this case the line intersects the horizontal and profile sides of an object.

FIG. 9.3. Intersection of a skew line with planes. (*A*) intersection with horizontal; (*B*) intersection with frontal and profile; (*C*) intersection with horizontal, frontal, and profile.

(A) INTERSECTION WITH TOP SURFACE

(B) NO INTERSECTION WITH TOP SURFACE

length and position of the line, only one or two intersections exist. Figure 9.3 illustrates all possibilities. At (*A*), the skew line from point *A* inside the object emanates upward, backward, and to the right, and obviously intersects the top (horizontal) surface of the object at *P*, observed first at P_F and P_R, where the top surface appears as an edge, and then projected to P_T. But line *AB* does not intersect any other surface of the object.

At (*B*) line *AB* is seen to intersect two surfaces of the object, the right side at *Q* and the front at *P*. Note that in each case the points are found first where the surface appears as an edge, Q_T and Q_F for point *Q*, and P_T and P_R for point *P*.

At (*C*) the top surface of the object is extended so that three intersections are possible. Physically this occurs on an object when two rectangular shapes are offset or when a base or lug extends. The line *AB* intersects the right side at *P* and the front at *Q*. The top surface and the line give an intersection at *R*, shown on the figure with dashed lines for the extensions.

Note in every case, (*A*), (*B*), and (*C*), of Fig. 9.3, that the intersection is found by observing where the line intersects the surface *in the edge view* of the surface.

For horizontal, frontal, and profile surfaces, two views always show the surface as an edge. Thus it is easily seen that, for example, at (*B*) the line crosses the *edge* view of the *right side* of the object in the top view at Q_T and in the front view at Q_F, and because point *Q* falls *within the confines* of the surface, a real point of intersection has been found. Also observe at (*A*) that line *AB apparently* crosses the edge view of the right side of the object *in the top view*. Nevertheless, reading the front view, line *AB* is seen to miss the right side and there is therefore no intersection of *AB* with the right side. To illustrate further, line *AB* of Fig. 9.4*A* apparently intersects the edge view of the top surface, as observed in the front view. But projecting Q_F to the top view at Q_T on *AB*, we see that Q_T falls within the confines of the top surface of the object and is therefore an intersection. However, at (*B*) when Q_F is projected to the top view, Q_T is outside the confines of the top surface and there is no intersection. From this it is clear that to determine a real point of intersection, (1) *two views must be consulted,* and (2) *the apparent point of intersection in one view must project within the confines of the surface in another view.*

FIG. 9.4. To determine an intersection. The intersection (piercing point) must fall within the surface area in two (or more) views.

FIG. 9.6. Intersection of a skew line and skew plane. An auxiliary (edge view) determines the intersection.

9.6. INTERSECTION OF A SKEW LINE WITH INCLINED PLANES.

An inclined plane appears as an edge in one view and, because of this, its intersection with any line is easily found. In Fig. 9.5*A* the inclined surface appears as an edge in the front view. The apparent intersection P_F is projected to P_T on $A_T B_T$, where it is seen that P_T falls within the confines of the inclined surface and therefore is a real point of intersection. Figure 9.5 shows the principle applied at (*B*) to a surface inclined to front and side and at (*C*) to a surface inclined to top and front. Note that at (*B*) the intersection will be located first in the top view, and at (*C*) it will be found first in the side view.

9.7. INTERSECTION OF A SKEW LINE WITH A SKEW SURFACE.

A skew surface does not appear as an edge in any principal view, so if the methods of paragraphs 9.3 to 9.6 are used, an edge view will have to be made. This is illustrated in Fig. 9.6 where the edge view has been made by looking in the direction of *SR*, a horizontal line of the skew surface. Line *AB* is now projected into the edge view, and the intersection *P* is located and then projected back to top, front, and side views.

It is not necessary, however, to employ an extra (edge) view. Figure 9.7 shows pictorially, a line and skew plane. If any edge-view plane is passed through the line, the intersection of this plane with the skew plane will contain the point of intersection between the line and the skew plane. The intersection of the edge-view plane and the skew plane is easily located, as shown in Fig. 9.8, where *AB* is a line and *RST* a skew plane. A plane *appearing as an edge in the top view,* passed

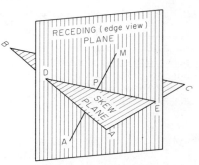

FIG. 9.7. A receding plane passed through a line.

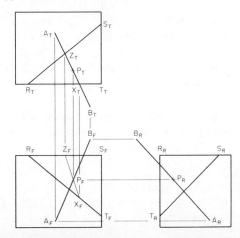

FIG. 9.8. Intersection of a skew line and skew plane. The intersection is determined by a receding plane (edge view plane in top view) passed through line *AB*.

FIG. 9.9. Intersection of a skew line and skew plane. This illustrates enlargement of the skew plane to eliminate difficult projection.

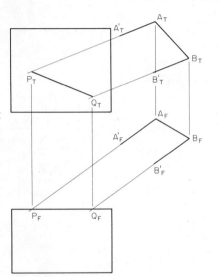

FIG. 9.10. Intersection of a skew plane with a plane in principal position. The edge view of the principal plane determines the intersection.

FIG. 9.11. Intersection of a skew plane with an inclined plane. The edge view of the inclined plane determines the intersection.

through AB, will intersect RS at Z_T and RT at X_T, and these points projected to the front view at Z_F and X_F establish ZX as the line of intersection between the edge-view plane and RST, the skew plane. The front view shows the intersection of AB with ZX at P_F, the point common to line, skew plane, and edge-view plane. To complete, P is projected to the top view at P_T.

Often, it happens that one edge of a skew surface is profile, as is ST in Figs. 9.8 and 9.9, and when the line, in this case AB, is in a position like that of Fig. 9.9, the intersection (with the skew plane) of an edge-view plane through the line is not easily projected. An accepted method in such cases is to *extend* the skew plane to eliminate the profile edge. In Fig. 9.9, RS has been extended to U, making the skew surface RUT, still the *same* surface, but larger. An edge-view plane (in the top view) passed as before gives XZ as its line of intersection with RUT. Point P, the point common to edge-view plane, skew plane, and line, is then located first in the front view at P_F and then projected to top and side views.

9.8. INTERSECTION OF A PLANE WITH A PLANE IN A PRINCIPAL POSITION. Any line of a given plane will intersect a sec-

ond plane *on the line of intersection* between two planes. Therefore, to establish the line of intersection between two planes, the intersection of either of two lines of one plane with the other plane (or one line of each plane with the opposite plane) will establish two points on the line of intersection of the planes. The simplest case is when one of the planes is in a principal position as is the top surface of the object in Fig. 9.10. Lines A-A' and B-B' are edges of a skew plane, which, extended, are seen to intersect the top surface of the rectangular object at P and Q, as explained in paragraph 9.5.

9.9. INTERSECTION OF A PLANE WITH AN INCLINED PLANE. Figure 9.11 is similar to Fig. 9.10 but the intersection this time is with the inclined surface of the object. The intersection is again found by extending A-A' and B-B' to the edge view of the inclined surface. Refer to paragraph 9.6.

9.10. INTERSECTION OF TWO SKEW PLANES. As before, the points of intersection of two lines determine the intersection of the planes. In Fig. 9.12 two edge-view (in the front view) planes have been passed through A-A' and B-B' extended. The edge-view planes then intersect the skew plane $RSTU$ in lines WX and YZ. Then P_T and Q_T, the intersections of A-A' and B-B' extended, in the top view determine the top view of the line of intersection, which, projected to the front view at P_F and Q_F, completes the solution. Compare Fig. 9.12 (edge-view plane in front view is used) with Fig. 9.8 (edge-view plane in top view is used). An edge-view plane can also be passed in a side view whenever it is convenient to do so.

9.12. To Find the Intersection of Two Pyramids

9.11. TO FIND THE INTERSECTION OF TWO PRISMS (FIG. 9.13). In general, find the line of intersection of a surface on one prism with all surfaces on the other. Then take a surface adjacent to the first surface, and find its intersection with the other prism. Continue in this manner until the complete line of intersection of the prisms is determined.

The method of locating end points on the line of intersection of two surfaces depends upon the position of the surfaces, as follows:

Both Surfaces Receding (Edge View). Their intersection appears as a point in the view in which they recede. Project the intersection to an adjacent view, locating the two ends of the intersection on the edges of one or both intersecting surfaces so that they will lie within the boundaries of the other surface. The intersection 4-5 of surfaces *QRST* and *EF*-3 was obtained in this manner.

One Surface Receding, the Other Skew. An edge of the oblique surface may appear to pierce the receding surface in a view in which these conditions exist. If, in an adjacent view, the piercing point lies on the edge of the oblique surface and within the boundaries of the other surface, it is an end point on the intersection of the surfaces. Point 5, lying on edge *F*-5 of the oblique surface *FG*-1-5 and the surface *QRST*, is located in the top view in this manner. Point 1 was similarly established. Point 6, lying on edge *ST*, is found by passing a vertical plane *AA* through edge *ST*. Plane *AA* cuts line 1-*c* from plane *GF*-5-1, giving point 6 where line 1-*c* crosses *ST*.

Both Surfaces Skew. Find the piercing point of an edge of one surface with the other surface, as follows: Pass a receding plane through an edge of one surface. Find the line of intersection of the receding plane and the other surface, as explained above. The piercing point of the edge and surface is located where the line of intersection, just found, and the edge intersect. Repeat this operation to establish the other end of the line of intersection of the surfaces. Point 3, on the line of intersection 2-3 of the oblique surfaces *NORS* and *EG*-1-3, was found in this manner by passing the receding plane *BB* through edge *E*-3, finding the intersection *b*-4 of the surfaces, and then locating point 3 at the intersection of *b*-4 and *E*-3.

9.12. TO FIND THE INTERSECTION OF TWO PYRAMIDS. In general, find the point where one edge on one pyramid pierces a surface of the other pyramid. Then find where a second edge pierces, and so on. To complete the line of intersection, the piercing points of the edges of the second pyramid with surfaces of the first will probably also have to be found. Figure 9.14 illustrates the method. Find where edge *AD* pierces plane *EHG*, by assuming a vertical cutting plane through edge *AD*. This plane cuts line 1-2 from plane *EHG*, and the piercing point is point *P*, located first on the front view and then projected to the top view. Next, find where *AD* pierces plane *EFG*,

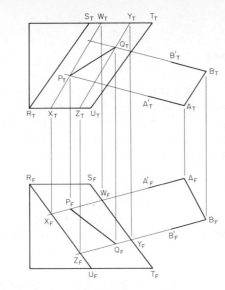

FIG. 9.12. Intersection of two skew planes. Receding planes, passed through two lines of one plane, determine the intersection.

FIG. 9.13. Intersection of two prisms. The edges of one, intersecting the faces of the other, determine the complete "line" of intersection.

FIG. 9.14. Intersection of two pyramids. The edges of one, intersecting the faces of the other, determine the intersection.

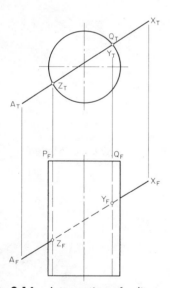

FIG. 9.15. Intersection of a prism and pyramid. The edges of one, intersecting the faces of the other, determine the intersection.

FIG. 9.16. Intersection of a line and cylinder. The edge view of the cylinder determines the two piercing points.

FIG. 9.17. Intersection of a plane and cylinder. A number of lines on the plane are used.

by using a vertical cutting plane through *AD*. This plane cuts line 3-4 from plane *EFG*, and the piercing point is point *Q*.

After finding point *P* on plane *EHG* and point *Q* on plane *EFG*, locate the piercing point of edge *EG* with plane *ABD* in order to draw lines of intersection. A vertical plane through *EG* cuts line 5-6 from plane *ABD*, and the intersection is point *R* on edge *EG*. Thus edges of the "first" pyramid pierce surfaces of the "second," and edges of the second pierce surfaces of the first. Continue in this manner until the complete line of intersection *PRQSTV* has been found.

The use of a vertical cutting plane to obtain the piercing points is perhaps the simplest method and the easiest to visualize. Nevertheless, it should be noted that a plane receding from the frontal or profile plane could also be used. As an example of the use of a plane receding from the frontal, consider that such a plane has been passed through line *CA* in the front view. This plane cuts line 7-8 from plane *EFG*, and the point of intersection is *S* on line *CA*. The use of a plane receding from the profile plane

would be basically the same but would require a side view.

9.13. TO FIND THE LINE OF INTERSECTION BETWEEN A PRISM AND A PYRAMID (FIG. 9.15). The method is basically the same as for two pyramids. Thus a vertical plane through edge *G* cuts line 1-2 from surface *AED*, and a vertical plane through edge *K* cuts line 3-4 from surface *AED*, giving the two piercing points *P* and *Q* on surface *AED*. A vertical plane through edge *AE* cuts elements 7 and 8 from the prism and gives piercing points *R* and *T*. Continue in this manner until the complete line of intersection *PQSTVR* is found.

9.14. INTERSECTIONS OF CURVED SURFACES. The intersections of single- and double-curved surfaces with lines and planes and with each other, especially when one or both of the surfaces are in a skew position, are properly a part of the study of engineering geometry and therefore not included here. However, the intersections of cylinders and cones in simple positions occur more or less frequently on machine parts, and so are discussed in the paragraphs that follow.

9.15. INTERSECTION OF A CYLINDER AND LINE. The common case occurs when the cylinder is in a simple position, as in Fig. 9.16, with one view the end view —the *edge* view of the surface and the other view showing the normal view of all the elements. Any line such as *AX* is therefore seen to intersect the cylinder where the surface appears as an edge, in this case the top view at Y_T and Z_T. These two points lie on elements of the cylinder *P* and *Q*, which are projected to the front view thus locating Y_F and Z_F.

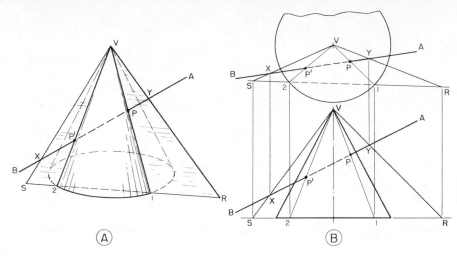

(A)

(B)

FIG. 9.18. Intersection of a line and cone. A plane passed through the line and simultaneously through the apex of the cone is the basis for determination.

9.16. INTERSECTION OF A CYLINDER AND PLANE.

Planes theoretically contain an infinite number of lines, and so, by the method of paragraph 9.15, the intersection of a number of *lines* of a plane will determine the intersection of a plane with a cylinder. In Fig. 9.17 the intersection of *ABC* with the cylinder is to be located. Any line *AX* is drawn on the plane and the intersections *Z* and *Y* found, giving two points on the curved line of intersection. The process repeated with a number of lines similar to *AX* will give points to complete the curve.

9.17. INTERSECTION OF A CONE AND A LINE.

Figure 9.18*A* illustrates pictorially the problem of finding the points where a line pierces a cone. Select a cutting plane, *VXY,* containing the given line *AB* and passing through the apex, *V,* of the cone. A plane passing through the apex of a cone will intersect the cone in straight lines. The lines of intersection of the cutting plane and the cone are lines *V-1* and *V-2*. These lines are determined by finding the line of intersection, *RS,* between the cutting plane and the base plane of the cone and then finding the points 1 and 2 where this line crosses the base curve. Line *AB* intersects both lines *V-1* and *V-2*, establishing the points *P* and *P'* where line *AB* pierces the cone.

The orthographic solution is illustrated at (*B*). Convenient points *X* and *Y* on line *AB* are selected so that plane *VXY* (a plane containing the apex of the cone and line *AB*) extended, will intersect the base plane of the cone in the line *RS*. In the top view *RS* cuts the base curve at 1 and 2, thus locating elements *V-1* and *V-2 in* the cutting plane and *on* the surface of the cone. *V-1* and *V-2* then intersect *BA* at *P* and *P'*, the piercing points of line *AB* and the cone.

9.18. INTERSECTION OF A CONE AND A PLANE.

Figure 9.19*A* illustrates pictorially the determination of the line of intersection between a cone and a plane. Lines (elements) of the cone, such as *V-1, V-2,* etc., will intersect the plane at *a, b,* etc., respectively. If the edge view of the plane appears in one of the views, as at (*B*), the solution is quite simple. Selected elements of the cone, *V-1, V-2,* etc., are drawn in both views. These elements are seen to intersect the plane in the front view at *a, b,* etc. Projection of these points to the top view then gives points through which a smooth curve is drawn to complete the solution. The edge view of the plane (within the confines of the cone) is, of course, the intersection in the front view.

(A)

(B)

FIG. 9.19. Intersection of a plane and cone. The edge view of the plane determines the intersection.

FIG. 9.20. Intersection of a plane and cone. (*A*) a series of planes, passed through the cone apex, locate points common to plane and cone; (*B*) an auxiliary (edge view of plane) determines points common to cone and plane.

Ⓐ   Ⓑ

If the plane intersecting the cone is skew, as in Fig. 9.20, the cutting-plane method is probably preferable because of the simplicity of the solution. Any plane passed through the apex of the cone will cut straight lines from the cone. Therefore, as shown at (*A*), if vertical cutting planes are used, all passing through *V*, the apex, these planes will cut lines such as *V*-2 and *V*-8 from the cone. At the same time, a vertical cutting plane will cut *XZ* from the plane. *XZ* then intersects *V*-2 at *b* and *V*-8 at *h*, giving two points on the line of intersection. A series of planes thus passed and points found will complete the solution.

Even though the above plane method is simple and requires only the given views for solution, it *might* be advantageous to draw an extra view (auxiliary), as at (*B*), where, by projecting parallel to a horizontal line of the plane, *the plane appears as an edge*. In this event, selected lines of the cone are seen to intersect the plane in the auxiliary view (where the plane appears as an edge), and the solution becomes basically the same as in Fig. 9.19*B*. In addition, points located first in the auxiliary view and then in the top view will have to be found in the front view by projection from the top view and measurement from the auxiliary, indicated by distance *X* on the figure.

9.19. INTERSECTION OF TWO CYLINDERS (FIG. 9.21). Cutting planes parallel to the axis of a cylinder will cut straight-line elements from the cylinder. The frontal cutting planes *A, B, C,* and *D, parallel to the axis of each cylinder,* cut elements from each cylinder, the intersections of which are points on the curve. The pictorial sketch shows a slice cut by a plane from the object, which has been treated as a solid in order to illustrate the method more easily.

When the axes of the cylinders do not intersect, as in Fig. 9.22, the same method is used. Certain "critical planes"

FIG. 9.21. Intersection of two cylinders. Planes cut straight-line elements from both.

give the limits and turning points of the curve. Such planes should always be taken through the contour elements. For the position shown, planes *A* and *D* give the depth of the curve, the plane *B* the extreme height, and the plane *C* the tangent or turning points on the contour element of the vertical cylinder. After the critical points have been determined, a sufficient number of other cutting planes are used to give an accurate curve.

9.20. INTERSECTION OF A CYLINDER AND A CONE (FIG. 9.23). Cutting planes may be taken, as at (*A*), so as to pass through the vertex of the cone and parallel to the axis of the cylinder, thus cutting the straight-line elements from both cylinder and cone; or, as at (*B*), with a right-circular cone, when the cylinder's axis is parallel or perpendicular to the cone's axis, cutting planes may be taken parallel to the base so as to cut circles from the cone. Both systems of planes are illustrated in the figure. The pictorial sketches show slices taken by each plane through the objects, which have been treated as solids in order to illustrate the method more easily. Some judgment is necessary in the selection of both the direction and the number of cutting planes. More points need to be found at the places of sudden curvature or change of direction of the projections of the line of intersections.

In Fig. 9.23*A* the cutting planes appear as edges in the right-side view, where the cylinder surface also appears as an edge. The observed intersections in the side view are then projected to the cone elements formed by the cutting planes, in the top and front views, to complete the solution.

At (*B*), horizontal cutting planes cut circles from the cone and straight-line elements from the cylinder. The top view then reveals intersections of cone circles and cylinder elements. Projection to the front view will complete the solution.

9.21. DEVELOPMENTS. In many different kinds of construction full-size patterns of some or all of the faces of an object are required; for example, in stonecutting, a template or pattern giving the shape of an irregular face, or in sheet-metal work, a pattern to which a sheet may be cut so that when rolled, folded, or formed it will make the object.

The complete surface laid out in a plane is called the "development" of the surface.

Surfaces about which a thin sheet of flexible material (such as paper or tin) can be wrapped smoothly are said to be developable; these include objects made up of planes and single-curved surfaces only. Warped and double-curved surfaces are nondevelopable; and when patterns are required for their construction, they can be made only by methods that are approximate, but, assisted by the ductility or pliability of the material, they give the required form. Thus while a ball cannot be wrapped smoothly, a two-piece pattern developed approximately and cut from leather can be stretched and sewed on in a smooth cover, or a flat disk of metal can be die-stamped, formed, or spun to a hemispherical or other shape.

9.22. BASIC CONSIDERATIONS. We have learned the method of finding the true size of a plane surface by projecting its normal view. If the true size of all the plane faces of an object are found and joined in order at their common edges so that all faces lie in a common plane,

FIG. 9.22. Intersection of two cylinders, axes not intersecting. Planes, parallel to each of the axes, cut straight-line elements from both surfaces.

FIG. 9.23. Intersection of a cylinder and cone. (*A*) elements of the cone are observed to intersect the cylinder in the side view (edge view of cylinder); or (*B*) horizontal planes cut circles from both surfaces and locate points common to both.

FIG. 9.24. Theory of development. The surface is composed into a plane by unfoldment.

the result will be the developed surface. Usually this may be done to the best advantage by finding the true length of the edges.

The development of a right cylinder is evidently a rectangle whose width is the altitude and length the rectified circumference (Fig. 9.24); and the development of a right-circular cone is a circular sector with a radius equal to the slant height of the cone and an arc equal in length to the circumference of its base (Fig. 9.24).

As illustrated in Fig. 9.24, developments are drawn with the inside face up. This is primarily the result of working to inside rather than outside dimensions of ducts. This procedure also facilitates the use of fold lines, identified by punch marks at each end, along which the metal is folded in forming the object.

In laying out real sheet-metal designs, an allowance must be made for seams and lap and, in heavy sheets, for the

thickness and crowding of the metal; there is also the consideration of the commercial sizes of material as well as the question of economy in cutting. In all of this some practical shop knowledge is necessary. Figure 9.40 and paragraph 9.34 indicate the usage of some of the more common joints, although the developments given in this chapter will be confined to the principles.

9.23.   TO DEVELOP A TRUNCATED HEXAGONAL PRISM (FIG. 9.25).   First draw two projections of the prism: (1) a normal view of a right section (a section or cut obtained by a plane perpendicular to the axis) and (2) a normal view of the lateral edges. The base *ABCDEF* is a right section shown in true size in the bottom view. Lay off on line *AA* of the development the perimeter of the base. This line is called by sheet-metal workers the "stretchout" or "girth" line. At points *A, B, C,* etc., erect perpendiculars called "measuring lines" or "bend lines," representing the lateral edges along which the pattern is folded to form the prism. Lay off on each of these its length *A*-1, *B*-2, *C*-3, etc., as given on the front view. Connect the points 1, 2, 3, etc., in succession, to complete the development of the lateral surfaces. Note on the pattern that the inside of the lateral faces is toward the observer. For the development of the entire surface in one piece, attach the true sizes of the upper end and the base as shown, finding the true size of the upper end by an auxiliary (normal) view as described in paragraph 7.4. For economy of solder or rivets and time, it is customary to make the seam on the shortest edge or surface. In seaming along the intersection of surfaces whose dihedral angle is other than 90°, as is the case

FIG. 9.25. Development of a prism. The true size of each side is laid out in successive order.

9.25. To Develop an Oblique Pyramid

here, the lap seam lends itself to convenient assembling. The flat lock could be used if the seam were made on one of the lateral faces.

9.24. TO DEVELOP A TRUNCATED RIGHT PYRAMID (FIG. 9.26).

Draw the projections of the pyramid which show (1) a normal view of the base or right section and (2) a normal view of the axis. Lay out the pattern for the pyramid, and then superimpose the pattern of the truncation.

Since this is a portion of a right regular pyramid, the lateral edges are all of equal length. The lateral edges OA and OD are parallel to the frontal plane and consequently show in their true length on the front view. With center O_1, taken at any convenient place, and a radius $O_F A_F$, draw an arc that is the stretchout of the pattern. On it step off the six equal sides of the hexagonal base, obtained from the top view, and connect these points successively with each other and with the vertex O_1, thus forming the pattern for the pyramid.

The intersection of the cutting plane and lateral surfaces is developed by laying off the true length of the intercept of each lateral edge on the corresponding line of the development. The true length of each of these intercepts, such as OH and OJ, is found by rotating it about the axis of the pyramid until they coincide with $O_F A_F$. The path of any point, as H, will be projected on the front view as a horizontal line. To obtain the development of the entire surface of the truncated pyramid, attach the base; also find the true size of the cut face and attach it on a common line.

The lap seam is suggested for use here for the same reason that was advanced in paragraph 9.23.

FIG. 9.28. Development of an oblique pyramid. Each lateral edge is of different length. The true length for each must be determined.

The right-rectangular pyramid, Fig. 9.27, is developed in a similar way, but as the edge OA is not parallel to the plane of projection, it must be rotated to $O_F A_R$ to obtain its true length.

9.25. TO DEVELOP AN OBLIQUE PYRAMID (FIG. 9.28).

Since the lateral edges are unequal in length, the true length of each must be found separately by rotating it parallel to the frontal plane. With O_1 taken at any convenient place, lay off the seam line $O_1 A_1$ equal to $O_F A_R$. With A_1 as center and radius $A_1 B_1$ equal to the true length of AB, describe an arc. With O_1 as center and radius $O_1 B_1$ equal to $O_F B_R$, describe a second arc intersecting the first in vertex B_1. Connect the vertices

FIG. 9.26. Development of a pyramid. This is a right pyramid. The true lengths of all edges (from the vertex to the base) are equal.

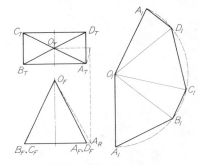

FIG. 9.27. Development of a pyramid. The true length from vertex to base is found by rotating one edge until frontal.

FIG. 9.29. Development of a cylinder. The cylinder is treated as a many-sided prism.

O_1, A_1, and B_1, thus forming the pattern for the lateral surface OAB. Similarly, lay out the patterns for the remaining three lateral surfaces, joining them on their common edges. The stretchout is equal to the summation of the base edges. If the complete development is required, attach the base on a common line. The lap seam is suggested as the most suitable for the given conditions.

9.26. TO DEVELOP A TRUNCATED RIGHT CYLINDER (FIG. 9.29). The development of a cylinder is similar to the development of a prism. Draw two projections of the cylinder: (1) a normal view of a right section and (2) a normal view of the elements. In rolling the cylinder out on a tangent plane, the base or right section, being perpendicular to the axis, will develop into a straight line. For convenience in drawing, divide the

normal view of the base, here shown in the bottom view, into a number of equal parts by points that represent elements. These divisions should be spaced so that the chordal distances closely enough approximate the arc to make the stretch-out practically equal to the periphery of the base or right section. Project these elements to the front view. Draw the stretchout and measuring lines as in Fig. 9.25, the cylinder now being treated as a many-sided prism. Transfer the lengths of the elements in order, by projection or with dividers, and join the points thus found by a smooth curve, sketching it in freehand very lightly before fitting the french curve to it. This development might be the pattern of one-half of a two-piece elbow. Three-piece, four-piece, or five-piece elbows can be drawn similarly, as illustrated in Fig. 9.30. As the base is symmetrical, only one-half of it need be drawn. In these cases, the intermediate pieces, as B, C, and D, are developed on a stretch-out line formed by laying off the perimeter of a right section. If the right section is taken through the middle of the piece, the stretchout line becomes the center line of the development.

Evidently any elbow could be cut from a single sheet without waste if the seams were made alternately on the long and short sides. The flat lock seam is recommended for Figs. 9.29 and 9.30, although other types could be used.

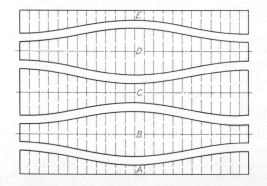

FIG. 9.30. Development of an elbow (cylinders). Note the identity of A and E and of B and D.

The octagonal dome (Fig. 9.31) illustrates an application of the development of cylinders. Each piece is a portion of a cylinder. The elements are parallel to the base of the dome and show in their true lengths in the top view. The true length of the stretchout line for sections A and A' shows in the front view at $O_F H_F$. By considering $O_T H_T$ as the edge of a plane cutting a right section, the problem is identical with the preceding problem.

Similarly, the stretchout line for sections B, B', D, and D' shows in true length at $O_F K_R$ in the front view, and for section C and C' at $O_S M_S$ in the side view.

The true shape of hip rafter ON is found by rotating it until it is parallel to the frontal plane, as at $O_F N_R$, in the same manner as in finding the true length of any line. A sufficient number of points should be taken to give a smooth curve.

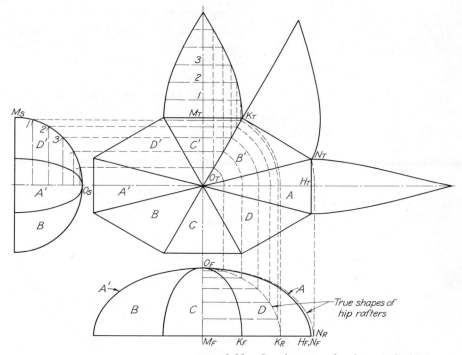

FIG. 9.31. Development of a dome (cylinders). Each cylindrical portion is unrolled separately.

9.27. TO DEVELOP A TRUNCATED RIGHT-CIRCULAR CONE (FIG. 9.32).

Draw the projections of the cone which will show (1) a normal view of the base or right section and (2) a normal view of the axis. First develop the surface of the complete cone and then superimpose the pattern for the truncation.

Divide the top view of the base into a sufficient number of equal parts so that the sum of the resulting chordal distances will closely approximate the periphery of the base. Project these points to the front view, and draw front views of the elements through them. With center A_1 and a radius equal to the slant height A_F-1_F, which is the true length of all the elements, draw an arc, which is the stretchout, and lay off on it the chordal divisions of the base, ob-

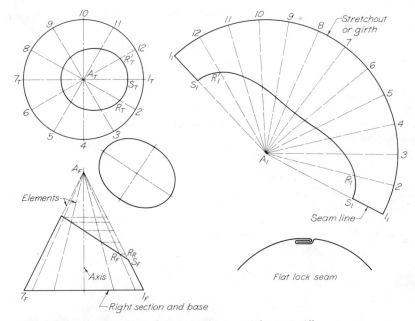

FIG. 9.32. Development of a cone. This is a right cone. All elements from vertex to base are the same length.

tained from the top view. Connect these points 1_1, 2, 3, etc., with A-1, thus forming the pattern for the cone. Find the true length of each element from vertex to cutting plane by rotating it to coincide with the contour element A-1, and lay off this distance on the corresponding line of the development. Draw a smooth curve through these points. The flat lock seam along element S-1 is recommended, although other types could be employed. The pattern for the inclined surface is obtained from the auxiliary (normal) view.

9.28. TRIANGULATION.

Nondevelopable surfaces are developed approximately by assuming them to be made of narrow sections of developable surfaces. The commonest and best method for approximate development is that of triangulation, that is, the surface is assumed to be made up of a large number of triangular strips, or plane triangles with very short bases. This method is used for all warped surfaces and also for oblique cones. Oblique cones are single-curved surfaces and thus are theoretically capable of true development, but they can be developed much more easily and accurately by triangulation.

The method is extremely simple. It consists merely of dividing the surface into triangles, finding the true lengths of the sides of each, and constructing them one at a time, joining these triangles on their common sides.

9.29. TO DEVELOP AN OBLIQUE CONE (FIG. 9.33).

An oblique cone differs from a cone of revolution in that the elements have different lengths. The development of the right-circular cone is, practically, made up of a number of equal triangles which meet at the vertex and whose sides are elements and whose bases are the chords of short arcs of the base of the cone. In the oblique cone each triangle must be found separately.

Draw two views of the cone showing (1) a normal view of the base and (2) a normal view of the altitude. Divide the true size of the base, here shown in the top view, into a sufficient number of equal parts so that the sum of the chordal distances will closely approximate the length of the base curve. Project these points to the front view of the base. Through these points and the vertex, draw the elements in each view. Since this cone is symmetrical about a frontal plane through the vertex, the elements are shown only on the front half of it. Also, only one-half of the development is drawn. With the seam on the shortest element, the element OC will be the center line of the development and can be drawn directly at O_1C_1, as its true length is given at O_FC_F. Find the true length of the elements by rotating them until parallel to the frontal plane or by constructing a "true-length diagram." The true length of any element would be the hypotenuse of a triangle, one leg being the length of the projected element as seen in the top view and the other leg being equal to the altitude of the cone. Thus to make the diagram, draw the leg OD coincid-

9.31. Transition Pieces

ing with or parallel to $O_F D_F$. At D and perpendicular to OD, draw the other leg, on which lay off the lengths D-1, D-2, etc., equal to D_T-1_T, D_T-2_T, etc., respectively. Distances from O to points on the base of the diagram are the true lengths of the elements.

Construct the pattern for the front half of the cone as follows: With O_1 as center and radius O-1, draw an arc. With C_1 as center and radius C_T-1_T, draw a second arc intersecting the first at 1_1; then O_1-1_1 will be the developed position of the element O-1. With 1_1 as center and radius 1_T-2_T, draw an arc intersecting a second arc with O_1 as center and radius O-2, thus locating 2_1. Continue this procedure until all the elements have been transferred to the development. Connect the points C_1, 1_1, 2_1, etc., with a smooth curve, the stretchout line, to complete the development. The flat lock seam is recommended for joining the ends of the pattern to form the cone.

9.30. A CONIC CONNECTION BETWEEN TWO PARALLEL CYLINDRICAL PIPES OF DIFFERENT DIAMETERS.

This is shown in Fig. 9.34. The method used in drawing the pattern is an application of the development of an oblique cone. One-half of the elliptical base is shown in true size in an auxiliary view, here attached to the front view. Find the true size of the base from its major and minor diameters, divide it into a number of equal parts so that the sum of these chordal distances closely approximates the periphery of the curve, and project these points to the front and top views. Draw the elements in each view through these points, and find the vertex O by extending the contour elements until they intersect. The true length of each element is found by using the vertical dis-

tance between its ends as the vertical leg of the diagram and its horizontal projection as the other leg. As each true length from vertex to base is found, project the upper end of the intercept horizontally across from the front view to the true length of the corresponding element to find the true length of the intercept. The development is drawn by laying out each triangle in turn, from vertex to base, as in paragraph 9.29, starting on the center line $O_1 C_1$ and then measuring on each element its intercept length. Draw smooth curves through these points to complete the pattern. Join the ends of the development with a flat lock seam to form the connection.

9.31. TRANSITION PIECES.

These are used to connect pipes or openings of different shapes of cross section. Figure 9.35, showing a transition piece for con-

FIG. 9.34. Development of a transition (oblique cone). This transition connects two cylindrical pipes of different diameters and offset in position.

FIG. 9.35. Development of transition. This transition connects a cylindrical with a rectangular pipe. The surface is made up of planes and portions of oblique cones.

necting a round pipe and a rectangular pipe, is typical. Transition pieces are always developed by triangulation. The piece shown in Fig. 9.35 is made up of four triangular planes, whose bases are the sides of the rectangle, and four parts of oblique cones, whose common bases are arcs of the circle and whose vertices are at the corners of the rectangle. To develop it, make a true-length diagram as in Fig. 9.33. When the true length of *O*-1 is found, all the sides of triangle *A* will be known. Attach the development of cones *B* and *B'*, then those of triangles *C* and *C'*, and so on.

Figure 9.36 is another transition piece joining a rectangular to a circular pipe whose axes are nonparallel. By using a partial right-side view of the round opening, the divisions of the bases of the oblique cones can be found (as the object is symmetrical, one-half only of the opening need be divided). The true lengths of the elements are obtained as in Fig. 9.34.

With the seam line the center line of the plane *E* in Figs. 9.35 and 9.36, the flat lock is recommended for joining the ends of the development.

9.32. TRIANGULATION OF WARPED SURFACES.

The approximate development of a warped surface is made by dividing it into a number of narrow quadrilaterals and then splitting each of these quadrilaterals into two triangles by a diagonal, which is assumed to be a straight line, although really a curve. Figure 9.37 shows a warped transition piece to connect an ovular (upper) pipe with a right-circular cylindrical pipe (lower). Find the true size of one-half the elliptical base by rotating it until horizontal about an axis through 1, when its true shape appears on the top view. The major diameter is $1\text{-}7_R$, and the minor diameter through 4_R will equal the diameter of the lower pipe. Divide the semiellipse into a sufficient number of equal parts, and project these to the top and front views. Divide the top semicircle into the same number of equal parts, and connect similar points on each end, thus dividing the surface into approximate quadrilaterals. Cut each into two triangles by a diagonal. On true-length diagrams find the lengths of the elements and the diagonals, and draw the development by constructing the true sizes of the triangles in regular order. The flat-lock seam is recommended for joining the ends of the development.

9.33. TO DEVELOP A SPHERE.

The sphere may be taken as typical of double-curved surfaces, which can be developed only approximately. It may be cut into a number of equal meridian sections, or lunes, as in Fig. 9.38, and these may be considered to be sections of cylinders. One of these sections, developed as the cylinder in Fig. 9.38, will give a pattern for the others.

Another method is to cut the sphere

FIG. 9.36. Development of a transition. This transition connects cylindrical and rectangular pipes with nonparallel axes. The surface is made up of planes and portions of oblique cones.

FIG. 9.37. Development of a transition (warped surface). This transition connects an oval and cylindrical pipe. Triangulation of surface portions is necessary.

Elements	Diagonals
7-7'	6-7'
6-6'	5-6'
5-5'	4-5'
4-4'	3-4'
3-3'	2-3'
2-2'	1-2'
1-1'	

FIG. 9.38. Development of a sphere (gore method). This is a double-curved surface and development is only approximate.

into horizontal sections, or zones, each of which may be taken as the frustum of a cone whose vertex is at the intersection of the extended chords (Fig. 9.39).

9.34. JOINTS, CONNECTORS, AND HEMS.

There are numerous joints used in seaming sheet-metal ducts and in connecting one duct to another. Figure 9.40 illustrates some of the more common types, which may be formed by hand on a break or by special seaming machines. No attempt to dimension the various seams and connections has been made here because of the variation in sizes for different gages of metal and in the forming machines of manufacturers.

Hemming is used in finishing the raw edges of the end of the duct. In wire hemming, an extra allowance of about 2½ times the diameter of the wire is made for wrapping around the wire. In flat hemming, the end of the duct is bent over once or twice to relieve the sharp edge of the metal.

FIG. 9.39. Development of a sphere (zone method). This is a double-curved surface and development is only approximate.

Wired edge   A   B   Flat lock   Soldered   Riveted
Hemmed edges   Lap joints

Pittsburgh corner lock   Riveted   Button punched   Elbow slip joint   Cup joint
Standing seams

A   B   C   S-hook slip joint   Cap strip connector
Side outlet joints

FIG. 9.40. Joints and finished edges. These are used in constructing sheet-metal parts.

PROBLEMS

Selections may be made from the following problems. Construct the figures accurately in pencil without inking. Any practical problem can be resolved into some combination of the "type solids," and the exercises given illustrate the principles involved in the various combinations.

An added interest in developments may be found by working problems on suitable paper, allowing for fastenings and lap, and cutting them out. It is recommended that at least one or two models be constructed in this manner.

In sheet-metal shops, development problems, unless very complicated, are usually laid out directly on the metal.

The following problems may be drawn on 8½ × 11 in. or 11 × 17 in. sheets. Assume the objects to be made of thin metal with open ends unless otherwise specified.

GROUP 1.   INTERSECTIONS OF PRISMATIC DUCTS

9.1.1 to 9.1.3.   Find the line of intersection, considering the prisms as pipes opening into each other. Use care in indicating visible and invisible parts of the line of intersection.

PROB. 9.1.1.

PROB. 9.1.2.

PROB. 9.1.3.

9.1.4 to 9.1.6.   Find the line of intersection, indicating visible and invisible parts and considering prisms as pipes opening into each other.

PROB. 9.1.4.

PROB. 9.1.5.

PROB. 9.1.6.

GROUP 2. INTERSECTIONS OF PYRAMIDAL OBJECTS

9.2.1 to 9.2.5. Find the lines of intersection.

| PROB. 9.2.1. | PROB. 9.2.2. | PROB. 9.2.3. | PROB. 9.2.4. | PROB. 9.2.5. |

GROUP 3. INTERSECTIONS OF CYLINDRICAL DUCTS

9.3.1 to 9.3.3. Find the line of intersection, indicating visible and invisible portions and considering cylinders as pipes opening into each other.

| PROB. 9.3.1. | PROB. 9.3.2. | PROB. 9.3.3. |

GROUP 4. INTERSECTIONS OF CONIC OBJECTS AND DUCTS

9.4.1 to 9.4.11. Find the line of intersection.

| PROB. 9.4.1. | PROB. 9.4.2. | PROB. 9.4.3. | PROB. 9.4.4. | PROB. 9.4.5. |

PROB. 9.4.6.

PROB. 9.4.7.

PROB. 9.4.8.

PROB. 9.4.9.

PROB. 9.4.10.

PROB. 9.4.11.

GROUP 5.   **DEVELOPMENTS OF PRISMS**

9.5.1 to 9.5.6.   Develop lateral surfaces of the prisms.

PROB. 9.5.1.   **PROB. 9.5.2.**   **PROB. 9.5.3.**   **PROB. 9.5.4.**   **PROB. 9.5.5.**   **PROB. 9.5.6.**

GROUP 6. DEVELOPMENTS OF PYRAMIDS

9.6.1 to 9.6.3. Develop lateral surfaces of the hoppers.

9.6.4 and 9.6.5. Develop lateral surfaces of the pyramids.

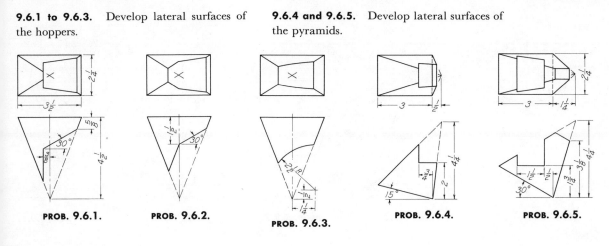

PROB. 9.6.1.   PROB. 9.6.2.   PROB. 9.6.3.   PROB. 9.6.4.   PROB. 9.6.5.

GROUP 7. DEVELOPMENTS OF CYLINDERS

9.7.1 to 9.7.7. Develop lateral surfaces of the cylinders.

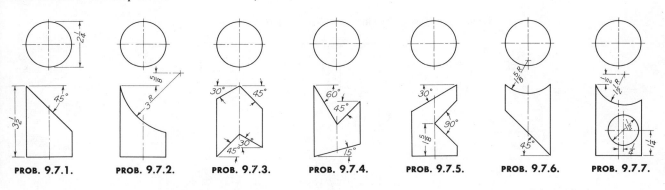

PROB. 9.7.1.   PROB. 9.7.2.   PROB. 9.7.3.   PROB. 9.7.4.   PROB. 9.7.5.   PROB. 9.7.6.   PROB. 9.7.7.

GROUP 8. DEVELOPMENTS OF COMBINATIONS OF PRISMS AND CYLINDERS

9.8.1 to 9.8.3. Develop lateral surfaces.

PROB. 9.8.1.   PROB. 9.8.2.   PROB. 9.8.3.

GROUP 9.   DEVELOPMENTS OF CONES

9.9.1 to 9.9.5.   Develop lateral surfaces.

PROB. 9.9.1.   PROB. 9.9.2.   PROB. 9.9.3.   PROB. 9.9.4.   PROB. 9.9.5.

GROUP 10.   DEVELOPMENTS OF COMBINATIONS OF SURFACES

9.10.1 to 9.10.4.   Develop lateral surfaces of the objects.

PROB. 9.10.1.   PROB. 9.10.2.   PROB. 9.10.3.   PROB. 9.10.4.

GROUP 11.   DEVELOPMENTS OF CONES AND TRANSITION PIECES

9.11.1 to 9.11.8.   Develop lateral surfaces of the objects (one-half in Probs. 9.11.1, 9.11.2, 9.11.4, 9.11.5, and 9.11.7).

PROB. 9.11.1

PROB. 9.11.2.

PROB. 9.11.3.

PROB. 9.11.4.

PROB. 9.11.5.

PROB. 9.11.6.

PROB. 9.11.7.

PROB. 9.11.8.

GROUP 12. DEVELOPMENTS OF FURNACE-PIPE FITTINGS

9.12.1 to 9.12.8. Develop surfaces and make paper models.

PROBS. 9.12.1 to 9.12.8.

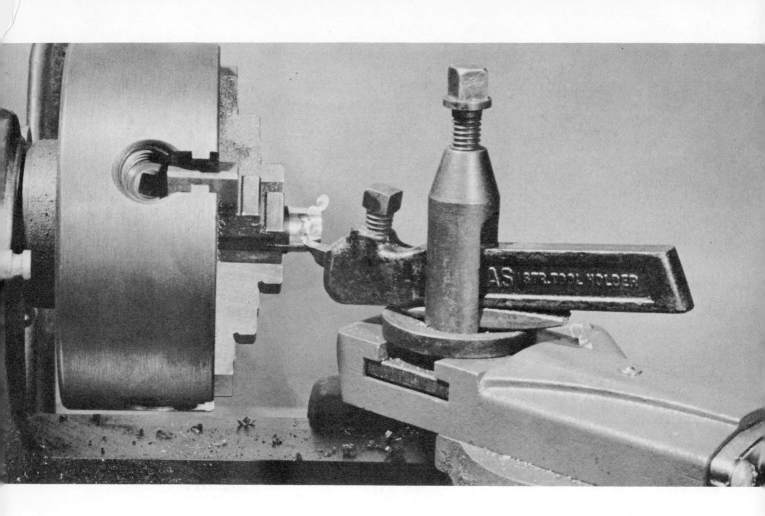

10

Drawings and the Shop

10.1. The test of any working drawing for legibility, completeness, and accuracy is the production of the object or assembly by the shop without further information than that given on the drawing. A knowledge of shop methods will, to a great extent, govern the effectiveness and completeness of the drawing. Study the glossary of shop terms to become familiar with the terms and the form of designation in notes. This chapter is given as an introduction to those on dimensioning (Chap. 11) and working drawings (Chap. 13).

The relation of drawings and the prints made from them to the operations of production is illustrated in the accompanying chart (Fig. 10.1). This chart shows in diagrammatic form the different steps in the development of drawings and their distribution and use in connection with shop operations from the time the order is received in the plant until the finished machine is delivered to the shipping room.

10.2. **EFFECT OF THE BASIC MANUFACTURING METHOD ON THE DRAWING.** In drawing any machine part, consider first the manufacturing process to be used, as on this depends the representation of the detailed features of the part and, to some extent, the choice of dimensions. Special or unusual methods may occasionally be used, but most machine parts are produced by (1) casting, (2)

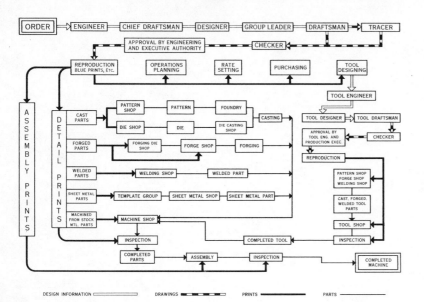

FIG. 10.1. Development and distribution of drawings. This shows the routing of drawings, prints, and parts through all design and manufacturing units.

forging, (3) machining from standard stock, (4) welding, or (5) forming from sheet stock.

Each of the different methods produces a characteristic detailed shape and appearance of the parts, and these features must be shown on the drawing.

FIG. 10.2. Drawing requirements for different manufacturing methods.

Figure 10.2 shows and lists typical features of each method and indicates the differences in drawing practice.

10.3.   THE DRAWINGS.   For the production of any part, a detail working drawing is necessary, complete with shape and size description and giving, where needed, the operations that are to be performed by the shop. Machined surfaces must be clearly indicated, with dimensions chosen and placed so as to be useful to the various shops without the necessity of adding or subtracting dimensions or scaling the drawing.

Two general practices are followed: (1) the "single-drawing" system, in which only one drawing, showing the finished part, is made to be used by all the shops involved in producing the part; and (2) the "multiple-drawing" system, in which different drawings are prepared, one for each shop, giving only the information required by the shop for which the drawing is made.

The second practice is recommended, as the drawings are easier to dimension without ambiguity, somewhat simpler and more direct, and therefore easier for the shop to use. Figure 10.3 is a single drawing, to be used by the pattern shop and the machine shop. Figures 11.107 and 11.108 are multiple drawings, Fig. 11.107 for the patternmaker and Fig. 11.108 for the machine shop.

10.4.   SAND CASTINGS.   Figure 10.3 shows (in the title strip) that the material to be used is cast iron (*C.I.*), indicating that the part will be formed by pouring molten iron into a mold (in this case a "sand mold"), resulting in a sand casting.

After casting, subsequent operations produce the finished part. Figure 10.4

illustrates the shop interpretation of the casting drawing in Fig. 10.3 and indicates the order of operations to be performed.

10.5. THE PATTERN SHOP.

The drawing is first used by the patternmaker, who makes a pattern, or "model," of the part in wood. From this, if a large quantity of castings is required, a metal pattern, often of aluminum, is made. The patternmaker provides for the shrinkage of the casting by making the pattern oversize, using a "shrink rule" for his measurements. He also provides additional metal (machining allowance) for the machined surfaces, indicated on the drawing by (1) finish marks, (2) dimensions indicating a degree of precision attainable only by machining, or (3) notes giving machining operations. The patternmaker also provides the "draft," or slight taper, not shown on the drawing, so that the pattern can be withdrawn easily from the sand. A "core box," for making sand cores for the hollow parts of the casting, is also made in the pattern shop. A knowledge of patternmaking is a great aid in dimensioning, as almost all the dimensions are used by the patternmaker, while only the dimensions for finished features are used by the machine shop.

10.6. DRAWINGS OF CASTINGS.

A casting drawing is usually made as a single drawing of the machined casting, with dimensions for both the patternmaker and the machinist (Fig. 10.3). If the multiple-drawing system is followed, a drawing of the unmachined casting, with allowances for machining accounted for and with no finish marks or finish dimensions, is made for the patternmaker; then a second drawing for the

machinist shows the finished shape and gives machining dimensions.

For complicated or difficult castings, a special "pattern drawing" may be made (Fig. 10.5), showing every detail of the pattern, including the amount of draft, the parting line, "core prints" for supporting the cores in the mold, and the pattern material. Similar detail drawings may also be made for the core boxes.

FIG. 10.4. Interpretation of the casting drawing in Fig. 10.3. These are the operations that must be performed to produce the part.

FIG. 10.6. Cross section of a two-part mold. This shows the cavity produced by the pattern in Fig. 10.5.

FIG. 10.7. Drop-forging dies and the forged part. These are the dies for the part shown in Fig. 10.8.

10.7. THE FOUNDRY. The pattern and core box or boxes are sent to the foundry, and sand molds are made so that molten metal can be poured into the molds and allowed to cool, forming the completed rough casting. Figure 10.6 is a cross section of a two-part mold, showing the space left by the pattern and the core in place. Only in occasional instances does the foundryman call for assistance from the drawing, as his job is simply to reproduce the pattern in metal.

Permanent molds, made of cast iron coated on the molding surfaces with a refractory material, are sometimes an advantage in that the mold can be used over and over again, thus saving the time to make an individual sand mold for each casting. This method is usually limited to small castings.

Die castings are made by forcing molten metal under pressure into a steel die mounted in a special die-casting machine. Alloys with a low melting point are used in order to avoid damaging the die. Because of the accuracy possible in mak-

ing a die, a fine finish and accurate dimensions of the part can be obtained; thus machining may be unnecessary.

10.8. FORGINGS. Forgings are made by heating metal to make it plastic and then forming it to shape on a power hammer with or without the aid of special steel dies. Large parts are often hammered with dies of generalized all-purpose shape. Smaller parts in quantity may warrant the expense of making special dies. Some small forgings are made with the metal cold.

Drop forgings are the most common and are made in dies of the kind shown in Fig. 10.7. The lower die is held on the bed of the drop hammer, and the upper die is raised by the hammer mechanism. The hot metal is placed between the dies, and the upper die is dropped several times, causing the metal to flow into the cavity of the dies. The slight excess of material will form a thin fin, or "flash," surrounding the forging at the parting plane of the dies (Fig. 10.7). This flash is then removed in a "trimming" die made for the purpose. Considerable draft must be provided for release of the forging from the dies.

10.9. DRAWINGS OF FORGINGS. Forging drawings are prepared according to the multiple-drawing system, one drawing for the diemaker and one for the machinist (Fig. 11.110); or the single-drawing system, one drawing for both (Fig. 10.8). In either case the parting line and draft should be shown and the amount of draft specified. On the single drawing (Fig. 10.8), the shape of the finished forging is shown in full outline, and the machining allowance is indicated by "alternate-position" lines, thus completing the shape of the rough forging. This single

FIG. 10.8. A working drawing of a forged part. Note the indication of parting line and extra material for machining.

drawing combines two drawings in one, with complete dimensions for both die-maker and machinist.

Figure 10.9 illustrates the shop interpretation of the forging drawing in Fig. 10.8 and indicates the order of operations to be performed.

10.10. THE MACHINE SHOP.

The machine shop produces parts machined from stock material and finishes castings, forgings, etc., requiring machined surfaces. Cylindrical and conic surfaces are machined on a lathe. Flat or plane surfaces are machined on a planer, shaper, milling machine, broaching machine, or in some cases (facing) a lathe. Holes are drilled, reamed, counterbored, and countersunk on a drill press or lathe; holes are bored on a boring mill or lathe. For exact work, grinding machines with wheels of abrasive material are used. Grinders are also coming into greatly increased use for operations formerly made with cutting tools. In quantity production many special machine tools and automatic machines are in use. The special tools, jigs, and fixtures made for the machine parts are held in the toolroom ready for the machine shop.

10.11. FUNDAMENTALS OF MACHINING.

All machining operations remove metal, either to make a smoother and more accurate surface, as by planing, facing, milling, etc., or to produce a surface not previously existing, as by drilling, punching, etc. The metal is removed by a hardened steel, carbide, or diamond cutting tool (machining) or an abrasive wheel (grinding); the product, or "work piece," as well as the tool or wheel, being held and guided by the machine. When steel cutting tools are used, the

⑥ Drill 2 holes, then ⑦ Tap (thread)
   (Drill Press)
② Face base surface
   (Shaper)
③ Face front surface of boss
   (Shaper)
① Forge basic part
④ Drill 4 holes, then ⑤ Spotface
   (Drill Press)

FIG. 10.9. Interpretation of the forging drawing in Fig. 10.8. These are the separate manufacturing steps.

product must remain relatively soft until after all machining has been performed upon it, but if diamond-tipped tools are used or if grinding wheels are employed, the product may be hardened by heat-treatment before finishing.

All machining methods are classified according to the operating principle of the machine performing the work:

1. The surface may be *generated* by moving the work with respect to a cutting tool or the tool with respect to the work, following the geometric laws for producing the surface.

2. The surface may be *formed* with a specially shaped cutting tool, moving either work or tool while the other is stationary.

The forming method is, in general, less accurate than the generating method, as any irregularities in the cutter are reproduced on the work. In some cases a combination of the two methods is used.

10.12. THE LATHE.

Called the "king of machine tools," the lathe is said to be capable of producing all other machine tools. Its primary function is machining cylindrical, conic, and other surfaces of revolution, but with special attachments it can perform a great variety of operations. Figure 10.10 shows the casting made from the drawing of Fig. 10.3

FIG. 10.10. Facing. The chuck (*A*) holds the part (*B*) and revolves it in the direction shown. The tool in the holder (*C*) is brought against the work surface by the lathe carriage, and the motion of the tool across the face is controlled by the cross slide (*D*).

FIG. 10.11. Turning. The chuck (A) holds the part (B) and revolves it in the direction shown. The tool in the holder (C) is brought against the work surface by the cross slide, and the motion of the tool is controlled by the lathe carriage (D).

FIG. 10.12. Threading. The chuck (A) holds the part (B) and revolves it in the direction shown. The tool, ground to the profile of the thread space, in the holder (C) is brought into the work surface by the angled cross slide (D), and the rate of travel is controlled by gears and a lead screw that moves the lathe carriage.

FIG. 10.13. Boring. The chuck (A) holds the part (B) and revolves it in the direction shown. The boring bar with the tool in the holder (C) is brought against the work surface by the cross slide, and advance is controlled by the lathe carriage (D).

held in the lathe chuck. As the work revolves, the cutting tool is moved across perpendicular to the axis of revolution, removing metal from the base and producing a plane surface by generation. This operation is called *facing*. After being faced, the casting is turned around, and the finished base is aligned against the face of the chuck, bringing the cylindrical surface into position for *turning* to the diameter indicated in the thread note on the drawing. The neck shown at the intersection of the base with the body is turned first, running the tool into the casting to a depth slightly greater than the depth of the thread. The cylindrical surface is then turned (generated) by moving the tool parallel to the axis of revolution (Fig. 10.11). Figure 10.12 shows the thread being cut on the finished cylinder. The tool is ground to the profile of the thread space, carefully lined up to the work, and moved parallel to the axis of revolution by the lead screw of the lathe. This operation is a combination of the fundamental processes, the thread profile being formed while the helix is generated.

The hole through the center of the casting, originally cored, is now finished by *boring*, as the cutting of an interior surface is called (Fig. 10.13). The tool

is held in a boring bar and moved parallel to the axis of revolution, thus generating an internal cylinder.

Note that in these operations the dimensions used by the machinist have been (1) the finish mark on the base and thickness of the base, (2) the thread note and outside diameter of the thread, (3) the dimensions of the neck, (4) the distance from the base to the shoulder, and (5) the diameter of the bored hole.

Long cylindrical pieces to be turned in the lathe are supported by conic centers, one at each end. Figure 10.22 illustrates the principle.

10.13. THE DRILL PRESS. The partially finished piece of Fig. 10.3 is now taken to the drill press for drilling and counterboring the holes in the base according to the dimensions on the drawing. These dimensions give the diameter of the drill, the diameter and depth of the counterbore, and the location of the holes. The casting is clamped to the drill-press table (Fig. 10.14) and the rotating drill brought into the work by a lever operating a rack and pinion in the head of the machine. The cutting is done by two ground lips on the end of the drill (Fig. 10.24). Drilling can also be done in a lathe, the work revolving while the drill is held in and moved by the tailstock. In Fig. 10.15 the drill has been replaced by a counterboring tool (Fig. 10.24) of which the diameter is the size specified on the drawing and which has a cylindrical pilot on the end to fit into the drilled hole, thus ensuring concentricity. This tool is fed in to the depth shown on the drawing.

Study the drawing of Fig. 10.3 with the illustrations of the operations, and check, first, the dimensions that would

FIG. 10.14. Drilling. The table (*A*) supports the part (*B*), sometimes clamped as shown. The drill in the chuck (*C*) revolves in the direction shown, and is forced downward by a gear and rack in the drill-press head, to make the hole.

FIG. 10.15. Counterboring. The table (*A*) supports the part (*B*), sometimes clamped as shown. The counterboring tool with piloted end to fit the previously drilled hole is held in the chuck (*C*) and revolves in the direction shown. The gear and rack in the drill-press head bring the tool into the work.

FIG. 10.16. Shaping. The vise (*A*) holds the part (*B*). The tool in the holder (*C*) is forced across the work surface by the ram (*D*) in the forward-stroke direction shown. The tool lifts on the return stroke by the pivot head on the ram. To make successive cuts, the table holding (*A*) and (*B*) moves in the direction shown.

be used by the patternmaker and, second, those required by the machinist.

10.14. THE SHAPER AND THE PLANER.

The drop forging of Fig. 10.8 requires machining on the base and boss surfaces.

Flat surfaces of this type are machined on a shaper or a planer. In this case the shaper (Fig. 10.16) is used because of the relatively small size of the part. The tool is held in a ram that moves back and forth across the work, taking a cut at each pass forward. Between the cuts, the table moves laterally so that closely spaced parallel cuts are made until the surface is completely machined.

The planer differs from the shaper in that its bed, carrying the work, moves back and forth under a stationary tool. It is generally used for a larger and heavier type of work than that done on a shaper.

10.15. PARTS MACHINED FROM STANDARD

STOCK. The shape of a part will often lend itself to machining directly from standard stock, such as bars, rods, tubing, plates, and blocks, or from extrusions and rolled shapes, such as angles and

FIG. 10.17. Working drawing of a part machined from stock. Note the specification of material and stock size in the title block.

channels. Hot-rolled (HR) and cold-rolled (CR) steel are common materials.

Parts produced from stock are usually finished on all surfaces, and the general note "Finish all over" on the drawing eliminates the use of finish marks. Figure 10.17 is the drawing of a part to be made from bar stock. Note the specification of material, stock size, etc., in the title.

FIG. 10.18. Interpretation of the drawing in Fig. 10.17. This lists machining operations.

FIG. 10.19. Turret-lathe operations (drilling and reaming). The chuck (A) holds, indexes (for length), and rotates the stock (B) in the direction shown. The turret (C) swings the drill (D) and reamer (E) successively into position.

Figure 10.18 illustrates the shop interpretation in Fig. 10.17 and indicates the order of machining operations to be performed.

10.16. THE TURRET LATHE. The *quill* of Fig. 10.17, produced in quantity, may be made on a turret lathe, except for the rack teeth and the outside-diameter grinding. The stock is held in the collet chuck of the lathe. First the end surface is faced, and then the cylindrical surface (OD) is turned. The work piece is then ready for drilling and reaming. The turret holds the various tools and swings them around into position as needed. A center drill starts a small hole to align the larger drill, and then the drill and reamer are brought successively into position. The drill provides a hole slightly undersize, and then the reamer, cutting with its fluted sides, cleans out the hole and gives a smooth surface finished to a

size within the dimensional limits on the drawing. Figure 10.19 shows the turret indexed so that the drill is out of the way and the reamer in position. At the right is seen the cutoff tool ready to cut the piece to the length shown on the drawing.

10.17. THE MILLING MACHINE. The dimensions of the rack teeth (Fig. 10.17) give the depth and spacing of the cuts and the specifications for the cutter to be used. This type of work may be done on a milling machine. The work piece is held in a vise and moved horizontally into the rotating milling cutter, which, in profile, is the shape of the space between the teeth (Fig. 10.20). The cuts are spaced by moving the table of the machine to correspond with the distance shown on the drawing. Note that this operation is a forming process, as the shape depends upon the contour of the cutter. With several cutters mounted together (gang milling), a number of teeth can be cut at the same time.

There are many types of milling cutters made to cut on their peripheries, their sides, or their ends, for forming flat, curved, or special surfaces. Three milling cutters are shown in Fig. 10.21.

10.18. THE GRINDER. The general purpose of grinding is to make a smoother and more accurate surface than can be

FIG. 10.20. Milling. The vise (A) holds the part (B) to the table (C), which moves laterally to index cuts and longitudinally, in the direction shown, for individual cuts. The milling cutter (D) revolves in the direction shown.

FIG. 10.21. Milling cutters.

obtained by turning, planing, milling, etc. In many cases pieces hardened by heat-treatment will warp slightly; and as ordinary machining methods are impractical with hardened materials, such parts are finish-ground after hardening.

The limit dimensions for the outside diameter of the quill (Fig. 10.17) indicate a grinding operation on a cylindrical grinder (Fig. 10.22). The abrasive wheel rotates at high speed, while the work piece, mounted on a mandrel between conic centers, rotates slowly in the opposite direction. The wheel usually moves laterally to cover the surface of the work piece. The work piece is gaged carefully during the operation to bring the size within the dimensional limits shown on the drawing and to check for a cylindrical surface without taper. The machine for flat surfaces, called a "surface grinder," holds the work piece on a flat table moving back and forth under the abrasive wheel. The table "indexes" laterally after each pass under the work.

10.19. LAPPING, HONING, AND SUPER-FINISHING.

These are methods of producing smooth, accurate, mirrorlike surfaces after grinding. All three methods use fine abrasives (1) powdered and carried in oil on a piece of formed soft metal (lapping) or (2) in the form of fine-grained compact stones (honing and superfinishing) to rub against the surface to be finished and reduce scratches and waviness.

10.20. THE BROACHING MACHINE.

A broach is a long, tapered bar with a series of cutting edges (teeth), each successively removing a small amount of material until the last edge forms the shape desired. For flat or irregular external surfaces, the broach and work

FIG. 10.22. Grinding. The cone centers (A) hold the mandrel, which mounts and rotates the part (B) in the direction shown. The wheel (C) moves laterally to traverse the entire surface of (B).

piece are held by the broaching machine, and the broach is passed across the surface of the work piece. For internal surfaces, the broach is pulled or pushed through a hole to give the finished size and shape.

Some machined shapes can be more economically produced by broaching than by any other method. Figure 10.23 shows several forms of broaches and the shapes they produce.

10.21. SMALL TOOLS.

The shop uses a variety of small tools, both in powered machines and as hand tools. Figure

Broaching a Keyway

Hexagon Broach

Surface Broach

FIG. 10.23. Broaches. Each tooth takes its small cut as the broach is forced across or through the work piece.

FIG. 10.24. Small tools.

10.24 shows a *twist drill,* available in a variety of sizes (numbered, lettered, fractional, and metric) for producing holes in almost any material; a *reamer,* used to enlarge and smooth a previously existing hole and to give greater accuracy than is possible by drilling alone; a *counterbore* and a *countersink,* both used to enlarge and alter the end of a hole (usually for screwheads). A *spot-facing tool* is similar to a counterbore. *Taper, plug,* and *bottoming taps* for cutting the thread of a tapped hole and a die for threading a rod or shaft are also shown.

10.22. WELDED PARTS. Simple shapes cut from standard rod, bar, or plate stock can be combined by welding to form a finished part. Some machining after welding is frequently necessary (Chap. 16).

10.23. PARTS FROM STANDARD SHEET. A relatively thin sheet or strip of standard thickness may first be cut to size "in the flat" and then bent, formed, punched,

etc., to form the final required part. The drawing should be made so as to give information for the "template maker" and the information required for bending and forming the sheet. Sometimes separate developments (Chap. 9) are made. The thickness of sheet stock is specified by giving (1) the gage (see table, Appendix) and the equivalent thickness in decimals of an inch or (2) only the decimal thickness (the practice followed in specifying aluminum sheet). Figure 11.111 shows a working drawing of a sheet-metal part.

10.24. PLASTICS. Plastics are available either in standard bar, rod, tubing, sheet, etc., from which parts can be made by machining, or in granular form to be used in "molding," a process similar to die-casting, in which the material is heated to a plastic state and compressed by a die (compression molding) or injected under pressure into a die (injection molding). Metal inserts for threads, wear bushings, etc., are sometimes cast into the part. Consideration should be given the diemaker when dimensioning the drawing.

10.25. HEAT-TREATMENT. This is a general term applied to the processing of metals by heat and chemicals to change the physical properties of the material.

The glossary of shop terms gives definitions of such heat-treatment processes as annealing, carburizing, casehardening, hardening, normalizing, and tempering.

The specification of heat-treatment may be given on the drawing in several ways: (1) by a general note listing the steps, temperatures, and baths to be used, (2) by a standard heat-treatment number (SAE or company standard) in the space provided in the title block, (3) by giving the Brinell or Rockwell hardness number to be attained, or (4) by giving the tensile strength, in pounds per square inch, to be attained through heat-treatment.

Figures 10.8, 11.67, 11.106, and 11.110 illustrate these methods.

10.26. TOOLS FOR MASS PRODUCTION. Many special machine tools, both semi-automatic and fully automatic, are used in modern factories. These machines are basically the same as ordinary lathes, grinders, etc., but contain mechanisms to control the movements of cutting tools and produce identical parts with little attention from the operator once the machine has been "tooled up." Automatic screw machines

and centerless grinders are examples.

10.27. JIGS AND FIXTURES. Jigs for holding the work and guiding the tool and fixtures for holding the work greatly extend the production rate for general-purpose machine tools (Chap. 15).

10.28. INSPECTION. Careful inspection is an important feature of modern production. Good practice requires inspection after each operation. For production in quantity, special gages are usually employed, but in small-quantity production, the usual measuring instruments, calipers and scale, micrometers, dial gages, etc., are used. For greater precision in gaging, electrical, air, or optical gages are often employed.

10.29. ASSEMBLY. The finished separate pieces come to the assembly department to be put together according to the assembly drawings. Sometimes it is desirable or necessary to perform some small machining operation during assembly, often drilling, reaming, or hand finishing. In such cases the assembly drawing should carry a note explaining the required operation and give dimensions for the alignment or location of the pieces. If some parts are to be combined before final assembly, a subassembly drawing or the detail drawings of each piece will give the required information; "⅛ drill in assembly with piece No. 107" is a typical note form for an assembly machining operation.

11

Dimensions, Notes, Limits, and Precision

11.1. After the shape of an object has been described by orthographic (or pictorial) views, the value of the drawing for the construction of the object depends upon dimensions and notes that describe the *size*. In general, the description of shape and size together gives complete information for producing the object represented.

The dimensions put on the drawing are *not necessarily* those used in making the drawing but are those required for the proper functioning of the part after assembly, selected so as to be readily usable by the workers who are to make the piece. Before dimensioning the drawing, study the machine and understand its functional requirements; then put yourself in the place of the pattern-maker, diemaker, machinist, etc., and mentally construct the object to discover which dimensions would best give the information.

11.2. METHOD. The basic factors in dimensioning practice are:

1. *Lines and Symbols.* The first requisite is a thorough knowledge of the elements used for dimensions and notes and of the weight and spacing of the lines on the drawing. These lines, symbols, and techniques are the "tools" for clear, concise representation of size.

2. *Selection of Distances.* The most important consideration for the ultimate operation of a machine and the

FIG. 11.1. Dimensions.

FIG. 11.2. A note.

FIG. 11.3. Open-style arrowhead strokes.

FIG. 11.4. Solid-style arrowhead strokes.

proper working of the individual parts is the selection of distances to be given. This selection is based upon the functional requirements, the "breakdown" of the part into its geometric elements, and the requirements of the shop for production.

3. *Placement of Dimensions.* After the distances to be given have been selected, the next step is the actual placement of the dimensions showing these distances on the drawing. The dimensions should be placed in an orderly arrangement that is easy to read and in positions where they can be readily found.

4. *Dimensioning Standard Features.* These include angles, chamfers, standard notes, specifications of holes, spherical shapes, round-end shapes, tapers, and others for which, through long usage and study, dimensioning practice has been standardized.

5. *Precision and Tolerance.* The ultimate operation of any device depends upon the proper interrelationship of the various parts so that they operate as planned. In quantity production, each part must meet standards of size and position to assure assembly and proper functioning. Through the dimensioning of the individual parts, the limits of size are controlled.

6. *Production Methods.* The method of manufacturing (casting, forging, etc.) affects the detailed information given on the drawing proper, and in notes and specifications. The operations of various shops must be known, in order to give concise information.

LINES AND SYMBOLS

11.3. DIMENSION FORMS. Two basic methods are used to give a distance on

a drawing: a *dimension* (Fig. 11.1) or a *note* (Fig. 11.2).

A dimension is used to give the distance between two points, lines, or planes, or between some combination of points, lines, and planes. The numerical value gives the actual distance, the dimension line indicates the direction in which the value applies, and the arrowheads indicate the points between which the value applies. Extension lines refer the dimension to the view when the dimension is placed outside the view.

A note provides a means of giving explanatory information along with a size. The leader and arrowhead refer the word statement of the note to the proper place on the drawing. Notes applying to the object as a whole are given without a leader in some convenient place on the drawing.

The lines and symbols used in dimensioning are dimension lines, arrowheads, extension lines, leaders, numerical values, notes, finish marks, etc.

11.4. LINE WEIGHTS. Dimension lines, extension lines, and leaders are made with fine full lines the same width as center lines so as to contrast with the heavier outlines of the views. Note the line widths given in the alphabet of lines, Figs. 2.56 and 2.57.

11.5. ARROWHEADS. These are carefully drawn freehand. The sides of the arrowhead are made either in one stroke, toward the point and then away from it, or in two strokes toward the point, as shown in enlarged form in Fig. 11.3. The general preference is for the solid head, as in Fig. 11.4. The solid head is usually made narrower and slightly longer than the open head and has practically no curvature to the sides. It is made in one stroke and then filled, if necessary, without lifting the pen or pencil; a rather blunt pencil or pen is required for this style of head. The bases of arrowheads should not be made wider than one-third the length. All arrowheads on the same drawing should be the same type, open or solid, and the same size, except in restricted spaces. Arrowhead lengths vary somewhat depending upon the size of the drawing. One-eighth inch is a good general length for small drawings and ³⁄₁₆ in. for larger drawings.

Poor arrowheads ruin the appearance of an otherwise carefully made drawing. Avoid the incorrect shapes and placements shown in Fig. 11.5.

11.6. EXTENSION LINES. These extend from the view to a dimension placed outside the view. They should not touch the outline of the view but should start about ¹⁄₁₆ in. from it and extend about ⅛ in. beyond the last dimension line (Fig. 11.6A). This example is printed approximately one-half size.

Dimensions may also terminate at *center lines* or *visible outlines of the view*. Where a measurement between centers is to be shown, as at (B), the center lines are continued to serve as extension lines, extending about ⅛ in. beyond the last dimension line. Usually the outline of the view becomes the terminal for arrowheads, as at (C), when a dimension must be placed inside the view. This might occur because of limited space, when extension lines crossing parts of the view would cause confusion, or when long extension lines would make the dimension difficult to read.

Extension lines for an angular dimension are shown in Fig. 11.7A, which also shows one of the extension lines

FIG. 11.5. Incorrect arrowheads. The first two examples show mistakes in placement. The last three illustrate shapes that are extremely poor.

FIG. 11.6. Dimension terminals.

used for a linear dimension, a common occurrence.

Extension lines should not be broken where they cross each other or an outline of a view, as shown in Fig. 11.6A and 11.7A. However, when space is restricted and the extension lines come close to arrowheads, the extension lines may be broken for clarity, as in Fig. 11.7B.

Where a point is located by extension lines alone, the extension lines should pass through the point, as at (C).

11.7. LEADERS. These are *straight* (not curved) lines leading from a dimension value or an explanatory note to the feature on the drawing to which the note applies (Fig. 11.8). An arrowhead is used at the pointing end of the leader but never at the note end. The note end of the leader should terminate with a short horizontal bar at the mid-height of the lettering and should run to the beginning or the end of the note, never to the middle.

Leaders should be drawn at an angle to contrast with the principal lines of the drawing, which are mainly horizontal and vertical. Thus leaders are usually drawn at 30°, 45°, or 60° to the horizontal; 60° looks best. When

FIG. 11.7. Technique of drawing extension lines.

FIG. 11.8. Leaders for notes. Observe that the leader emanates from the *beginning* or the *end* of the lettered information.

FIG. 11.9. Leaders. (*A*) special terminal; (*B*) and (*C*) proper angle.

FIG. 11.10. Placement of dimension values.

FIG. 11.11. Technique for lettering values with common fractions.

several leaders are used, the appearance of the drawing is improved if the leaders can be kept parallel.

The ASA allows the use of a "dot" for termination of a leader, as in Fig. 11.9*A,* when the dot is considered to be a clearer representation than an arrowhead. The dot should fall within the outline of the object.

When dimensioning a circular feature with a note, the leader should be *radial* as shown at (*B*). A leader directed to a flat surface should meet the surface at an angle of *at least* 30°; an angle of 45° or 60° as at (*C*) is best.

If possible *avoid* crossing leaders; *avoid* long leaders; *avoid* leaders in a horizontal or vertical direction; *avoid* leaders parallel to adjacent dimension lines, extension lines, or crosshatching; and *avoid* small angles between leaders and the lines they terminate on.

11.8. FIGURES.   For dimension values, figures must be carefully lettered in vertical or inclined style. In an effort to achieve neatness, the beginner often gets them too small. One-eighth inch for small drawings and $\frac{5}{32}$ in. for larger drawings are good general heights.

The general practice is to leave a space in the dimension line for the dimension value (Fig. 11.10). It is universal in structural practice and common in architectural practice to place the value above a continuous dimension line (Fig. 11.10).

11.9. COMMON FRACTIONS.   These should be made with the fraction bar parallel to the guide lines for making the figure and with the numerator and denominator each somewhat smaller than the height of the whole number so that the *total* fraction height is twice that of the integer (Fig. 11.11). Avoid

the incorrect forms shown. The figures should not touch the fraction bar.

11.10. FEET AND INCHES.   Indicate these thus: 9'-6". When there are no inches, it should be so indicated, as 9'-0", 9'-0½". When dimensions are all in inches, the inch mark is preferably omitted from all the dimensions and notes unless there is some possibility of misunderstanding; if that is the case, "1 bore," for example, should be given for clarity as "1" bore."

In some machine industries, all dimensions are given in inches. In others where feet and inches are used, the ASA recommends that dimensions up to and including 72 in. be given in inches and greater lengths in feet and inches.

In structural drawing, length dimensions should be given in feet and inches. Plate widths, beam sizes, etc., are given in inches. Inch marks are omitted, even though the dimension is in feet and inches (Fig. 11.10).

In the United States, if no foot or inch marks appear on a drawing, the dimension values indicate inches unless a different unit of measurement is indicated by a general note. Drawings made in foreign countries employing the metric system are commonly dimensioned in millimeters.

11.11. READING DIRECTION OF FIGURES.   This is arranged according to the aligned system or the unidirectional system.

The *aligned system* is the older of the two methods. The figures are oriented to be read from a position *perpendicular* to the dimension line; thus the guide lines for the figures will be parallel to the dimension line, and the fraction bar in line with the dimension line (Fig. 11.12). The figures should be arranged so as to be read from the *bottom* or *right*

11.12. Systems of Writing Dimension Values

side of the drawing. Avoid running dimensions in the directions included in the shaded area of Fig. 11.12; if this is unavoidable, they should read downward with the line.

The *unidirectional system* originated in the automotive and aircraft industries, and is sometimes called the "horizontal system." All figures are oriented to read from the bottom of the drawing. Thus the guide lines and fraction bars are horizontal regardless of the direction of the dimension (Fig. 11.13). The "avoid" zone of Fig. 11.12 has no significance with this system.

Notes must be lettered horizontally and read from the bottom of the drawing in either system.

FIG. 11.12. Reading direction of values (aligned system). The drawing is read from the bottom and right side.

FIG. 11.13. Reading direction of values (unidirectional system). The drawing is read from the bottom.

11.12. SYSTEMS OF WRITING DIMENSION VALUES.

Dimension values may be given as common fractions, ¼, ⅜, etc., or as decimal fractions, 0.25, 0.375, etc.; and from these, three systems are evolved.

The *common-fraction system,* used in general drawing practice, including architectural and structural work, has all dimension values written as units and common fractions, as 3½, 1¼, ⅜, 1⁄16, 3⁄32, 1⁄64. Values thus written can be laid out with a steel tape or scale graduated in sixty-fourths of an inch.

The *common-fraction, decimal-fraction system* is used principally in machine drawing whenever the degree of precision required calls for fractions of an inch smaller than those on the ordinary steel scale. To continue the use of common fractions below 1⁄64, such as 1⁄128 or 1⁄256, is considered impractical. The method followed is to give values: (1) in units and common fractions for distances not requiring an accuracy closer than 1⁄64 in.; and (2) in units and decimal fractions, as 2.375, 1.250, 0.1875, etc.,

for distances requiring greater precision. The decimal fractions are given to as many decimal places as needed for the degree of precision required.

The *complete decimal system* uses decimal fractions exclusively for all dimension values. This system has the advantages of the metric system but uses the inch as its basis, thus making it possible to use present measuring equipment.

The ASA complete decimal system[1] uses a two-place decimal for all values where common fractions would ordinarily be used. The digits after the decimal point are preferably written to even fiftieths, .02, .10, .36, etc., so that when halved, as for radii, etc., two-place decimals will result. Writing the values in even fiftieths allows the use of scales divided in fiftieths (Fig. 11.14), which are much easier to read than scales divided in hundredths.

Dimension values for distances requiring greater precision than that expressed by the two-place decimal are written to three, four, or more decimal places as needed for precision.

[1] Z14.1—1946.

FIG. 11.14. Decimal scale. Graduations are in fiftieths.

FIG. 11.15. A drawing dimensioned in the decimal system.

than is necessary or desirable for use as a dimension value, and in such cases the decimal should be adjusted, or "rounded off," to a smaller number of decimal places. The following procedure from the American Standard[2] is recommended:

When the figure beyond the last figure to be retained is less than 5, the last figure retained should not be changed. Example: 3.46325, if cut off to three places, should be 3.463.

When the figure beyond the last figure to be retained is more than 5, the last figure retained should be increased by 1. Example: 8.37652, if cut off to three places, should be 8.377.

When the figure beyond the last place to be retained is exactly 5 with only zeros following, the preceding number, if even, should be unchanged; if odd, should be increased by 1. Example: 4.365 becomes 4.36 when cut off to two places. Also, 4.355 becomes 4.36 when cut off to two places.

11.13. FINISH MARKS. These are used to indicate that certain surfaces of metal parts are to be machined and that allowance must therefore be provided for finish. Finish marks need not be used for parts made by machining from rolled stock, as the surfaces are necessarily machined. Neither are they necessary on drilled, reamed, or counterbored holes or on similar machined features when the machining operation is specified by note. Also, when limit dimensions are given, the accuracy required is thereby stated, and a finish mark on the surface is unnecessary.

The standard finish mark recommended by the ASA is a 60° **V** with its point touching the line representing the

[2] Z25.1—1940.

Figure 11.15 is a detail drawing dimensioned according to the ASA decimal system. The advantage of this system in calculating, adding, and checking and in doing away with all conversion tables, as well as in lessening chances for error, is apparent.

Designers and draftsmen working in the complete decimal system find it necessary to think in terms of tenths and hundredths of inches instead of common fractions. New designs must be made in decimal sizes without reference to common fractional sizes. However, until standard-stock materials, tools, and commercial parts are available in decimal sizes, some dimensions will have to be given as the decimal equivalent of a common fraction. Thus, for example, a standard ⅜-16UNC-2A thread would be given as 0.375-16UNC-2A.

Decimal equivalents of some common fractions come out to a greater number of decimal places (significant digits)

edge view of the surface to be machined. The **V** is placed on the "air side" of the surface. Figure 11.16 shows the normal size of the **V** and its position for lines in various directions as given on a drawing.

Finish marks should be placed on all views in which the surface to be machined appears as a line, including dashed lines. If the part is to be machined on all surfaces, the note "Finish all over," or "FAO," is used, and the marks on the views are omitted.

In addition to using the finish mark to indicate a machined surface, it may be necessary in some cases to indicate the degree of smoothness of the surface. The ASA gives a set of symbols to indicate the degree of smoothness of a surface, the various conditions of *surface quality*. These symbols are explained and illustrated in paragraph 11.79.

11.14. SCALE OF THE DRAWING. Even though a workman is never expected to scale a distance on a drawing to obtain a dimension value, the scale to which the drawing is made should be stated in the title block. Standard scales are listed in Fig. 2.34.

11.15. REVISION OF DIMENSIONS. As a project is being developed, changes in design, in engineering methods, etc., may make it necessary to change some drawings either before or after they have been released to the shop. If the change is a major one, the drawing may have to be remade. But in many cases it is merely a question of altering the dimension values and leaving the shape description unchanged. For changes in dimensions, the out-of-scale dimensions should be indicated by one of the methods in Fig. 11.17. Drawing changes should be listed in tabular form, in con-

nection with the title block or in the upper right corner, with reference letters and the date, as explained in paragraph 13.19.

11.16. ABBREVIATIONS. Many abbreviations are used on drawings to save time and space. The common ones such as DIA, THD, MAX, MIN, ID, and OD are universally understood. Uncommon abbreviations such as PH BRZ (Phosphor bronze) should be used cautiously because of the possibility of misinterpretation. Abbreviations should conform to ASA Z32.13—1950 or revisions thereof (see Appendix).

11.17. DECIMAL POINTS. These should be made distinctly, in a full letter space, and should be aligned with the bottom edges of digits and letters.

11.18. DASHES. These are used in many standard expressions such as ½—20 and should be made clearly, one letter space in length, at the mid-height of letters or digits and parallel to the direction of the expression.

SELECTION OF DISTANCES

11.19. THEORY OF DIMENSIONING. Any object can be broken down into a combination of basic geometric shapes, principally prisms and cylinders. Occasionally, however, there will be parts of pyramids and cones, now and then a double-curved surface, and rarely, except for surfaces of screw threads, a warped surface. Any of the basic shapes may be positive or negative, in the sense that a hole is a negative cylinder. Figure 5.98 illustrates a machine part broken down into its fundamental shapes.

FIG. 11.16. The ASA finish mark. It indicates removal of material to produce the desired surface.

FIG. 11.17. Out-of-scale dimensions.

FIG. 11.18. Size dimensions. (*A*) prism; (*B*) cylinder; (*C*) cone; (*D*) pyramid.

If the *size* of each of these elementary shapes is dimensioned and the relative position of each is given, measuring from center to center, from base lines, or from surfaces, the dimensioning of any piece can be done systematically. Dimensions can thus be classified as dimensions of *size* and dimensions of *position*.

11.20.   DIMENSIONS OF SIZE.   Since every solid has three dimensions, each of the geometric shapes making up the object must have its height, width, and depth indicated in the dimensioning.

The *prism,* often in plinth or flat form, is the most common shape and requires three dimensions for square, rectangular, or triangular (Fig. 11.18*A*). For regular hexagonal or octagonal types, usually only two dimensions are given, either the distance "across corners" and the length or the distance "across flats" and the length.

The *cylinder,* found on nearly all mechanical pieces as a shaft, boss, or hole, is the second most common shape. A cylinder obviously requires only two dimensions, diameter and length (*B*). Partial cylinders, such as fillets and rounds, are dimensioned by radius instead of diameter. A good general rule is to dimension complete circles with the diameter and circle arcs (partial circles) with the radius.

Right cones can be dimensioned by giving the altitude and the diameter of the base. They usually occur as frustums, however, and require the diameters of the ends and the length (*C*). Sometimes it is desirable to dimension cone frustums as *tapers* or with an angular dimension, as described in paragraph 11.41.

Right pyramids are dimensioned by

giving the dimensions of the base and the altitude. Right pyramids are often frustums, requiring dimensions of both bases (*D*).

Oblique cones and *pyramids* are dimensioned in the same way as right cones and pyramids but with an additional dimension parallel to the base to give the offset of the vertex.

Spheres are dimensioned by giving the diameter and other surfaces of revolution by dimensioning the generating curve.

Warped surfaces are dimensioned according to their method of generation; and as their representation requires numerous sections, each of these must be fully dimensioned by ordinate and abscissa dimensions.

11.21.   DIMENSIONS OF POSITION.   After the basic geometric shapes have been dimensioned for size, the position of each relative to the others must be given. *Position must be established in height, width, and depth directions.* Rectangular shapes are positioned with reference to their faces, cylindrical and conic shapes with reference to their center lines and their ends.

One basic shape will often coincide or align with another on one or more of its faces. In such cases the alignment serves partially to locate the parts and eliminates the need of a dimension of position in a direction perpendicular to the line of coincidence. Thus in Fig. 11.19, prism *A* requires only one dimension for complete positioning with respect to prism *B*, as two surfaces are in alignment and two in contact.

Coincident center lines often eliminate the need for position dimensions. In the cylinder in Fig. 11.18*B* the center lines of the hole and of the cylinder

11.23. Correlation of Dimensions

coincide, and no dimensions of position are needed. The two holes of Fig. 11.19 are on the same center line, and the dimension perpendicular to the common center line positions both holes in that direction.

11.22. SELECTION OF DIMENSIONS. The dimensions arrived at by reducing the part to its basic geometric shapes will, in general, fulfill the requirements of practical dimensioning. However, sometimes other dimensions are required to ensure satisfactory functioning of the part and to give the information in the best way from the standpoint of production.

The draftsman must therefore correlate the dimensions on drawings of mating parts to ensure satisfactory functioning and, at the same time, select dimensions convenient for the workmen to use.

Here our study of drawing as a language must be supplemented by a knowledge of shop methods. To be successful, the machine draftsman must have an intimate knowledge of pattern-making, foundry practice, forging, and machine-shop practice, as well as, in some cases, sheet-metal working, metal and plastic die casting, welding, and structural-steel fabrication.

The beginning student who is without this knowledge should not depend upon his instructor alone but should learn by observing work going through the shops and reading books and periodicals on methods used in modern production work.

The *selection of dimensions of size* arrived at by shape breakdown will usually meet the requirements of the shop since the basic shapes result from the fundamental shop operations. However, a shop often prefers to receive dimensions of

FIG. 11.19. Dimensions of size and position. *S* indicates size, *P* position.

size in note form rather than as regular dimensions when a shop process is involved, such as drilling, reaming, counterboring, and punching.

Selecting dimensions of position ordinarily requires more consideration than selecting dimensions of size because there are usually several ways in which a position might be given. In general, positional dimensions are given between finished surfaces, center lines, or a combination thereof (Fig. 11.22). Remember that rough castings or forgings vary in size; so do not position machined surfaces from unfinished surfaces—except in one situation: A machined surface may be positioned from an unmachined surface only when the *initial,* or *starting,* dimension gives the position for the first surface to be machined—a position from which the other machined surfaces will in turn be positioned. *Coinciding center lines of unfinished and finished surfaces often take the place of a starting dimension.*

The position of a point or center by offset dimensions from two center lines or surfaces (Fig. 11.20) is preferable to angular dimensions (Fig. 11.21) unless the angular dimension is more practical from the standpoint of construction.

11.23. CORRELATION OF DIMENSIONS. Mating parts must have their dimensions correlated so that the two parts will

FIG. 11.20. Position by offsets.

FIG. 11.21. Position by angle.

BRACKET

BODY

FIG. 11.22. Correlation of dimensions. Dimensions must be given so that parts will assemble properly.

lated with the dimensions of the mating part, but the accuracy to which these distances are produced must meet certain requirements, or the parts still may not fit and function properly. Distances between the surfaces or center lines of finished features of an object must usually be more accurately made than distances between unfinished features. In Fig. 11.23, note that the position dimensions between center lines or surfaces of finished features are given as three-place decimals, as dimension *A*. Dimensions of position for unfinished features are given as common fractions, as dimension *B*. The decimal dimensions call for greater precision in manufacture than do the common fractions. Dimension *B* is in this case used by the patternmaker to position cylinder *C* from the right end of the piece. The machinist will first locate the finished hole in this cylinder, making it concentric with the cylinder; then all other machined surfaces will be positioned from this hole, as, for example, the spline position by dimension *A*. The four spot-faced holes are positioned with reference to each other with fractional dimensions since the holes are oversize for the fastenings used, allowing enough shifting of the fastenings in the holes so that great accuracy in location is not necessary. The mating part, with its holes to receive the screws, would be similarly dimensioned.

Study Fig. 11.23 and note the classification, size, and position of each dimension.

11.24. SUPERFLUOUS DIMENSIONS. *Duplicate* or *unnecessary* dimensions are to be avoided because they may cause confusion and delay. When a drawing is changed or revised, a duplicate dimension may not be noticed and changed

fit and function as intended. Figure 11.22 illustrates this principle. Note that the tongue of the bracket is to fit the groove in the body, and that the drilled holes in both pieces must align. Study the dimensioning of both pieces and observe that the dimensions of position (*P*) are correlated so that the intended alignment and fitting of the parts will be accomplished.

Not only must dimensions be corre-

FIG. 11.23. An example of dimensioning. See text for detailed explanation.

along with its counterpart; hence a distance will have two different values, one incorrect. An unnecessary dimension is any dimension, other than a duplicate, that is not essential in making the piece. Because of the allowable variation permitted the manufacturer on each dimension (see paragraph 11.54), difficulties will be encountered if unnecessary dimensions occur when parts are to be interchangeable. Actually, if the proper dimensions have been selected, it will be possible to establish a point on the object in any given direction with only one dimension. Unnecessary dimensions always occur when all the individual dimensions are given, in addition to the over-all dimension (Fig. 11.24). One dimension of the series must be omitted if the over-all dimension is used, thus allowing only one possible positioning from each dimension (Fig. 11.25).

In architectural and structural work, where the interchangeability of parts is usually irrelevant, unnecessary dimensions cause no difficulty and all dimensions are given.

Although it is important not to "over-dimension" a part, it is equally important to give all the dimensions that are needed to locate every point, line, or surface of the object. Every dimension that the workman will require in making the part must be given.

Dimensions for similar features, such as the thickness of several ribs obviously of the same size, need not be repeated (Fig. 11.26). Also, such details as the size of fillets and rounds can be provided for with a general note. Any superfluous or omitted dimensions can be easily discovered by mentally going through the manufacture, or even the drawing, of the part, checking each dimension as it is needed.

11.25. REFERENCE DIMENSIONS. Occasionally it is useful, for reference and checking purposes, to give all dimensions in a series as well as the overall dimension. In such cases one dimension is marked with the abbreviation "REF" as shown in Fig. 11.26. According to ASA definition, a reference dimension is "a dimension without tolerance, used for informational purposes only, and does not govern machining or inspection operations."

11.26. DIMENSIONS FROM DATUM. Datum points, lines, and edges of surfaces of a part are features that are assumed to be exact for purposes of computation or reference, and *from* which the position of other features is established. In Fig. 11.27*A* the left side and bottom surfaces of the part are the datum surfaces, and at (*B*) the center lines of the central hole in the part are datum lines. Where positions are specified by dimensions from a datum, different features are always positioned from this datum and *not* with respect to one another.

11.27. SELECTION OF A DATUM. A feature selected to serve as a datum must be clearly identified and readily recognizable. Note in Fig. 11.27 that the datum lines and edges are obvious. On an actual part, the datum features must be accessible during manufacture so that there will be no difficulty in making measurements. In addition, *corresponding*

FIG. 11.24.   One unnecessary dimension.

FIG. 11.25.   Unnecessary dimension omitted.

FIG. 11.26.   One reference dimension.

FIG. 11.27.   Dimensions from datum. (*A*) datum surfaces; (*B*) datum center.

FIG. 11.28. Maximum and minimum sizes. Mating edges at (A) are dimensioned as at (B) and (C) so that there will be no assembly interference.

FIG. 11.29. The contour principle. Dimensions are placed where the feature dimensioned is most easily recognized.

FIG. 11.30. Dimensions for cylinders. (A) shows usual practice for cylindrical parts; (B), (C), and (D), for holes.

features on mating parts must be employed as datum features to assure assembly and proper functioning.

A datum surface (on a physical part) must be more accurate than the allowable variation on any dimension of position which is referred to the datum. Thus, it may be necessary to specify the perfection of datum surfaces for flatness, straightness, roundness, etc. See paragraphs 11.77 and 11.78.

11.28. BASIC DIMENSIONS. Any dimension on a drawing specified as BASIC is a *theoretical* value used to describe the exact size, shape, or position of a feature. It is used as a reference from which permissible variations are established.

11.29. MAXIMUM AND MINIMUM SIZES. In some cases a maximum or a minimum size represents a limit beyond which any variation in size cannot be permitted, but in the *opposite* direction there is no difficulty. To illustrate, Fig. 11.28A shows a shaft and hub assembly. If the change in diameter of the shaft (rounded) is too large or the hub edge (chamfer) too small, the hub will not seat against the shaft shoulder, but if the shaft radius is somewhat smaller or the hub edge somewhat larger, no difficulty exists. Therefore in the dimensioning of both, at (B) and (C), MAX and MIN are applied to the dimensions. This method is often used in connection with depths of holes, lengths of threads, chamfers, and radii.

PLACEMENT OF DIMENSIONS

11.30. PLACEMENT OF DIMENSIONS. After the distances have been selected, it is possible to decide (1) the *view* on which the distance will be indicated, (2) the particular *place* on that view, and (3) the *form* of the dimension itself. Numerous principles, some with the force of a rule, can be given, but in all cases the important consideration is *clarity*.

11.31. VIEWS: *The Contour Principle.* One of the views of an object will usually describe the shape of some detailed feature better than will the other view or views, and the feature is then said to be "characteristic" in that particular view. In reading a drawing, it is natural to look for the dimensions of a given feature wherever that feature appears most characteristic, and an advantage in clarity and in ease of reading will certainly result if the dimension is placed there. In Fig. 11.29 the rounded corner, the drilled hole, and the lower notched corner are all characteristic in, and dimensioned on, the front view. The projecting shape on the front of the object is more characteristic in the top view and is dimensioned there.

Dimensions for prisms should be placed so that two of the three dimensions are on the view showing the contour shape and the third on one of the other views (Figs. 11.18 and 11.29).

Dimensions for cylinders, the diameter

FIG. 11.31. Dimensions inside the view.

11.31. Views

and length, are usually best placed on the noncircular view (Fig. 11.30*A*). This practice keeps the dimensions on one view, a convenience for the workman. Occasionally a cylindrical hole is dimensioned with the diameter at an angle on the circular view, as indicated at (*B*). This practice should never be used unless there is a clear space for the dimension value. In some cases, however, the value can be carried outside the view, as at (*C*). When a round hole is specified by a note, as at (*D*), the leader should point to the circular view if possible. The note has an advantage in that the diameter, operation, and depth can all be given together. Giving the diameter on the circular view as at (*B*), (*C*), and (*D*) may make for ease of reading, as the dimensions of position will probably be given there also, as indicated at (*D*). When it is not obvious from the drawing, a dimension may be indicated as a diameter by following the value with the letter *D*, as shown in Fig. 11.31.

PRINCIPLES FOR THE PLACEMENT OF DIMENSIONS

1. Dimensions outside the view are preferred, unless added clearness, simplicity, and ease of reading will result from placing some of them inside. For good appearance, dimensions should be kept off the cut surfaces of sections. When it is not possible to do this, the section lining is omitted around the numbers, as shown in Fig. 11.31 (see paragraph 11.35).

2. Dimensions between the views are preferred unless there is some reason for placing them elsewhere, as in Fig. 11.29 where the dimensions for the lower notched corner and the position of the hole must come at the bottom of the front view.

Avoid   Correct

FIG. 11.32. Dimensions applied to one view only.

3. Dimensions should be applied to one view only; that is, with dimensions between views, the extension lines should be drawn from one view, not from both views (Fig. 11.32).

4. Dimensions should be placed on the view that shows the distance in its true length (Fig. 11.33).

5. Dimension lines should be spaced, in general, ½ in. away from the outlines of the view. This applies to a single dimension or to the first dimension of several in a series.

6. Parallel dimension lines should be spaced uniformly with at least ⅜ in. between lines.

7. Values should be midway between the arrowheads, except when a center line interferes (Fig. 11.34) or when the values of several parallel dimensions are staggered (Fig. 11.35).

8. Continuous or staggered dimension lines may be used, depending upon convenience and readability. Continuous dimension lines are preferred where possible (Fig. 11.36 and 11.37).

9. Always place a longer dimension line outside a shorter one to avoid crossing dimension lines with the extension lines of other dimensions. Thus an overall dimension (maximum size of piece in a given direction) will be outside all other dimensions.

FIG. 11.33. Dimensioned distance given in normal view.

FIG. 11.34. Values midway between arrowheads.

FIG. 11.35. Values staggered for clarity.

FIG. 11.36. Dimensions arranged in continuous form.

FIG. 11.37. Dimensions staggered.

FIG. 11.38. Dimensions in limited space.

FIG. 11.39. Use of enlarged view to clarify dimensions.

10. Dimensions should never be crowded. If the space is small, follow one of the methods given in paragraph 11.32.

11. Center lines are used to indicate the symmetry of shapes, and frequently eliminate the need for a positioning dimension. They should be considered as part of the dimensioning and drawn in finished form at the time of dimensioning. They should extend about ⅛ in. beyond the shape for which they indicate symmetry unless they are carried further to serve as extension lines. Center lines should not be continued between views.

12. All notes must read horizontally (from the bottom of the drawing).

CAUTIONS

1. Never use a center line, a line of a view, or an extension line as a dimension line.

2. Never place a dimension line on a center line or place a dimension line where a center line should properly be.

3. Never allow a line of any kind to pass through a dimension figure.

4. Never allow the crossing of two dimension lines or an extension line and a dimension line.

5. Avoid dimensioning to dashed lines if possible.

11.32. DIMENSIONING IN LIMITED SPACE. Dimensions should never be crowded into a space too small to contain them. One of the methods in Fig. 11.38 can be used where space is limited. Sometimes a note is appropriate. If the space is small and crowded, an enlarged removed section or part view can be used (Fig. 11.39).

11.33. ORDER OF DIMENSIONING. A systematic order of working is a great help in placing dimensions. Figure 11.40 illustrates the procedure. First complete the shape description (*A*). Then place the extension lines and extend the center lines where necessary (*B*), thus planning for the location of both size and position dimensions; study the placement of each dimension and make alterations if desirable or necessary. Add the dimension lines (*C*). Draw arrowheads and leaders for notes (*D*). Then add values and letter notes (*E* and *F*).

It is desirable to add the notes *after* the dimensions have been placed. If the notes are placed first, they may occupy a space needed for a dimension. Because of the freedom allowed in the use of leaders, notes may be given in almost any available space.

11.34. DIMENSIONING OF AUXILIARY VIEWS. In placing dimensions on an auxiliary view, the same principles of dimensioning apply as for any other drawing, but special attention is paid to the contour principle given in paragraph 11.31. An auxiliary view is made for the purpose of showing the normal view (size)

FIG. 11.40. Order of dimensioning. See text for details.

of some inclined or skew face, and for this reason the dimensioning of the face should be placed where it is easiest to read, *which will be on the normal view.* Note in Fig. 11.41 that the spacing and size of holes as well as the size of the inclined face are dimensioned on the auxiliary view. Note further that the angle and dimension of position tying the inclined face to the rest of the object could not be placed on the auxiliary view.

11.35. DIMENSIONING OF SECTIONAL VIEWS.

Dimensions that must be placed on sectional views are usually placed outside the view so as not to be crowded within crosshatched areas. However, sometimes a dimension *must* be placed across a crosshatched area. When this is the case, the crosshatching is left out around the dimension figures, as illustrated in Fig. 11.31. Examples showing dimensioning practice on sectional views are given in Probs. 13.2.3, 13.2.4, and 13.3.11.

11.36. DIMENSIONING A HALF SECTION.

In general, the half section is difficult to dimension clearly without some possibility of crowding and giving misleading or ambiguous information. Generous use of notes and careful placement of dimension lines, leaders, and figures will in most cases make the dimensioning clear; but if a half section cannot be clearly dimensioned, an extra view or part view should be added on which to describe the size.

Inside diameters should be followed by the letter *D* and the dimension line carried over the center line, as in Fig. 11.42, to prevent the possibility of reading the dimension as a radius. Sometimes the view and the dimensioning

FIG. 11.41. Dimensioning on an auxiliary (normal) view.

can both be clarified by showing the dashed lines on the unsectioned side. Dimensions of internal parts, if placed inside the view, will prevent confusion between extension lines and the outline of external portions.

11.37. DIMENSIONING OF PICTORIAL DRAWINGS.

Pictorial drawings are often more difficult to dimension than orthographic drawings because there is one view instead of several, and the dimensioning may become crowded unless the placement is carefully planned. In general, the principles of dimensioning for orthographic drawings should be followed whenever possible. The following rules should be observed:

FIG. 11.42. Dimensioning a half section.

FIG. 11.43. Recommended wording of notes.

NOTE (appears on)	PC. No.	NOTE (appears on)	PC. No.	NOTE (appears on)	PC. No.	NOTE (appears on)	PC. No.
Bore	4	Fillet	11,12	Peen	9	Section	2
Broach	9	Finish	8(V),9(f),13,14	Pickle	17	Spot	7
Chamfer	8	Grind	6	Plate	2,18,19	Spotface	3
Core	3,8	Heat-treat	6,15	Polish	1,19	Tap	3,9
Counterbore	9	Keyseat	1,7	Ream	1,3	Taper	4,6
Countersink	2	Keyway	4	Relief (thread)	7	Template	21
Crown	4	Knurl	6	Rounds	11,12	Thread	1,5,9
Drill	1,2,3,9	Neck	6	Sandblast	20	Tumble	22
Draft	10	Pattern	16	Sawcut	9	Undercut	8

1. Dimension and extension lines should be placed so as to lie *in* or *perpendicular* to the face on which the dimension applies. See Probs. 13.1.4 and 13.1.5.

2. Dimension numerals should be placed so as to lie in the plane in which the dimension and extension lines lie. See Probs. 13.1.8 and 13.1.14.

3. Leaders for notes and the lettered note should be placed so as to lie in a plane parallel or perpendicular to the face on which the note applies. See Probs. 13.1.18 and 13.4.7.

4. Finish may be indicated by the standard finish symbol (**V**). The symbol is applied *perpendicular to* the face with its point touching a short line lying in the surface. The symbol and line should be parallel to one of the principal axes. If the symbol cannot be applied in the above manner, the finish symbol may be attached to a leader pointing to the face. See Probs. 13.1.5 and 13.1.18.

5. Lettering of dimension values and of notes should be made so that the lettering appears to lie in or parallel to one of the principal faces of the pictorial drawing. To do this, the lettering must be the *pictorial representation of vertical figures*. Note the placement and lettering of the dimension values and the notes in Probs. 13.4.2 and 13.4.4.

The American Standard permits lettering of pictorial drawings according to the unidirectional system, with either vertical or slant lettering. This is principally to make possible the use of mechanical lettering devices. If the unidirectional system is employed,

1. Dimension values are lettered to read from the bottom of the sheet.

2. Notes are lettered so that they lie *in the picture plane,* to read from the bottom of the sheet. Notes should be kept off the view, if possible.

DIMENSIONING STANDARD FEATURES

11.38. NOTES. These are word statements giving information that cannot be given by the views and dimensions. They almost always specify some standard shape, operation, or material, and are classified as *general* or *specific*. A general note applies to the entire part, and a specific note applies to an individual feature. Occasionally a note will save making an additional view; or even an entire drawing, for example by indicating right- and left-hand parts.

Do not be afraid to put notes on drawings. Supplement the graphic language with the English language whenever added information can be conveyed by so doing, but be careful to word the note so clearly that the meaning cannot possibly be misunderstood.

General notes do not require the use of a leader and should be grouped together above the title block. Examples are "Finish all over," "Fillets ¼ R, rounds ⅛ R, unless otherwise specified," "All draft angles 7°," "Remove burs," etc.

Much of the information provided in the title strip of a machine drawing is a grouping of general notes. Stock size, material, heat-treatment, etc., are general notes in the title of the drawing of Fig. 11.106.

Specific notes almost always require a leader and should therefore be placed fairly close to the feature to which they apply. Most common are notes giving an operation with a size, as "½ Drill, 4 holes."

Recommended wordings for notes occurring more or less frequently are given in Fig. 11.43.

When lower-case lettering is used, capitalization of words in notes depends largely on company policy. One common practice is to capitalize all important words. However, for long notes, as on civil engineering or architectural drawings, the grammatical rules for capitalization usually prevail.

11.39. ANGLES. The dimension line for an angle is a circle arc with its center at the intersection of the sides of the angle (Fig. 11.44). The value is placed to read horizontally, with the exception that in the aligned system large arcs have the value aligned with the dimension arc. Angular values should be written in the form 35°7′ with no dash between the degrees and the minutes.

11.40. CHAMFERS. Chamfers may be dimensioned by note, as in Fig. 11.45*A*, if the angle is 45°. The linear size is understood to be a short side of the chamfer triangle; the dimensioning without a note shown at (*B*) is in conformity with this. If the chamfer angle is other than 45°, it is dimensioned as at (*C*).

11.41. TAPERS. The term "taper" as used in machine work usually means the surface of a cone frustum. The dimensioning will depend on the method of manufacture and the accuracy required. If a standardized taper (see Appendix) is used, the specification should be accompanied by one diameter and the length as shown at (*A*) in Fig. 11.46. The general method of giving the diameters of both ends and the taper per foot is illustrated at (*B*). An

FIG. 11.44. Dimensions for angles.

FIG. 11.45. Dimensioning of chamfers.

FIG. 11.46. Dimensioning of tapers.

FIG. 11.47. Dimensioning of batters and slopes.

Aligned

Unidirectional

FIG. 11.48. Dimensioning of radii.

FIG. 11.49. Dimensioning of radii having inaccessible centers. Note that the positioning dimension is marked out of scale.

FIG. 11.50. Dimensioning a curve made up of radii. The position of centers must be given.

alternate method is to give one diameter, the length, and the taper per foot. Taper per foot is defined as the difference in diameter in inches for 1 ft of length. The method of dimensioning for precision work, where a close fit between the parts as well as a control of entry distance is required, is shown at (*C*). Because of the inaccuracy resulting from measuring at one of the ends, a gage line is established where the diameter is to be measured. The entry distance is controlled through the allowable variation in the location of the gage line, and the fit of the taper is controlled by the accuracy called for in the specification of the angle.

11.42. BATTERS, SLOPES, AND GRADE. *Batter* is a deviation from the vertical, such as is found on the sides of retaining walls, piers, etc., and *slope* is a deviation from the horizontal. Both are expressed as a ratio with one factor equal to unity, as illustrated in Fig. 11.47. *Grade* is identical with slope but is expressed in percentage, the inclination in feet per hundred feet. In structural work angular measurements are shown by giving the ratio of run to rise with the larger side 12 in.

11.43. ARCS. Arcs should be dimensioned by giving the radius on the view that shows the true shape of the curve. The dimension line for a radius should always be drawn as a radial line at an angle (Fig. 11.48), never horizontal or vertical; and only one arrowhead is used. There is no arrowhead at the arc

FIG. 11.51. A curve dimensioned by offsets.

center. The numerical value should be followed by the letter *R*. Depending upon the size of the radius and the available space for the value, the dimension line and value are both inside the arc, or the line is inside and the value outside, or, for small arcs, both are outside, as shown in the illustration.

When the center of an arc lies outside the limits of the drawing, the center is moved closer along a center line of the arc and the dimension line is jogged to meet the new center (Fig. 11.49). The portion of the dimension line adjacent to the arc is a radial line of the true center.

A curved line made up of circle arcs is dimensioned by radii with the centers located, as in Fig. 11.50.

11.44. CURVES. Curves for which great accuracy is not required are dimensioned by offsets, as in Fig. 11.51. For greater accuracy, dimensions from datum features, as in Fig. 11.52, are recommended. Note in Fig. 11.52 that *any* pair of dimensions (indicated at *x*) could be given to greater accuracy than the others, in order to position a point for which greater accuracy is required.

11.45. SHAPES WITH ROUNDED ENDS. These should be dimensioned according to their method of manufacture. Figure 11.53 shows several similar contours and the typical dimensioning for each. The link (*A*), to be cut from thin material, has the radius of the ends and the center distance given as it would be laid out. At (*B*) is shown a cast pad di-

FIG. 11.52. A curve dimensioned from datum edges.

FIG. 11.53. Dimensioning of round-end shapes.

FIG. 11.54. Dimensioning of drilled and reamed holes.

FIG. 11.55. Dimensioning of counterbored holes.

FIG. 11.56. Dimensioning of countersunk holes.

FIG. 11.57. Dimensioning of spotfaced holes.

mensioned as at (*A*), with the dimensions most usable for the patternmaker. The drawing at (*C*) shows a slot machined from solid stock with an end-milling cutter. The dimensions give the diameter of the cutter and the travel of the milling-machine table. The slot at (*D*) is similar to that at (*C*) but it is dimensioned for quantity production, where, instead of the table travel, the over-all length is wanted for gaging purposes. Pratt and Whitney keys and key seats are dimensioned by the method shown at (*D*).

11.46. DIMENSIONS AND SPECIFICATIONS FOR HOLES. Drilled, reamed, bored, punched, or cored holes are usually specified by note giving the diameter, operation, and depth if required. If there is more than one hole of the same kind, the leader needs to point to but one hole, and the number of holes is stated in the note (Fig. 11.54). Several operations involving one hole may be grouped in a common note. Figures

11.54 to 11.57 show typical dimensioning practice for drilled and reamed, counterbored, countersunk, and spotfaced holes.

The ASA specifies that standard drill sizes be given as decimal fractions, such as 0.250, 0.375, 0.750, and 1.500. If the size is given as a common fraction, the decimal equivalent should be added.

The leader to a hole should point to the *circular* view if possible. The pointing direction is toward the center (Fig. 11.9*B*). With concentric circles, the arrowhead should touch the inner circle (usually the first operation) unless an outer circle would pass through the arrowhead. In such a case, the arrow should be drawn to touch the outer circle.

FIG. 11.58. Method of specifying several operations on a hole.

FIG. 11.59. Dimensions of position for holes.

FIG. 11.60. Dimensions of position for holes.

Holes made up of several diameters and involving several stages of manufacture may be dimensioned as shown in Fig. 11.58. This method of dimensioning combines notes with the regular dimensions.

Threaded holes are dimensioned and specified as described in Chap. 12.

11.47. POSITIONING OF HOLES. Mating parts held together by bolts, screws, rivets, etc., must have holes for fastenings positioned from common datum surfaces or lines in order to assure matching of the holes. When two or more holes are on an established center line, the holes will require a dimension of position in one direction only (Fig. 11.59). If the holes are not on a common center line, they will require positioning in two directions, as in Fig. 11.60. The method at (B) is preferred when it is important to have the positions of both holes established from datum features (left and lower sides of the part).

The coordinate method for the positioning of holes (Fig. 11.61A) is preferred in precision work. The hole circle is often drawn and its diameter given for reference purposes, as in the figure. The diameter of a hole circle is invariably given on the circular view. The datum lines in this case are the center lines of the part.

Hole circles are circular center lines, often called "bolt circles," on which the centers of a number of holes are located.

One practice is to give the diameter of the hole circle and a note specifying the size of the holes, the number required, and the spacing, as in Fig. 11.61B. If one or more holes are not in the regular equally spaced position, their location may be given by an offset dimension, as shown at (C).

Figure 11.62 shows holes located by polar coordinates. This method should be used only when modern, accurate shop equipment is available for locating holes by angle.

11.48. CYLINDRICAL SURFACES. Cylindrical surfaces on a drawing having an end view may be dimensioned as in Fig. 11.63A; if there is no end view, "DIA" should be placed after each value as in Fig. 11.63B.

11.49. SPHERICAL SURFACES. Spherical surfaces should be dimensioned as in Fig. 11.64, that is, by placing the abbreviation "SPHER" after the dimension value.

11.50. CURVED SURFACES. A position on a curved part may be misconstrued unless there is a specification showing the *surface* of the part to which the dimension applies, as in Fig. 11.65.

11.51. THREADS, FASTENERS, KEYWAYS, AND KEYSEATS. The dimensioning of these is given in Chap. 12.

FIG. 11.61. Positioning of holes on "hole circles." (*A*) from datum lines; (*B*) equally spaced; (*C*) one hole offset.

FIG. 11.62. Holes positioned by angle from datum line.

FIG. 11.63. Dimensioning of cylinders. (A) end view shown; (B) no end view.

11.52. THE METRIC SYSTEM.

A knowledge of the metric system is advantageous, as it is used on all drawings from countries where this system is standard and with increasing frequency on drawings made in the United States. The first instance of international standardization of a mechanical device is that of ball bearings, which have been standardized in the metric system.

Scale drawings in the metric system are not made to English or American scales, but are based on divisions of 10 as full size and then 1 to 2, 1 to 2½, 1 to 5, 1 to 10, 1 to 20, 1 to 50, and 1 to 100. The unit of measurement is the millimeter (mm), and the figures are all understood to be millimeters, without any indicating marks. Figure 11.66 is an example of metric dimensioning. A table of metric equivalents is given in the Appendix.

11.53. STANDARD SIZES, PARTS, AND TOOLS.

In dimensioning any machine part, it is often necessary to specify some standard thickness or diameter or the size produced by some standard tool. The American Standard, prevailing company standard, or manufacturer's standard should be consulted in order to assure giving correct information.

Wire and sheet-metal gages are given by number and are followed by the equivalent thickness or diameter in decimal form.

Bolts and screws are supplied in fractional and numbered sizes.

Keys are available in manufacturer's numbered sizes or, for square and flat keys, in fractional sizes.

Rivets, depending upon the variety, are supplied in fractional or numbered sizes.

Drills are available in numbered, lettered, fractional, and metric sizes.

Reamers, milling cutters, and other standard tools are available in a variety of standard sizes.

The Appendix gives tables of standard wire and metal gages, bolt and screw sizes, key sizes, etc. ASA or manufacturer's standards will give further information required.

PRECISION AND TOLERANCE

11.54. PRECISION AND TOLERANCE.

In the manufacture of any machine or structure, quality is a primary consideration. The manufacturing care put into the product determines its quality in relation to competitive products on the market and, in part, its accompanying relative cost and selling price.

FIG. 11.64. Dimensioning a spherical surface.

FIG. 11.65. Dimensioning a position on a curved surface.

FIG. 11.66. A metric drawing. Dimensions are in millimeters.

Neck for Grinding, $\frac{1}{8}$ wide x $\frac{1}{64}$ deep
Neck $\frac{1}{8}$ wide x $\frac{1}{16}$ deep
$2\frac{5}{16}$-16N-3
Neck for Grinding, $\frac{1}{8}$ wide x $\frac{1}{64}$ deep
Neck $\frac{1}{8}$ wide x $\frac{1}{16}$ deep
$1\frac{3}{8}$-16N-3
Seat for Wood-ruff Key #808
$1\frac{1}{4}$-16N-3

DWN	A. B. C.	1-17-47	LIMITS, UNLESS OTHERWISE NOTED: FRACTIONAL $\pm\frac{1}{64}$. DECIMAL $\pm$.010, ANGULAR $\pm\frac{1}{2}°$		REVISION	DATE	CHANGE OR ADDITION		
TCD	H. ROWE	2-14-47							
CKD	Al Smith	2-16-47	PART NO.	REQD	NAME	MATERIAL	STOCK SIZE	HEAT TR.	FINISH
APPD	T. C. C.	2-16-47	H-22	1	CLUTCH SPINDLE	2335	$3\frac{1}{8}$D x $10\frac{1}{2}$	Brin.225	✓
	NAME	DATE	UNIT OR ASSEMBLY		MODEL "S" HEADSTOCK				

| B | 3-9-47 | Added $\frac{1}{32}$ Radii |
| A | 2-24-47 | $1\frac{1}{8}$ was $1\frac{1}{16}$ |

SCALE Full
ASSY. DR. NO. E-27340
COMPANY NAME CITY
DRAWING NO. E-27461
NO. OF

FIG. 11.67. Toleranced dimensions. The title strip gives tolerances on fractional, decimal, and angular dimensions. All other tolerances are specified directly as limits.

Precision is the degree of accuracy necessary to ensure the functioning of a part as intended. As an example, a cast part usually has two types of surfaces: mating surfaces and nonmating surfaces. The mating surfaces are machined to the proper smoothness and to be at the correct distance from each other. The nonmating surfaces, exposed to the air and with no important relationship to other parts or surfaces, are left in their original rough-cast form. Thus mating surfaces ordinarily require much greater manufacturing precision than nonmating surfaces. The dimensions on a drawing must indicate which surfaces are to be finished and the degree of precision required in finishing. However, because it is impossible to produce any distance to an absolute size, some variation must be allowed in manufacture.

Tolerance is the allowable variation for any given size and provides a practical means of achieving the precision

required. The tolerance on any given dimension varies according to the degree of precision necessary for the particular surface. For nonmating surfaces, the tolerance may vary from 0.01 in. for small parts to as much as 1 in. on very large parts. For mating surfaces, tolerances as small as a few millionths of an inch are sometimes necessary (for extremely close-fitting surfaces), but usually surfaces are finished to an accuracy of 0.001 to 0.010, depending upon the function of the part. Figure 11.67 shows variously toleranced dimensions on a machine drawing. Methods of expressing tolerances are given in paragraph 11.61.

In some cases, particularly in structural and architectural work, tolerances are not stated on the drawing but are given in a set of specifications or are understood to be of an order standard for the industry.

11.55. FITS OF MATING PARTS. The working parts of any machine have some definite relationship to their mating parts in order to achieve a particular function, such as free rotation, free longitudinal movement, clamping action, permanent fixed position, etc. To ensure the proper relationship, the old practice was to mark the drawings of both parts with the same fractional dimension and add a note such as "running fit" or "drive fit," leaving the difference in size required (the allowance) to the experience and judgment of the machinist.

The tongue of Fig. 11.68 is to slide longitudinally in the slot. Thus, if the slot is machined first and measures 1.499 in. and the machinist, from his experience, assumes an allowance of 0.004 in., he will carefully machine the tongue to 1.495 in.; the parts will fit and function as desired. In making up a second machine, if the slot measured, say, 1.504 in. after machining, the tongue would be made 1.500 in. and an identical fit obtained; but the tongue of the first machine would be much too loose in the slot of the second machine, and the tongue of the second would not enter the slot of the first. The parts would, therefore, not be interchangeable.

Since it is not possible to work to absolute sizes, it is necessary where interchangeable assembly is required to give the dimensions of mating parts with "limits," that is, the maximum and minimum sizes within which the actual measurements must fall in order for the part to be accepted. The dimensions for each piece are given by three- or four-place decimals, the engineering department taking all the responsibility for the correctness of fit required.

Figure 11.69 shows the same tongue and slot as in Fig. 11.68 but dimensioned for interchangeability of parts. In this case, for satisfactory functioning, it has been decided that the tongue must be at least 0.002 in. smaller than the slot but not more than 0.006 in. smaller. This would provide an average fit similar to that used in the previous example. The maximum and minimum sizes acceptable for each part are then figured.

The value 1.500 in. has been assigned as the size of the minimum acceptable slot. This value minus the minimum clearance, 0.002 in., gives a size for the maximum tongue of 1.498. The maximum allowable clearance, 0.006, minus the minimum allowable clearance, 0.002, gives the amount, 0.004, available as the total manufacturing tolerance for both parts. This has been evenly divided and applied as 0.002 to the slot and 0.002 to the tongue. Thus the size of the maximum slot will be the size of the minimum slot *plus* the slot tolerance, or $1.500 + 0.002 = 1.502$. The size of the minimum tongue will be the size of the maximum tongue *minus* the tongue tolerance, or $1.498 - 0.002 = 1.496$.

A study of Fig. 11.69 will show that, made in any quantity, the two parts will allow interchangeable assembly and that any pair will fit approximately as any other pair, as planned. This system is essential in modern quantity-production manufacture. Quantity-production and unit-production methods are discussed in paragraph 11.80.

11.56.   NOMENCLATURE.   The terms used in limit dimensioning are so interconnected that their meaning should be clearly understood before a detailed study of the method is attempted.

The following are adapted from ASA definitions:

Nominal Size.   The nominal size is the designation that is used for the purpose of general identification.

Dimension.   A dimension is a geometric characteristic such as diameter, length, angle, or center distance.

Size.   Size is a designation of magnitude. When a value is assigned to a dimension, it is referred to as the size of that dimension.

Allowance.   An allowance is an intentional difference between the maximum material limits of mating parts. (See definition of "Fit.") It is a minimum clearance (positive allowance) or maximum interference (negative allowance) between mating parts.

Tolerance.   A tolerance is the total permissible variation of a size. The tolerance is the difference between the limits of size.

FIG. 11.68.   Dimensioning a fit. According to this practice the machinist fits one part to the other.

FIG. 11.69.   Dimensioning a fit with limits. Tolerance on tongue, 0.002 in.; tolerance on groove, 0.002 in.; allowance, 0.002 in.

FIG. 11.70. An example of limit dimensioning. Tolerance on tongue, 0.002 in.; tolerance on groove, 0.001 in.; allowance, 0.004 in.

FIG. 11.71. A clearance fit. The tightest fit is 0.005 in. clearance; the loosest, 0.009 in. clearance.

Basic Size. The basic size is that size from which the limits of size are derived by the application of allowances and tolerances.

Design Size. The design size is that size from which the limits of size are derived by the application of tolerances. When there is no allowance, the design size is the same as the basic size.

Actual Size. An actual size is a measured size.

Limits of Size. The limits of size are the applicable maximum and minimum sizes.

Maximum Material Limit. A maximum material limit is the maximum limit of size of an external dimension or the minimum limit of size of an internal dimension.

Minimum Material Limit. A minimum material limit is the minimum limit of size of an external dimension or the maximum limit of size of an internal dimension.

Tolerance Limit. A tolerance limit is the variation, positive or negative, by which a size is permitted to depart from the design size.

Unilateral Tolerance. A unilateral tolerance is a tolerance in which variation is permitted only in one direction from the design size.

Bilateral Tolerance. A bilateral tolerance is a tolerance in which variation is permitted in both directions from the design size.

Unilateral Tolerance System. A design plan that uses only unilateral tolerance is known as a Unilateral Tolerance System.

Bilateral Tolerance System. A design plan that uses only bilateral tolerances is known as a Bilateral Tolerance System.

Fit. Fit is the general term used to signify the range of tightness which may result from the application of a specific combination of allowances and tolerances in the design of mating parts.

Actual Fit. The actual fit between two mating parts is the relation existing between them with respect to the amount of clearance or interference that is present when they are assembled.

Clearance Fit. A clearance fit is one having limits of size so prescribed that a clearance always results when mating parts are assembled.

Interference Fit. An interference fit is one having limits of size so prescribed that an interference always results when mating parts are assembled.

Transition Fit. A transition fit is one having limits of size so prescribed that either a clearance or an interference may result when mating parts are assembled.

Basic-Hole System. A basic-hole system is a system of fits in which the design size of the hole is the basic size and the allowance is applied to the shaft.

Basic-Shaft System. A basic-shaft system is a system of fits in which the design size of the shaft is the basic size and the allowance is applied to the hole.

In illustration of some of these terms, a pair of mating parts is dimensioned in Fig. 11.70. In this example the *nominal size* is 1½ in. The *basic size* is 1.500. The *allowance* is 0.004. The *tolerance* on the tongue is 0.002, and on the slot it is 0.001. The *limits* are, for the tongue, 1.496 (maximum) and 1.494 (minimum) and, for the slot, 1.501 (maximum) and 1.500 (minimum).

11.57. GENERAL FIT CLASSES. The fits established on machine parts are classified as follows:

A *clearance fit* is the condition in which

the internal part is smaller than the external part, as illustrated by the dimensioning in Fig. 11.71. In this case the largest shaft is 1.495 in. and the smallest hole 1.500 in., leaving a clearance of 0.005 for the tightest possible fit.

An *interference fit* is the opposite of a clearance fit, having a definite interference of metal for all possible conditions. The parts must be assembled by pressure or by heat expansion of the external member. Figure 11.72 is an illustration. The shaft is 0.001 in. larger than the hole for the loosest possible fit. The allowance in this case is 0.003 in. interference.

A *transition fit* is the condition in which either a clearance fit or an interference fit may be had. Figure 11.73 illustrates a transition fit; the smallest shaft in the largest hole results in 0.0003 in. clearance and the largest shaft in the smallest hole results in 0.0007 in. interference.

11.58. SELECTIVE ASSEMBLY. Sometimes the fit desired may be so close and the tolerances so small that the cost of producing interchangeable parts is prohibitive. In such cases tolerances as small as practical are established; then the parts are gaged and graded as, say, *small, medium,* and *large.* A small shaft in a small hole, medium in medium, or large in large will produce approximately the same fit allowance. Transition and interference fits often require a selection of parts in order to get the amount of clearance or interference desired. Antifriction bearings are usually assembled selectively.

11.59. BASIC-HOLE AND BASIC-SHAFT SYSTEMS. Production economy depends to some extent upon which mating part

is taken as a standard size. In the *basic-hole system,* the minimum size of the hole is taken as a base from which all variations are made; the hole can often be made with a standard tool.

Where a number of different fits of the same nominal size are required on one shaft, as, for example, when bearings are fitted to line shafting, the *basic-shaft system* is employed, in which the maximum shaft size is taken as the basic size.

11.60. UNILATERAL AND BILATERAL TOLERANCES. A unilateral tolerance is one in which the total allowable variation is in *one* direction, plus or minus (not both) from the basic value. A bilateral tolerance is one in which the tolerance is divided, with part plus and the remainder minus from the basic value.

11.61. METHODS OF EXPRESSING TOLERANCES. Tolerances may be *specific,* given with the dimension value; or *general,* given as a note in the title block. The general tolerances apply to all dimensions not carrying a specific tolerance. The general tolerance should be allowed to apply whenever possible, using specific tolerances only when necessary. If no tolerances are specified, the value usually assumed for fractional dimensions is $\pm\frac{1}{64}$ in.; for angular dimensions $\pm\frac{1}{2}°$; and for decimal dimensions plus or minus the nearest significant figure, as, for example, ±0.01 in. for a two-place decimal and ±0.001 in. for a three-place decimal.

There are several methods of expressing tolerances. The method preferred in quantity-production work, where gages are employed extensively, is to write the two limits representing the maximum and minimum acceptable

FIG. 11.72. An interference fit. The loosest fit is 0.001 in. interference; the tightest, 0.003 in. interference.

FIG. 11.73. A transition fit. The loosest fit is 0.0003 in. clearance; the tightest, 0.0007 in. interference.

FIG. 11.74. A tolerance expressed as limits.

FIG. 11.75. Tolerances plus and minus.

sizes as in Fig. 11.74. An internal dimension has the *minimum* size above the line, and an external dimension has the *maximum* size above the line. This arrangement is for convenience in machining.

Another method is to give the basic size followed by the tolerance, plus and minus (with the plus above the minus), as in Fig. 11.75. If only one tolerance value is given, as at (*B*), the other value is assumed to be zero.

Unilateral tolerances are expressed by giving the two limits, as in Fig. 11.74, or by giving one limiting size and the tolerance, as $2.750 + 0.005$ or $2.750 \begin{smallmatrix} +0.005 \\ -0.000 \end{smallmatrix}$; for fractional dimensions, $\frac{1}{2} - \frac{1}{32}$ or $\frac{1}{2} \begin{smallmatrix} +0 \\ -\frac{1}{32} \end{smallmatrix}$; for angular dimensions, $64°15'30'' + 0°45'0''$ or $64°15'30'' \begin{smallmatrix} +0°45'0'' \\ -0°0'0'' \end{smallmatrix}$.

Bilateral tolerances are expressed by giving the basic value followed by the divided tolerance, both plus and minus (commonly equal in amount), as $1.500 \begin{smallmatrix} +0.002 \\ -0.002 \end{smallmatrix}$ or 1.500 ± 0.002; for fractional dimensions, $1\frac{1}{2} \begin{smallmatrix} +\frac{1}{64} \\ -\frac{1}{64} \end{smallmatrix}$ or $1\frac{1}{2} \pm \frac{1}{64}$; for angular dimensions, $30°0' \begin{smallmatrix} +0°10' \\ -0°10' \end{smallmatrix}$ or $30°0' \pm 0°10'$.

11.62. DECIMAL PLACES. A dimension value should be carried to the same number of decimal places as the tolerance. For example, with a tolerance of 0.0005 on a nominal dimension of 1½ in., the basic value should be written 1.5000. Tolerances for common fractional values should be given as common fractions, as $\frac{7}{8} \pm \frac{1}{64}$. Tolerances for decimal values should be given as decimal fractions, as 0.750 ± 0.010.

11.63. FUNDAMENTALS FOR TOLERANCE SELECTION. Before the engineer can decide on the precision necessary for a particular part and specify the proper fits and tolerances, he must have experience in the manufacturing process used and understand the particular mechanism involved. The following quotation from the ASA Standard is pertinent: "Many factors, such as length of engagement, bearing load, speed, lubrication, temperature, humidity, and materials, must be taken into consideration in the selection of fits for a particular application."

A table of fits, such as the ASA table of cylindrical fits (Appendix) explained in paragraph 11.67, may be taken as a guide for ordinary work.

In many cases practical experience is necessary in determining the fit conditions guaranteeing proper performance. Often it is difficult to determine the definite size at which performance fails, and critical tolerances are sometimes determined through exhaustive testing of experimental models.

It is essential to know the precision attainable with various machine tools and machining methods. As an example, holes to be produced by drilling must not be specified to a smaller tolerance than can be attained by drilling. Attainable manufacturing precision is discussed in paragraph 11.64. A knowledge of kinds and types of equipment is needed to assure that the tolerances specified can be attained.

11.64. MANUFACTURING PRECISION. The different manufacturing processes all have inherent minimum possible accuracies, depending upon the size of the work, the condition of the equipment, and, to some extent, the skill of the workmen. The following *minimum* tolerances are given as a guide and are based on the assumption that the work is to be done on a quantity-production basis with equipment in good condition. Greater precision can be attained by highly skilled workmen on a unit-production basis.

In general, the following are recommended as tolerances for dimensions having *no effect on the function of the part;* for sizes of 0 to 6 in., ±1/64; 6 to 18 in., ±1/32; 18 in. and larger, ±1/16 (or more).

Sand Castings. For unmachined surfaces, a tolerance of ±1/32 is recommended for small castings and a tolerance of ±1/16 for medium-sized castings. On larger castings the tolerance should be increased to suit the size. Small and medium-sized castings are rarely below the nominal size since the pattern is "rapped" for easy removal from the sand, and this tends to increase the size.

Die Castings and Plastic Molding. A tolerance of ±1/64 or less can easily be held with small and medium-sized parts; for large parts, the tolerance should be increased slightly. Hole-center distances can be maintained within 0.005 to 0.010, depending on the distance of separation. Certain alloys can be die-cast to tolerances of 0.001 or less.

Forgings. The rough surfaces of drop forgings weighing 1 lb or less can be held to ±1/32; for weights up to 10 lb, ±1/16; for weights up to 60 lb, ±1/8. Because of die wear, drop forgings tend to increase in size as production from the die increases.

Drilling. For drills from no. 60 to no. 30, allow a tolerance of +0.002 − 0.000; from no. 29 to no. 1, +0.004 − 0.000; from 1/4 to 1/2 in., +0.005 − 0.000; from 1/2 to 3/4 in., +0.008 − 0.000; from 3/4 to 1 in., +0.010 − 0.000; from 1 to 2 in., a tolerance of +0.015 − 0.000.

Reaming. In general, a tolerance of +0.0005 − 0.0000 can be held with diameters up to 1/2 in. For diameters from 1/2 to 1 in., +0.001 − 0.000; from 1 in. and larger, +0.0015 − 0.0000.

Lathe Turning: Rough Work. For diameters of 1/4 to 1/2 in., allow a total tolerance of 0.005; for diameters of 1/2 to 1 in., 0.007; for diameters of 1 to 2 in., 0.010; for diameters of 2 in. and larger, 0.015.

Finish Turning. For diameters of 1/4 to 1/2 in., allow a total tolerance of 0.002; for diameters of 1/2 to 1 in., 0.003; for diameters of 1 to 2 in., 0.005; for diameters of 2 in. and larger, 0.007.

Milling. When single surfaces are to be milled, tolerances of 0.002 to 0.003 can be maintained. When two or more surfaces are to be milled, the most important can be toleranced to 0.002 and the remainder to 0.005. In general, 0.005 is a good value to use with most milling work.

Planing and Shaping. These operations are not commonly used with small parts in quantity-production work. For larger parts, tolerances of 0.005 to 0.010 can be maintained.

Broaching. Diameters up to 1 in. can be held within 0.001; diameters of 1 to 2 in., 0.002; diameters of 2 to 4 in., 0.003. Surfaces up to 1 in. apart can be held within 0.002; 1 to 4 in. apart, 0.003; 4 in. apart and over, 0.004.

Threads. Tolerances for ASA threads are provided on the pitch diameter through the thread class given with the specification. For a given class, the tolerances increase as the size of the thread increases.

Grinding. For both cylindrical and surface grinding, a tolerance of 0.0005 can be maintained.

FIG. 11.76. Limits calculated from maximum and minimum clearances. See text for details.

11.65. SELECTION OF TOLERANCES. A common method of determining and applying tolerances is to determine at the outset how much clearance or interference there can be between the mating parts *without impeding their proper functioning*. The difference between the tightest and loosest conditions will be the *sum* of the tolerances of both parts. To obtain tolerances for the individual parts, take half of this value; or if it seems desirable because of easier machining on one part, use slightly less tolerance for that part, with a proportionately larger tolerance for the part more difficult to machine. The following example will illustrate the procedure:

Assume that a running fit is to be arranged between a 2-in. shaft and bearing. It has been determined that in order to provide clearance for a film of oil, the parts cannot fit closer than 0.002 in., and in order to prevent excessive looseness and radial movement of the shaft, the parts cannot be looser than 0.007 in. Then we have the following calculations:

Loosest fit	= 0.007	(maximum clearance)
Tightest fit	= 0.002	(minimum clearance—allowance)
Difference	= 0.005	(sum of tolerances)
½ of difference	= 0.0025	(possible value for each tolerance)

Assuming that the shaft will be ground and the bearing reamed, 0.002 can be used for the shaft tolerance and 0.003 for the bearing tolerance since these values conform better to the precision attainable by these methods of production.

Figure 11.76 illustrates the completed dimensions. Note that the minimum hole is taken as the basic size of 2.000 and the tolerance of 0.003 applied. Then the largest shaft size will be the basic size minus the value for the tightest fit (the allowance); the shaft tolerance then subtracted from the maximum shaft size gives the minimum shaft size. From the figure, the 2.003 bearing minus the 1.996 shaft gives 0.007, the loosest fit; the 2.000 bearing minus the 1.998 shaft gives 0.002, the tightest fit.

11.66. ASA PREFERRED LIMITS AND FITS FOR CYLINDRICAL PARTS.[3] This standard conforms with the recommendations of American-British-Canadian conferences. Agreement has been reached for diameters up to 20 in., and larger diameters are under study.

11.67. DESIGNATION OF ASA FITS. The standard ASA fits are designated by symbols that facilitate reference for educational purposes. These symbols are not to be shown on manufacturing drawings; instead, sizes should be specified. The letter symbols used are as follows:

RC, running or sliding fit
LC, locational clearance fit
LT, transition fit
LN, locational interference fit
FN, force or shrink fit

These letter symbols are used in conjunction with numbers for the class of

[3] Excerpted from American Standard preferred limits and fits for cylindrical parts (ASA B4.1—1955) with the permission of the publisher, the American Society of Mechanical Engineers, 29 West 39th Street, New York 18, N.Y.

fit; thus FN4 represents a class 4 force fit. Each symbol (two letters and a number) represents a complete fit, for which the minimum and maximum clearance or interference and the limits of size for the mating parts are given in the Appendix.

11.68. DESCRIPTION OF FITS. The following is a description of each class of fit, with a reference in each case to the tables in the Appendix.

Running and Sliding Fits (Table 1). These fits provide a similar running performance, with suitable lubrication allowance, throughout the range of sizes. The clearances for the first two classes, used chiefly as slide fits, increase more slowly than for the other classes, so that accurate location is maintained, even when this is at the expense of free relative motion.

RC 1, *close sliding fits* accurately locate parts that must assemble without perceptible play.

RC 2, *sliding fits* are for accurate location, but with greater maximum clearance than RC 1. Parts move and turn easily but do not run freely, and in the larger sizes may seize with small temperature changes.

RC 3, *precision running fits* are about the closest fits expected to run freely, and are for precision work at slow speeds and light journal pressures. They are not suitable under appreciable temperature differences.

RC 4, *close running fits* are chiefly for running fits on accurate machinery with moderate surface speeds and journal pressures, where accurate location and minimum play are desired.

RC 5 and RC 6, *medium running fits* are for higher running speeds, heavy journal pressures, or both.

RC 7, *free running fits* are for use where accuracy is not essential, where large temperature variations are likely, or under both these conditions.

RC 8 and RC 9, *loose running fits* are for materials such as cold-rolled shafting and tubing, made to commercial tolerances.

Locational Fits (Tables 2, 3, and 4). These fits determine only the location of mating parts and may provide rigid or accurate location—as in interference fits—or some freedom of location—as in clearance fits. They fall into three groups:

LC, *locational clearance fits* are for normally stationary parts that can be freely assembled or disassembled. They run from snug fits for parts requiring accuracy of location, through the medium clearance fits for parts such as spigots, to the looser fastener fits where freedom of assembly is of prime importance.

LT, *transition locational fits* fall between clearance and interference fits for application where accuracy of location is important, but small amount of clearance or interference is permissible.

LN, *locational interference fits* are used where accuracy of location is of prime importance, and for parts needing rigidity and alignment with no special requirements for bore pressure. Such fits are not for parts that transmit frictional loads from one part to another by virtue of the tightness of fit; these conditions are met by force fits.

Force Fits (Table 5). A force fit is a special type of interference fit, normally characterized by maintenance of constant bore pressures throughout the range of sizes. Thus the interference varies almost directly with diameter, and to maintain the resulting pressures

FIG. 11.77. An ASA clearance fit. This one is class RC 6. Tolerance on shaft, 0.0012 in.; tolerance on hole, 0.0012 in.; allowance, 0.0016 in. clearance.

FIG. 11.78. An ASA interference fit. This one is class FN 4. Tolerance on shaft, 0.0007 in.; tolerance on hole, 0.0012 in.; allowance, 0.0042 in. interference.

FIG. 11.79. Successive dimensioning. Tolerances accumulate.

FIG. 11.80. Dimensions from datum. Position from datum is subject to only one tolerance, but the center distance between two holes positioned from datum is subject to variation of two tolerances.

within reasonable limits, the difference between its minimum and maximum value is small.

FN 1, *light drive fits* require light assembly pressures and produce more or less permanent assemblies. They are suitable for thin sections, long fits, or cast-iron external members.

FN 2, *medium drive fits* are for ordinary steel parts or for shrink fits on light sections. They are about the tightest fits that can be used with high-grade cast-iron external members.

FN 3, *heavy drive fits* are suitable for heavier steel parts or for shrink fits in medium sections.

FN 4 and FN 5, *force fits* are for parts that can be highly stressed, or for shrink fits where heavy pressing forces are impractical.

11.69. EXAMPLES OF DIMENSIONING STANDARD ASA FITS. Assume that a 1-in. shaft is to run with moderate speed but with a fairly heavy journal pressure. The fit class chosen is RC 6. From Table 1 (Appendix) the limits given are:

Hole: $\begin{array}{l} +1.2 \\ -0 \end{array}$

Shaft: $\begin{array}{l} -1.6 \\ -2.8 \end{array}$

These values are thousandths of an inch. The basic size is 1.0000. Therefore, for the hole, 1.0000 + 0.0012 gives 1.0012 as the maximum limit, and 1.0000 + 0.0000 gives 1.0000 for the minimum limit. For the shaft, 1.0000 − 0.0016 gives 0.9984 for the maximum limit, and 1.0000 − 0.0028 gives 0.9972 for the minimum limit. The dimensioning is shown in Fig. 11.77. To analyze the fit, the tightest condition (largest shaft in smallest hole) is 1.0000 − 0.9984, or 0.0016, clearance. This is the

allowance. The loosest condition (smallest shaft in largest hole) is 1.0012 − 0.9972, or 0.0040, clearance. The values of these two limits are given in the table under "limits of clearance."

To illustrate further, suppose a 2-in. shaft and hub are to be fastened permanently with a drive fit. The hub is high-grade steel. Fit FN 4 has been chosen. Table 5 gives:

Hole: $\begin{array}{l} +1.2 \\ -0 \end{array}$

Shaft: $\begin{array}{l} +4.2 \\ +3.5 \end{array}$

These values are in thousandths of an inch. The basic size is 2.0000. Thus, for the hole 2.0000 + 0.0012 gives 2.0012 for the maximum limit, and 2.0000 − 0.0000 gives 2.0000 as the minimum limit. For the shaft, 2.0000 + 0.0042 gives 2.0042 for the maximum limit, and 2.0000 + 0.0035 gives 2.0035 for the minimum limit. The limits of fit are 0.0023 minimum interference and 0.0042 maximum interference. The allowance is 0.0042. The dimensioning of this fit is shown in Fig. 11.78.

Note in both the above cases that, in dimensioning, the maximum limit of the hole and the minimum limit of the shaft are placed below the dimension line. This is for convenience in reading the drawing and to help prevent mistakes by the machinist.

The ASA fits are based on standard hole practice. Note in the tables (1 to 5) that the minimum hole size is always the basic size.

11.70. CUMULATIVE TOLERANCES. Tolerances are said to be cumulative when a position in a given direction is controlled by more than one tolerance. In Fig. 11.79 the holes are positioned one from another. Thus, the distance between two holes separated by two, three, or four dimensions will vary in position by the sum of the tolerances on all the dimensions. This difficulty can be eliminated by dimensioning from *one* position, which is used as a datum for all dimensions, as shown in Fig. 11.80. This system is commonly called baseline dimensioning.

Figure 11.81 is a further example of the effect of cumulative tolerances. The position of surface *Y* with respect to surface *W* is controlled by the additive tolerances on dimensions *A* and *B*. If it is important, functionally, to hold surface *Y* with respect to surface *X,* the dimensioning used is good. If, however, it is more important to hold surface *Y* with respect to surface *W,* the harmful effect of cumulative tolerances can be avoided by dimensioning as in Fig. 11.82. Cumulative tolerance, however, is always present; in Fig. 11.82 the position of surface *Y* with respect to surface *X* is now subject to the cumulative tolerances of dimensions *A* and *C*.

In machine drawing, overdimensioning a drawing may cause confusion in the shop due to cumulative tolerances. This is illustrated in Fig. 11.83, where one of the surfaces will be positioned by two dimensions, both of which are subject to a tolerance. Thus surface *Z* may be positioned with respect to surface *W* by means of dimensions *A, B,* and *D* and be within ±0.003 in. of the basic position; this variation is inconsistent with the tolerance on dimension *E*. The situation can be clarified by assigning smaller tolerances to dimensions *A, B,* and *D* so that, cumulatively, they will be equal to ±0.001 or less. This is poor practice, however, since it will probably increase the production cost. Another

solution is to increase the tolerance on dimension *E* to ±0.003 if the function of the part will permit. The best solution, however, is to eliminate one of the four dimensions, since one dimension is superfluous. If all four dimensions are given, one should be marked "REF," and its tolerance thus eliminated.

11.71. TOLERANCE BETWEEN CENTERS. In all cases where centers are arranged for interchangeable assembly, the tolerance on shafts, pins, etc., and the tolerance on bearings or holes in the mating pieces will affect the possible tolerance between centers. In Fig. 11.84, observe that smaller tolerances on the holes would necessitate a smaller tolerance on the center distances. A smaller allowance for the fit of the pins would make a tighter fit and reduce the possible tolerances for the center-to-center dimensions. Study carefully the dimensions of both pieces.

11.72. TOLERANCE OF CONCENTRICITY. Tolerance of concentricity is a special case of tolerance in which there is a coincidence of centers. In most cases, concentric cylinders, cones, etc., generated about common axes in manufacture, will be concentric to a degree of precision more than adequate for functional requirements, and no statement is required on the drawing concerning the allowable variation. However, mating pairs of two (or more) precise, close-fitting, machined cylindrical surfaces must have the axes of adjoined cylinders closely coinciding in order to permit assembly of the parts; thus it is sometimes necessary to give the permissible deviation from concentricity. Since the center lines of adjoining cylinders coincide on a drawing, the tolerance

FIG. 11.81. Control of surface position through different toleranced dimensions. Here one dimension is successive.

FIG. 11.82. Control of surface position through different toleranced dimensions. All dimensions are from datum.

FIG. 11.83. Control of surface position through different toleranced dimensions. This drawing is overdimensioned.

FIG. 11.84. Tolerance on centers. The parts will not assemble unless all features are held within the limits shown.

Dimensions C, D and E concentric within 0.0005 full indicator reading.

FIG. 11.85. Tolerance of concentricity. (*A*) shown by general note; (*B*) shown by note with leaders to surfaces.

cannot be given as a dimension. One method of indicating it is to mark the diameters with reference letters and give the tolerance in note form as in Fig. 11.85*A*. The reference letters can be dispensed with if the note is applied directly to the surfaces, as at (*B*).

11.73. TOLERANCE FOR ANGULAR DIMENSIONS. When it is necessary to give the limits of an angular dimension, the tolerance is generally bilateral, as $32 \pm \frac{1}{2}°$. When the tolerance is given in minutes, it is written $\pm 0°10'$; and when given in seconds, it is written $\pm 0'30''$. Where the location of a hole or other feature depends upon an angular dimension, the length along the leg of the angle governs the angular tolerance permitted. A tolerance of $\pm 1°$ gives a variation of

0.035 in. for a length of 1 in. and can be used as a basis for computing the tolerance in any given problem.

As an example, assume an allowable variation of 0.007 in.; then $(0.007/0.035) \times 1° = \frac{1}{5}°$ is the angular tolerance at 1 in. If the length is assumed as 2 in., the tolerance would be one-half the tolerance computed for 1 in., or $\frac{1}{5}° \times \frac{1}{2} = \frac{1}{10}°$, or $0°6'$.

11.74. COINCIDING CENTER LINES AND DIMENSIONS. In many cases the center lines for two different features of a part will coincide. Often one center line is for an unfinished feature and the other (and coincident) center line for a finished feature. Figure 11.86*A* shows the drawing of a link dimensioned for the patternmaker. If holes are to be machined in this link, the drawing would be as at (*B*); the patternmaker would not use the dimension between centers, as shown, but would assume the nominal dimension of 1½ in. with the usual pattern tolerance of $\pm \frac{1}{32}$ in. The clearest dimensioning in this case would be as at (*C*).

In any instance where there is a coincidence of centers, it may be difficult to indicate the limits within which the coincidence must be maintained. At (*C*) there are actually two horizontal center lines, one for the cast link and another for the hole centers. One method of controlling the deviation from coincidence is to give the wall thickness as a minimum, which is understood to apply in all radial directions.

In cases where the coincident center lines are both for finished features with differing tolerances, there may be a serious ambiguity on the drawing unless the dimensioning is specially arranged. Figure 11.87*A* shows a milled slot with

FIG. 11.86. Coinciding center lines and dimensions. Clarification is obtained by giving dimensions for separate operations.

nominal dimensions and, on the coincident center lines, two accurate holes with a closely toleranced center distance. Unless the dimensioning is cleared by two separate dimensions, as shown, the machinist would not know the difference in tolerance. A somewhat more difficult case is shown at (*B*) where pairing holes are diagonally opposite. Unless all the holes are to be toleranced the same on their center distance, the dimensioning must be made clear with notes,. as shown.

11.75. POSITIONAL TOLERANCES.

Figures 11.61 and 11.62 show holes positioned by rectangular or polar coordinates. This method of positioning by tolerances on two dimensions produces a square tolerance zone for the common case where the positioning dimensions are at right angles to each other. The engineering intent can often be specified more accurately by giving information that states the *true position,* with tolerances to indicate how far actual position on the part can vary from true position. True position denotes the basic or theoretically exact position of a feature. This method results in a circular tolerance zone when the tolerance applies in all directions from true position.

Features such as holes may be allowed to vary in any direction from the specified true position. Features such as slots may be allowed to vary from the specified true position on either side of the true-position plane. Thus there are two methods of applying true-position tolerances. Both methods are shown in Fig. 11.88.

When a feature is allowed to vary in any direction, a note in one of the following forms should be used:

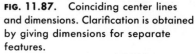

(*a*) 6 holes located at true position within 0.010 dia.

(*b*) 6 holes located within $0.005R$ of true position.

When features are allowed to vary from a true-position plane, a note in one of the following forms should be used:

(*a*) 6 slots located at true position within 0.010 wide zone.

(*b*) 6 slots located within 0.005 either side of true position.

When a feature is allowed to vary in any direction from true position, the position of the feature is given by untoleranced dimensions, as shown in Figs. 11.88 and 11.89. The fact that there is no allowable variation on the positioning dimensions should be indicated either on the drawing, in the title block, or in a separate specification, by a note —"Dimensions locating true position are basic." If this is not done, the word "basic" should be shown on each dimension subject to true-position tolerance.

11.76. MAXIMUM MATERIAL CONDITION.

Since all features of a part have allowable variations in size, for *mating* parts the least favorable assembly condition exists when the mating parts are both at their maximum material condition. This means that a hole is at its minimum size and a shaft at its maximum.

FIG. 11.87. Coinciding center lines and dimensions. Clarification is obtained by giving dimensions for separate features.

FIG. 11.88. True position dimensioning (ASA).

FIG. 11.89. True position dimensioning (ASA).

FIG. 11.90. Zone tolerances (ASA).

FIG. 11.91. Form tolerances. Straightness, flatness, and parallelism (ASA).

In terms of the cylindrical surface of a hole, it means that no point on the surface will be inside a cylinder having a diameter equal to the *actual* diameter of the hole, minus the true-position tolerance (diameter or twice the radius of the tolerance circle), the axis of the cylinder being at true position.

Where the maximum material condition applies, it is stated by the addition of "maximum material condition" to the true-position note, or by using the abbreviation "MMC," as shown in Fig. 11.89. Also, MMC may be stated in a general note or a specification.

In some cases it may be necessary to state a positional tolerance without reference to MMC. This is done by the reference "regardless of feature size" (abbreviated RFS), as shown on Fig. 11.89, or by a general note or specification.

In most cases the datum for true position is obvious from the dimensioning itself, but where there may be any

doubt, the positional tolerance note should read "XX holes located within .xxxR of true position in relation to datum *A*." Of course, datum *A* must be clearly marked on the drawing.

For a complete discussion of true-position tolerancing and related details, see ASA Y14.5—1957 or any subsequent revisions thereof.

11.77. ZONE TOLERANCES. A zone tolerance may be specified where a uniform variation can be permitted along a contour, as in Fig. 11.90. For complete coverage, see ASA Y14.5—1957 or any subsequent revisions thereof.

11.78. FORM TOLERANCES. Tolerances of form state how far actual surfaces may vary from the perfect geometry implied by the drawing. The methods of indicating straightness, flatness, and parallelism are shown in Fig. 11.91; squareness in Fig. 11.92; angularity, symmetry, concentricity, and roundness in Fig. 11.93; and parallelism with a surface and another hole in Fig. 11.94. For complete details on form tolerances, see ASA Y14.5—1957.

11.79. SURFACE QUALITY. The proper functioning and wear life of a part frequently depend upon the smoothness quality of its surfaces. American Standard B46.1—1955 defines the factors of surface quality and describes the mean-

FIG. 11.92. Form tolerances. Squareness (ASA).

FIG. 11.93. Form tolerances. Angularity, symmetry, concentricity, and roundness (ASA).

.625 DIA HOLE LOCATED AT TRUE POSITION WITHIN .010 DIA AND PARALLEL TO A WITHIN .003 TOTAL

.250 DIA LOCATED AT TRUE POSITION WITHIN .010 DIA IN RELATION TO A AND PARALLEL TO A WITHIN .003 TOTAL

FIG. 11.94. Form tolerances. Parallel to surface and parallel to hole (ASA).

ing and use of symbols on drawings. Any surface, despite its apparent smoothness, has minute peaks and valleys, the height of which is termed "surface roughness" and which may or may not be superimposed on a more general "*waviness*." The most prominent direction of tool marks and minute scratches is called "lay."

Roughness, produced principally by cutting edges and tool feed, is expressed as the arithmetical average from the mean in microinches (Fig. 11.95).

Roughness width is rated in inches as the maximum permissible spacing between repetitive units of the surface pattern (Fig. 11.95).

Roughness-width cutoff is the maximum width in inches of surface irregularities to be included in the measurement of roughness height (Fig. 11.95).

Waviness designates irregularities of greater spacing than the roughness, resulting from factors such as deflection and vibration (Fig. 11.95). The height is rated in inches as peak-to-valley height. The width is rated in inches as the spacing of adjacent waves.

Lay is the direction of the predominant surface pattern, produced by tool marks or grains of the surface ordinarily determined by the production method used (Fig. 11.95).

Although other instruments are used, the common method of measuring surface roughness employs electrical amplification of the motion of a stylus over the surface.

The symbol for indicating surface irregularities is a "check mark" with the

FIG. 11.95. Surface roughness (ASA).

SYMBOL

MEANING—

FIG. 11.96. Symbol. The roughness height rating is placed at the left of the long leg.

FIG. 11.97. Symbol. The specification of maximum and minimum roughness height indicates the allowable range.

FIG. 11.98. Symbol. The maximum waviness height rating is placed above the horizontal extension.

FIG. 11.99. Symbol. The maximum waviness width rating is placed to the right of the waviness height rating.

FIG. 11.100. Symbol. To specify the contact area, when required, the percentage value is placed above the extension line.

FIG. 11.101. Symbol. Lay designation is given by the lay symbol placed to the right of the long leg.

TABLE 11.1

Recommended roughness-height values (microinches)				
0.25	5	20	80	320
0.5	6	25	100	400
1.0	8	32	125	500
2.0	10	40	160	600
3.0	13	50	200	800
4.0	16	63	250	1000

Recommended waviness-height values (inches)					
0.00002	0.00008	0.0003	0.001	0.005	0.015
0.00003	0.0001	0.0005	0.002	0.008	0.020
0.00005	0.0002	0.0008	0.003	0.010	

Recommended roughness-width-cutoff values (inches)					
0.003	0.010	0.030	0.100	0.300	1.0000

horizontal extension as shown in Figs. 11.96 to 11.103. Symbols for lay and the application of the symbols on a drawing are shown in Fig. 11.104. The caption explains each case.

Values for roughness height, waviness height, and roughness-width cutoff are shown in Table 11.1.

Figure 11.105 is a chart adapted from several sources, giving the range of surface roughness for various methods.

PRODUCTION METHODS

11.80. PRODUCTION METHODS AND DIMENSIONING PRACTICE. Production methods can be classified as (1) *unit production,* when one or only a few devices or structures are to be built, and (2) *quantity* or *mass production,* when a large number of practically identical ma-

FIG. 11.102. Symbol. The roughness-width-cutoff rating is placed below the horizontal extension.

chines or devices are to be made with the parts interchangeable from one machine to another.

Unit-production methods almost always apply to large machines and structures, especially if they are custom-made. The large size to some extent eliminates the need for great accuracy. Each individual part is produced to fit or is fitted to the adjacent parts, frequently on the job, by experienced workmen in accordance with common fractional dimensions and directions given on the drawings. Since interchangeability of parts is no object, tolerances are not ordinarily used.

Similar methods are employed for unit production of smaller machines and mechanical devices. The drawings may have common fractional dimensions exclusively, on the assumption that the parts will be individually fitted in the shop. If this practice is followed, the manufacturing group accepts the responsibility for the proper functioning of the machine, and in some cases even for designing some of the parts. Skilled workmen are employed for this work. Usually one machine is completed before another is started, and the parts are not interchangeable.

Quantity-production methods are used whenever a great many identical products are made. After a part has been detailed, the operations-planning group of the engineering department plans the shop operations step by step. Then special tools are designed by the tool-design group so that, in production, semiskilled workmen can perform operations that would otherwise require skilled work-

FIG. 11.103. Symbol. When it is required, the maximum roughness width rating is placed at the right of the lay symbol.

FIG. 11.104. Lay symbols and application of surface-quality symbols on the drawing.

men. These tools, built by a highly skilled toolmaker, simplify and greatly increase the rate of production.

One workman performs a single operation on a part; then it is passed to a second workman, who performs another operation; and so on until the part has been completed. Specially designed tools and equipment make it possible to produce economical parts that have dimensional exactness consistent with the requirements for interchangeability. The assembly may also be made by semi-skilled workers using special assembly fixtures and tools.

With this system nothing can be left to the judgment of the workman. In preparing drawings intended for quantity production, the engineering department must assume full responsibility for the success of the machine by making the drawings so exact and complete that, if followed to the letter, the resulting parts cannot fail to be satisfactory. The engineering department alone is in a position to correlate corresponding dimensions of mating parts, establish dimensional tolerances, and give complete directions for the entire manufacturing job.

It is sometimes expedient for concerns doing unit or small-production work to follow the methods of the quantity-production system. The advantage they gain is interchangeability of parts, which can be produced without reference or fitting to mating parts.

11.81.   PRINCIPLES FOR THE SELECTION OF DIMENSIONS. Systematic selection of dimensions demands consideration of the *use* or *function* of the part and the *manufacturing process* to be used in producing it.

The *functional principle* recognizes that it is essential to dimension between points or surfaces associated through their functional relationship with points or surfaces of mating parts. This is accomplished by correlating the dimensions on a drawing of one part with the mating dimensions on the drawing of a mating part and arranging the tolerances of these dimensions to ensure interchangeability and proper functioning.

The *process principle,* or "workman's rule," as it is sometimes called, recognizes that the work of manufacture can be made easier by giving directly the dimensions the shop will find most convenient to "work to" in producing the part. Here a knowledge of manufacturing processes and procedure is necessary, as explained in Chap. 10.

In some cases there may be a conflict between these two principles. Whenever

FIG. 11.105.   Surface-roughness values.

there is, the functional principle must take precedence, as any attempt to satisfy both principles would result in overdimensioning, as described in paragraph 11.24, causing confusion for the workmen and possible malfunctioning of the part. With few exceptions, however, dimensions can be chosen to satisfy both principles.

11.82. PROCEDURE FOR THE SELECTION OF DIMENSIONS. A systematic procedure for selecting dimensions is of course desirable. The following steps can serve as a guide:

1. Carefully study the part along with its mating part or parts. Pay particular attention to the mating and controlling surfaces. Plan dimensions meeting functional requirements before placing any dimensions on the drawing so that you can correlate dimensions of mating parts.

2. Study the part to determine whether or not the manufacturing processes can be simplified by an alteration of any of the functional dimensions. Do not make changes if the functioning of the part would be impaired in any way.

3. Select the nonfunctional dimensions, being guided by the process principle, so that the dimensions will be readily usable by the workmen. Avoid overdimensioning and duplication.

In general, dimensions for mating surfaces are governed by the functional and process principles, and the dimensions for nonmating surfaces are governed by the process principle only.

Occasionally the manufacturing process will not be known at the time of dimensioning. This may happen when there are optional methods of manufacture, all equally good, or when the details of the manufacturing equipment

of a contracting firm are not known. When this is the case, the dimensions should be selected and toleranced in a logical manner so that the part, regardless of the method by which it is produced, cannot fail to be satisfactory. The size and location dimensions arrived at by the shape-breakdown system described in paragraph 11.22 apply here to a great extent since these dimensions fulfill most production requirements. Contracting firms often redraw incoming part drawings, dimensioning them for the most economical production with their own shop equipment.

11.83. METHODS OF PART PRODUCTION. In following the process principle, the basic methods of part production—casting, forging, etc.—as described in Chap. 10, must be known. The manufacturing procedures followed with the particular type of part involved are then considered in selecting the dimensions. The only workman to be considered in dimensioning a part cut from solid stock is the machinist. For parts produced by casting, the workmen to be considered are the patternmaker (for sand castings) or the diemaker (for die castings) and, for finishing, the machinist. Forged parts subject to quantity production are dimensioned for the diemaker and machinist. For parts produced from sheet stock, the template maker, the diemaker, and the machinist must be considered; information for making the template and for forming the blank is obtained from a detail drawing showing the part as it should be when completed. In every case one drawing, appropriately dimensioned, must show the finished part.

The paragraphs that follow give examples of the dimensioning of machine parts for quantity production.

11.84. DIMENSIONING A PART MACHINED FROM STOCK.   Figure 11.106 is a detail drawing of the stud from the rail-transport hanger in Prob. 13.3.13. Study this assembly drawing to determine the function of the stud. The stud is produced by machining on a lathe. Cold-rolled steel stock, 1¼ in. in diameter, is used. The stock diameter is the same as the large end of the stud, thus eliminating one machining operation.

Shape breakdown of the part results in a series of cylinders each requiring two dimensions—diameter and length. The important functional dimensions have been marked (on Fig. 11.106) with the letters *A*, *B*, *C*, and *D*. Diameter *A* is given to correlate with the bore of the bearings; a four-place decimal limit provides for the desired fit. Dimension *B* is a three-place decimal limit to correlate with a similar dimension for the hole in the hanger. Dimension *C* is made 0.03 in. larger than the combined width of the two bearings in order to allow the inner races of the bearings to "creep." Dimension *C*, a two-place decimal, can vary ±0.030 in., but clearance for the bearings is assured under all conditions. Dimension *D* is made approximately 0.05 in. less than the length of the hanger hub to ensure that the nut will bear against the hanger rather than on the shoulder of the stud.

Functional dimensions need not always be extremely accurate. Note that dimensions *C* and *D*, with the relatively broad tolerance of two-place decimals, will allow the part to function as intended.

The thread specification can be con-

FIG. 11.106. Dimensioning a part machined from stock.

sidered as a functional dimension with the tolerance provided through the thread class.

The remainder of the dimensions selected are those that best suit shop requirements. Note that the thread length and over-all dimension cannot both be given, or the part would be overdimensioned.

11.85. DIMENSIONING A CASTING.   The dimensions required for sand castings can be classified as those used by the patternmaker and those used by the machinist. Since a cast part has two distinct phases in its manufacture, we will discuss a particular case first with the drawings made according to the multiple system explained in Chap. 10,

For "Machining" see Dwg. 87343.

Rounds $\frac{1}{8}$ R.
Fillets $\frac{1}{4}$ R.

DWN	R.S.	6-7-47	LIMITS, UNLESS OTHERWISE NOTED: FRACTIONAL $\pm\frac{1}{64}$, DECIMAL $\pm.010$, ANGULAR $\pm\frac{1}{2}°$				REVISION	DATE		CHANGE OR ADDITION	
TCD	R.S.	6-7-47					MATERIAL	STOCK SIZE	HEAT TR.		FINISH
CKD	L.K.D.	6-8-47	PART NO.	REQD	NAME		C.I.				
APPD	James	6-10-47	142-C	4	ROCKER ARM		SCALE ½ Size		COMPANY NAME CITY		DRAWING NO. NO. OF
	NAME	DATE	UNIT OR ASSEMBLY		MODEL 47 DIESEL		ASSY. DR. NO. 87200				87342

FIG. 11.107.   Dimensioning an unmachined casting.

For "Casting" see Dwg. 87342.

$\frac{1}{2}$ Drill

3.000 +.003 Bore

DWN	R.S.	6-7-47	LIMITS, UNLESS OTHERWISE NOTED: FRACTIONAL $\pm\frac{1}{64}$, DECIMAL $\pm.010$, ANGULAR $\pm\frac{1}{2}°$				REVISION	DATE		CHANGE OR ADDITION	
TCD	R.S.	6-7-47					MATERIAL	STOCK SIZE	HEAT TR.		FINISH
CKD	L.K.D.	6-8-47	PART NO.	REQD	NAME		C.I.	87342 Casting			As Shown
APPD	James	6-10-47	142	4	ROCKER ARM		SCALE ½ Size		COMPANY NAME CITY		DRAWING NO. NO. OF
	NAME	DATE	UNIT OR ASSEMBLY		MODEL 47 DIESEL		ASSY. DR. NO. 87200				87343

FIG. 11.108.   Dimensions for machining a casting.

one for the patternmaker (Fig. 11.107) and one for the machinist (Fig. 11.108).

The *casting drawing* gives the shape of the unmachined casting and carries dimensions for the patternmaker only. Shape breakdown will show that each geometric shape has been dimensioned for size and then positioned, thus providing dimensions easily usable by the workman. Some of the dimensions might be altered, depending upon how the pattern is made; the most logical and easily usable combination should be given. Note that the main central shape is dimensioned as it would be laid out on a board. Note also that several of the dimensions have been selected to agree with required functional dimensions of the machined part although the dimensions employed have been selected so as to be directly usable by the patternmaker; they also achieve the *main objective,* which is to state *the sizes that the unmachined casting must fulfill when produced.*

The *machining drawing* shows only the dimensions required by the machinist. These are almost all functional dimensions and have been selected to correlate with mating parts. It is important to note that a starting point must be established in each of the three principal directions for machining the casting. In this case a starting point is provided by (1) the coincidence of the center lines of the large hole and cylinder (positioning in two directions) and (2) dimension *A* to position the machined surface on the back, from which is positioned the drilled hole. Dimension *A* is a common fraction carrying the broad tolerance of $\pm\frac{1}{64}$ in., as there is no functional reason for working to greater precision.

Figure 11.109 is a drawing of the same part used in Figs. 11.107 and 11.108 but with the casting drawing dispensed with and the patternmaker's dimensions incorporated in the drawing of the finished part. In combining the two drawings, some dimensions have been eliminated, as the inclusion of all the dimensions of both drawings would result in over-dimensioning; thus the patternmaker must make use of certain machining dimensions in his work. In working from the drawing in Fig. 11.109, the patternmaker provides for machining allowance, being guided by the finish marks. In the drawing in Fig. 11.107 the engineering department provides for the machining allowance by showing and dimensioning the rough casting oversize where necessary for machining, and no finish marks are used.

11.86. DIMENSIONING A DROP FORGING.
Figure 11.110 is a drawing of a drop forging showing, at the left, the unmachined forging and, at the right, the machined forging. The drawing of the unmachined forging carries the dimensions it must fulfill when produced; these dimensions have been selected so as to be most useful to the diemaker for producing the forging dies. As the draft on drop forgings is considerable, it is shown on the drawing and dimensioned (usually) by a note. If the draft varies for different portions of the part, the angles may be given on the views. The dimensions parallel to the horizontal surfaces of the die are usually given so as to specify the size at the *bottom of the die cavity*. Thus, in dimensioning, visualize the draft as stripped off; then its apparent complication will no longer be a difficulty.

The machining drawing shows the dimensions for finishing. These are all functional, selected from the standpoint of the required function of the part. Study the illustration carefully.

FIG. 11.109. All dimensions for a casting.

FIG. 11.110. Dimensioning a drop forging.

.130 +.005 Punch 8 Holes

L.H. Bracket shown. Make R.H. opposite. Bend radii ⅛

DWN	M.E.P.	3-1-47	LIMITS, UNLESS OTHERWISE NOTED: FRACTIONAL ±¹⁄₆₄. DECIMAL ±.010. ANGULAR ±½°			REVISION	DATE	CHANGE OR ADDITION	
TCD	P.M.	3-9-47				MATERIAL	STOCK SIZE	HEAT TR.	FINISH
CKD	Olin	4-10-47	PART NO.	REQD	NAME	1010 C.R.	No.16 (.0613) Gage	As rec.	
APPD	Smith	4-13-47	R17 R/L	1R-1L	BRACKET	SCALE Full		DRAWING NO.	
			UNIT OR ASSEMBLY		RADIATOR – 1949 STD.	ASSY. DR. NO. 274851	COMPANY NAME CITY	NO. OF 274833 ⁴/R	

FIG. 11.111. Dimensioning a sheet-metal part.

11.87. DIMENSIONING A SHEET-METAL PART. Parts to be made of thin materials are usually drawn showing the

part in its finished form, as in Fig. 11.111. The template maker first uses the drawing to lay out a flat pattern of the part. If only a few parts are to be made, this template will serve as a pattern for cutting the blanks. Then the part will be formed and completed by hand. If a large number of parts are to be made, the diemaker will use the template and drawing in making up the necessary dies for blanking, punching, and forming. The work of both template maker and diemaker is simplified by giving the dimensions to the same side of the material inside or outside, whichever is more important from the functional standpoint, as shown in Fig. 11.111. Dimensions to rounded edges (bends) are given to the theoretical sharp edges, which are called *mold lines*. The thickness of the material is given in the "stock" block of the title strip. Note in the figure that the holes are positioned in groups (because of functional requirements) and that important functional dimensions are three-place decimals.

PROBLEMS

The following problems are given as studies in dimensioning in which the principles presented in this chapter are to be applied. Attention should be given to the methods of manufacture, as described in Chap. 10. Assume a function for the part in order to fix the position of finished surfaces and limit possibilities in the selection of dimensions.

GROUP 1. DIMENSIONED DRAWINGS FROM PICTORIAL VIEWS

The problems that are presented in pictorial form in Chaps. 5 to 8 can be used as dimensioning problems. Either dimension a drawing you have already made as an exercise in shape description or, for variety, select another. Because of the difference in method of representation, the dimensions on a pictorial drawing and those on an orthographic drawing of the same object will not necessarily correspond; therefore, pay no attention to the placement of dimensions on the pictorial drawings except for obtaining the sizes needed. A selection of 11 problems, graded in order of difficulty, is given below.

11.1.1. Make a dimensioned orthographic drawing of Prob. 5.2.1, beam support. No finished surfaces.

11.1.2. Make a dimensioned orthographic drawing of Prob. 5.2.5, slotted wedge. Slot and base are finished.

11.1.3. Make a dimensioned orthographic drawing of Prob. 5.2.8, corner stop. Slot at top, cut corner, and base are finished.

11.1.4. Make a dimensioned orthographic drawing of Prob. 5.2.11, guide base. Vertical slot, boss on front, and base are finished.

11.1.5. Make a dimensioned orthographic drawing of Prob. 5.2.19, shifter fork. All contact surfaces are finished.

11.1.6. Make a dimensioned orthographic drawing of Prob. 5.2.29, shaft guide. L-shaped pad and end of hub are finished.

11.1.7. Make a dimensioned orthographic drawing of Prob. 7.1.13, jig angle. Finished all over.

11.1.8. Make a dimensioned orthographic drawing of Prob. 7.1.19, angle-shaft base. Base and slanting surface are finished.

11.1.9. Make a dimensioned orthographic drawing of Prob. 7.1.18, radial swing block. All contact surfaces are finished.

11.1.10. Make a dimensioned orthographic drawing of Prob. 7.2.6, transverse connection. Base pads are finished.

11.1.11. Make a dimensioned orthographic drawing of Prob. 7.2.7, chamfer-tool base. Contact surfaces are finished.

GROUP 2.   DIMENSIONED DRAWINGS FROM MODELS

Excellent practice in dimensioning is afforded by making a detail drawing from a pattern, casting, or forging or from a model made for the purpose. Old or obsolete patterns can often be obtained from companies manufacturing a variety of small parts, and "throw-out" castings or forgings are occasionally available. In taking measurements from a pattern, a shrink rule should be used; allowance must be made for finished surfaces.

GROUP 3.   PIECES TO BE DRAWN AND DIMENSIONED

The problem illustrations are printed to scale, as indicated in each problem. Transfer distances with dividers or by scaling, and draw the objects to a convenient scale on paper of the size to suit. For proper placement of dimensions, more space should be provided between the views than is shown in the illustrations.

Use the aligned or horizontal dimensioning system, as desired. It is suggested that some problems be dimensioned in the complete decimal system.

11.3.1. Stud shaft, shown half size. Machined from steel-bar stock.

PROB. 11.3.1.   Stud shaft.

PROB. 11.3.2. Shaft bracket.

11.3.2. Shaft bracket, shown half size. Malleable iron. Hole in base is drilled and counterbored for a socket-head cap screw. Base slot and front surface of hub are finished. Hole in hub is bored and reamed. The function of this part is to support a shaft at a fixed distance from a machine bed, as indicated by the small pictorial view.

11.3.3. Idler bracket, shown half size. Cast iron. Hole is bored and reamed. Slot is milled.

11.3.3A. See Prob. 11.3.3. Draw and dimension the right-hand part.

11.3.4. Filter flange, shown half size. Cast

PROB. 11.3.3. Idler bracket, left hand.

aluminum. The small holes are drilled. Add spot faces.

11.3.5. Boom-pin rest. Steel drop forging. Shown half size; draw half size or full size. Add top view if desired. Show machining allowance with alternate position lines, and dimension as in Fig. 10.8. All draft angles 7°. Holes are drilled, corner notches milled.

11.3.5*A*. Same as Prob. 11.3.5., but make two drawings; (*a*) the unmachined forging dimensioned for the diemaker and (*b*) the machined forging dimensioned for the machinist. Reference: Fig. 11.110.

PROB. 11.3.4. Filter flange.

PROB. 11.3.5. Boom-pin rest.

11.3.6. Clutch lever. Aluminum drop forging. Shown half size, draw full size or twice size. Add top view if desired. Holes are drilled and reamed; ends of hub are finished; left-end lug is straddle milled; slot in lower lug is milled. Show machining allowance with alternate position lines, and dimension as in Fig. 10.8. All draft angles 7°.

11.3.6A. Same as Prob 11.3.6, but make two drawings: (a) the unmachined forging di- mensioned for the diemaker and (b) the machined forging dimensioned for the machinist. Reference: Fig. 11.110.

11.3.7. Radiator mounting clip, LH, no. 16 (0.0625) steel sheet. Shown half size. Holes and slot are punched. Reference: Fig. 11.111.

11.3.8. Pulley bracket. Shown half size. Aluminum sheet, 24-ST, 0.032 in. thick. Reference: Fig. 11.111.

PROB. 11.3.6. Clutch lever.

PROB. 11.3.7. Radiator mounting clip, left hand.

PROB. 11.3.8. Pulley bracket.

GROUP 4. DIMENSIONED DRAWINGS FROM AN ASSEMBLY OR DESIGN DRAWING

The assembly drawings given in the problem section of Chap. 13 are well suited for exercises in dimensioning detail working drawings. The assembly shows the position of each part, and the function can be understood by a study of the motion, relationship, etc., of the different parts. Note particularly the mating and controlling surfaces and the logical reference surfaces for dimensions of position. Inasmuch as the dimensioning of an assembly drawing is crowded, and it will probably not even have the same views as the detail drawing of one of the parts, disregard the position and selection of the assembly dimensions, and use them only to obtain sizes. The following are suggested:

11.4.1.   Detail drawing of shaft, Prob. 13.3.3.

11.4.2.   Detail drawing of bushing, Prob. 13.3.3.

11.4.3.   Detail drawing of bracket, Prob. 13.3.3.

11.4.4.   Detail drawing of body, Prob. 13.3.7.

11.4.5.   Detail drawing of hanger, Prob. 13.3.13.

11.4.6.   Detail drawing of rack, Prob. 13.3.9.

11.4.7.   Detail drawing of rack housing, Prob. 13.3.9.

11.4.8.   Detail drawing of cover, Prob. 13.3.9.

11.4.9.   Detail drawing of base, Prob. 13.3.1.

11.4.10.   Detail drawing of base, Prob. 13.7.3.

11.4.11.   Detail drawing of jaw, Prob. 13.7.3.

11.4.12.   Detail drawing of screw, Prob. 13.7.3.

11.4.13.   Detail drawing of screw bushing, Prob. 13.7.3.

11.4.14.   Detail drawing of body (drop forging), Prob. 13.4.7.

11.4.15.   Detail drawing of base, Prob. 13.7.1.

11.4.16.   Detail drawing of frame, Prob. 13.7.1.

11.4.17.   Detail drawing of frame, Prob. 13.7.2.

11.4.18.   Detail drawing of ram, Prob. 13.7.2.

11.4.19.   Detail drawing of pinion shaft, Prob. 13.7.2.

11.4.20.   Detail drawing of base, Prob. 13.7.2.

11.4.21.   Detail drawing of cover, Prob. 13.7.2.

11.4.22.   Detail drawing of sleeve ball, Prob. 13.7.2.

11.4.23.   Detail drawing of stud ball, Prob. 13.7.2.

11.4.24.   Detail drawing of body, Prob. 13.4.5.

11.4.25.   Detail drawing of spring, Prob. 13.4.5.

12

Screw Threads, Fasteners, Keys, Rivets, and Springs

12.1. A screw thread is the functional element used on bolts, nuts, cap screws, wood screws, and the like and on shafts or similar parts employed for transmitting power or for adjustment. Screw threads occur in one form or another on practically all engineering products. Consequently, in making working drawings, there is the repeated necessity to *represent* and *specify* screw threads.

12.2. **HISTORY.** The earliest records of the screw are found in the writings of Archimedes (278 to 212 B.C.). Although specimens of ancient Greek and Roman screws are so rare as to indicate that they were seldom used, there are many

from the later Middle Ages; and it is known that crude lathes and dies were used to cut threads in the latter period. Most early screws were made by hand, by forging the head, cutting the slot with a saw, and fashioning the screw with a file. In America in colonial times wood screws were blunt on the ends; the gimlet point did not appear until 1846. Iron screws were made for each threaded hole. There was no interchanging of parts, and nuts had to be tied to their own bolts. In England, Sir Joseph Whitworth made the first attempt to set up a uniform standard in 1841. His system was generally adopted there but not in the United States.

FIG. 12.1. Screw-thread terminology. See paragraph 12.4 for details.

FIG. 12.2. Multiple threads. Note that, for a single thread, lead and pitch are identical values; for a double thread, lead is twice the pitch; and for a triple thread, lead is three times the pitch.

12.3. **STANDARDIZATION.** The initial attempt to standardize screw threads in the United States came in 1864 with the adoption of a report prepared by a committee appointed by the Franklin Institute. The system, designed by William Sellers, came into general use and was known as the "Franklin Institute thread," the "Sellers thread," or the "United States thread." It fulfilled the need for a general-purpose thread at that period; but with the coming of the automobile, the airplane, and other modern equipment, it became inadequate. Through the efforts of the various engineering societies, the Bureau of Standards, and others, the National Screw Thread Commission was authorized by act of Congress in 1918 and inaugurated the present standards. The work has been carried on by the ASA and by the Interdepartmental Screw Thread Committee of the U.S. Departments of Defense, Army, Navy, Air Force, and Commerce. Later, these organizations, working in cooperation with representatives of the British and Canadian governments and standards associations, developed an agreement covering a general-purpose thread that fulfills the basic requirements for interchangeability of threaded products produced in the three countries. The "Declaration of Accord" establishing the Unified Screw Thread was signed in Washington, D.C., on November 18, 1948.

Essential features of the Unified and other threads are given in this chapter, while standards covering them are listed in the Appendix.

12.4. **SCREW-THREAD TERMINOLOGY**

Screw Thread (Thread). A ridge of uniform section in the form of a helix on the external or internal surface of a cylinder or cone.

Straight Thread. A thread formed on a cylinder (Fig. 12.1).

Taper Thread. A thread formed on a cone.

External Thread (Screw). A thread on the external surface of a cylinder or cone (Fig. 12.1).

Internal Thread (Nut). A thread on the internal surface of a cylinder or cone (Fig. 12.1).

Right-hand Thread. A thread which, when viewed axially, winds in a clockwise and receding direction. Threads are always right-hand unless otherwise specified.

Left-hand Thread. A thread which, when viewed axially, winds in a counterclockwise and receding direction. All left-hand threads are designated "LH."

Form. The profile (cross section) of the thread. Figure 12.3 shows various forms.

Crest. The edge or surface that joins the sides of a thread and is farthest from the cylinder or cone from which the thread projects (Fig. 12.1).

Root. The edge or surface that joins the sides of adjacent thread forms and coincides with the cylinder or cone from which the thread projects (Fig. 12.1).

Pitch. The distance between corresponding points on adjacent thread forms measured parallel to the axis (Fig. 12.1). This distance is a measure of the size of the thread form used.

Lead. The distance a threaded part moves axially, with respect to a fixed mating part, in one complete revolution. See multiple thread (below) and Fig. 12.2.

Threads per Inch. The reciprocal of the pitch and the value specified to govern the size of the thread form.

Major Diameter. The largest diameter of a screw thread (Fig. 12.1). .

Minor Diameter. The smallest diameter of a screw thread (Fig. 12.1).

Pitch Diameter. On a straight thread, the diameter of an imaginary cylinder, the surface of which cuts the thread forms where the width of the thread and groove are equal (Fig. 12.1). The clearance between two mating threads is controlled largely by closely toleranced pitch diameters.

Depth of Thread. The distance between crest and root measured normal to the axis (Fig. 12.1).

Single Thread. A thread having the thread form produced on but one helix of the cylinder (Fig. 12.2). See multiple thread (below). On a single thread, the lead and pitch are equivalent. Threads are always single unless otherwise specified.

Multiple Thread. A thread combination having the same form produced on two or more helices of the cylinder (Fig. 12.2). For a multiple thread, the lead is an integral multiple of the pitch, that is, on a *double thread* the lead is twice the pitch, on a *triple thread,* three times the pitch, etc. A multiple thread permits a more rapid advance without a coarser (larger) thread form. Note that the helices of a double thread start 180° apart; those of a triple thread, 120° apart; and those of a quadruple thread, 90° apart.

12.5. THREAD FORMS. Screw threads are used on fasteners, on devices for making adjustments, and for the transmission of power and motion. For these different purposes, a number of thread forms are in use (Fig. 12.3). The dimensions given in the figure are those of the basic thread forms. In practical usage,

clearance must be provided between the external and internal threads.

The *sharp V,* formerly used to a limited extent, is rarely employed now; it is difficult to maintain sharp roots in quantity production. The form is of interest, however, as the basis of more practical V-type threads; also, because of its simplicity, it is used on drawings as a conventional representation for other (V-type) threads.

V-type threads are employed primarily on fasteners and for making adjustments. For these purposes, the standard thread form in the United States is the *American National.* This form is also the basis for the Unified Screw Thread standard of the United States, Canada, and Great Britain and as such is known as the *Unified* thread. As illustrated in Fig. 12.3, the form is that of the maximum external thread. Observe that while the crest may be flat or rounded, the root is rounded by design or as a result of tool wear. The American National thread is by far the most commonly used thread in this country.

The 60° *stub* form is sometimes preferred when, instead of multiple threads, a single National-form thread would be too deep.

FIG. 12.3. Thread profiles. See paragraph 12.5 for the explanation of each type.

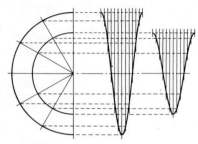

FIG. 12.4. True representation of a square thread, external and internal. Each thread (crest and root) line is a plotted helix.

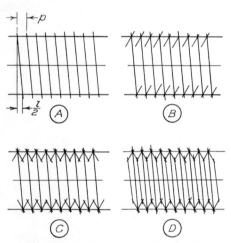

FIG. 12.5. Stages in construction for drawing a single V thread. Lay out pitch and half-lead and draw crest lines (*A*), start thread contour (*B*), complete thread contour (*C*), and draw root lines (*D*).

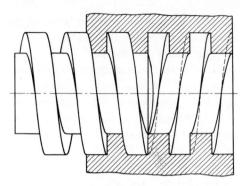

The former British standard was the *Whitworth,* at 55°, with crests and roots rounded. The *British Association Standard,* at 47½°, measured in the metric system, is used for small threads. The *French* and the *International Metric Standards* have a form similar to the American National but are dimensioned in the metric system.

The V shapes are not desirable for transmitting power since part of the thrust tends to burst the nut. This does not happen when a *square thread* is used as it transmits all the forces nearly parallel to the axis of the screw. The square thread can have, evidently, only half the number of threads in the same axial space as a V thread of the same pitch, and thus in shear it is only half as strong. Because of manufacturing difficulties, the square-thread form is sometimes modified by providing a slight (5°) taper to the sides.

The *Acme* has generally replaced the square thread in use. It is stronger, more easily produced, and permits the use of a disengaging or split nut that cannot be used on a square thread.

The *Stub Acme* is a strong thread suited to power applications where space limitation makes it desirable.

The *buttress,* for transmitting power in only one direction, has the efficiency of the square and the strength of the V thread. It was formerly produced with a perpendicular pressure flank (face); the newer 7° slope is more easily manufactured. Sometimes called the "breech-block" thread, it is used to withhold the pressure on breech blocks of large guns.

The *knuckle* thread is especially suitable when threads are to be molded or rolled in sheet metal. It can be observed on glass jars and in a shallow form on the bases of ordinary incandescent lamps.

Internal screw threads are produced by cutting, while external threads are made by cutting or rolling. Tests show that rolled threads are considerably stronger than cut threads. Through cold forging, rolling adds toughness and strength to the threaded portion of the metal.

12.6.   THREAD REPRESENTATION. The true representation of a screw thread is almost never used in making working drawings. In true representation, the crest and root lines (Fig. 12.4) appear as the projections of helices (see Helix, paragraph 3.71), which are extremely laborious to draw. For instances where true representation is desirable, that is, on advertising, elaborate display drawings, etc., templates can be made of cardboard or celluloid to assist in drawing the helices.

On practical working drawings, threads are given a semiconventional or symbolic representation, which provides thread pictures adequate for manufacturing purposes. The methods of

FIG. 12.6. Stages in drawing a single Acme thread. Because of the shape of the thread, the pitch diameter must first be located (*A*); then the thread form is drawn (*B*) and completed (*C*) and (*D*).

12.7. Semiconventional Representation

representing threads are discussed in the following paragraphs.

12.7. SEMICONVENTIONAL REPRESENTATION.

This simplifies the drawing of the thread principally by conventionalizing the projection of the helix into a straight line. Where applicable with certain thread forms, further simplifications are made. For example, the 29° angle of the Acme and 29° stub forms are drawn at 30°, and the American National form is represented by the sharp V. In general, true pitch should be shown, although a small increase or decrease in pitch is permissible so as to have even units of measure in making the drawing. Thus seven threads per inch may be increased to eight, or four and one-half may be decreased to four. Keep in mind that this is only to simplify the drawing and that the actual threads per inch must be specified in the dimensioning.

To draw a thread semiconventionally, you must know whether it is external or internal, the form, the major diameter, the pitch, its multiplicity, and whether it is right- or left-hand. Figure 12.5 illustrates the stages in drawing an American National, or sharp V; Fig. 12.6, an Acme; and Fig. 12.7, a square thread. Figure 12.5, showing the V thread, illustrates the method of drawing a thread semiconventionally. At (A) the diameter is laid out, and on it the pitch is measured on the upper line. This thread is a single thread; therefore, the pitch is equal to the lead, and the helix will advance $p/2 = l/2$ in 180°. This distance is laid off on the bottom diameter line, and the crest lines are drawn in. One side of the V form is drawn at (B), and it is completed at (C). At (D), the root lines are

FIG. 12.7. Stages in drawing a double square thread. The lead is twice the pitch. Note that after spacing the lead and pitch (A), crest and root lines are drawn (B) and (C); then the base line of the thread is added (D).

Length of Thread

FIG. 12.8. Thread representation on a long screw. The "repeat" lines save much drawing time.

added. As can be seen from Figs. 12.5 to 12.7, the stages in drawing any thread semiconventionally are similar; the principal difference is in the thread form. The square thread in Fig. 12.7 is double, while that in Fig. 12.8 is single and left-hand. Observe in Fig. 12.8 that it is unnecessary to draw the threads the whole length of a long screw. If the thread is left-hand, the crest and root lines are slanted in the opposite direction from those shown in Figs. 12.5 to 12.7, as illustrated by the left-hand square thread in Fig. 12.8. Figure 12.9

FIG. 12.9. Semiconventional thread representation. This method is used for threads drawn 1 in. or larger on both assembly and detail drawings.

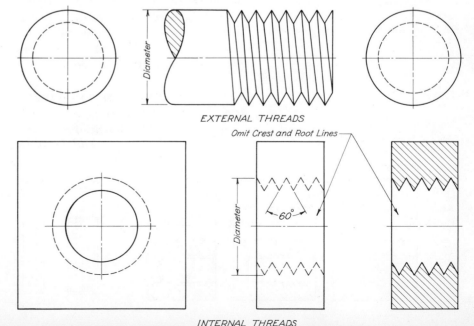

EXTERNAL THREADS

Omit Crest and Root Lines

INTERNAL THREADS

FIG. 12.10. ASA regular thread symbols. These are used for threads drawn under 1 in. on assembly drawings.

lines perpendicular to the axis. However, exceptions are made for internal threads not drawn in section and external threads drawn in section as shown in the figure.

12.10. ASA SIMPLIFIED SYMBOLS (FIG. 12.11). The simplified symbols omit both form and crest lines and indicate the threaded portion by dashed lines parallel to the axis at the approximate depth of thread. The simplified symbols are less descriptive than the regular symbols, but they are quicker to draw and for this reason are preferred on detail drawings.

12.11. TO DRAW THE ASA SYMBOLS. The two sets of symbols should be carefully studied and compared. Note that the regular and simplified symbols are identical for hidden threads. Note also that the end view of an external thread differs from the end view of an internal thread but that regular and simplified end-view symbols are identical.

No attempt need be made to show the actual pitch of the threads or their depth by the spacing of lines in the symbol. Identical symbols may be used for several threads of the same diameter but of different pitch. Only in the larger sizes for which the symbols are used could the actual pitch and the true depth of thread be shown without a confusion of lines that would defeat the purpose of the symbol. The symbols should therefore be made so as to read clearly and look well on the drawing, without other considerations.

To draw a symbol for any given thread, only the major diameter and length of thread must be known, and for a blind tapped hole, the depth of the tap drill is also needed.

illustrates semiconventional treatment for both external and internal V threads. Note that the crest and root lines are omitted on internal threads.

In general, threads should be represented semiconventionally except for the smaller sizes, which are ordinarily pictured by means of the ASA thread symbols. It is suggested that threads of 1 in. and larger in actual measurement on the drawing be represented semiconventionally.

12.8. THREAD SYMBOLS. The ASA provides two types of thread symbols: "regular" and "simplified." It is recommended that the ASA symbols be used for indicating the smaller threads, those drawn under 1 in., and that the regular symbols be used on assembly drawings and the simplified symbols on detail drawings. The following paragraphs describe these symbols in detail.

12.9. ASA REGULAR THREAD SYMBOLS (FIG. 12.10). The regular symbols omit the profile on longitudinal views and indicate the crests and roots by

FIG. 12.11. ASA simplified thread symbols. These are used for threads drawn under 1 in. on detail drawings.

12.11. To Draw the ASA Symbols

A *regular or simplified symbol for a tapped hole* is drawn in the stages shown in Fig. 12.12. The lines representing depth of thread are not drawn to actual scale but are spaced so as to look well on the drawing and to avoid crowding of the lines.

A *regular symbol for a tapped hole in section* is drawn in the stages shown in Fig. 12.13. The lines representing the crests are spaced by eye or scale to look well and need not conform to the actual thread pitch. The lines representing the roots of the thread are equally spaced by eye between the crest lines and are usually drawn heavier. Their length need not indicate the actual depth of thread but should be kept uniform by using light guide lines.

A *simplified symbol for an external thread* is drawn in the stages shown in Fig. 12.14. The 45° chamfer extends to the root line of the thread. Note that in the end view the chamfer line is shown.

A *regular symbol for external threads* is drawn in the stages shown in Fig. 12.15. The chamfer is 45° and to the depth of thread. Crest lines are spaced by eye or scale. Root lines are spaced by eye, are usually drawn heavier, and need not conform to actual thread depth.

Line Spacings. Table 12.1 gives suggested values of "pitch" and "depth of thread" for purposes of drawing the

TABLE 12.1. Suggested Values for Drawing Thread Symbols

Major diam. of thread D	Pitch p for dwg. purposes	Depth of thread $p/2$ for dwg. purposes
⅛ and 3/16	1/16 scant	1/32 scant
¼ and ⅜	1/16	1/32
½ and ⅝	⅛	1/16
¾ and ⅞	3/16	3/32

FIG. 12.12. Stages in drawing internal-thread symbols in external views. Regular and simplified symbols are identical here. See Table 12.1 for suggested depth of thread spacing.

FIG. 12.13. Stages in drawing regular internal-thread symbols in sectional views. See Table 12.1 for suggested depth of thread and pitch spacing.

FIG. 12.14. Stages in drawing simplified external-thread symbols. See Table 12.1 for suggested depth of thread spacing.

FIG. 12.15. Stages in drawing regular external-thread symbols. See Table 12.1 for suggested depth of thread and pitch spacing.

ASA symbols. Figure 12.16 shows both regular and simplified symbols, full size, drawn according to the values given in Table 12.1. No distinction is made in the symbol between coarse and fine threads.

12.12. THREADS IN SECTION. Figure 12.4 shows the true form of an internal square thread in section. Observe that the far side of the thread is visible, causing the root and crest lines to slope in the opposite direction from those on the external thread. Figure 12.9 shows the semiconventional treatment for V threads 1 in. or larger in diameter. Note that the crest and root lines are omitted. The regular and simplified symbols for threads in section are shown in Figs. 12.10 and 12.11. When two pieces screwed together are shown in section, the thread form should be drawn to aid in reading (Fig. 12.17). With small diameters, it is desirable to decrease the number of threads per inch, thus eliminating monotonous detail and greatly improving the readability of the drawing.

12.13. UNIFIED AND AMERICAN (NATIONAL) SCREW THREADS. The Unified thread standards adopted by the United States, Canada, and Great Britain for the bulk of threaded products basically constitutes the American Standard "Unified and American Screw Threads"

(ASA B1.1—1949). The form of thread employed has been described in paragraph 12.5 and is essentially that of the former (1935) American Standard. Threads produced according to the former and present American Standards will interchange. Important differences between the two standards are in the liberalization of manufacturing tolerances, the provision of allowances for most classes of threads, and the changes in thread designations. The new American Standard contains, in addition to the Unified diameter-pitch combinations and thread classes (adopted in common by the three countries), additional diameter-pitch combinations and two thread classes retained from the 1935 standard.

12.14. THREAD SERIES. Threads are classified in "series" according to the number of threads per inch used with a specific diameter. For example, an American (Unified) thread having 20 threads per inch applied to a ¼-in. diameter results in a thread belonging to the coarse-thread series, while one with 28 threads per inch on the same diameter gives a thread belonging to the fine-thread series.

In the United States the thread forms that have been subjected to series standardization by the ASA include the Unified or American National, the Acme, Stub Acme, pipe threads, buttress, and the knuckle thread as used on electric sockets and lamp bases. Except for the Unified, or American National, only one series is provided for each of the thread forms so standardized (see Appendix for Acme and Stub Acme threads and for pipe threads).

The American Standard "Unified and American (National) Screw Threads" covers six series of screw threads and, in

Regular

Simplified

FIG. 12.16. Thread symbols, actual drawing size.

addition, certain other preferred special diameter-pitch combinations. In the descriptions of the series which follow, the letters "U" and "N" used in the series designations stand for the words "Unified" and "National (form)," respectively.

The *coarse-thread series,* designated "UNC" or "NC," is recommended for general use where conditions do not require a fine thread.

The *fine-thread series,* designated "UNF" or "NF," is recommended for general use in automotive and aircraft work and where special conditions require a fine thread.

The *extrafine-thread series,* designated "UNEF" or "NEF," is used particularly in aircraft work, where an extremely shallow thread or a maximum number of threads within a given length is required.

The *8-thread series,* designated "8N," is a uniform-pitch series using eight threads per inch for all diameters concerned. Bolts for high-pressure pipe flanges, cylinder-head studs, and similar fasteners against pressure require that an initial tension be set up by elastic deformation of the fastener and that the components be held together so that the joint will not open when steam or other pressure is applied. To secure a proper initial tension, it is not practicable that the pitch should increase with the diameter of the thread, as the torque required to assemble would be excessive. Accordingly, for such purposes, the 8-thread series has come into general use in many classes of engineering work and as a substitute for the coarse-thread series.

The *12-thread series,* designated "12UN" or "12N," is a uniform-pitch series using 12 threads per inch for all diameters concerned. Sizes of 12-pitch threads from ½ to 1¾ in. in diameter

FIG. 12.17. Threads in section, actual drawing size.

are used in boiler practice, which requires that worn stud holes be retapped with the next larger size. The 12-thread series is also widely used in machine construction for thin nuts on shafts and sleeves and provides continuation of the fine-thread series for diameters larger than 1½ in.

The *16-thread series,* designated "16UN" or "16N," is a uniform-pitch series using 16 threads per inch for all diameters concerned. This series is intended for applications requiring a very fine thread, such as threaded adjusting collars and bearing retaining nuts. It also provides continuation of the extrafine-thread series for diameters larger than 2 in.

Special threads, designated "UN," "UNS," or "NS," as covered in the standards include nonstandard or special combinations of diameter, pitch, and length of engagement.

The diameter-pitch combinations of the above series will be found in the Appendix, where the Unified combinations (combinations common to the standards of the United States, Canada, and Great Britain) are printed in bold type.

12.15. UNIFIED AND AMERICAN SCREW-THREAD CLASSES. A class of thread is distinguished by the tolerance and allowance specified for the member threads and is therefore a control of the looseness or tightness of the fit between mating screws and nuts. The Unified and American (National) and Acme are at present the only threads in this country standardized to the extent of providing several thread classes to control the fit.

The classes provided by the American Standard "Unified and American Screw Threads" are classes 1A, 2A, and 3A, applied to *external threads only;* classes 1B, 2B, and 3B, applied to *internal threads only;* and classes 2 and 3, applied to *both external and internal threads.* These classes are achieved through toleranced thread dimensions given in the standards.

Classes 1A and 1B are intended for ordnance and other special uses where free assembly and easy production are important. Tolerances and allowance are largest with this class.

Classes 2A and 2B are the recognized standards for the bulk of screws, bolts, and nuts produced and are suitable for a wide variety of applications. A moderate allowance provides a minimum clearance between mating threads to minimize galling and seizure.

Classes 3A and 3B provide a class where accuracy and closeness of fit are important. No allowance is provided.

Classes 2 and 3, each applying to both external and internal threads, have

been retained from the former (1935) American Standard. No allowance is provided with either class, and tolerances are in general closer than with the corresponding new classes.

12.16. UNIFIED THREADS. Not all the diameter-pitch combinations listed in the American Standard "Unified and American Standard Screw Threads" appear in the British and Canadian standards. Combinations used in common by the three countries are called Unified threads and are identified by the letter U in the series designation; they are printed in bold type in the Appendix table. Unified threads may employ classes 1A and 1B, 2A and 2B, and 3A and 3B only. When one of these classes is used and the U does not appear in the designation, the thread conforms to the principles on which Unified threads are based.

The Unified and American National screw-thread table (Appendix) indicates the classes for which each series has data tabulated in the standards. Threads of standard diameter-pitch combinations but of a class for which data are not tabulated in the standard are designated UNS if a Unified combination and NS if not.

12.17. ACME AND STUB ACME THREADS. Acme and Stub Acme threads have been standardized by the ASA in one series of diameter-pitch combinations (see Appendix). In addition, the standard provides for two general applications of Acme threads: general purpose and centralizing. The three thread classes 2G, 3G, and 4G, standardized for general-purpose applications, have clearances on all diameters for free movement. Centralizing Acme threads have a close fit on the major diameter

FIG. 12.18. Specifications of external threads. (*A*) is American National, (*B*) Unified, (*C*) American National, (*D*) Acme, (*E*) square.

to maintain alignment of the screw and nut and are standardized in five thread classes, 2C, 3C, 4C, 5C, and 6C. The Stub Acme has only one thread class for general usage.

12.18. BUTTRESS THREADS.

Buttress threads have been standardized in a different fashion from the other types. Thread form and class of fit is completely defined. Thread series is not defined, but a table of recommended thread diameters and associated thread pitches is provided. Since the number of associated thread pitches varies from three to eleven (depending upon the thread diameter), the designation of a thread series would merely add complication. Three classes of fit are standard: class 1 (free), class 2 (medium), and class 3 (close).

12.19. THREAD SPECIFICATION.

The orthographic views of a thread are necessary in order to locate the position of the thread dimensionally on the part. In addition, the views describe whether the thread is external or internal. All other information, called the "specification," is normally conveyed by means of a note or dimensions and a note. In addition to appearing on drawings, the specification may be needed in correspondence, on stock and parts lists, etc.

Features of a thread on which information is essential for manufacture are form, nominal (major) diameter, threads per inch, and thread class or toleranced dimensions. In addition, if the thread is left-hand, the letters LH must be included in the specification; also, if the thread is other than single, its multiplicity must be indicated.

In general, threads other than the Unified and American National, Acme, Stub Acme, and buttress require toler-

anced dimensions to control the fit (Fig. 12.18E).

Unified and American National threads are specified completely by note. The form of the specification always follows the same order: The nominal size is given first, then the number of threads per inch and the series designation (UNC, NC, etc.), and then the thread class (Fig. 12.18A to C). If the thread is left-hand, the letters LH follow the class (Fig. 12.18A). Examples:

¼-20UNC-3A	¼-20NC-2
1-12UNF-2B-LH	1-20NEF-3
2-8N-2	2-12UN-2A
2-16UN-2B	2-6NS-2A

Note that, when the Unified-thread classes are employed, the letters A and B indicate whether the thread is external or internal.

Acme and Stub Acme threads are also specified by note. The form of the specification follows that of the Unified (Fig. 12.18D). Examples:

1¾-4Acme-2G (general-purpose class 2 Acme; 1¾ in. major diameter, 0.25 in. pitch; single, right-hand)

1-5Acme-4C-LH (centralizing class 4 Acme; 1 in. major diameter, 0.2 in. pitch; single, left-hand)

2½-0.333p-0.666L-Acme-3G (general-purpose class 3 Acme; 2½ in. major diameter, 0.333 in. pitch, 0.666 in. lead; double, right-hand)

¾-6Stub Acme (Stub Acme; ¾ in. major diameter, 0.1667 in. pitch; right-hand) .

Buttress threads can be completely specified by note but require one additional item of information in addition to diameter, threads per inch, type of thread, and class of fit: the direction of pressure as exerted by the internal

$\frac{5}{16}$ Drill, $\frac{3}{8}$-16NC-2

Thread relief $\frac{3}{16}$ wide to $1\frac{17}{32}$D

$\frac{1.284}{1.290}$ Bore, $1\frac{1}{2}$-6NC-3

$1\frac{1}{2}$

$\frac{5}{16}$ Drill x $\frac{7}{8}$ deep, $\frac{3}{8}$-16NC-2 x $\frac{5}{8}$ deep

FIG. 12.19. Specifications of internal threads. All shown here are American National.

member (screw). The following symbols are recommended for this purpose:

($\leftarrow$ screw *pushing* to left (screw pressure flank facing left)

$\leftarrow$(screw *pulling* to right (screw pressure flank facing right)

Note that the arrow points left but that the parenthesis mark indicates the direction of pressure flank. Where the buttress thread is multiple, the pitch and lead distances should be given instead of threads per inch. Examples:

⅝-20($\leftarrow$N. Butt.-1
4-8$\leftarrow$(N. Butt.-2LH
10-0.1p-0.2L($\leftarrow$N. Butt.-1

12.20.   TAPPED-HOLE SPECIFICATIONS.
Always specify by note, giving the tap-drill diameter and depth of hole followed by the thread specification and

length of thread (Fig. 12.19). For tap-drill sizes, see the Appendix. It is general commercial practice to use 75 per cent of the theoretical depth of thread for tapped holes. This gives about 95 per cent of the strength of a full thread and is much easier to cut.

12.21.   DEPTH OF TAPPED HOLES AND ENTRANCE LENGTH.   For threaded rods, studs, cap screws, machine screws, and similar fasteners, the depth of tapped holes and entrance length may be found by using an empirical formula based on the diameter of the fastener and the material tapped. See Fig. 12.20 and Table 12.2.

12.22.   THREADED FASTENERS.   All engineering products, structures, etc., are composed of separate parts that must be held together by some means of fastening. Compared with permanent methods of fastening, such as welding and riveting, threaded fasteners provide an advantage in that they can be removed, thus allowing disassembly of the parts. As distinguished from other fastening devices such as pins, rivets, and keys, a *threaded* fastener is a cylinder of metal with a screw thread on one end and, usually, a head on the other.

The quantity of threaded fasteners used each year is tremendous. Many varieties are obtainable, some standardized and others special. The standardization of such widely used products results in uniform and interchangeable parts obtainable without complicated and detailed specification and at low cost. Standardized fasteners should be employed wherever possible.

Most fasteners have descriptive names, as the "setscrew," which holds a part in a set, or fixed, position. The bolt derives its name from an early-English use; it

Tap drill diameter (See Appendix)

F

HOLE DRILLED

Thread diameter

D

C

E

HOLE TAPPED

FIG. 12.20. Proportions for tapped holes. See Table 12.2 for values of *A* to *F*.

A

B

CAP SCREW IN TAPPED HOLE

TABLE 12.2.   Detailed Depths for Drilling and Tapping Holes in Common Materials

Material	Entrance length for cap screws, etc., A	Thread clearance at bottom of hole B	Thread depth C	Unthreaded portion at bottom of hole E	Depth of drilled hole F
Aluminum	$2D$	$4/n$	$2D + 4/n$	$4/n$	$C + E$
Cast iron	$1\frac{1}{2}D$	$4/n$	$1\frac{1}{2}D + 4/n$	$4/n$	$C + E$
Brass	$1\frac{1}{2}D$	$4/n$	$1\frac{1}{2}D + 4/n$	$4/n$	$C + E$
Bronze	$1\frac{1}{2}D$	$4/n$	$1\frac{1}{2}D + 4/n$	$4/n$	$C + E$
Steel	D	$4/n$	$D + 4/n$	$4/n$	$C + E$

A = entrance length for fastener.
B = thread clearance at bottom of hole.
C = total thread depth.
D = diameter of fastener.

E = unthreaded portion at bottom of hole.
F = depth of tap-drill hole.
n = threads per inch.

was employed as a fastener or pin for bolting a door. Five types—the bolt, stud, cap screw, machine screw, and setscrew—represent the bulk of threaded fasteners.

12.23. AMERICAN STANDARD BOLTS AND NUTS. A *bolt* (Fig. 12.21*A*), having an integral head on one end and a thread on the other end, is passed through clearance holes in two parts and draws them together by means of a nut screwed on the threaded end.

Two major groups of bolts have been standardized: round-head bolts and wrench-head bolts (sometimes called "machine bolts").

Round-head bolts are used as through fasteners with a nut, usually square. Eleven head types have standard proportions and include carriage bolts, step bolts, elevator bolts, and spline bolts. Several head types are intended for wood construction and have square sections, ribs, or fins under the head to prevent the bolts from turning. These bolts are hot or cold formed, with no machining except threading; hence they present a somewhat coarse and irregular appearance. A table in the Appendix shows the various head forms and

gives nominal dimensions suitable for drawing purposes.

Wrench-head (machine) bolts have two standard head forms: square and hexagonal. Although intended for use as a through fastener with a nut, machine bolts are sometimes used as cap screws. Nuts to match the bolthead form and grade are available, but any nut of correct thread will fit a bolt. Machine bolts vary in grade from coarsely finished products resembling round-head bolts to a well-finished product matching a hexagon cap screw in appearance. Dimensions for drawing purposes are given in the Appendix.

12.24. STUDS. A *stud* (Fig. 12.21*B*) is a rod threaded on each end. As used normally, the fastener passes through a clearance hole in one piece and screws permanently into a tapped hole in the

FIG. 12.21. Common types of fasteners. (*A*) bolt; (*B*) stud; (*C*) cap screw; (*D*) machine screws; (*E*) setscrew.

other. A nut then draws the parts together. The stud (Fig. 12.22) is used when through bolts are not suitable for parts that must be removed frequently, such as cylinder heads and chest covers. One end is screwed tightly into a tapped hole, and the projecting stud guides the removable piece to position. The end to be screwed permanently into position is called the "stud end"; and the opposite end, the "nut end." The nut end is sometimes identified by rounding instead of chamfering. Studs have not been standardized by the ASA. The length of thread on the stud end is governed by the material tapped, as indicated in paragraph 12.20. The threads should jam at the top of the hole to prevent the stud from turning out when the nut is removed. The fit of the thread between the stud and tapped hole should be tight.

The length of thread on the nut end should be such that there is no danger of the nut binding before the parts are drawn together. The name "stud bolt" is often applied to a stud used as a through fastener with a nut on each end. The stud, a nonstandard part, is usually described on a detail drawing

(Fig. 12.22B). The nut, being a standard part, is described by note on the assembly drawing (Fig. 12.22A) or on the parts list.

12.25. CAP SCREWS. A *cap screw* (Fig. 12.21C) passes through a clearance hole in one piece and screws into a tapped hole in the other. The head, an integral part of the screw, draws the parts together as the screw enters the tapped hole. Cap screws are used on machine tools and other products requiring close dimensions and finished appearances. They are well-finished products; for example, the heads of the slotted- and socket-head screws are machined, and all have chamfered points. The five types of heads shown in Fig. 12.23 are standard. Detail dimensions and length increments are given in the Appendix.

12.26. MACHINE SCREWS. A *machine screw* (Fig. 12.21D) is a small fastener used with a nut to function in the same manner as a bolt; or without a nut, to function as a cap screw. Machine screws are small fasteners used principally in numbered diameter sizes. The finish is regularly bright, and the material used

FIG. 12.22. Stud and nut. (*A*) is the assembly drawing and (*B*) is the detail drawing of the stud.

FIG. 12.23. American Standard cap screws. Note that the head type is given in the specification.

is commonly steel or brass. The nine standardized head shapes (Fig. 12.24), except for the hexagon, are available in slotted form as shown or with cross recesses (Fig. 12.25). The size of the recess varies with the size of the screw. Two recess types occur: intersecting slots with parallel sides converging to a sharp apex at the bottom of the recess (the same driver is used for all size recesses) and large center opening, tapered wings, and a blunt bottom (five sizes of drivers needed).

The hexagon machine screw is not made with a cross recess but may be optionally slotted. Dimensions for drawing machine screw heads will be found in the Appendix.

12.27. SETSCREWS. A *setscrew* (Fig. 12.21*E*) screws into a tapped hole in an outer part, often a hub, and bears with its point against an inner part, usually a shaft. Setscrews are made of hardened steel and hold two parts in relative position by having the point set against the inner part. The American Standard square-head and headless screws are shown in Fig. 12.26. Types of points are shown in Fig. 12.27. Headless setscrews are made to comply with the safety code of factory-inspection laws, which are strict regarding the use of projecting screws on moving parts. Square-head setscrews have head proportions following the formulas in Fig. 12.26 and can be drawn by using the radii suggested there. A neck or a radius may be used under the head, and the points have the same dimensions as headless screws. Dimensions for headless setscrews are given in the Appendix.

12.28. AMERICAN STANDARD NUTS. These are available in two wrench-type styles: square and hexagonal. In addi-

tion to the plain form usually associated with bolts, several special-purpose styles are available. Jam, hexagonal slotted, and hexagonal castle nuts are shown in Fig. 12.28. Machine screw and stovebolt nuts are available in small sizes only.

12.29. STANDARD FASTENERS. The ASA Standards provide uniform dimensions and proportions for all fasteners (except studs) listed in the preceding paragraphs. With the exception of machine bolts, the only options for any of the preceding fasteners are the head style and thread series. Wrench head bolts are available in two head styles, two head weights, three finishes, and three thread series. Table 12.3 lists the available standard options, and paragraph 12.30 describes the differences:

FIG. 12.24. American Standard machine-screw heads.

FIG. 12.25. Recessed head and driver.

FIG. 12.26. American Standard setscrews. (*A*) and (*B*) square head; (*C*), (*D*), and (*E*) headless.

FIG. 12.27. American Standard setscrew points.

FIG. 12.28. American Standard nuts.

TABLE 12.3. Available Types and Thread Details of Standard Fasteners

Fastener group	Head styles	Thread series	Thread class
Round-head bolts	All	UNC	2A
Cap screws	Hexagonal	UNC, UNF, 8UN	2A
	Slotted		2A
	Socket		3A
Machine screws	All	NC, NF	2
Setscrews	Socket	UNC, UNF, 8UN, UNC, UNF	3A
	Square		2A
	Slotted		2A

Wrench-head (Machine) Bolts

| Finish class | Square | | Hexagonal | | Thread | |
	Regular	Heavy	Regular	Heavy	Series	Class
Unfaced	X	. . .	X	X	UNC	2A
Semifinished	. . .	. . .	X	X	UNC	2A
Finished	. . .	. . .	X	X	UNC, UNF, 8UN	2A

American Standard Nuts

| Finish class | Square | | Hexagonal | | | Hexagonal slotted | | |
	Regular	Heavy	Regular	Heavy	Thick	Regular	Heavy	Thick
Unfaced	X	X	X*	X				
Semifinished	. . .	. . .	X*	X	. . .	X*	X	
Finished	. . .	. . .	X	. . .	X	X	. . .	X

* ASA Standard B18.2—1955 lists ¼ to ⅝ sizes as not recommended for new designs.

12.30. FASTENER TERMS. *Nominal Diameter*. The basic major diameter of the thread.

Width across Flats—W. The distance separating parallel sides of the square or hexagonal head or nut, corresponding with the nominal size of the wrench. See table in Appendix for dimension *W*.

Tops of Boltheads and Nuts. The tops of heads and nuts are flat with a chamfer to remove the sharp corners. The angle of chamfer with the top surface is 25° for the square form and 30° for the hexagonal form; both are drawn at 30°. The diameter of the top circle is equal to the width across flats.

Washer Face. The washer face is a circular boss turned or otherwise formed on the bearing surface of a bolthead or nut to make a smooth surface. The diameter is equal to the width across flats. The thickness is ⅟₆₄ in. for all fasteners. A circular bearing surface can be obtained on a nut by chamfering the corners. The angle of chamfer with the bearing face is 30°; the diameter of the circle is equal to the width across flats.

Fastener Length.   The nominal length is the distance from the bearing surface to the point. For flat-head fasteners and for headless setscrews it is the over-all length.

Regular Series.   Regular boltheads and nuts are for general use. The dimensions and the resulting strengths are based on the theoretical analysis of the stresses and on results of numerous tests.

Heavy Series.   Boltheads and nuts in this series are for use where greater bearing surface is necessary. Therefore, for the same nominal size, they are larger in over-all dimensions than regular heads and nuts. They are used where a large clearance between the bolt and hole or a greater wrench-bearing surface is considered essential.

Thick Nuts.   These have the same dimensions as regular nuts, except that they are higher.

Class of Finish.   Unfaced bolts and nuts are not machined on any surface except the threads. The bearing surface is plain. Dimensional tolerances are as large as practicable.

Semifinished Boltheads and Nuts.   These have a smooth bearing surface machined or formed at right angles to the axis (see Fig. 12.29). For boltheads, this is a washer face; and for nuts, a washer face or a circular bearing surface produced by chamfering the corners. Dimensional tolerances of the fastener are otherwise the same as for the unfaced group.

Finished Bolts and Nuts.   These differ from the semifinished in two ways: The bearing surface may be washer-faced or produced by double chamfering (see Fig. 12.29). Dimensional tolerances are smaller than for the semifinished form. Finished hexagonal bolts have dimensional tolerances and workmanship similar to hexagonal cap screws.

12.31. STANDARD FASTENER SPECIFICATIONS.   All standard fasteners may be specified on drawings or parts lists by notes. The following items may be included in a fastener specification in the order listed. Obviously, many of the items will not apply to some fastener types.

1. Thread specification (without length)
2. Fastener length
3. Fastener series (bolts only)
4. Class of finish (bolts only)
5. Material (if other than steel)
6. Head style or form
7. Point type (setscrews only)
8. Fastener group name

Sample specifications follow. Note carefully the machine-bolt notes.

½-13UNC-2A × 3
  Reg Sq Bolt

¼-20UNC-2A × 4
  Reg Semifin Hex Bolt

⅜-16UNC-2A × 3½
  Hvy Semifin Hex Bolt

¾-16UNF-2A × 2½
  Finished Hex Bolt (omit Reg)

⅝-11UNC-2A × 4¼
  Hvy Finished Hex Bolt

#10-24NC-2 × 2
  Brass Slotted Flat Hd Mach Scr

#6-32NC-2 × ½
  Recess Fil Hd Mach Scr

¼-20UNC-2A × ¾
  Sq Hd Cone Pt Setscrew

½-13UNC-3A × 2
  Soc, Flt Pt Setscrew

See Fig. 12.23 for cap-screw notes.

HEADS
Bearing Surface
Plain
Fillet under Head

Bearing Surface
Washer Faced
Body Diameter
45°
Height of Head (H)
⟨¹⁄₆₄ (all sizes)⟩
Length

NUTS
Bearing Surface
Plain or Washer Faced
Thickness (T)
Both Sides Chamfered

FIG. 12.29.   Details of form for hexagonal bolts and nuts.

END VIEW OF SQUARE BOLTHEAD

Draw a circle of diameter *W*, and then draw the square with T square and 45° triangle.

FACE VIEW OF SQUARE BOLTHEAD

1. Establish the diameter and the height of head.

2. Draw, lightly, the vertical edges of the faces, projecting from the end view.

| 3. Set compass to radius of *C/2*, and draw the circle arcs locating centers P_1 and P_2. | 3. Set compass to radius of *W*, and draw the circle arc locating the center *P*. |

4. Draw chamfer arcs, using radii and centers shown.

5. Complete the views. Show 30° chamfer on across-corners view.

FIG. 12.30. Stages in drawing a square head.

12.32. THE DRAWING OF FASTENERS. Before drawing a fastener, its *type, nominal diameter,* and *length,* if a bolt or screw, must be known. Knowing the type and diameter, other dimensions can be found in the tables (see Appendix).

12.33. TO DRAW SQUARE AND HEXAGON-FORM FASTENERS. Square and hexagonal heads and nuts are drawn "across corners" in all views showing the faces unless a special reason exists for drawing them "across flats." Figure 12.30 shows stages in drawing square heads both across corners and across flats, and Fig. 12.31 shows the same for hexagonal heads. The principles apply equally to the drawing of nuts. The following infor-

END VIEW OF HEXAGONAL BOLTHEAD

Draw a circle of diameter *W,* and then draw the hexagon with T square and 30-60° triangle.

FACE VIEW OF HEXAGONAL BOLTHEAD

1. Establish the diameter, height of head, and washer-face thickness. The actual thickness of the washer face for all fasteners is 1/64 in. but may be increased up to 1/32 in. for the drawing.

2. Draw, lightly, the vertical edges of the faces, projecting from the end view.

3. With radius of *W/2* draw the circle arcs locating centers P_1 and P_2.

4. Draw chamfer arcs, using radii and centers shown.

5. Complete the views. Washer-face diameter is equal to *W.* For across-corners view, show 30° chamfer.

FIG. 12.31. Stages in drawing a hexagonal head.

mation must be known: (1) type of head or nut, (2) whether regular or heavy, (3) whether unfinished or semifinished, and (4) the nominal diameter. Using this information, additional data *W* (width across flats), *H* (height of head), and *T* (thickness of nut) are obtained from the tables (see Appendix).

Figure 12.32 shows a regular semifin-

ished hexagonal bolt and nut, drawn by the method of Fig. 12.31, showing the head across flats and the nut across corners. The length is selected from the bolt-

FIG. 12.32. American Standard regular hexagonal semifinished bolt and nut. See Appendix for detailed sizes.

FIG. 12.33. ASA regular square bolt and regular unfaced hexagonal nut. See Appendix for detailed sizes.

$\frac{5}{8}$-11 UNC-2A x 2 Reg Sq Bolt

$\frac{5}{8}$-11 UNC-2B Reg Hex Nut

$\frac{5}{8}$-11 UNC-2A x 2 Reg Semifin Hex Bolt

$\frac{5}{8}$-11 UNC-2B Reg Semifin Hex Nut

FIG. 12.34. ASA regular semifinished hexagonal bolt and regular semifinished hexagonal nut. See Appendix for detailed sizes.

$\frac{5}{8}$-11 UNC-2A x 2 Brass Heavy Semifin Hex Bolt

$\frac{5}{8}$-11 UNC-2B Brass Heavy Semifin Hex Nut

FIG. 12.35. ASA heavy semifinished hexagonal bolt and heavy semifinished hexagonal nut. See Appendix for detailed sizes.

$\frac{5}{8}$-11 NC-2 x 2 Sq Bolt & Nut

FIG. 12.36. ASA regular unfaced square bolt and nut. See Appendix for detailed sizes.

FIG. 12.37. American Standard shoulder screw. The body is accurately finished. See Appendix.

length tables and the length of thread determined from the footnote to the bolt table (see Appendix). Observe that the washer face shown in Fig. 12.31 will occur only with semifinished hexagonal fasteners and is sometimes omitted from the drawings of these. Other views of bolts and nuts are shown in Figs. 12.33 to 12.36.

The drawing may require considerable time when, for example, clearance conditions necessitate an accurately drawn fastener, using exact dimensions from tables. Often, however, the representation of fasteners may be approximate or even symbolic because the note specifications invariably accompany and exactly specify them. If an accurate drawing of the fastener is not essential, the *W, H,* and *T* dimensions of hexagonal and square heads and nuts may be obtained from the nominal diameter and the following formulas; the resulting values will be quite close to the actual

dimensions. For the regular series, $W = 1\frac{1}{2}D$, $H = \frac{2}{3}D$, and $T = \frac{7}{8}D$; for the heavy series, $W = 1\frac{1}{2}D + \frac{1}{8}$ in., $H = \frac{3}{4}D$, and $T = D$.

A wide variety of *templates* to facilitate the drawing of fasteners is available.

12.34. SPECIALIZED FASTENERS. There are a great many special fasteners, a number of which are the developments of the companies that supply a variety of forms. The common types are discussed in the following paragraphs.

12.35. SHOULDER SCREWS (FIG. 12.37). These are widely used for holding machine parts together and providing pivots, such as with cams, linkages, etc. They are also used with punch and die sets for attaching stripper plates and are then commonly called "stripper bolts." Threads are coarse series, class 3. Detail dimensions are given in the Appendix.

12.36. PLOW BOLTS (FIG. 12.38). These are used principally in agricultural equipment. The No. 3 and No. 7 heads are recommended for most new work. Threads are coarse series, class 2A. For particulars and proportions, see ASA B18.9—1950.

12.37. AMERICAN STANDARD TAPPING SCREWS. Tapping screws are hardened fasteners that form their own mating internal threads when driven into a hole of the proper size. For certain conditions and materials, these screws give a combination of speed and low production cost, which makes them preferred. Many special types are available. The ASA has standardized head types conforming with all machine-screw heads except the binding and 100° flat heads. For draw-

No.3 Head   No.7 Head   No.4 Repair Hd   No.6 Repair Hd

FIG. 12.38. American Standard plow bolts.

ing purposes, dimensions of machine-screw heads may be used. Sizes conform, in general, with machine-screw sizes. The ASA provides three types of thread and point combinations (Fig. 12.39). The threads are 60° with flattened crest and root; types (*A*) and (*B*) are interrupted threads, and all fasteners are threaded to the head. Full details are given in ASA B18.6—1947.

12.38. **FASTENERS FOR WOOD.** Many forms of threaded fasteners for use in wood are available. Some are illustrated in Fig. 12.40. Threads are interrupted, 60° form, with a gimlet point. The ASA has standardized lag bolts with square heads and also wood screws with flat, round, and oval heads. Lag boltheads follow the same dimensions and, in general, the same nominal sizes as regular square bolts. Specific information is given in ASA B18—1951. Wood screws follow the same head dimensions and, in general, the same nominal sizes as the corresponding flat-, round-, and oval-head machine screws. The nominal sizes, however, are carried to higher numbers. See table in the Appendix. Like machine screws, wood-screw heads may be plain slotted or have either style of cross recess. Several kinds of finish are available, for example, bright steel, blued, or nickel-plated. Material is usually steel or brass.

12.39. **OTHER FORMS OF THREADED FASTENERS.** Many other forms of threaded fasteners, most of which have not been standardized, are in common use. Figure 12.41 illustrates some of these.

12.40. **LOCK NUTS AND LOCKING DEVICES (FIG. 12.42).** Many different locking devices are used to prevent nuts from working loose. A screw thread holds se-

FIG. 12.39. American Standard tapping screw points. These are hardened and made to form their own thread in a drilled or punched hole.

FIG. 12.40. Fasteners used in wood.

FIG. 12.41. Miscellaneous threaded fasteners. Many special fasteners are available.

FIG. 12.42. Various locking devices. See paragraph 12.40.

FIG. 12.43. Key nomenclature.

FIG. 12.44. Square (or flat) key. One-half of the key is in the keyway, one-half in the key seat.

FIG. 12.45. Gib-head key. The head shape provides removal.

FIG. 12.46. Pratt and Whitney key. The ends of the key are rounded.

FIG. 12.47. Woodruff keys, cutter, and key seat. This is most widely used.

curely unless the parts are subject to impact and vibration, as in a railroad-track joint or an automobile engine. A common device is the *jam nut* shown at (*A*). *Slotted nuts* (*L*) and *castle nuts* (*M*), to be held with a cotter or wire, are commonly used in automotive and allied work. For additional information on jam, slotted, and castle nuts, see paragraph 12.28.

At (*B*) is shown a *round nut* locked by means of a setscrew. A brass plug is placed under the setscrew to prevent damage to the thread. This is a common type of adjusting nut used in machine-tool practice. (*C*) is a *lock nut,* in which the threads are deformed after cutting. Patented *spring washers,* such as are shown at (*D*), (*E*), and (*F*), are common devices. Special patented nuts with plastic or fiber inserts or with distorted threads are in common use as locking devices. The locking action of (*J*), (*K*), (*N*), and (*O*) should be evident from the figure.

12.41. ASA STANDARD PLAIN AND LOCK WASHERS. There are four standard ASA spring lock washers: light, medium, heavy, and extra heavy. These are shown in Fig. 12.42*G* and *H* and are specified by giving nominal diameter and series, for example,

½ Heavy Lock Washer

ASA plain washers are also standardized in four series—light, medium, heavy, and extra heavy—and are specified by giving nominal diameter and series, for example,

⁷⁄₁₆ Light Plain Washer

FIG. 12.48. Keys for light duty. (*A*) saddle, (*B*) flat, (*C*) Nordberg.

Dimensions of ASA plain and lock washers are given in the Appendix.

12.42. KEYS. In making machine drawings there is frequent occasion for representing key fasteners, used to prevent the rotation of wheels, gears, etc., on their shafts. A key is a piece of metal (Fig. 12.43) placed so that part of it lies in a groove, called the "key seat," cut in a shaft. The key then extends somewhat above the shaft and fits into a "keyway" cut in a hub. Thus, after assembly, the key is partly in the shaft and partly in the hub, locking the two together so that one cannot rotate without the other.

12.43. KEY TYPES. The simplest key, geometrically, is the square key, placed *half* in the shaft and *half* in the hub (Fig. 12.44). A flat key is rectangular in cross section and is used in the same manner as the square key. The gib-head key (Fig. 12.45) is tapered on its upper surface and is driven in to form a very secure fastening. Both square and flat (parallel and tapered stock) keys have been standardized by the ASA. Tables of standard sizes are given in the Appendix.

The Pratt and Whitney key (Fig. 12.46) is a variation on the square key. It is rectangular in cross section and has rounded ends. It is placed two-thirds in the shaft and one-third in the hub. The key is proportioned so that the key seat is square and the keyway is half as deep as it is wide. Sizes are given in the Appendix.

Perhaps the most common key is the Woodruff (Fig. 12.47). This key is a flat segmental disk with a flat (*A*) or round (*B*) bottom. The key seat is semicylindrical and cut to a depth so that *half* the *width* of the key extends above the shaft

FIG. 12.49. Keys for heavy duty. (A) Barth, (B) Kennedy, (C) Lewis.

FIG. 12.50. Splined shafts and hubs. (A) straight-radial, (B) involute. Both provide strong resistance to torque forces.

FIG. 12.51. Nominal dimensions of key seats and keyways (square and Woodruff). See paragraph 12.45.

FIG. 12.52. Limit dimensions of key seats and keyways (square and Woodruff). See paragraph 12.45.

and into the hub. Tables of dimensions are given in the Appendix. A good basic rule for proportioning a Woodruff key to a given shaft is to have the width of the key one-fourth the diameter of the shaft and its radius equal to the radius of the shaft, selecting the standard key that comes nearest to these proportions. In drawing Woodruff keys, take care to place the center for the arc above the top of the key to a distance equal to one-half the thickness of the saw used in splitting the blank. This amount is given in column E of the table in the Appendix.

Figure 12.48 shows three keys for light duty: the saddle key (A), the flat key (B), and the pin, or Nordberg, key (C), which is used at the end of a shaft, as, for example, in fastening a handwheel.

Figure 12.49 shows some forms of heavy-duty keys. (A) is the Barth key, (B) the Kennedy key, and (C) the Lewis key for driving in one direction. In the latter two, the line of shear is on the diagonal.

For very heavy duty, keys are not sufficiently strong and splines (grooves) are cut in both shaft and hub, arranged so that they fit one within the other (Fig. 12.50). (A) and (B) are two forms of splines widely used instead of keys. (B) is the newer ASA involute spline (B5.15—1946).

12.44. SPECIFICATION OF KEYS. Keys are specified by note or number, depending upon the type.

Square and flat keys are specified by a note giving the width, height, and length, for example,

½ Square Key 2½ Lg

½ × ⅜ Flat Key 2½ Lg

Plain taper stock keys are specified by giving the width, the height at the large end, and the length. The height at the large end is measured at the distance W (width) from the large end. The taper is 1 to 96 (see Appendix). For example,

⅜ × ⅜ × 1½ Square Plain Taper Key

½ × ⅜ × 1¼ Flat Plain Taper Key

Gib-head taper stock keys are specified by giving, except for name, the same information as for square or flat taper keys (see Appendix), for example,

¾ × ¾ × 2¼ Square Gib-head Taper Key

⅞ × ⅝ × 2½ Flat Gib-head Taper Key

Pratt and Whitney keys are specified by number or letter (see Appendix), for example,

Pratt and Whitney Key No. 6

Woodruff keys are specified by number (see Appendix).

Dimensions and specifications of other key types may be found in handbooks or manufacturers' catalogues.

12.45. DIMENSIONING KEY SEATS AND KEYWAYS. The dimensioning of the *seat* and *way* for keys depends upon the purpose for which the drawing is intended. For unit production, when the keys are expected to be fitted by the machinist, nominal dimensions may be given, as in Fig. 12.51. For quantity production, the limits of width (and depth, if necessary) should be given as in Fig. 12.52. Pratt and Whitney key seats and keyways are dimensioned as in Fig. 12.53. Note that

FIG. 12.53. Dimensioning for a Pratt and Whitney key seat and keyway.

Button   High Button   Cone

Flat-top Countersunk   Round-top Countersunk   Pan

FIG. 12.55. Large rivet heads. These are used for structural steel.

FIG. 12.56. Lap and butt joints. See paragraph 12.46.

the *length* of the key seat is given to correspond with the specification of the key. If interchangeability is important and when careful gaging is necessary, the dimensions should be given as in Fig. 12.54 and the values expressed with limits.

12.46. RIVETS. Rivets are used for making permanent fastenings, generally between pieces of sheet or rolled metal. They are round bars of steel or wrought iron with a head formed on one end and are often put in place red hot so that a head can be formed on the other end by pressing or hammering. Rivet holes are punched, punched and reamed, or drilled larger than the diameter of the rivet, and the shank of the rivet is made just long enough to give sufficient metal to fill the hole completely and make the head.

Large rivets are used in structural-steel construction and in boiler and tank work. In structural work, only a few kinds of heads are normally needed: the button, high button, and flat-top countersunk heads (Fig. 12.55).

For boiler and tank work, the button, cone, round-top countersunk, and pan heads are used. Plates are connected by either lap or butt joints. Figure 12.56A is a single-riveted lap joint; (B) is a double-riveted lap joint; (C) is a single-strap butt joint; and (D) a double-strap butt joint.

Large rivets are available in diameters of ½ to 1¾ in., by increments of even ⅛ in. The length needed is governed by the "grip," as shown at Fig. 12.56D, plus the length needed to form the head. Length of rivets for various grip distances may be found in the handbook "Steel Construction" published by the American Institute of Steel Construction.

Small rivets are used for fabricating light structural shapes and sheet metal. ASA small-rivet heads are shown in Fig. 12.57. Small rivets are available in diameters of ³⁄₃₂ to ⁷⁄₁₆ in., by increments of even ¹⁄₃₂ in. to ⅜ in. diameter.

Tinners', coopers', and belt rivets are used for fastening thin sheet metal, wood, leather, rubber, etc. Standard heads and proportions are given in the Appendix.

12.47. SPRINGS. A spring can be defined as an elastic body designed to store energy when deflected. Springs are classified according to their geometric form: helical or flat.

12.48. HELICAL SPRINGS. These are further classified as (1) compression, (2) extension, or (3) torsion, according to the intended action. On working drawings, helical springs are drawn as a single-line convention, as in Fig. 12.58; or semiconventionally, as in Figs. 12.59 to 12.61, by laying out the diameter (D) and pitch (P) of coils and then drawing a construction circle for the wire size at the limiting positions and conventionalizing the helix with straight lines. Helical springs may be wound of round-, square-, or special-section wire.

Compression springs are wound with the coils separated so that the unit can be compressed, and the ends may be open or closed and may be left plain or ground,

FIG. 12.57. American Standard small-rivet heads. These are used principally for thin material.

FIG. 12.58. Conventional representation of springs. The single-line treatment saves drawing time.

as shown in Fig. 12.59. The information that must be given for a compression spring is as follows:

1. Controlling diameter: (*a*) outside, (*b*) inside, (*c*) operates inside a tube, or (*d*) operates over a rod

2. Wire or bar size

3. Material (kind and grade)

4. Coils: (*a*) total number and (*b*) right- or left-hand

5. Style of ends

6. Load at deflected length of ___

7. Load rate between ___ inches and ___ inches

8. Maximum solid height

9. Minimum compressed height in use

Extension springs are wound with the loops in contact so that the unit can be extended, and the ends are usually made as a loop, as shown in Fig. 12.60. Special ends are sometimes required and are described by the ASA. The information that must be given for an extension spring is as follows:

1. Free length: (*a*) over-all, (*b*) over coil, or (*c*) inside of hooks

2. Controlling diameter: (*a*) outside diameter, (*b*) inside diameter, or (*c*) operates inside a tube

3. Wire size

4. Material (kind and grade)

5. Coils: (*a*) total number and (*b*) right- or left-hand

FIG. 12.59. Representation and dimensioning of compression springs.

FIG. 12.60. Representation and dimensioning of extension springs.

FIG. 12.61. Representation and dimensioning of torsion springs.

Simple Flat Spring

Belleville Spring

Semi-elliptic Leaf Spring

Elliptic Leaf Spring

Power Spring

FIG. 12.62. Flat spring types. The variety is such that these require individual representation and specification.

6. Style of ends

7. Load at inside hooks

8. Load rate, pounds per 1-in. deflection

9. Maximum extended length

Torsion springs are wound with closed or open coils, and the load is applied torsionally (at right angles to the spring axis). The ends may be shaped as hooks or as straight torsion arms, as indicated in Fig. 12.61. The information that must be given for a torsion spring is as follows:

1. Free length (dimension *A,* Fig. 12.61)

2. Controlling diameter: (*a*) outside diameter, (*b*) inside diameter, (*c*) operates inside a hole, or (*d*) operates over a rod

3. Wire size

4. Material (kind and grade)

5. Coils: (*a*) total number and (*b*) right- or left-hand

6. Torque, pounds at ___ degrees of deflection

7. Maximum deflection (degrees from free position)

8. Style of ends

12.49. FLAT SPRINGS. A flat spring can be defined as any spring made of flat or strip material. Flat springs (Fig. 12.62) are classified as (1) simple flat springs, formed so that the desired force will be applied when the spring is deflected in a direction opposite to the force; (2) power springs, made as a straight piece and then coiled inside an enclosing case; (3) Belleville springs, stamped of thin material and shaped so as to store energy when deflected; and (4) leaf springs, in elliptic or semielliptic form, made of several pieces of varying length, shaped so as to straighten when a load is applied. The information that must be given for a flat spring is as follows:

1. Detailed shape and dimensions of the spring shown in a drawing

2. Material and heat-treatment

3. Finish

PROBLEMS

GROUP 1. HELICES

12.1.1. Draw three complete turns of a helix; diameter, 3 in.; pitch, 1¼ in. See Chap. 3.

12.1.2. Draw three complete turns of a conic helix, end and front views, with 1½-in. pitch, whose large diameter is 4 in. and small diameter is 1½ in. See Chap. 3.

GROUP 2. SCREW THREADS

12.2.1. Draw in section the following screw-thread forms, 1-in. pitch: American National, Acme, stub Acme, square.

12.2.2. Draw two views of a square-thread screw and a section of the nut separated; diameter, 2½ in.; pitch, ¾ in.; length of screw, 3 in.

12.2.3. Same as Prob. 12.2.2 but for V thread with ½-in. pitch.

12.2.4. Draw screws 2 in. in diameter and 3½ in. long: single square thread, pitch ½ in.; single V thread, pitch ¼ in.; double V thread, pitch ½ in.; left-hand double square thread, pitch ½ in.

12.2.5. Working space, 7 by 10½ in. Divide space as shown and in left space draw and label thread profiles, as follows: at *A*, sharp V, ½-in. pitch; at *B*, American National (Unified), ½-in. pitch; at *C*, square, 1-in. pitch; at *D*, Acme, 1-in. pitch. Show five threads each at *A* and *B* and three at *C* and *D*.

In right space, complete the views of the object by showing at *E* a 3½-4UNC-2B threaded hole in section. The thread runs out at a 3¹⁷/₃₂-in.-diameter by ¼-in.-wide thread relief. The lower line for the thread relief is shown. At *F*, show a 1¾-5UNC-3A thread. The thread is 1 in. long and runs out at a neck that is 1⅜ in. in diameter by ¼ in. wide. The free end of the thread should be chamfered at 45°. At *G*, show the shank threaded ⅝-18UNF-3A by 1 in. long; at *H*, show ⅜-16UNC-2B through tapped holes in section, four required. Completely specify all threads.

12.2.6. Working space, 7 by 10½ in. Com-plete the views and show threaded features as follows: at *A*, a ½-20UNF-3B through tapped hole; at *B*, a ⅝-11UNC-2B by ¾-in.-deep tapped hole with tap drill 1⅛ in. deep; at *C*, a ⅜-16UNC-2B by ¼-in.-deep tapped hole with the tap drill through to the 1-in. hole; at *D*, a 1½-8N-2 threaded hole running out at the large cored hole. Completely specify all threads.

12.2.7. Complete the offset support, showing threaded holes as follows: at *A*, 1⅜-6UNC-2B; at *B*, ½-13NC-2; at *C*, ⅝-18UNF-3B. *A* and *C* are through holes. *B* is a blind hole to receive a stud. Material is cast iron. Specify the threaded holes.

12.2.8. Complete the views of the cast-steel rocker, showing threads as follows: on center line *A-A*, 2-8N-2; on center line *B-B*, a ½-20UNF-2B tapped hole, ⅝ in. deep, with tap drill ⅞ in. deep; on center line *C-C*, a 2¾-12UN-2A external thread; on center line *D-D*, a ⅞-14UNF-3A external thread.

PROB. 12.2.5. Screw threads.

PROB. 12.2.6. Intermediate lever.

PROB. 12.2.7. Offset support.

PROB. 12.2.8. Rocker.

12.2.9. Minimum working space, 10½ by 15 in. Complete the views of the objects, and show threads and other details as follows: *upper left,* on center line *A-A,* show in section a ¾-10UNC-2B tapped hole, 1½ in. deep, with tap-drill hole 2½ in. deep. At *B,* show a 1¾-8N-2 external thread in section. At *C,* show a ¾-10UNC-2A thread in section. From *D* on center line *A-A,* show a ¼-in. drilled hole extending to the tap-drill hole. At *E,* show six ¼-in. drilled holes, ¼ in. deep, equally

spaced for spanner wrench. *Upper right,* at *F,* show a 1½-6UNC-2A thread. *Lower left,* at *G,* show (three) ⅜-16UNC-2B through holes. At *H,* show a ⅞-9UNC-2B tapped hole, 1⅛ in. deep, with the tap-drill hole going through the piece. On center line *K-K,* show a ⅞-14UNF-3B through tapped hole. *Lower center,* at *M,* show a ⅝-18UNF-3A thread 1¾ in. long. *Lower right,* on center line *P,* show a 2-4½UNC-2B hole in section.

Completely specify all threads.

PROB. 12.2.9. Screw threads.

GROUP 3.   THREADED FASTENERS

12.3.1. Draw one view of regular semi-finished hexagonal bolt and nut, across corners; diameter, 1 in.; length, 5 in.

12.3.2. Same as Prob. 12.3.1 for a heavy unfinished bolt and nut.

12.3.3. Same as Prob. 12.3.1 for a square bolt and nut.

12.3.4. Draw four ½- by 1½-in. cap screws, each with a different kind of head. Specify each.

12.3.5. Show the pieces fastened together on center line *E-E* with a ¾-in. hexagonal-head cap screw and light lock washer. On center line *A-A* show a ⅝- by 1½-in. shoulder screw.

12.3.6. Show pieces fastened together with a ¾-in. square bolt and heavy square nut. Place nut at bottom.

12.3.7. Fasten pieces together with a ¾-in. stud and regular semifinished hexagonal nut.

12.3.8. Fasten pieces together with a ¾-in. fillister-head cap screw.

12.3.9. Draw one view of a round-head square-neck (carriage) bolt; diameter, 1 in.; length, 5 in.; with regular square nut.

12.3.10. Draw one view of a round-head rib-neck (carriage) bolt; diameter, ¾ in.; length, 4 in.; with regular square nut.

12.3.11. Draw two views of a shoulder screw; diameter, ¾ in.; shoulder length, 5 in.

12.3.12. Draw two views of a socket-head cap screw; diameter, 1¼ in.; length, 6 in.

12.3.13. Draw the stuffing box and gland, showing the required fasteners. At *A*, show ½-in. hexagonal-head cap screws (six required). At *B*, show ½-in. studs and regular semi-finished hexagonal nuts. Specify fasteners.

12.3.14. Draw the bearing plate, showing the required fasteners. At *C*, show ½-in. regular semifinished hexagonal bolts and nuts (four required). At *D*, show ½-in. socket set-screw. At *E*, show ½-in. square-head setscrew. Setscrews are to have cone points. Specify fasteners.

Problems 12.3.13 and 12.3.14 may be drawn together on an 11- by 17-in. sheet or on separate sheets, showing full diameter of flanges.

PROB. 12.3.5. L lug.

PROB. 12.3.6. Double cover.

PROB. 12.3.7. Bracket and support.

PROB. 12.3.8. Centered closure.

PROB. 12.3.13. Stuffing box and gland.

PROB. 12.3.14. Bearing plate.

12.3.15. Draw the ball-bearing head, showing the required fasteners. At *A*, show ½- by 1¾-in. regular semifinished hexagonal bolts and nuts (six required), with heads to left and across flats. Note that this design prevents the heads from turning. At *B*, show 5⁄16- by ¾-in. fillister-head cap screws (four required). At *C*, show a ⅜- by ½-in. slotted flat-point setscrew with fiber disk to protect threads of spindle. Specify fasteners.

12.3.16. Draw the plain bearing head, showing the required fasteners. At *D*, show ½- by 2-in. studs and regular semifinished hexagonal nuts (six required); spot-face 1 in. diameter by 1⁄16 in. deep. At *E*, show ⅜- by 1-in. hexagonal-head cap screws (four required). At *F*, show a 7⁄16- by ⅞-in. square-head cup-point setscrew. At *G*, show a ⅛-27NPT hole with a pipe plug. Show the 11⁄32-in. tap drill through for gun packing the gland. Specify fasteners.

Problems 12.3.15 and 12.3.16 may be drawn together on an 11- by 17-in. sheet or on separate sheets, showing full diameter of flanges.

PROB. 12.3.15. Ball-bearing head.

PROB. 12.3.16. Plain bearing head.

GROUP 4. KEYS

Key sizes are given in the Appendix.

12.4.1. Draw hub and shaft as shown, with a Woodruff key in position.

12.4.2. Draw hub and shaft as shown, with a square key 2 in. long in position.

12.4.3. Draw hub and shaft as shown, with a gib-head key in position.

12.4.4. Draw hub and shaft as shown, with a Pratt and Whitney key in position.

PROB. 12.4.1. Hub and shaft. **PROB. 12.4.2.** Hub and shaft.   **PROB. 12.4.3.** Hub and shaft.   **PROB. 12.4.4.** Hub and shaft.

GROUP 5. RIVETS

12.5.1. Draw top view and section of a single-riveted butt joint 10⅜ in. long. Pitch of rivets is 1¾ in. Use cone-head rivets.

12.5.2. Draw a column section made of 15-in. by 33.9-lb channels with cover plates as shown, using ⅞-in. rivets (dimensions from the handbook of the American Institute of Steel Construction). Use button-head rivets on left side and flat-top countersunk-head rivets on right side so that the outside surface is flush.

PROB. 12.5.1. Butt joint.

PROB. 12.5.2. Column.

GROUP 6. SPRINGS

12.6.1. Draw a compression spring as follows: inside diameter, ¾ in.; wire size, ⅛ in. diameter; coils 14, right-hand; squared and ground ends; free length, 3½ in.

12.6.2. Draw a compression spring as follows: outside diameter, 1 in.; wire size, 3/32 in. diameter; coils 12, left-hand; open ends, not ground; free length, 4 in.

12.6.3. Draw an extension spring as follows: free length over coils, 2 in.; outside diameter, 1⅛ in.; wire size, ⅛ in. diameter; coils 11, right-hand; the ends parallel, closed loops.

12.6.4. Draw an extension spring as follows: free length inside hooks, 2¾ in.; inside diameter, ¾ in.; wire size, ⅛ in. diameter; coils 11, left-hand; the ends parallel, closed half loops.

12.6.5. Draw a torsion spring as follows: free length over coils ¾ in.; inside diameter, 1⅛ in.; wire size, ⅛ in. diameter; coils 5, right-hand; ends straight and turned to follow radial lines to center of spring and extend ½ in. from outside diameter of spring.

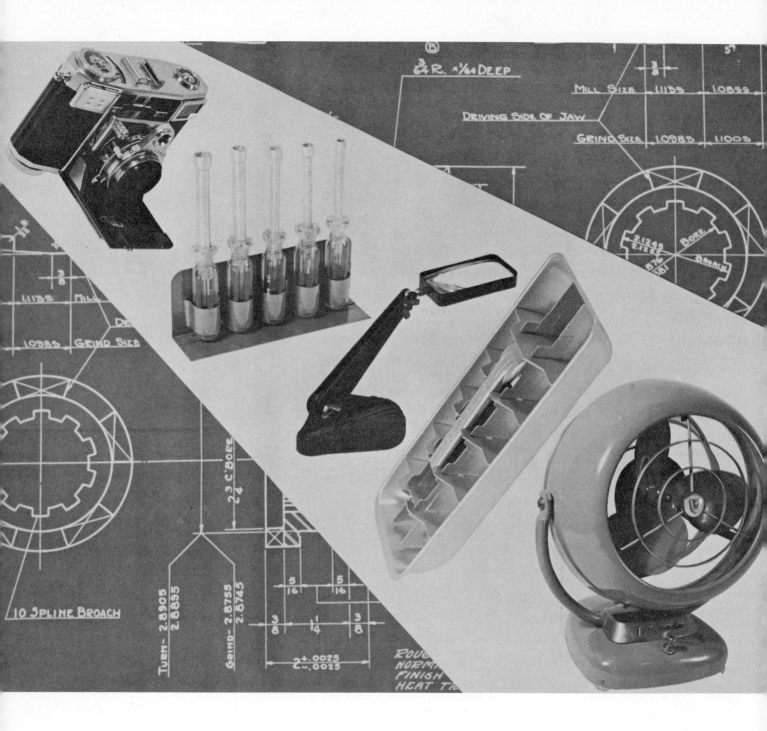

13

Working Drawings

13.1. DEFINITION.

A working drawing is any drawing used to give information for the manufacture or construction of a machine or the erection of a structure. Complete knowledge for the production of a machine or structure is given by a *set* of working drawings conveying all the facts fully and explicitly so that further instructions are not required.

The description given by the set of drawings will include:

1. The full graphic representation of the shape of each part (shape description).

2. The figured dimensions of each part (size description).

3. Explanatory notes, general and specific, on the individual drawings, giving the specifications of material, heat-treatment, finish, etc. Often, particularly in architectural and structural work, the notes of explanation and information concerning details of materials and workmanship are too extensive to be included on the drawings and so are made up separately in typed or printed form and called the "specifications"—thus the term "drawings and specifications."

4. A descriptive title on each drawing.

5. A description of the relationship of each part to the others (assembly).

6. A parts list or bill of material.

A set of drawings will include, in general, two classes of drawings: *detail drawings,* giving the information in-

FIG. 13.1. A portion of a design drawing. Notes and specifications accompany the drawing.

show all the intricate detail; only the essential dimensions, such as basic calculated sizes, are given. On the drawing, or separately as a set of written notes, will be the designer's general specifications for materials, heat-treatments, finishes, clearances or interferences, etc., and any other information needed by the draftsman in making up the individual drawings of the separate parts.

Working from the design drawing and notes, draftsmen (detailers) then make up the individual detail drawings. Figure 13.2 shows a detail drawing taken from the design drawing of Fig. 13.1. On a detail drawing, all the views necessary for complete shape description of a part are provided, and all the necessary dimensions and manufacturing directions are given. Dimension values for nonmating surfaces are obtained by scaling the design drawing, and the more critical values are determined from the design notes and from drafting-room standards. The detailer correlates the dimensions of mating parts and gives all necessary manufacturing information.

The set of drawings is completed with the addition of an assembly drawing and a parts list or bill of material.

If a machine is to be quantity produced, "operation" or "job" sheets will be prepared describing the separate manufacturing steps required and indicating the use and kind of special tools, jigs, fixtures, etc. The tool-design group, working from the detail drawings and the operation sheets, designs and makes the drawings for the special tools needed.

cluded in items 1 to 4; and an *assembly drawing,* giving the location and relationship of the parts, item 5.

13.2. ENGINEERING PROCEDURE. When a new machine or structure is designed, the first drawings are usually in the form of freehand sketches on which the original ideas, scheming, and inventing are worked out. These drawings are accompanied or followed by calculations to prove the suitability of the design. Working from the sketches and calculations, the design department produces a *design assembly* (also called a "design layout" or "design drawing") (Fig. 13.1). This is a preliminary pencil drawing on which more details of the design are worked out. It is accurately made with instruments, full size if possible, and shows the shape and position of the various parts. Little attempt is made to

13.3. ASSEMBLY DRAWINGS. An *assembly drawing* is, as its name implies, a drawing of the machine or structure put together, showing the relative positions of the different parts.

The term "assembly drawings" includes preliminary design drawings and layouts, piping plans, unit assembly drawings, installation diagrams, and final complete drawings used for assembling or erecting the machine or structure.

The design drawing is the preliminary layout on which the scheming, inventing, and designing are accurately worked out. The assembly drawing is in some cases made by tracing from the design drawing. More often it is drawn from the dimensions of the detail drawings; this provides a valuable check on the correctness of the detail drawings.

The assembly drawing sometimes gives the over-all dimensions and the distances between centers or from part to part of the different pieces, thus fixing the relation of the parts to each other and aiding in erecting the machine. However, many assembly drawings need no dimensions. An assembly drawing should not be overloaded with detail, particularly hidden detail. Unnecessary dashed lines should not be used on any drawing, least of all on an assembly drawing.

Assembly drawings usually have reference letters or numbers designating the different parts. These "piece numbers," sometimes enclosed in circles (called "balloons" by draftsmen) with a leader pointing to the piece (Fig. 13.3), are used in connection with the details and bill of material.

A *unit assembly drawing* or subassembly (Fig. 13.3) is a drawing of a related group of parts used to show the assembly of complicated machinery where it would be practically impossible to show all the features on one drawing. Thus,

FIG. 13.3. A unit assembly drawing. For complex machines, a number of units may be used in place of one complete assembly drawing.

FIG. 13.4. An outline assembly drawing (tabular). Tabulation gives the dimensions for different-sized units.

| CODE WORD | PIPE SIZES | | A | B | C | D | E | F | G | H | J | K | L | M | N | O | P | Q | R | S | T | U | W | X |
	DISCH.	SUCT'N																						
JAY	1½"	2"	TAPPED OPENINGS						5⅛	6⅝	6⅛	7¾	20⅜	3¼	8¾	⅜								
JABBER	2"	2½"		4¼	4-⅜	7	5½	4-⅜	5⅝⅜	7¼	6½	7¾	20¹⁄₁₆	3	8¼	⅜								
JACKET	3"	3"	7½	6	4-⅜	7½	6	4-⅜	6¼	7¹⁄₁₆	7	7¾	20¹⁄₁₆	3¾	8¼	⅜								
JACK	4"	4"	9	7½	8-⅜	9	7½	8-⅜	7¼	8¾	7¾	8¹²⁄₁₆	22¹⁄₁₆	4½	10	½								
JACOBUS	5"	5"	10	8½	8-⅜	10	8½	8-⅜	8⅝	9⅞	8¼	8¹³⁄₁₆	22¹⁵⁄₁₆	5	10¼	½								

ABOVE DIMENSIONS DETERMINED BY SIZE OF MOTOR AND BASE USED

in the drawing of a lathe, there would be included unit assemblies of groups of parts such as the headstock, tailstock, gearbox, etc.

An *outline assembly drawing* is used to give a general idea of the exterior shape of a machine or structure, and contains only the principal dimensions (Fig.

13.4). When it is made for catalogues or other illustrative purposes, dimensions are often omitted. Outline assembly drawings are frequently used to give the information required for the installation or erection of equipment and are then called *installation drawings.*

An *assembly working drawing* gives complete information for producing a machine or structure on one drawing. This is done by providing adequate orthographic views together with dimensions, notes, and a descriptive title. The figure for Prob. 13.3.7 is an example.

A *diagram drawing* is an assembly showing, symbolically, the erection or installation of equipment. Erection and piping and wiring diagrams are examples. Diagram drawings are often made in pictorial form.

13.4. DETAIL DRAWINGS. A *detail* drawing is the drawing of a single piece, giving a complete and exact description of its form, dimensions, and construction. A successful detail drawing will tell the workman *simply* and *directly* the shape, size, material, and finish of a part; what shop operations are necessary; what limits of accuracy must be observed; the number of parts wanted; etc. It should be so exact in description that, if followed, a satisfactory part will result. Figure 13.5 illustrates a commercial detail drawing.

Detailing practice varies somewhat according to the industry and the requirements of the shop system. For example, in structural work, details are often grouped together on one sheet, while in modern mechanical practice a separate sheet is used for each part.

If the parts are grouped on one sheet, the detailed pieces should be set, if possible, in the same relative position as on the assembly and, to facilitate reading,

FIG. 13.5. A detail drawing. Note the completeness of manufacturing information given on the drawing.

placed as nearly as possible in natural relationship. Parts of the same material or character are usually grouped together, as, for example, forgings on one sheet, castings on another, and parts machined from stock on another. A subtitle must be provided for each part, giving the part number, material, number required for each assembly, etc.

The accepted and best system in mechanical work is to have each piece, no matter how small, on a separate sheet. As described in paragraph 10.3, if the single-drawing system is followed, one drawing will be used by all shops. If the multiple system is used, a separate drawing must be made for each shop; thus there may be a *pattern drawing*, a *casting drawing*, and a *machining drawing*, all for a single cast part. A detail drawing should be a complete unit for the purpose intended and should not be dependent in any way upon any other detail drawing.

13.5. TABULAR DRAWINGS. A tabular drawing, either assembly or detail, is one on which the dimension values are replaced by reference letters, an accompanying table on the drawing listing the corresponding dimensions for a series of sizes of the machine or part, thus making one drawing serve for the range covered. Some companies manufacturing parts in a variety of sizes use this tabular system of size description, but a serious danger with it is the possibility of misreading the table. Figure 13.4 illustrates a tabular assembly drawing.

13.6. STANDARD DRAWINGS. To avoid the difficulties experienced with tabular drawings, some companies make a "standard drawing," complete except for the actual figured dimensions. This drawing is reproduced by offset printing or black-and-white reproduction on vellum paper, and the reproductions are dimensioned separately for the various sizes of parts. This method gives a separate complete drawing for each size of part; and when a new size is needed, the drawing is easily and quickly made. Figure 13.6 shows a standard drawing, and Fig. 13.7 the drawing filled in, making a completed working drawing.

13.7. STANDARD PARTS. Purchased or company standard parts are specified by name and size or by number and, consequently, do not need to be detailed. All standard parts, such as bolts, screws, antifriction bearings, etc., are shown on the assembly drawing and are given a part number. The complete specifications for their purchase are given in the parts list.

Sometimes, however, a part is made by *altering* a standard or previously produced part. In this case a detail drawing is made, showing and specifying the original part with changes and dimensions for the alteration.

13.8. THE BILL OF MATERIAL, OR PARTS LIST. This is a tabulated statement, usually placed on a separate sheet in the case of quantity production (as in Prob. 13.2.4) or on the assembly drawing in other cases (as in Prob. 13.3.12). This table gives the piece number, name, quantity, material, sometimes the stock size of raw material, detail drawing numbers, weight of each piece, etc. A final column is usually left for remarks. The term "bill of material" is ordinarily used in structural and architectural drawing. The term "parts list" applies more accurately in machine-drawing

COLLAR _____
Material _____
Heat-treat. _____
No. Req'd. _____

FIG. 13.6. A standard drawing. This is reproduced on tracing paper to provide the shape description needed for the drawing.

COLLAR _X6_
Material _S.A.E. 1020_
Heat-treat. _S.A.E. 2_
No. Req'd. _50_

FIG. 13.7. A filled-in standard drawing. With the addition of dimensions a standard drawing becomes a completed drawing to be used for manufacturing purposes.

practice. In general, the parts are listed in the order of their importance, with the larger parts first and the standard parts such as screws, pins, etc., at the end.

The blank ruling for a bill of material should not be crowded. Lines should never be spaced closer than ¼ in.; ⁵⁄₁₆ or ⅜ in. spacing is better, with the height of the lettering not more than half the space and centered between the lines. Instead of being lettered, bills of material are frequently typed on forms printed on thin paper. Intensifying the impression by typing with carbon paper on the back increases the opacity of the letters, and a clearer blueprint will result.

13.9. SET OF DRAWINGS. A *complete set* of working drawings consists of detail sheets and assembly sheets, the former giving all necessary information for the manufacture of each of the individual parts which cannot be purchased and the latter showing the parts assembled as a finished unit or machine. The set includes the bill of material or parts list and may also contain special drawings for the purchaser, such as foundation plans or oiling diagrams.

13.10. MAKING A WORKING DRAWING: BASIC CONCEPTS. Although pictorial drawings are used to some extent in special cases, the basis of all working drawings is orthographic projection. Thus, to represent an object completely, at least two views are ordinarily needed, often more. The only general rule is: *make as many views as are necessary to describe the object clearly—and no more.* Instances may occur in which the third dimension is so evident as to make one view sufficient, as, for example, in the drawing of a shaft or bolt. In other cases, perhaps a half-dozen views will be required to describe a piece completely. Sometimes half, partial, or broken views can be used to advantage.

Select for the front view the face showing the largest dimension, preferably the obvious front of the object when in its functioning position, and then decide what other views are necessary. A vertical cylindrical piece, for example, would require only a front and a top view; a horizontal cylindrical piece, only a front and a side view. Determine which side view to use or whether both are needed. The one with the fewest dashed lines should be preferred. In some cases the best representation will be obtained by using *both* side views with all unnecessary dashed lines omitted. See whether an auxiliary view or a note will eliminate one or more other views and whether a section is better than an exterior view. One statement can be made with the force of a rule: *If anything in clearness can be gained by violating a principle of projection, violate it.*

Paragraphs 8.12 to 8.26 give a number of examples of conventions that are in violation of theoretical representation but are in the interest of clearness. The draftsman must remember that his responsibility is to the reader of the drawing and that he is not justified in saving himself any time or trouble at the expense of the drawing, by making it less plain or easy to read. The time so saved by the draftsman may be lost to the company a hundredfold in the shop, where the drawing is used not once but repeatedly.

There is a *style* in drawing, just as there is in literature, which indicates itself in one way by ease of reading.

Some drawings stand out, while others, which may contain all the information, are difficult to decipher. Although dealing with mechanical thought, there is a place for some artistic sense in mechanical drawing. The number, selection, and disposition of views; the omission of anything unnecessary, ambiguous, or misleading; the size and placement of dimensions and lettering; and the contrast of lines are all elements in the style.

In commercial drafting, *accuracy* and *speed* are the two requirements. The drafting room is an expensive department, and time is an important element. The draftsman must therefore have a ready knowledge not only of the principles of drawing but of the conventional methods and abbreviations and of any device or system that will save time without sacrificing clearness.

The usual criticism of the beginner by the employer is the result of the former's lack of appreciation of the necessity for speed.

13.11. MATERIALS USED FOR WORKING DRAWINGS. Working drawings go to the shop in the form of blueprints, black-line prints, or other similar forms of reproduction, and the drawings must therefore be made on translucent material, either directly or as tracings. Pencil drawings may be made on tracing paper or on pencil cloth; inked drawings, on tracing paper or on tracing cloth.

Tracing paper is a thin translucent material, commonly called "vellum." Considerable time and expense may be saved by making the original pencil drawing on this material. Excellent prints can be obtained if the lines are of sufficient blackness and intensity.

Pencil cloth is a transparentized fabric with one or both sides of its surface prepared to take pencil so that the original drawing can be made on it and prints made either from the pencil drawing directly or after it has been inked. Some of the newer cloths are moisture resistant, others are really waterproof. Pencil cloth is made for pencil drawings, and perfect blueprints can be made from drawings made on it with sharp, hard pencils. Ink lines, however, do not adhere well and have a tendency to chip or rub off in cleaning.

Tracing cloth is a fine-thread fabric sized and transparentized with a starch preparation. The smooth side is considered by the makers as the working side, but most draftsmen prefer to work on the dull side, which will take pencil marks. The cloth should be fastened down smoothly over the pencil drawing and its selvage torn off. To remove the traces of grease that sometimes prevent the flow of ink, dust the tracing cloth with chalk or prepared pounce (a blackboard eraser may be used) and then rub it off with a cloth. Carbon tetrachloride is an effective cleaning agent. Rub a moistened cloth over the surface—any excess will evaporate in a moment.

A *plastic material,* known as "Mylar,"[1] is now available for both pencil and ink drawings. It is evenly translucent, has a fine matte surface, good lasting qualities, and requires no special storage precautions.

13.12. DRAWING SIZES. Drawing paper and cloth are available in rolls of various widths and in standard trimmed sizes. Most drafting rooms use standard sheets, printed with border and title block. The recommended sizes shown in Table 13.1, based on multiples of 8½ by 11 in. and 9

[1] DuPont Manufacturing Co.

TABLE 13.1.   Finished Flat-sheet Sizes

Designation	Width	Length	Designation	Width	Length
A	8½	11	A	9	12
B	11	17	B	12	18
C	17	22	C	18	24
D	22	34	D	24	36
E	34	44	E	36	48
F*	28	40	F*	28	40

* Not a multiple of the basic size. To be used when width of *E* size is not adaptable.

by 12 in., permit the filing of prints in a standard letter file.

Figure 13.8 shows the most common trimmed sizes. Larger drawings can be made on rolled stock of standard width, with the length as a multiple of 11 or 12 in., not to exceed 144 in.

13.13.   ORDER OF PENCILING.   After the scheming, inventing, and calculating have been done and the design drawing has been completed, the order of procedure for making the detail drawings is:

1. Select a suitable standard sheet or lay off a sheet to standard size, with the excess paper to the right, as a convenient space for making sketches and calculations, and block out the space for the title.

2. Decide what scale to use, choosing one large enough to show all dimensions without crowding, and plan the arrangement of the sheet by making a little preliminary freehand sketch, estimating the space each view will occupy and placing the views to the best advantage for preserving, if possible, a balance in the appearance of the sheet. Be sure to leave sufficient space *between* views for the dimensions.

3. Draw the center lines for each view, and on these "block in" the views by laying off the principal dimensions and outlines, using *light, sharp, accurate* pencil lines. Center lines are drawn for the axes of symmetry of all symmetrical views or parts of views. Thus every cylindrical part should have a center line—the projection of the axis of the piece. Every circle should have two center lines intersecting at its center.

4. Draw the views, beginning with the most dominant features and progressing to the subordinate. Carry the different views on together, projecting a characteristic shape as shown on one view to the other views and *not* finishing one view before starting another. Draw the lines to the final finished weight (wherever possible), using a minimum of construction. *Never* make a drawing lightly and "heavy" it later.

5. Finish the projections, putting in last the minor details. Check the projec-

Accordion Folding

FIG. 13.8.   ASA trimmed sizes of paper and cloth. ASA sizes are based on multiples of 8½ by 11 in. and 9 by 12 in. (see Table 13.1).

tions and make sure that all views are complete and correct.

6. Draw all necessary dimension lines; then put in the dimension values.

7. Draw guide lines for the notes, and then letter them.

8. Lay out the title.

9. Check the drawing carefully.

The overrunning lines of the constructive stage should not be erased before tracing or inking. These extensions are often convenient in showing the stopping points. Avoid unnecessary erasing as it abrades the surface of the paper so that it catches dirt more readily.

As an aid in stopping tangent arcs in inking, it is desirable to mark the tangent point on the pencil drawing with a short piece of the normal to the curve at the point of tangency.

Figure 13.9 illustrates the stages of penciling.

13.14. ORDER OF INKING.

To ensure good printing, the ink should be perfectly black and the ruling pens in good condition. Red ink should not be used unless it is desired to have some lines inconspicuous on the print. Blue ink will not print well. Sometimes, on maps, diagrams, etc., it is desirable to use colored inks on the tracing to avoid confusion of lines; in such cases, add a little Chinese white to the colored inks and it will render them sufficiently opaque to print.

Ink lines can be removed from tracing cloth by rubbing with a hard pencil eraser, slipping a triangle under the tracing to give a harder surface. The rubbed surface should afterward be burnished with a burnisher or fingernail. In tracing a part that has been section-lined, a piece of white paper can be slipped under the cloth and the section lining

done without reference to the section lines underneath.

Tracing cloth is sensitive to atmospheric variations, often changing overnight so as to require restretching. If a large tracing cannot be finished in one day, some views should be finished and no figure left with only part of its lines traced.

In making a large tracing, it is well to cut the required piece from the roll and lay it exposed, flat, for a short time before fastening it down.

Water will ruin a tracing on starch-coated cloth, and moist hands or arms should not come in contact with it. Form the habit of keeping the hands off drawings. In both drawing and tracing on large sheets, it is a good plan to cut a

FIG. 13.9. Order of penciling. (1) Layout; (2) details progress to (3); completion at (4). See paragraph 13.13.

FIG. 13.10. Order of inking. (1) Layout; (2) details progress to (3); completion at (4). See paragraph 13.14.

mask of drawing paper to cover all but the view being worked on. Unfinished drawings should be covered overnight.

Tracings can be cleaned of pencil marks and dirt by wiping with a cloth moistened with benzine or carbon tetrachloride. To prevent smearing when using this method of cleaning, borders and titles should be printed in an ink not affected by benzine.

Order of Inking

1. Ink all full-line circles, beginning with the smallest, and then circle arcs.

2. Ink dashed circles and arcs in the same order as full-line circles.

3. Ink any irregular curved lines.

4. Ink straight full lines in this order: horizontal, vertical, and inclined.

5. Ink straight dashed lines in the same order.

6. Ink center lines.

7. Ink extension and dimension lines.

8. Ink arrowheads and dimensions.

9. Section-line all areas representing cut surfaces.

10. Letter notes and titles. (On tracings, draw pencil guide lines first.)

11. Ink the border.

12. Check the inked drawing.

Figure 13.10 shows the stages of inking.

13.15. TITLE BLOCKS. The title of a working drawing is usually placed in the lower right-hand corner of the sheet, the size of the space varying with the amount of information to be given. The spacing and arrangement are designed to provide the information most helpful in a particular line of work.

In general, the title of a machine drawing should contain the following information:

1. Name of company and its location

2. Name of machine or unit

3. Name of part (if a detail drawing)

4. Drawing number

5. Part number (if a detail drawing)

6. Number of parts required (for each assembly)

7. Scale

8. Assembly-drawing number (given on a detail drawing to identify the part in assembly)

9. Drafting-room record: names or initials of draftsman, tracer, checker, approving authority; each with date

10. Material

To these, depending upon the need for the information, may be added:

11. Stock size

12. Heat-treatment

13. Finish

14. Name of purchaser, if special machine

15. Drawing "supersedes" and "superseded by"

Form of Title. Every drafting room has its own standard form for titles. In large offices the blank form is often printed in type on the tracing paper or cloth. Figures 13.11 and 13.12 are characteristic examples.

A form of title that is used to some extent is the *record strip,* a strip marked off across the lower part or right end of the sheet, containing the information required in the title and space for the recording of orders, revisions, changes, etc., that should be noted, with the date, as they occur. Figure 13.13 illustrates one form.

It is sometimes desired to keep the records of orders and other private information on the tracing but not to have them appear on the print. In such cases a record strip is put outside the border and trimmed off the print before sending it out.

To Letter a Title. The title should be lettered freehand in single-stroke capitals, vertical or inclined—not both styles in the same title. Write out the contents on a separate piece of paper; then refer to paragraph 4.17, where full instructions have been given.

13.16.   **ZONING.** As an aid in locating some item on a large drawing, the lower and right borders may be ruled and marked as shown on the *D*-size drawing in Fig. 13.8. Item *Q* would be located in zone *b*2. A separate column in the change-record block is often used to indicate the position of each drawing change.

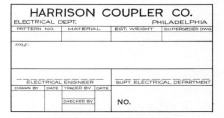

FIG. 13.11. A printed title form. This one contains a "change-record" block.

13.17.   **CHECKING.** When a working drawing is finished, it must be checked by an experienced person, who, in signing his name to it, becomes responsible for any errors. This is the final "proofreading" and cannot be done by the one who has made the drawing nearly so well as by another person. In small offices all the work is checked by the chief draftsman, or sometimes draftsmen check one another's work; in large drafting rooms one or more checkers are employed who devote all their time to this kind of work. All notes, computations, and checking layouts should be preserved for future reference.

Students can gain experience in this work by checking one another's drawings.

To be effective, checking must be done in an absolutely systematic way and with thorough concentration.

13.18.   **ORDER OF CHECKING.** Each of the following items should be gone through separately. As each dimension or feature is verified, a check mark in colored pencil should be placed on or above it and corrections indicated with a different-colored pencil.

1. Put yourself in the position of those who are to read the drawing, and find out whether it is easy to read and

FIG. 13.12. A printed title form. This one is for an electrical department.

FIG. 13.13. A strip title. This type extends across one side of the drawing.

tells a straight story. Always do this before checking any individual features, in other words, before you have had time to become accustomed to the contents.

2. See that each piece is correctly designed and illustrated and that all necessary views are shown but none that is not necessary.

3. Check all the dimensions by scaling and, where advisable, also by calculation. Preserve the calculations.

4. See that dimensions for the shop are given as required by the shop and that the shop is not left to do any adding or subtracting in order to get a needed dimension.

5. Check for tolerances. See that they are neither too "fine" nor too "coarse" for the particular conditions of the machine, so that they will not, on the one hand, increase unnecessarily the cost of production or, on the other, impair accuracy of operation or duplication.

6. Go over each piece and see that finishes are properly specified.

7. See that every specification of material is correct and that all necessary ones are given.

8. Look out for "interferences." This means that each detail must be checked with the parts that will be adjacent to it in the assembled machine to see that proper clearances have been allowed.

9. When checking for clearances in connection with a mechanical movement, lay out the movement to scale, figure the principal angles of motion, and see that proper clearances are maintained in all positions, drawing small mechanisms to double size or larger.

10. Check to see that all the small details such as screws, bolts, pins, and rivets are standard and that, where it is possible, stock sizes have been employed.

11. Check every feature of the title or record strip and bill of material.

12. Review the drawing in its entirety, adding such explanatory notes as will increase its efficiency.

13.19. ALTERATIONS. Once a drawing has been printed and the prints have been released to the shop, any alterations or changes should be recorded on the drawing and new prints issued. If the changes are extensive, the drawing may be *obsoleted* and a new drawing made which *supersedes* the old drawing. Many drawing rooms have "change-record" blocks printed in conjunction with the title, where minor changes are recorded (Fig. 13.11). The change is identified in the record and on the face of the drawing by a letter.

New designs may be changed so often that the alterations cannot be made fast enough to reach the shop when needed. In this case sketches showing the changes are rapidly made, reproduced, and sent to the shop, where they are fastened to each print of the drawing. These sketches, commonly known as "engineering orders," are later incorporated on the drawing.

Portions of a drawing can be canceled by drawing closely spaced parallel lines, usually at 45°, over the area to be voided.

13.20. WORKING SKETCHES. Facility in making freehand orthographic drawings is an essential part of the equipment of every engineer. Routine men such as tracers and detailers may get along with skill and speed in mechanical execution, but the designer must be able to record his ideas freehand. In all inventive mechanical thinking, in all preliminary designing, in all explanations and instructions to draftsmen, freehand sketching is the mode of expression. Its mastery means mastery of the language, and it is gained only after full proficiency in drawing with instruments has been acquired. It is mastery which the engineer, inventor, designer, chief draftsman, and contractor, with all of whom time is too valuable to spend in mechanical execution, must have.

Working sketches may be made in orthographic or pictorial form. Chapter 5 gives the fundamentals for orthographic freehand drawings, and Chap. 6 discusses pictorial sketching.

13.21. KINDS OF WORKING SKETCHES.

Working sketches can be divided into two general classes: (1) those made before the structure is built and (2) those made after the structure is built.

In the first class are included the sketches made in connection with the designing of the structure. These can be classified as (*a*) *scheme* or *idea* sketches, used in studying and developing the arrangement and proportion of parts; (*b*) *computation sketches,* made in connection with the figured calculations for motion and strength; (*c*) *executive sketches,* made by the chief engineer, inventor, or consulting engineer to give instructions for special arrangements or ideas that must be embodied in the design; (*d*) *design sketches,* used in working up the schemes and ideas into suitable form so that the design drawing can be started; and (*e*) *detail sketches,* made as substitutes for detail drawings.

The second class includes (*a*) *detail sketches,* drawn from existing models or parts, with complete notes and dimensions, from which duplicate parts can be constructed directly or from which work-

GUIDE - C.I. - 1 Req'd.

BLOCK - C.I.- 1 Req'd.
¾" Cap Screw 3¾"Lg. -1 Req'd,
Washer for Screw - 1 Req'd,

FIG. 13.14. A detail sketch. This is a sketch of two parts, the guide and block, parts for a leveling device.

ing drawings can be made (Fig. 13.14); (*b*) *assembly sketches,* made from an assembled machine to show the relative positions of the various parts, with center and location dimensions, or sometimes for a simple machine, with complete dimensions and specifications; and (*c*) *outline* or *diagrammatic sketches,* generally made for the purpose of location: sometimes, for example, to give the size and location of pulleys and shafting, piping, or wiring, that is, information for use in connection with the setting up of machinery; sometimes to locate a single machine, giving the over-all dimensions, sizes, and center distances for foundation bolts and other necessary information.

13.22. MAKING A WORKING SKETCH.

In making a working sketch, the principles of projection and the rules of practice for working drawings are to be remembered and applied. A systematic order should be followed for both idea sketches and sketches from objects, as listed below:

1. Visualize the object.
2. Decide on the treatment, orthographic or pictorial.

FIG. 13.15. A one-view sketch. Notes and the dimensioning details make another view unnecessary.

FIG. 13.16. A sketch on coordinate paper.

FIG. 13.17. Outside caliper. It is used for measuring diameters or thicknesses.

FIG. 13.18. Inside transfer caliper. It is used for measuring internal distances when a shoulder prevents direct removal.

3. Determine the view or views.

4. Determine the size of the sketch.

5. Locate the center lines.

6. Block in the main outlines.

7. Complete the detail.

8. Add dimension lines and arrowheads.

9. Put on the dimension values.

10. Letter notes and title, with date.

11. Check the drawing.

Before a good graphic description of an object or idea can be developed, it is essential that the mental image of it be definite and clear. The clearness of the sketch is a direct function of this mental picture. Hence the first step is to concentrate on visualization, which leads directly to the second step: determination of the best method of representation.

The method of representation will probably not be just the same as would be used in a scale drawing. For example, a note in regard to thickness or shape of section will often be used in a working drawing to save a view (Fig. 13.15); thus one view of a piece that is circular in cross section would be sufficient. In other cases additional part views and extra sections may be sketched rather than complicate the regular views with added lines that might confuse the sketch,

although the same lines might be perfectly clear in a measured drawing.

The third step is to determine the view (pictorial) or views (orthographic). Draw the object in its functioning position, if possible, but if another position will show the features to better advantage, use it. A machine should, of course, be represented right-side up, in its natural working position. If symmetrical about an axis, often only one-half need be sketched. If a whole view cannot be made on one sheet, it may be put on two, each part being drawn up to a break line used as a datum line.

The fourth step is to proportion the size of the sketch to the sheet. Have it large enough to show all detail clearly, but allow plenty of room for dimensions, notes, and memorandums. Small parts can be sketched larger than full size. Do not try to crowd all the views on one sheet of paper. Use as many sheets as may be required, but name each view, indicating the direction in which it is taken. Sometimes one view alone will require a whole sheet.

In drawing on plain paper, the location of the principal points, centers, etc., should be so judged that the sketches will fit on the sheet, and the whole sketch, with as many views, sections, and auxiliary views as are necessary to describe the piece, will be drawn in as nearly correct proportion as the eye can determine, *without making any measurements.*

Cross-section Paper. Sketches are often made on coordinate paper ruled faintly in ⅟₁₆, ⅛, or ¼ in., used simply as an aid in drawing straight lines and judging proportions, or for drawing to approximate scale by assigning suitable values to the unit spaces. The latter use is more applicable to design sketches than to sketches from the object (Fig. 13.16).

In order to gain skill through practice, sketches should be made entirely freehand. However, in commercial work the engineer often saves time by making a hybrid sketch, drawing circles with the compass or even with a coin from his pocket, ruling some lines with a pocket scale or a triangle and making some freehand but always keeping a workmanlike quality and good proportion.

13.23. DIMENSIONING AND FINISHING.
After completing the views of a piece, go over it and add *dimension lines* for all the dimensions needed for its construction, drawing extension lines and arrowheads carefully and checking to see that none is omitted.

The dimension values are now added. If the sketch is made from reference drawings and specifications, these sources give the dimension values. If the sketch is of an existing part or model, measurements must be made to determine the dimension values, as explained in paragraph 13.24.

Add all remarks and notes that seem to be of possible value. The title should be written or lettered on the sketch.

Always Date a Sketch., Valuable in-

ventions have been lost through inability to prove priority because the first sketches had not been dated. In commercial work the draftsman's notebook with sketches and calculations is preserved as a permanent record, and its sketches should be made so as to stand the test of time and be legible after the details of their making have been forgotten.

13.24. MEASURING AND DIMENSIONING.
Before adding values, *if the sketch is of an existing model or part,* the object has not been handled, and so the drawing has been kept clean. The measurements for the dimensions indicated on the drawing are now needed. A flexible rule or steel scale will serve for getting most of the dimensions. Never use a draftsman's scale for measuring castings, as it would become soiled and its edges marred. The diameter of cylindrical shapes or the distance between outside surfaces can be measured by using outside calipers and scale (Fig. 13.17); and the sizes of holes or internal surfaces, by using inside calipers. Figure 13.18 illustrates the inside transfer caliper, used when a projecting portion prevents removing the ordinary caliper. The outside transfer caliper is used for a similar condition occurring with an outside measurement. The depth of a hole is easily measured with the depth gage (Fig. 13.19*A*). Screw threads are measured by calipering the body diameter and either counting the number of threads per inch or gaging with a screw-pitch gage (Fig. 13.19*B*). A fillet-and-round gage measures radii, the gage fitting to the circular contour (Fig. 13.19*C*). It is often necessary to lay a straightedge across a surface, as in Fig. 13.20. This type of measurement could be made

FIG. 13.19. Gages. (*A*) depth gage; (*B*) screw-pitch gage; (*C*) fillet-and-round gage.

FIG. 13.20. Making a measurement.

FIG. 13.21. Combination square. (*A*) standard head; (*B*) adjustable head.

FIG. 13.22. Outside micrometer caliper.

conveniently with a combination square or with a surface gage. The combination square has two different heads, the regular 90-45° head (Fig. 13.21*A*) for a variety of measurements, and the protractor head (Fig. 13.21*B*) for measuring or laying out angles. For accurate measurements, outside or inside micrometer calipers are necessary. The outside type is illustrated in Fig. 13.22. Readings to 0.001 in. are easily obtained. Accurate measurements of holes can be made with a telescopic gage in conjunction with an outside micrometer.

A variety of gages made for special purposes, such as a wire gage, gage for sheet metal, can be used as occasion demands. With some ingenuity, measurements can often be made with the simpler instruments when special ones are not available.

Always measure from finished surfaces, if possible. Judgment must be exercised in measuring rough castings so as not to record inequalities.

In finding the distance between centers of two holes of the same size, measure from the edge of one to the corresponding edge of the other. Curves are measured by coordinates or offsets, as shown in Figs. 11.51 and 11.52. A curved outline can be recorded by laying a sheet of paper on it and making a rubbing.

13.25. CHECKING THE SKETCH. The final step is to check the sketch. It is a curious fact that when a beginner omits a dimension, it is usually a basic, vital one, such as that of the center height of a machine or an over-all length.

Sketches are not always made on paper with a printed title, but essentially the same information as for an instru-

ment drawing should be recorded in some convenient place on the sheet. All notes and special directions should be checked for accuracy along with the drawing proper. In general, follow the order of checking given in paragraph 13.17.

13.26. REPRODUCTION OF DRAWINGS. Working drawings go to the shop in the form of prints made from the original drawings. Several different printing processes are in use, all of which give the best results from tracings inked on tracing cloth or paper. However, quite satisfactory prints can be obtained from pencil drawings on translucent paper when the penciling is done skillfully, with uniform, opaque lines. In fact, most of the drawings of industry are not inked; only those of a permanent nature, such as maps, charts, etc., and tracings that must be printed a great many times, are inked.

Blueprints. The simplest and most generally used copying process is the blueprinting process, in which the prints are made by exposing a piece of sensitized paper and a tracing in close surface contact with each other to sunlight or electric light in a printing frame or machine made for the purpose. On exposure to the light, a chemical action takes place, which, when fixed by washing in water, gives a strong blue color. The parts protected from the light by the black lines of the tracing wash out, leaving the white paper.

Vandyke Paper. This is a thin sensitized paper that turns dark brown when exposed to light and properly "fixed." A reversed negative of a tracing can be made on it by exposing it to light with the inked side of the drawing next to the sensitized side of the paper; then this negative can be printed on blueprint paper, giving a positive print with blue lines on white.

BW Prints and Directo Prints. These have black lines on a white ground and are made directly from the original tracing, in a blueprinting machine (and developed by hand) or in a special machine made for the purpose. They are used extensively when positive prints are desired.

Ozalid Prints. This process is based on the chemical action of light-sensitive diazo compounds. It is a contact method of reproduction in which the exposure is made in a regular blueprinting machine or an ozalid "whiteprint" machine, and the exposed print is developed dry with ammonia vapors in a developing machine. Standard papers giving black, blue, and maroon lines on a white ground are available. Dry developing has the distinct advantage of giving prints without distortion, and it also makes possible the use of transparent papers, cloth, and foils, which effects savings in drawing time, as these transparent replicas can be changed by additions or erasures and prints made from them without altering the original tracing.

Photostat Prints. These are extensively used by large corporations. By this method, a print with white lines on a dark background is made directly from any drawing or tracing, to any desired reduction or enlargement, through the use of a large, specially designed camera. This print can be again photostated, giving a brown-black line on a white ground. This method is extremely useful to engineers for drawings to be included in reports and for matching drawings of different scales which may have to be combined into one.

Duplicating Tracings. Tracings with all the qualities of ordinary inked ones are made photographically from pencil drawings by using a sensitized tracing cloth.

Lithoprinting. When a number of copies of a drawing (50 or more) are needed, they may be reproduced by lithoprinting, a simplified form of photolithography, at comparatively small cost.

Copying Methods. Copying methods such as the mimeograph, ditto machine, and other forms of the hectograph or gelatin pad are often used for small drawings.

Photo-copying Methods. Negative copies on high-contrast film are reproduced on paper or cloth either to the same size as the original or to a reduced or increased size. Micromaster copies (Keuffel & Esser Co.) are well known. The reproductions are very good, and when the process is used for reproduction of an old drawing, wrinkles and other blemishes can be eliminated by using opaque on the film negative.

13.27. FILING AND STORING DRAWINGS. Drawings are filed in steel or wooden cabinets made for the purpose. Many engineering offices store their drawings in fireproof vaults and remove them only for making alterations or for printing. Photographic copies are sometimes made as a separate permanent record. Drawings are always filed flat or rolled. Prints, however, are folded for filing or mailing. The usual method is the "accordion" fold illustrated in Fig. 13.8. To aid in the filing of accordion-folded prints, a supplementary number block may be added, as shown.

PROBLEMS

GROUP 1.   DETAIL DRAWINGS

This group of problems gives practice in making drawings with sectional views, auxiliaries, and conventional representation.

Several methods of part production are included: casting, forging, forming of sheet metal, and plastic molding.

13.1.1.   Make complete working drawing with necessary sectional views. Cast iron.

13.1.2.   Working drawing of friction-shaft bearing. Cast iron.

13.1.3.   Working drawing of mixing-valve body. Cast brass.

13.1.4.   Working drawing of conveyer hanger. Determine what views and part views will best describe the piece. Cast steel.

13.1.5.   Working drawing of strut base. Determine what views and part views will best describe the piece. Cast aluminum.

PROB. 13.1.1.   Gear-shifter bracket.

PROB. 13.1.2.   Friction-shaft bearing.

PROB. 13.1.3.   Mixing-valve body.

PROB. 13.1.4.   Conveyor hanger.

PROB. 13.1.5.   Strut base.

13.1.6. Draw given front view. Add part views and auxiliaries to describe the piece best. Cast aluminum.

13.1.7. Working drawing of valve cage. Cast bronze.

13.1.8. Determine what views and part views

will most adequately describe the piece. Malleable iron.

13.1.9. Working drawing of water-pump cover. Aluminum alloy die casting.

13.1.10. Working drawing of slotted spider. Malleable iron.

PROB. 13.1.6. Hinge bracket.

PROB. 13.1.7. Valve cage.

PROB. 13.1.8. Brace plate.

PROB. 13.1.9. Water-pump cover.

PROB. 13.1.10. Slotted spider.

13.1.11. Make working drawing of relief-valve body. Cast brass.

13.1.12. Working drawing of breaker. Steel.

13.1.13. Working drawing of meter case. Molded bakelite.

13.1.14. (*a*) Make detail working drawings on same sheet, one for *rough* forging and one for *machining;* or (*b*) make one detail drawing for forging and machining. Alloy steel.

PROB. 13.1.11. Relief-valve body.

0.062 Stock

PROB. 13.1.12. Breaker.

PROB. 13.1.13. Meter case.

Forging   Machining

PROB. 13.1.14. Steering knuckle.

13.1.15. Working drawing of automotive connecting rod. Drop forging, alloy steel. Drawings same as Prob. 13.1.14.

13.1.16. Working drawing of puller body. Press forging, steel. Drawings same as Prob. 13.1.14.

13.1.17. Make working drawing of buffer stand. Steel drop forging. Drawings same as Prob. 13.1.14.

13.1.18. Working drawing of torque-tube support. Drop forging, aluminum alloy. Drawings same as Prob. 13.1.14.

PROB. **13.1.16.** Puller body.

PROB. **13.1.15.** Automotive connecting rod.

PROB. **13.1.17.** Buffer stand.

PROB. **13.1.18.** Torque-tube support.

13.1.19. Working drawing of supply head. Cast iron.

13.1.20. Working drawing of bearing block, cast iron.

13.1.21. Working drawing of elevator control bracket. Aluminum alloy, welded.

13.1.22. Working drawing of flap link. High-strength aluminum alloy.

PROB. 13.1.19. Supply head.

PROB. 13.1.20. Bearing block.

PROB. 13.1.21. Elevator control bracket.

PROB. 13.1.22. Flap link.

13.1.23. Working drawing of wing fitting. High-strength aluminum alloy.

13.1.24. Working drawing of micro-switch bracket. Aluminum sheet, 0.15 thick.

13.1.25. Working drawing of tab link. High-strength aluminum alloy.

13.1.26. Working drawing of drag strut. High-strength aluminum alloy.

PROB. 13.1.23. Wing fitting.

PROB. 13.1.24. Micro-switch bracket.

PROB. 13.1.25. Tab link.

PROB. 13.1.26. Drag strut.

GROUP 2.   AN ASSEMBLY DRAWING FROM THE DETAILS

13.2.1.   Assembly drawing of sealed shaft unit. Bracket and gland are cast iron. Shaft, collar, and studs are steel. Bushing is bronze.

PROB. 13.2.1.   Sealed shaft unit.

13.2.2. Make an assembly drawing of the crane hook from details given. Standard parts 7 to 10 are not detailed; see Appendix or handbook for sizes.

13.2.3. Make an assembly drawing, front view in section, of caster.

13.2.3A. Redesign caster for ball-bearing installation.

PC. NO.	NAME	QUAN.	NOTES
1	SIDE PLATE	2	S.A.E.-1030-PLATE
2	PULLEY	2	" 1020-CASTING
3	PULLEY PIN	2	" 1045-FORGING
4	NUT LOCK PIN	1	" 1030-CR
5	CRANE HOOK	1	" 3140-FORGING
6	HOOK TRUNION	1	" 1045 "
7	SEMIFIN HEX NUT	6	2¼-4UNC-2B
8	HEX SLOTTED NUT	1	3-6NS-2B
9	WASHER	2	3" HEAVY
10	COTTER PIN	2	NO. 11 × 1" LONG

PROB. 13.2.2. Crane hook.

PROB. 13.2.3. Caster.

13.2.4. Make an assembly drawing of the Brown and Sharpe rotary geared pump, with top view, longitudinal section, and side view. Show direction of rotation of shafts and flow of liquid with arrows. Give dimensions for base holes to be used in setting; also give distance from base to center of driving shaft and size of shaft and key.

For the parts that are not detailed, see the parts list.

PC. NO.	DRAW SIZE	NAME	QUAN.	MAT.	STOCK DIA.	STOCK LGTH.	USED ON NAME	USED ON PC. NO.	REMARKS
101		Base	1	C.I.					
102		Body	1	C.I.					
103		Cover	1	C.I.					
104		Pulley	1	C.I.					
105		Gland	1	C.I.					
106		Gland Bushing	1	Bro.					
107		Gear Bushing	4	Bro.					
108		Driving Gear	1	S.A.E. #1045	1 9/16	5 7/8			
109		Driven Gear	1	S.A.E. #1045	1 9/16	2 9/16			
110		Gasket	2	Sheet Copper			Body	102	#26 B&S Gage (0.0159)
111		#10-32 x 1 5/8 Slotted Hex. Hd. Mach. Scr. & Nut	4				Cover	103	
112		#10-32 x 1 5/8 Slotted Hex. Hd. Cap Scr.	2				Cover	103	
113		#10-32 x 7/8 Slotted Hex. Hd. Cap Scr.	2				Gland	105	
114		Woodruff Key #405	1				Driving Gear	108	
115		3/8 x 3/8 Headless Set Scr., 3/8-16NC-2	1				Pulley	104	
116		3/16 x 1 7/16 Dowel Pin	2	C.R.S.			Cover	103	
		Packing	To Suit						Garlock Rotopac #239

Table title (spanning): **PARTS LIST** — BROWN AND SHARPE No. 1 ROTARY GEARED PUMP

PROB. 13.2.4. Rotary geared pump and parts list.

Problems

GROUP 3. DETAIL DRAWINGS FROM THE ASSEMBLY

13.3.1. Make detail drawings of the jig table. Parts, cast iron.

13.3.2. Make detail drawings of the door catch.

PROB. 13.3.1. Jig table.

PROB. 13.3.2. Door catch.

13.3.3.   Make detail drawings of belt drive. The pulley and bracket are cast iron; the gear and shaft, steel. The bushing is bronze.

13.3.4.   Make detail drawings of swing table.

PROB. 13.3.3.   Belt drive.

PC. NO.	NAME	MAT.	QUAN.	NOTES
101	Base	C.I.	1	
102	Table	C.I.	1	
103	Trunnion Stud	Steel	1	

PROB. 13.3.4.   Swing table.

13.3.5. Make detail drawings of sealed ball joint.

13.3.6. Make detail drawings of belt tight-

ener. The bracket, pulley, and collar are cast iron. The bushing is bronze; the shaft, steel.

PC. NO.	NAME	MAT.	QUAN	NOTES
101	Base	Mal. I.	1	
102	Cover	Mal. I.	1	
103	Sleeve Ball	Steel	1	
104	Stud Ball	Steel	1	
105	Diaphragm	Fabric	1	Purchased

PROB. 13.3.5. Sealed ball joint.

PROB. 13.3.6. Belt tightener.

13.3.7.   Make detail drawings of rotary pressure joint.

13.3.8.   Make detail drawings of ball-bearing idler pulley.

13.3.9.   Make detail drawings of butterfly valve.

13.3.10.   Make detail drawings for V-belt drive.

PC.NO.	NAME	MAT.	QUAN.				
1	Body	C.I.	1	5	Thrust Collar	C.I.	1
2	Head	C.I.	1	6	Seal Ring	No.61 Graphitar	2
3	Nipple Tube	Steel	1	7	Spring	Stainless Steel	1
4	Nipple Body	C.I.	1	8	Gasket	Durabla	1
				9	Key	Steel	1

PROB. 13.3.7.   Rotary pressure joint.

PC.NO.	NAME	MAT.	QUAN.	NOTES
101	Bracket	C.I.	1	
102	Pulley	C.I.	1	
103	Flange	C.I.	2	
104	Shaft	Steel	1	
105	Sleeve	Steel	1	
106	Nut	Steel	1	

PROB. 13.3.8.   Ball-bearing idler pulley.

PC. NO.	NAME		MAT.	QUAN.	NOTES
101	Butterfly Housing		Mal. I.	1	
102	Rack Housing		Mal. I.	1	
103	Butterfly	(.0625"thick)	Steel	1	#16 U.S.S. Gage
104	Butterfly Shaft		Steel	1	
105	Pinion		Steel	1	
106	Rack		Steel	1	16 Pitch
107	Key Screw		Steel	1	
108	Cover	(.0625"thick)	Steel	1	#16 U.S.S. Gage

PROB. 13.3.9. Butterfly valve.

PC. NO.	NAME	MAT.	QUAN.	NOTES
101	Bracket	C.I.	1	
102	Gear	C.I.	1	
103	Shaft	Steel	1	
104	Gland	C.I.	1	
105	Pulley	Al.	1	Die Cast
106	Bushing	Bro.	1	

PROB. 13.3.10. V-belt drive.

PC. NO.	NAME	MAT.	QUAN.	NOTES
101	Bracket	C.I.	1	
102	Cylinder	C.I.	1	
103	Piston	C.I.	1	
104	Cylinder Head	C.I.	1	
105	Sleeve Stop	C.I.	1	
106	Sleeve	Steel	1	
107	Sleeve Nut	Steel	1	
108	Punch	Steel	1	
109	Punch Cap	Steel	1	
110	Packing Plate	Steel	1	
111	Packing	Leather	1	Purchase
112	Piston Rod	Steel	1	
113	Sleeve Spring	Steel	1	Purchase
114	Punch Spring	Steel	1	Purchase

PROB. 13.3.11. Hydraulic punch.

PC. NO.	NAME	MAT.	QUAN.	NOTES
101	Cylinder Head, Front	C.I.	1	
102	Cylinder Head, Rear	C.I.	1	Use Cast. 101
103	Packing Gland	C.I.	1	
104	Piston	C.I.	1	
105	Piston Rod	Steel	1	
106	Piston Plate	Steel	2	
107	Cylinder	Steel	1	Shelby Tubing
108	Tie Rod	Steel	4	
109	Stop Collar	Steel	1	
110	Piston Packing	Leath.	2	Purchase
111	Gasket	Fiber	2	Purchase

PROB. 13.3.12. Double-acting air cylinder.

13.3.11. Make detail drawings of hydraulic punch. In action, the punch assembly proper advances until the cap, piece 109, comes against the work. The assembly (piece 106 and attached parts) is then stationary, and the tension of the punch spring (piece 114) holds the work as the punch advances through the work and returns.

13.3.12. Make detail drawings of double-acting air cylinder. Length of stroke to be as-

signed. Fix length of cylinder to allow for clearance of 1 in. at ends of stroke. Note that pieces 101 and 102 are identical except for the extra machining of the central hole in piece 101 for the shaft, packing, and gland. Make separate drawings for this piece, one for the pattern shop and two for the machine shop.

13.3.13. Make detail drawings of rail-transport hanger. Rail is 10-lb ASCE.

PROB. 13.3.13.   Rail-transport hanger.

PC. NO.	NAME	MAT.	QUAN.	NOTES
101	Hanger	C.S.	1	
102	Wheel	C.I.	1	
103	Stud	Steel	1	
104	Plate	Steel	2	#13 U.S. Gage (.0938)
105	Eyebolt	D.F.	1	Purchase

GROUP 4.   A SET OF DRAWINGS FROM AN EXPLODED PICTORIAL

The problems that are given in this group have been arranged as complete exercises in making a set of working drawings. Remember that the dimensions given on the pictorial views are to be used only to obtain distances or information needed. In some cases the data needed for a particular part may have to be obtained from the mating part.

The detail drawings should be made with each part on a separate sheet. Drawings of cast or forged parts may be made in the single-drawing or the multiple-drawing system described in Chap. 11.

The assembly drawing should include any necessary dimensions, such as number, size, and spacing of mounting holes, that might be required by a purchaser or needed for checking with the machine on which a subassembly is used.

For the style and items to be included in the parts list, see Prob. 13.2.4.

13.4.1. Make a complete set of working drawings for the antivibration mount.

13.4.2. Make a complete set of drawings for pivot hanger, including detail drawings, assembly drawing, and parts list. All parts are steel. This assembly consists of a yoke, base, collar, and standard parts.

PROB. 13.4.2. Pivot hanger.

PROB. 13.4.1. Antivibration mount.

13.4.3. Make a complete set of drawings for pump valve. The valve seat, stem, and spring are brass; the disk is hard-rubber composition. In operation, pressure of a fluid upward against the disk raises it and allows flow. Pressure downward forces the disk tighter against the seat and prevents flow.

13.4.4. Make a complete set of working drawings for the cartridge-case trimmer. Note that some of the dimensions will have to be obtained from the mating part. A tabular drawing may be made of the case holder, covering holders for various cartridge cases. The dimensions to be tabulated are (a) holder length, (b) diameter, and (c) taper of hole.

NAME	MAT.
Base	1020
Base Rod	1020
Stop Screw	B-1113
Stop Nut	B-1113
Case Holder	B-1113
Cutter Bearing	B-1113
Cutter (Harden)	1.05-1.10 Carbon Tool Steel
Handle	1020
Ball	Bro
Fibre Disc	
Slotted Flat Pt Setscrew	
Fil Hd Mach Screw	
Semifin Hex Nut	
Lock Nut (alter std. nut)	

PROB. 13.4.4. Cartridge-case trimmer.

PROB. 13.4.3. Pump valve.

13.4.5. Make a complete set of working drawings of the hydraulic check valve. Spring is stainless steel; gasket is soft aluminum; all other parts are steel.

13.4.6. Make a complete set of working drawings of the boring-bar holder. All parts are steel. Note that the *body* is made in one piece, then split with a ⅛-in.-wide cut (exaggerated in the picture). The holder can be seen in use in Fig. 10.13.

PROB. 13.4.5. Hydraulic check valve.

PROB. 13.4.6. Boring-bar holder.

13.4.6A. Design three boring bars (see Fig. 10.13) to fit the boring-bar holder, and make a tabular drawing.

13.4.7. Make a complete set of working drawings of the ratchet wrench.

13.4.8. Make detail and assembly drawings of landing-gear door hinge. High-strength aluminum alloy.

13.4.9. Make a complete set of working drawings for access-door support.

NAME	MAT.	REQ	NOTES
Body	3240	1	Drop forging, Heat-treat
Cover	1025	1	
Ratchet Wheel	2315	1	Caseharden
Ratchet	2315	1	Caseharden
Lever	1025	1	
Spring, 5/32 OD	Music Wire	2	No.8 Ga, 5 Coils, 5/16 F.L.
Ball	Steel	2	5/32 D, Hardened
Flat Hd Mach Scr		2	Recess drive

PROB. 13.4.7. Ratchet wrench.

PROB. 13.4.8. Landing-gear door hinge.

PROB. 13.4.9. Access-door support.

GROUP 5.   A SET OF DRAWINGS FROM A PICTORIAL ASSEMBLY

13.5.1.   Make a complete set of working drawings of the high-tension coil mount.

13.5.2.   Make a complete set of working drawings of the pipe clamp. The flange is cast steel.

13.5.3.   Make a complete set of working drawings of the stay-rod pivot. Parts are malleable iron.

13.5.4.   Make a complete set of working drawings of the tool post. All parts are steel.

13.5.5.   Make a unit-assembly working drawing of the wing-nose rib.

PROB. 13.5.3.   Stay-rod pivot.

PROB. 13.5.1.   High-tension coil mount.

PROB. 13.5.2.   Pipe clamp.

PROB. 13.5.4.   Tool post.

PROB. 13.5.5.   Wing-nose rib.

GROUP 6. WORKING DRAWINGS FROM PHOTO-DRAWINGS

Photo-drawings are coming into use commercially, especially in the processing industries. These problems give practice in making detail and assembly drawings, and illustrate the possibilities of drawings produced from photographs of models or test parts.

13.6.1. Detail drawing of conveyor link. SAE 1040 steel.

13.6.2. Detail drawing of hydro-cylinder support. Aluminum sheet.

13.6.3. Detail drawing of lift-strut pivot. Forged aluminum.

13.6.4. Detail drawing of length adjuster-tube. SAE 1220 steel.

13.6.5. Detail and unit assembly of pivot shaft. Shaft is bronze; nuts are steel.

PROB. 13.6.1. Conveyor link.

PROB. 13.6.2. Hydro-cylinder support.

PROB. 13.6.3. Lift-strut pivot.

PROB. 13.6.4. Length adjuster-tube.

PROB. 13.6.5. Pivot shaft.

13.6.6. Detail drawing of third terminal (temperature control). Material is red brass (85% CU).

13.6.7. Set of working drawings of conveyor link unit. All parts are steel.

PROB. 13.6.6. Third terminal.

PROB. 13.6.7. Conveyor link unit.

GROUP 7.   A SET OF DRAWINGS FROM THE DESIGN DRAWING

13.7.1. Marking machine. From design drawing, shown half size, make complete set of drawings. Base, piece 1, is malleable-iron casting. Frame, piece 2, is cast iron. Ram, piece 3, is 1020 HR; bushing, piece 4, is 1020 cold-drawn tubing; heat-treatment for both is car-burize at 1650 to 1700°F, quench direct, temper at 250 to 325°F. Spring, piece 5, is piano wire, No. 20 (0.045) gage, six coils, free length 2 in., heat-treatment is "as received." Marking dies and holders are made up to suit objects to be stamped.

PROB. 13.7.1. Marking machine (one-half size).

13.7.2. Arbor press. From design drawing, shown one-quarter size, make complete set of drawings. All necessary information is given on the design drawing.

PROB. **13.7.2.** One-ton arbor press (one-quarter size).

13.7.3. Number 2 flanged vise. From design drawing, make complete set of drawings, including details, parts list, and assembly. Design drawing is shown one-third size. All necessary information will be found on the design drawing.

PROB. **13.7.3.** No. 2 flanged vise (one-third size). .

PC. NO.	NAME	MAT.	REQ	NOTES
1	Base	2335	1	Steel Casting
2	Jaw	2335	1	Steel Casting
3	Eccentric	2340 HR	1	
4	Blade	1095 HR	2	
5	Handle	1040	1	Drop Forging
6	Shoulder Screw		1	
7	Flat Head Cap Screw		4	
8	Socket Set Screw		1	Flat Point
9	Semifin Hex Jam Nut		1	
10	Semifin Hex Jam Nut		2	
11	Semifin Hex Jam Nut		2	
12	Cut Washer	1112 CR	1	
13	Cut Washer	1112 CR	1	
14	Key	Key Stock	1	

PROB. 13.7.4. Bench shears, 2¾-in. (one-half size).

13.7.4. Bench shears. Design drawing is half size. Make a complete set of drawings. For dimensions where close fits are involved, either the decimal limits or the tolerance to be applied to the scaled basic size are given on the design drawing. Heat-treatments should be specified as follows: for base and jaw, "normalize at 1550°F"; for eccentric, "as received"; for blade, "to Rockwell C57-60"; for handle, none. Finish for blades, "grind." Washers are special but may be specified on the parts list by giving inside diameter, outside diameter, and thickness. The key may be specified on the parts list by giving width, thickness, and length.

Following are some specifications for limits and tolerances:

Diameter of shoulder screw and hole in both base and jaw:

Screws (as manufactured): $\dfrac{0.623}{0.621}$

Hole: $\dfrac{0.624}{0.626}$

Diameter of eccentric and hole in handle:

Eccentric: $\dfrac{0.999}{0.997}$

Handle: $\dfrac{0.999}{1.001}$

Diameter of eccentric and hole in base:

Eccentric: $\dfrac{1.3745}{1.3740}$

Base: $\dfrac{1.3750}{1.3755}$

Diameter of eccentric and width of slot in jaw:

Eccentric: $\dfrac{0.874}{0.872}$

Jaw: $\dfrac{0.875}{0.877}$

Width of keyway in both handle and eccentric:

Key (as purchased): $\dfrac{0.250}{0.249}$

Key seat and keyway: $\dfrac{0.250}{0.251}$

Depth of keyway and key seat in both handle and eccentric:

$\frac{3}{32}'' + \frac{1}{64} - 0$

Control of clearance between blades:

Thickness of blade: $\dfrac{0.1250}{0.1245}$

Dimension A: $\dfrac{0.562}{0.561}$

Dimension B: $\dfrac{0.812}{0.813}$

Tolerance on shoulder screw and eccentric hole locations: For base and jaw (two dimensions on each part)

± 0.002

Limits for eccentric offset:

Center to center: $\dfrac{0.248}{0.252}$

Length of handle:

Center of hub to center of ball: 12 in.

GROUP 8. WORKING SKETCHES

13.8.1. Select one of the problems in Group 1, and make a detail working sketch.

13.8.2. Select one of the problems in Group 2, and make an assembly sketch.

13.8.3. Select a single part from one of the assemblies of Groups 3 to 5, and make a working sketch.

13.8.4. Select a single part from one of the Probs. 13.1.1 to 13.4.7, and make a pictorial working sketch.

13.8.5. Select one of the problems that are given in Group 3, and make detail working sketches.

13.8.6. Select one of the problems in Group 4 or 5, and make a complete set of working sketches.

$$14$$

Charts, Graphs, and Diagrams

14.1. This chapter is given as an introduction to the use of graphic methods in tabulating data for analysis, solving problems, and presenting facts. We will discuss the value of this application of graphics in engineering and suggest ways of studying the subject further.

The graphic chart is an excellent method for presenting a series of quantitative facts quickly. When properly constructed, charts, graphs, and diagrams constitute a powerful tool for computation, analysis of engineering data, and the presentation of statistics for comparison or prediction.

14.2. CLASSIFICATION. Charts, graphs, and diagrams fall roughly into two classes: (1) those used for purely technical purposes and (2) those used in advertising 'or in presenting information in a way that will have popular appeal. The engineer is concerned mainly with those of the first class, but he should be acquainted also with the preparation of those of the second and understand their potential influence. The aim here is to give a short study of the types of charts, graphs, and diagrams with which engineers and those in allied professions should be familiar.

It is assumed that the student is familiar with the use of rectangular coordinates and that such terms as "axes," "ordinates," "abscissas," "coordinates," and "variables," are understood.

14.3. REPRESENTATION OF DATA: RECTILINEAR CHARTS. Because the preliminary chart work in experimental engineering is done on rectilinear graph paper, the student should become familiar with this form of chart early in his course. The rectilinear chart is made on a sheet ruled with equispaced horizontal lines crossing equispaced vertical lines. The spacing is optional. One commercial graph paper is divided into squares of ½0 in., with every fifth line heavier, to aid in plotting and reading. Sheets are available with various other rulings, such as 4, 6, 8, 10, 12, and 16 divisions per inch.

It is universal practice to use the upper right-hand quadrant for plotting experimental-data curves, making the lower left-hand corner the origin. In case both positive and negative values of a function are to be plotted, as occurs with many mathematical curves, the origin must be placed so as to include all desired values.

Figure 14.1 shows a usual form of rectilinear chart, such as might be made for inclusion in a written report.

14.4. DRAWING THE CURVE. In drawing graphs from experimental data, it is often a question whether the curve should pass through all the points plotted or strike a mean between them. In general, observed data not backed up by definite theory or mathematical law are shown by connecting the points plotted with straight lines, as in Fig. 14.2*A*. An empirical relationship between curve and plotted points may be used, as at (*B*), when, in the opinion of the engineer, the curve should exactly follow some points and go to one side of others. Consistency of observation is indicated at (*C*), in which case the curve should closely follow a true theoretical curve.

14.5. TITLES AND NOTATION. The title is an important part of a chart, and its wording should be clear and concise. In every case, it should contain sufficient description to tell what the chart is, the source or authority, the name of the observer, and the date. Approved practice places the title at the top of the sheet, arranged in phrases symmetrically about a center line. If it is placed within the ruled space, a border line or box should set it apart from the sheet. Each sheet of curves should have a title; and when more than one curve is shown on a sheet, the different curves should be drawn so as to be easily distinguishable. This can be done by varying the character of the lines, using full, dashed, and dot-and-dash lines, with a tabular key for identification, or by lettering the names of the curves directly along them. When the charts are not intended for reproduction, inks of different colors can be used.

14.6. TO DRAW A CHART. In drawing a coordinate chart, the general order is: (1) compute and assemble all data; (2) determine the size and kind of chart best adapted and whether to use printed or

FIG. 14.1. A rectilinear chart. This type of chart shows how one variable changes with respect to another. Corresponding values can be determined.

Axial Deflection Curve
Non-Preloaded Angular Contact Bearing

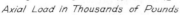

plain paper; (3) determine, from the limits of the data, the scales for abscissas and ordinates to give the best effect to the resulting curve; (4) lay off the independent variable (often *time*) on the horizontal, or X, axis and the dependent variable on the vertical, or Y, axis; (5) plot points from the data and pencil the curves; (6) ink the curve; (7) compose and letter the title and coordinates.

The construction of a graphic chart requires good draftsmanship, especially for the lettering, but in engineering and scientific work the primary considerations are judgment in the proper selection of coordinates, accuracy in plotting points and drawing the graph, and an understanding of the functions and limitations of the resulting chart.

When the chart is drawn on a printed form, to be blueprinted, the curve can be drawn on the reverse side of the paper, enabling erasures to be made without injuring the ruled surface.

Green is becoming the standard color for printed forms. Blue will not print or photograph; red is trying on the eyes.

If the curve is for purposes of computation, it should be drawn with a fine, accurate line; if for demonstration, it should be fairly heavy, for contrast and effect.

The following rules are adapted from ASA Y15 (formerly Z15):

Standards for Graphic Presentations

1. A graph should be free of all lines and lettering that are not essential to the reader's clear understanding of its message.

2. All lettering and numbers on a graph should be placed so as to be easily read from the bottom and from the right-hand side of the graph, not the left-hand side.

3. Standard abbreviations should be used where space is limited as, for example, in denoting the unit of measurement in scale captions.

4. The range of scales should be chosen so as to ensure effective and efficient use of the coordinate area in attaining the objective of the chart.

5. The zero line should be included if visual comparison of plotted magnitudes is desired.

6. When it is desired to show whether the rate of change of the dependent variable is increasing, constant, or decreasing, a logarithmic vertical scale should be used in conjunction with an arithmetical horizontal scale.

7. The horizontal (independent variable) scale values should usually increase from left to right and the vertical (dependent variable) scale values from bottom to top.

8. Scale values and scale captions should be placed outside the grid area, normally at the bottom for the horizontal scale and at the left side for the vertical scale. On wide graphs it may be desirable to repeat the vertical scale at the right side.

9. For arithmetical scales, the scale numbers shown on the graph and the space between coordinate rulings should preferably correspond to 1, 2, or 5 units of measurement, multiplied or divided by 1, 10, 100, etc.

10. The use of many digits in scale numbers should be avoided.

11. The scale caption should indicate both the variable measured and the unit of measurement. For example: EXPOSURE TIME IN DAYS.

12. Coordinate rulings should be limited in number to those necessary to guide the eye in making a reading to the desired degree of approximation. Closely

FIG. 14.2.   Methods of drawing curves. (*A*) "curve" for data not supported by theory and therefore not necessarily producing a smooth curve; (*B*) and (*C*) curves for data known to produce smooth curves.

spaced coordinate rulings are appropriate for computation charts but not for graphs intended primarily to show relationship.

13. Curves should preferably be represented by solid lines.

14. When more than one curve is presented on a graph, relative emphasis or differentiation of the curves may be secured by using different types of line, that is, solid, dashed, dotted, etc., or by different widths of line. A solid line is recommended for the most important curve.

15. The observed points should preferably be designated by circles.

16. Circles, squares, and triangles should be used rather than crosses or filled-in symbols to differentiate observed points of several curves on a graph.

17. Curves should, if practicable, be designated by brief labels placed close to the curves (horizontally or along the curves) rather than by letters, numbers, or other devices requiring a key.

18. If a key is used, it should preferably be placed within the grid in an isolated position, and enclosed by a light line border—grid lines, if convenient.

19. The title should be as clear and concise as possible. Explanatory material, if necessary to ensure clearness, should be added as a subtitle.

20. Scale captions, designations, curves, and blank spaces should, so far as practicable, be arranged to give a sense of balance around vertical and horizontal axes.

21. The appearance and the effectiveness of a graph depend in large measure on the relative widths of line used for its component parts. The widest line should be used for the principal curve. If several curves are presented on the same graph, the line width used for the curves should be less than that used when a single curve is presented.

22. A simple style of lettering, such as Gothic with its uniform line width and no serifs, should in general be used.

14.7. LOGARITHMIC SCALES. An important type of chart is that in which the divisions are made proportional to the logarithms of the numbers instead of to the numbers themselves, and accordingly

FIG. 14.3. A semilogarithmic chart. The ordinate axis (in this case) is logarithmic, the abscissa uniform.

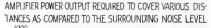

are not equally spaced. When ruled logarithmically in one direction with equal spacing at right angles, the spacing is called "semilogarithmic."

Logarithmic spacing may be done directly from the graduations on one of the scales of a slide rule. Logarithmic paper is sold in various combinations of ruling. It is available in one, two, three, or more cycles; in multiples of 10; and also in part-cycle and split-cycle form. In using logarithmic paper, interpolations should be made logarithmically; arithmetical interpolation with coarse divisions might lead to considerable error.

14.8. SEMILOGARITHMIC CHARTS.

These charts have equal spacing on one axis, usually the X axis, and logarithmic spacing on the other axis. Owing to a property by virtue of which the slope of the curve at any point is an exact measure of the rate of increase or decrease in the data plotted, the semilogarithmic chart is frequently called a "ratio chart." Often called the "rate-of-change" chart as distinguished from the rectilinear, or "amount-of-change," chart, it is extremely useful in statistical work as it shows at a glance the rate at which a variable changes. By the use of this chart it is possible to predict a trend, such as the future increase of a business, growth of population, etc.

In choosing between rectilinear ruling and semilogarithmic ruling, the important point to consider is whether the chart is to represent *numerical* increases and decreases or *percentage* increases and decreases. In many cases it is desirable to emphasize the percentage, or rate, change, not the numerical change; for these a semilogarithmic chart should be used.

An example of a semilogarithmic chart is given in Fig. 14.3. This curve was drawn from data compiled for the *World Almanac*. The dashed line shows the actual production by years, and the full line is the trend curve, the extension of which predicts future production.

Exponential equations of the form $y = ae^{bx}$ plot on semilogarithmic coordinates as a straight line. This represents the type of relationship in which a quantity increases or decreases at a rate proportional to the amount present at any time. For example, the passage of light through a translucent substance varies (in intensity) exponentially with the thickness of material.

14.9. LOGARITHMIC CHARTS.

These are charts in which both abscissas and ordinates are spaced logarithmically. Any equation of the form $y = ax^b$, in which one quantity varies directly as some power of another, will plot as a straight line on logarithmic coordinates. Thus, multiplication, division, powers, and roots are examples. Figure 14.4 shows a logarithmic plot of sound intensity (and the power required to produce it) which varies as a power of the distance from the source. Other examples are the distance-time relationship of a falling body and the period of a simple pendulum.

14.10. POLAR CHARTS.

The use of polar coordinate paper for representing intensity of illumination, intensity of heat, polar forms of curves, etc., is common. Figure 14.5 shows a candle-power distribution curve for an ordinary Mazda B lamp, and Fig. 14.6 the curve for a certain type of reflector. The candle power in any given direction is determined by reading off the distance from

FIG. 14.4.   A logarithmic chart. Both ordinate and abscissa are divided logarithmically.

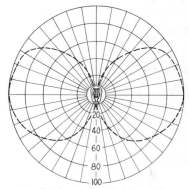

FIG. 14.5.   A polar chart. This type is used when direction from a point (pole) must be shown.

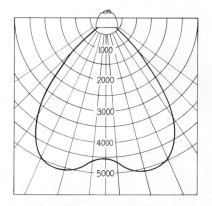

FIG. 14.6.   A polar chart. This one shows the area of illumination from a reflector.

the origin to the curve. Use of polar forms of curves enables the determination of the foot-candle intensity at any point.

14.11. TRILINEAR CHARTS. The trilinear chart, or "triaxial diagram," as it is sometimes called, affords a valuable means of studying the properties of chemical compounds consisting of three elements, alloys of three metals or compounds, and mixtures containing three variables. The chart has the form of an equilateral triangle, the altitude of which represents 100 per cent of each of the three constituents. Figure 14.7, showing the ultimate tensile strength of copper-tin-zinc alloys, is a typical example of its application. The usefulness of such diagrams depends upon the geometric principle that the sum of the perpendiculars to the sides from any point within an equilateral triangle is a constant and is equal to the altitude.

14.12. CHOICE OF TYPE AND PRESENTATION. The function of a chart is to reveal facts. It may be entirely misleading if wrong paper or coordinates are chosen. The growth of an operation plotted on a rectilinear chart might, for example, entirely mislead an owner analyzing the trend of his business, while if plotted on

FIG. 14.7. A trilinear chart. This type is used to represent properties of three combined elements.

a semilogarithmic chart, it would give a true picture of conditions. Intentionally misleading charts have been used many times in advertising; the commonest form is the chart with a greatly exaggerated vertical scale. In engineering work it is essential to present the facts honestly and with scientific accuracy.

14.13. ANALYSIS OF EXPERIMENTAL DATA. So far we have discussed only the representation of data. In many cases representation alone, on suitable coordinates gives an accurate description—for, from the plot, the *value* of one variable relative to a second variable can be ascertained. Nevertheless, the equation of a relationship can often be obtained from the data. To do this, the data must be plotted on coordinates that will "justify" the curve to a straight line. The equation of a straight line on any system of coordinates is easily determined. Equations thus resolved are known as *empirical* equations.

The standard procedure is first to plot the data on rectangular coordinates. If a straight line results, it is known that the equation is of the first degree (linear). If a curve results from the plot, the equation is of a higher form, and semilogarithmic coordinates or logarithmic coordinates should be tried; if the data justifies to a straight line on either system, the equation can be determined.

14.14. RECTANGULAR PLOTS: LINEAR EQUATIONS. If a plot of data results in a straight line on rectilinear coordinates, the equation is of the first degree. Figure 14.8 shows a plot that justifies to a straight line on rectilinear coordinates. To determine the equation of the line, select two points, such as y_1x_1 and y_2x_2 shown in Fig. 14.8. Then by simple proportion

$$\frac{y - y_1}{x - x_1} = \frac{y_2 - y_1}{x_2 - x_1}$$

and from Fig. 14.8

$y_1 = 13.8, y_2 = 43.5; x_1 = 8, x_2 = 35.0$

substituting,

$$\frac{y - 13.8}{x - 8.0} = \frac{43.5 - 13.8}{35.0 - 8.0}$$

whence,

$$\frac{y - 13.8}{x - 8.0} = 1.1$$

and $y = 5.0 + 1.1x$

Thus, this equation is of a straight line, $y = a + bx$, where $a = 5.0$ and $b = 1.1$.

The coefficient 1.1 is the slope of the line and the constant 5.0 is the ordinate-axis intercept.

14.15. LOGARITHMIC PLOTS: POWER EQUATIONS.

If the data justifies to a straight line on logarithmic coordinates, the equation is a power relationship of the form $y = ax^b$. Figure 14.9 shows a plot that justifies to a straight line on logarithmic coordinates. Two selected points give

$x_1 = 2.5 \qquad y_1 = 3.8$
$x_2 = 55.0 \qquad y_2 = 26.5$

Because the plot is logarithmic,

$$\frac{\log y - \log 3.8}{\log x - \log 2.5} = \frac{\log 26.5 - \log 3.8}{\log 55.0 - \log 2.5}$$

whence,

$$\log y = 0.330 + 0.628 \log x$$

and

$$y = 2.14x^{0.628}$$

14.16. SEMILOGARITHMIC PLOTS: EXPONENTIAL EQUATIONS.

If plotted data justifies to a straight line on semilogarithmic coordinates, the equation is

FIG. 14.8. A straight-line plot on rectilinear coordinates. The equation of the line is linear, $y = a + bx$.

an exponential form, $y = ae^{bx}$ or $y = a10^{bx}$ (for base 10 logarithms). Figure 14.10 shows a typical plot. Two selected points give

$x_1 = 0.8 \qquad y_1 = 3.8$
$x_2 = 4.5 \qquad y_2 = 50.0$

Writing the equation of the straight line,

$$\frac{\ln y - \ln 3.8}{x - 0.8} = \frac{\ln 50.0 - \ln 3.8}{4.5 - 0.8}$$

whence,

$$\ln y = 0.777 + 0.697x$$

and

$$y = 2.18e^{0.697x}$$

14.17. NOMOGRAPHY.

After the equation of a relationship has been determined, specific values of the variables can be found by substitution in the equation. To facilitate such calculations, a chart called a nomogram can be made in which the variables are represented by plotted scales arranged so that a straightedge placed across the scales will give corresponding values of the variables. A simple example of a nomogram (conversion chart) is shown in Fig. 14.11.

FIG. 14.9. A straight-line plot on logarithmic coordinates. The equation of the line is a power form, $y = ax^b$.

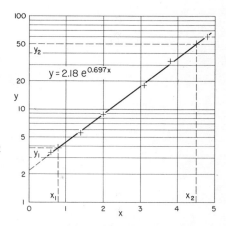

FIG. 14.10. A straight-line plot on semilogarithmic coordinates. The equation of the line is an exponential form, $y = ae^{bx}$.

FIG. 14.11. A nomogram. This one is a conversion chart for specific gravity to degrees API.

FIG. 14.12. A classification chart. This type of chart shows the relationship of parts of a whole.

The construction of a nomogram requires a knowledge of functional scales, chart forms, and the necessary mathematics. Thus, nomography is a special graphic field and is beyond the scope of this book. For a discussion of it, see "Graphic Science" by Thomas E. French and Charles J. Vierck.[1]

14.18. GRAPHIC CALCULUS. Considered in the same light as nomography, this is a specialized field of chart construction in which the rates of change of variables are determined graphically. This field is also beyond the scope of this book. For a discussion of graphic calculus, see "Graphic Science" by Thomas E. French and Charles J. Vierck.[1]

[1] McGraw-Hill, New York, 1958.

14.19. CLASSIFICATION CHARTS, ROUTE CHARTS, AND FLOW SHEETS. The uses to which these three classes of charts can be put are widely different; but their underlying principles are similar, and so they have been grouped together for convenience.

A *classification chart,* illustrated in Fig. 14.12, is intended to show the subdivisions of a whole and the interrelation of its parts with one another. Such a chart often takes the place of a written outline as it gives a better visualization of the facts than can be achieved with words alone. A common application is an organization chart of a corporation or business. It is customary to enclose the names of the divisions in rectangles, although circles or other shapes may be used. The rectangle has the advantage of being convenient for lettering, while the circle can be drawn more quickly and possesses greater popular appeal. Often a combination of both is used.

The *route chart* is used mainly for the purpose of showing the various steps in a process, either of manufacturing or other business. The *flow sheet,* illustrated in Fig. 14.13, is an example of a route chart applied to a chemical process. Charts of this type show in a dynamic way facts that might require considerable study to be understood from a written description. Figure 10.1, showing the course of a drawing through the shops, illustrates a different form of route chart.

FIG. 14.13. A flow sheet. This is an effective way to show the fundamentals of a process or method.

14.20. POPULAR CHARTS. Engineers and draftsmen are frequently called upon to prepare charts and diagrams that will be understood by nontechnical readers. For such charts it is often advisable to present the facts, not by means of curves on coordinate paper, but in a way that is more easily read, even though the representation may be somewhat less accurate. Charts for popular use must be made so that the impression they produce is both quick and accurate. They are seldom studied critically but are taken in at a glance; hence the method of presentation requires the exercise of careful judgment and the application of a certain amount of psychology.

14.21. BAR CHARTS. The bar chart is a type of chart easily understood by nontechnical readers. One of its simplest forms is the *100 per cent bar* for showing the relations of the constituents to a given total. Figure 14.14 is an example. The different segments should be crosshatched, shaded, or distinguished in some other effective manner, the percentage represented should be placed on the related portion of the diagram or directly opposite, and the meaning of each segment should be clearly stated. Bars may be placed vertically or horizontally, the vertical position giving an advantage for lettering and the horizontal an advantage in readability, as the eye judges horizontal distances readily.

Figure 14.15 is an example of a *multiple-bar chart,* in which the length of each bar is proportional to the magnitude of the quantity represented. Means should be provided for reading numerical values represented by the bars. If it is necessary to give the exact value rep-

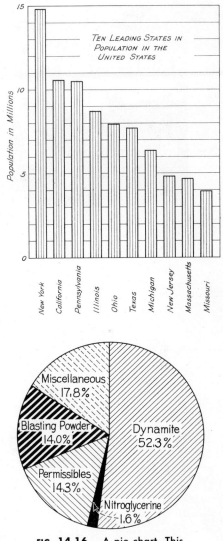

WEIGHT PERCENTAGE ANALYSIS FOR AN INTERNALLY BRACED CABIN MONOPLANE

26.4%   22.4%   33.1%   15.6%

Wing Group   Body Group   Power Plant   Fixed
Tail Group 2.5%   Equip.

FIG. 14.14. A 100 per cent bar chart. This is a simple and impressive method of showing percentages of a whole.

FIG. 14.15. A multiple-bar chart. Each bar gives (graphically) the magnitude of the item represented.

TEN LEADING STATES IN POPULATION IN THE UNITED STATES

Population in Millions

New York, California, Pennsylvania, Illinois, Ohio, Texas, Michigan, New Jersey, Massachusetts, Missouri

Miscellaneous 17.8%
Blasting Powder 14.0%
Permissibles 14.3%
Dynamite 52.3%
Nitroglycerine 1.6%

FIG. 14.16. A pie chart. This chart shows percentages of a whole. Compare it with a 100 per cent bar chart.

resented by the individual bars, the values should not be lettered at the ends of the bars as this would increase their apparent length. This type of chart is made horizontally, with the description at the base, and vertically. The vertical form is sometimes called the "pipe-organ chart." When vertical bars are drawn close together, touching along the sides, the diagram is called a "staircase chart." This chart is more often made as the "staircase curve," a line plotted on coordinate paper representing the profile of the tops of the bars.

A *compound-bar chart* is made when it is desirable to show two or more components in each bar. It is really a set of 100 per cent bars of different lengths set together in pipe-organ or horizontal form.

14.22. PIE CHARTS. The "pie diagram," or 100 per cent circle (Fig. 14.16) is much inferior to the bar chart but is used constantly because of its popular appeal. It is a simple form of chart and, except for the lettering, is easily constructed. It can be regarded as a 100 per cent bar bent into circular

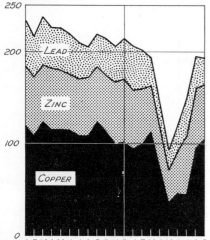

MANUFACTURERS' PURCHASES
OF COPPER, ZINC AND LEAD
Thousands of Tons

FIG. 14.17. A strata chart. The individual charts are superimposed.

form. The circumference of the circle is divided into 100 parts, and sectors are used to represent percentages of the total.

To be effective, this diagram must be carefully lettered and the percentages marked on the sectors or at the circumference opposite the sectors. For contrast, it is best to crosshatch or shade the individual sectors. If the original drawing is to be displayed, the sectors may be colored and the diagram supplied with a key showing the meaning of each color. The percentage notation should always be placed where it can be read without removing the eyes from the diagram.

14.23. STRATA AND VOLUME DIAGRAMS. The use of strata and volume diagrams has been common although they are usually the most deceptive of the graphic methods of representation. Figure 14.17 is a strata chart showing a change in amounts over a period of time. The area between the curves is shaded to emphasize each variable represented. However, in reading it should be remembered that the areas *between* curves have no significance.

14.24. PICTORIAL CHARTS. Pictorial charts were formerly much used for comparisons, for example of costs, populations, standing armies, livestock, and various products. It was customary to represent the data by human or other figures whose heights were proportional to numerical values or by silhouettes of the animals or products concerned whose heights or sometimes areas were proportional. Since volumes vary as the cubes of the linear dimensions, such charts are grossly misleading. Bar charts or charts such as the one shown in Fig.

14.18, where the diameter of the column is constant, should be used for the type of comparisons that are shown in pictorial charts.

14.25. CHARTS FOR REPRODUCTION. Charts for reproduction by the zinc-etching process should be carefully penciled to about twice the size of the required cut. Observe the following order in inking: First, ink the circles around plotted points; second, ink the curves with strong lines. A border pen is useful for heavy lines, and a Leroy pen (in socket holder) may be used to advantage, particularly for dashed lines. Third, ink the title box and all lettering; fourth, ink the coordinates with fine black lines, putting in only as many as are necessary for easy reading and breaking them wherever they interfere with title or lettering or where they cross plotted points.

14.26. CHARTS FOR DISPLAY. Large charts for demonstration purposes are sometimes required. These can be drawn on sheets 22 by 28 in. or 28 by 44 in. known as "printer's blanks." The quickest way to make them is with show-card colors and single-stroke sign-writer's brushes. Large bar charts can be made with strips of black adhesive tape. Lettering can be done with the brush or with gummed letters.

14.27. STANDARDS. Many standards are available for graphic presentations of data. Of particular interest are the ASA standards for graphic symbols (Z32), letter symbols (Z10), and time-series charts (Z15.2—1947), and ASA Y15 "Guide for Preparing Technical Illustrations for Publications and Projections."

MILL PRICE OF BAR STOCK
Cents per Pound

FIG. 14.18. A pictorial chart. Pictorialism adds to popular interest but detracts from accuracy of representation.

PROBLEMS

These problems are given for practice in preparing various types of charts, graphs, and diagrams for technical or popular presentation.

14.1.1. The data given below were obtained in a tension test of a machine-steel bar. Plot the data on rectangular coordinates, using the elongation as the independent variable, the applied load as the dependent variable.

Applied load, lb per sq in.	Elongation per in. of length
0	0
3,000	0.00011
5,000	0.00018
10,000	0.00033
15,000	0.00051
20,000	0.00067
25,000	0.00083
30,000	0.00099
35,000	0.00115
40,000	0.00134
42,000	0.00142

14.1.2. A test of the corrosive effect of 5 per cent sulfuric acid, both air-free and air-saturated, on 70 per cent nickel, 30 per cent copper alloy (Monel) over a temperature range from 20 to 120°C resulted in the data tabulated below. Plot this data on rectangular coordinates with corrosion rate as ordinate versus temperature as abscissa.

Temp., °C	Corrosion rate, MDD (mg per sq dm per day)	
	Acid sat. with air	Acid air-free, sat. with N_2
20	195	35
30	240	45
40	315	50
50	425	63
60	565	70
70	670	74
80	725	72
83	715	70
85	700	68
92	580	57
95	470	42
101	60	12

14.1.3. In testing a small 1-kw transformer for efficiency at various loads, the following data were obtained: Watts delivered: 948, 728, 458, 252, 000. Losses: 73, 62, 53, 49, 47.

Plot curves on rectangular coordinate paper showing the relation between percentage of load and efficiency, using watts delivered as the independent variable and remembering that efficiency = output ÷ (output + losses).

14.1.4. The following data were obtained from a test of an automobile engine:

Rpm	Length of run, min	Fuel per run, lb	Bhp
1,006	11.08	1.0	5.5
1,001	4.25	0.5	8.5
997	7.53	1.0	13.0
1,000	5.77	1.0	16.3
1,002	2.38	0.5	21.1

Plot curves on rectangular coordinate paper, showing the relation between fuel used per brake horsepower-hour and brake horsepower developed. Show also the relation between thermal efficiency and brake horsepower developed, assuming the heat value of the gasoline to be 19,000 Btu per lb.

14.1.5. During the year 1950 the consumption of wood pulp by various grades in the United States was as follows:

Grade of pulp	Consumption in paper and board manufacture, tons
Sulfate	8,380,864
Sulfite	3,331,668
Groundwood	2,483,980
Defibrated, exploded, etc.	971,912
Soda	564,355
All other	754,331
Total (all grades)	16,487,110

Show these facts by means of a 100 per cent bar, a pie diagram, and a multiple-bar chart.

14.1.6. Put the data of Fig. 14.16 into 100 per cent bar form.

14.1.7. Put the data of Fig. 14.14 into pie-chart form.

14.1.8. A test of the resistance of alloy steels to high-temperature steam resulted in the data tabulated below. Represent the results of the test graphically by means of a multiple-bar chart.

Corrosion of Steel Bars in Contact with Steam at 1100°F for 2,000 Hr

Steel	Average penetration, in.
SAE 1010	0.001700
1.25 Cr-Mo	0.001169
4.6 Cr-Mo	0.000956
9 Cr 1.22 Mo	0.000694
12 Cr	0.000045
18-8-Cb	0.000012

14.1.9. From the data below, plot curves showing the "thinking distance" and "braking distance." From these curves, plot the sum curve "total distance." Title "Automobile Minimum Travel Distances When Stopping—Average Driver."

Mph	Ft per sec	Thinking distance, ft	Braking distance, ft
20	29	22	18
30	44	33	40
40	59	44	71
50	74	55	111
60	88	66	160
70	103	77	218

14.1.10. Make a semilogarithmic chart showing the comparative rate of growth of the five largest American cities from 1880 to 1950. Data for this chart are given below:

Population

City	1880	1890	1900	1910
New York, N.Y.	1,911,698	2,507,414	3,437,202	4,766,883
Chicago, Ill.	503,185	1,099,850	1,698,757	2,185,283
Philadelphia, Pa.	847,170	1,046,964	1,293,697	1,549,008
Los Angeles, Calif.	11,181	50,395	102,479	319,198
Detroit, Mich.	116,340	205,876	285,704	465,766

City	1920	1930	1940	1950
New York, N.Y.	5,620,048	6,930,446	7,454,995	7,835,099
Chicago, Ill.	2,701,705	3,376,438	3,396,808	3,606,436
Philadelphia, Pa.	1,823,779	1,950,961	1,931,334	2,064,794
Los Angeles, Calif.	576,673	1,238,048	1,504,277	1,957,692
Detroit, Mich.	993,678	1,568,662	1,623,452	1,838,517

14.1.11. On polar coordinate paper, plot a curve for the first set of data given below as a solid line (Fig. 14.6) and a curve for the second set as a broken line (Fig. 14.5). The lower end of the vertical center lines is to be taken as the zero-degree line. The curves will be symmetrical about this line, two points being plotted for each angle, one to the left and one to the right. Mark the candle power along this center line also.

Angle, °	(1) Mazda lamp and porcelain enameled reflector, candle power	(2) Type S-1 sun lamp, candle power
0	600	1,000
5	655	925
10	695	790
15	725	640
20	760	460
25	800	350
30	815	260
35	825	205
40	830	170
45	815	150
50	785	130
55	740	120
60	640	0
65	485	—
70	330	—
75	200	—
80	90	—
85	25	—
90	0	—

14.1.12. On trilinear coordinate paper plot the data given below. Complete the chart, identifying the curves and lettering the title below the coordinate lines (Fig. 14.7).

Freezing Points of Solutions of Glycerol and Methanol in Water

Weight, per cent			Freezing points, °F
Water	Methanol	Glycerol	
86	14	0	+14
82	8	10	+14
78	6	16	+14
76	24		−4
74	2	24	+14

Freezing Points of Solutions of Glycerol and Methanol in Water (Cont.)

Water	Weight, per cent Methanol	Glycerol	Freezing points, °F
71	17	12	− 4
70	0	30	+14
68	32	0	−22
65	10	25	− 4
62	23	15	−22
60	40	0	−40
58	5	37	− 4
57	17	26	−22
55	0	45	− 4
54	28	18	−40
53	47	0	−58
52	10	38	−22
50	20	30	−40
47	31	22	−58
45	0	55	−22
42	7	51	−40
39	12	49	−58
37	0	63	−40
36	8	56	−58
33	0	67	−58

14.1.13. Thermal conductivities of a bonded-asbestos-fiber insulating material at various mean temperatures are tabulated below:

Mean temperature (hot to cold surface) T, °F	Thermal conductivity K, Btu per hr-sq ft-°F temp diff-in. thickness
100	0.365
200	0.415
320	0.470
400	0.520
460	0.563
600	0.628
730	0.688
900	0.780

Plotting the data on uniform rectangular coordinates with thermal conductivity as ordinate and mean temperature as abscissa, evaluate the constants a and b in the linear equation $K = a + bT$ relating the variables.

14.1.14. Corrosion tests on specimens of pure magnesium resulted in values for weight increase in pure oxygen at 525°C tabulated in the next column:

Elapsed time T, hr	Weight increase W, mg per sq cm
0	0
2.0	0.17
4.0	0.36
8.2	0.65
11.5	1.00
20.0	1.68
24.1	2.09
30.0	2.57

Plotting the data on uniform rectangular coordinates with weight increase as ordinate and elapsed time as abscissa, evaluate the constant a in the linear equation $W = aT$ relating the variables.

14.1.15. Approximate rates of discharge of water under various heads of fall through a 1,000-ft length of 4-in. pipe having an average number of bends and fittings are tabulated below:

Head of fall H, ft	Discharge Q, gal per min	Head of fall H, ft	Discharge Q, gal per min
1	35.8	20	159.7
2	50.6	25	178.9
4	71.6	30	195.8
6	87.7	40	225.8
9	107.5	50	252.2
12	123.7	75	309.8
16	142.9	100	357.9

Plotting the data on logarithmic coordinates with discharge as ordinate and head as abscissa, evaluate the constants a and b in the power equation $Q = aH^b$ relating the variables.

14.1.16. Creep-strength tests of a high-chromium (23 to 27 per cent) ferritic steel used in high-temperature service resulted in the stress values, to produce a 1 per cent deformation in 10,000 hr at various temperatures, tabulated in the right margin:

Plotting the data on semilogarithmic coordinates with stress as ordinate on a logarithmic scale and temperature as abscissa on a uniform scale, evaluate the constants a and b in the exponential equation $S = a10^{bT}$ relating the variables.

Temperature T, °F	Stress S, lb per sq in.
1,000	6,450
1,100	2,700
1,200	1,250
1,300	570
1,400	270

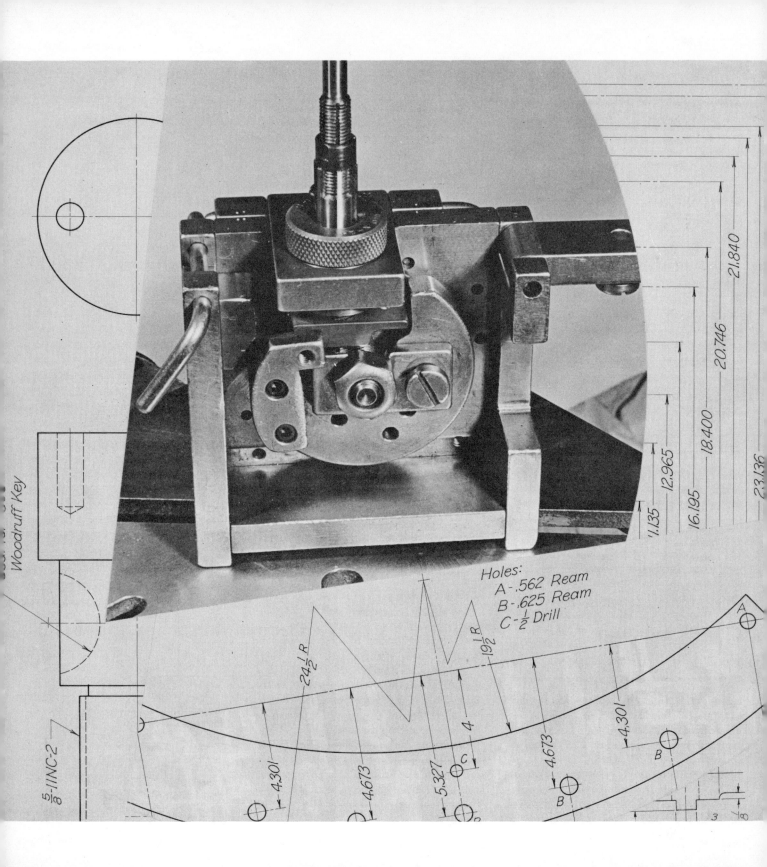

Woodruff Key

$\frac{5}{8}$-11NC-2

Holes:
A - .562 Ream
B - .625 Ream
C - $\frac{1}{2}$ Drill

11.135
12.965
16.195
18.400
20.746
21.840
23.136

24$\frac{1}{2}$ R

19$\frac{1}{2}$ R

4.301
4.673
5.327
4
4.673
4.301

C
B
B
A

3
$\frac{1}{8}$

15

Drawings of Jigs and Fixtures

15.1. Manufacturing methods for producing a single unit or very few units require individual measurements for locations, careful and accurate gaging during machining, and meticulous care to bring parts to required specifications. All this must be done by trained and experienced workers, an expensive procedure because the parts are virtually handmade.

Many products—for example, automobiles, home appliances, and components such as valves, motors—are manufactured by the thousands, even millions. Manufacturing parts in such quantities by ordinary unit methods would be impractical not only from the standpoint of the time and care required but, more important, because parts thus produced would be costly and not consistently interchangeable.

Even when producing only a few parts, say up to 100, the use of devices known as jigs and fixtures assists greatly in obtaining uniform parts at reduced cost.

15.2. JIGS.   A *jig* is a device that holds a production and guides a rotating tool that performs some machining operation. Thus a jig is used for drilling, reaming, counterboring, countersinking, tapping, or combinations of these operations. The part being processed is often called "the production" or "the subject." Figure 15.1 is a picture of a small jig for performing several drilling operations on a part. The jig is placed on the table of a drill press, and the drill is passed through a "drill bushing" in the jig. The drill is thus accurately located (positioned) and guided by the bushing to drill a hole in the production. The production is accurately located and clamped tightly in the jig so that each part produced will be essentially identical. The accuracy built into the jig controls the accuracy of the finished product and eliminates the necessity for measurements on each (individual) part in order to locate the holes.

15.3.   PRINCIPLES OF DESIGN.

To illustrate some of the principles of jig design, a simple jig for drilling two ¾-in. holes and reaming one 1-in. hole in a pawl carrier is shown in Fig. 15.2. The principles that should be followed as far as possible in designing a jig are:

1. The production must go into the jig easily and quickly.

2. The production must be located accurately.

3. The bushings must be accessible to the operator.

4. The production must be securely clamped in the jig.

5. The production must be removable easily and quickly.

It is universal practice in jig drawing to show the production in *red;* the jig itself is drawn in *black*. Visible features are drawn as they would be if the production were not in place. On blueprints and direct-process prints, the red lines that show the production print

FIG. 15.1. A jig. The product to be processed (*A*) is placed in the jig (*B*) where it is located against finished surfaces and held in position by clamps (*C*). The drill then passes through a bushing at (*D*) to make the hole in part (*A*).

lighter than the black lines. Thus, also on the print, the production is distinguishable from the jig or fixture. All the jig and fixture drawings in this chapter illustrate prints of drawings; therefore the production shows in gray lines.

In all jig designs four main points of design related to the above principles must be considered. Briefly they are:

1. Locating the production accurately
2. Clamping the production securely
3. Selecting bushings of correct style and size
4. Designing the jig body to accommodate the production and satisfy the principles

By observing these four cardinal points, a drill jig can be designed that will satisfy the requirements of commercial production. Study each of the four aspects of the design carefully to determine the best solution. There are many different methods of providing for each. Select the one that will be most suitable in combination with the method of providing for the other three. We will discuss several methods of meeting each of the four requirements, but selection is not confined to these in designing a particular piece of work.

15.4.   LOCATING THE PRODUCTION.
The shape of the production, previous finishing before drilling, and other points of design will influence the type of locator best suited for the production. Location must be thoroughly considered, as it is perhaps the most important of the four points for accuracy in the jig.

Finished surfaces are often used to locate—a finished surface of the production is placed against a finished surface of the jig; or, when necessary, an unfinished surface of the production is placed against a finished surface of the

ITEM	NAME	MATL.	DESCRIPTION
1	Body	C.I.	
2	Clamp	C.R.S.	
3	Set Screw	Std.	½ × 1⅜ Sq Hd Rd Pt.
4	Quarter Turn Scr	C.R.S.	½–13 NC-2 Thd
5	Hinge Pin	D.Rd	½ × 2⅜ Lg.
6	Set Screw	Std.	½ × 1⅛ Slot Hd'less Rd Pt
7	Hex Nut	Std.	½–13 NC-2
8	Pop Pin	T.S.	
9	Spring	Stl.	To Suit
10	Screw Plug	"	¾–10 NC-2 × ⅞ Lg.
11	Bushing	"	Hdls f/O.Dx⅜lg. for ⅜ Drill
12	"	"	Liner ⅝ O.D x1⅜lg. x1⅜ I.D.
13	"	"	R.S.⅛⅜ O.D x⅜lg. for⅜Drill
14	"	"	R.S.⅛⅜ O.Dx⅞lg.for 1" Ream
15	Lockscrew	Std.	½–18 NC-2

FIG. 15.2. Jig for pawl carrier. The product is located against finished surfaces and setscrews (pieces 6 and 7). Clamping is done by piece 2 and setscrew (3). Processing is done through bushings (pieces 11 to 15). The product, in red on the drawing, reproduces in gray lines on a print—and in this illustration.

jig. Location surfaces may take the form of pads, counterbores, or two finished surfaces at right angles to each other.

Pins give an easy and relatively inexpensive method of location and at the same time a very accurate one. A finished or an unfinished surface of the production is held against a pin and a finished surface, or against two or three pins, by a clamp or screws (Fig. 15.3).

In the jig in Fig. 15.6 two pins, one circular and the other flattened, are used to locate. Both pins are accurate to the size necessary to fit into two

FIG. 15.3. Jig for cover plate. This design illustrates the use of pins and a V slide for location. The product, in red on the drawing, reproduces in gray lines on a print—and in this illustration.

FIG. 15.4. Drill-and-ream jig for gear case. The six bushings (three on the front and three on the rear) locate the production in front-to-rear direction. The product, in red on the drawing, reproduces in gray lines on a print—and in this illustration.

FIG. 15.5. Jig for trip arm. The product is located against a V block and finished surface. Clamping is done by pieces 4, 10, 11, 12, and 13. The product, in red on the drawing, reproduces in gray lines on a print—and in this illustration.

These Bosses not shown in side view

Note—File Break All Sharp Corners

Item	Quan	Name	Specification
4	1	Set Screw	⅜×1 Sq.Hd.Flat Pt. ⅜-16NC-2
6	4	Mach. "	10-32 × ½ Fil.Hd.
9	2	" "	10-32 × ¾ Flat Hd.
10	1	Set "	⅜ × ⅝ Sq.Hd.Flat Pt. ⅜-16NC-2
12	1	Spring	⅞ O.D. To Suit
13	1	Plug	½ø×¾ Slotted Hd'less ½-18NF-3
14	1	Set Screw	¼×⅜ " ¼-20NC-2
15	1	Jam Nut	Hex. ¼-20NC-2
16	2	Bushing	Hd'ls ½ O.D.×⅜ lg.for ¼ Drill
17	1	"	" ²⁷⁄₆₄ O.D.×⅜ lg.for ¹⁵⁄₆₄ Drill
18	1	"	" ⁷⁄₁₆ O.D.×⅜ lg.for ¼ Drill
19	1	"	" ⅜ O.D.×⅜ lg. for ⁷⁄₁₆ Drill

FIG. **15.6.**   Jig for making a jig. This type of jig is often used to obtain accuracy for identical sets of holes.

previously drilled or reamed holes in the production. (One pin must be flattened because the center-to-center distances of the holes may vary enough to make a fit impossible with two round pins.) The round pin locates along the line of centers, and both pins locate at right angles to the line of centers, since the flats of the flattened pin are always placed perpendicular to the line of centers. Note that the pins are made so that they can be pressed into the fixtures only up to the shoulder. The ends are chamfered, preferably at 30°, to allow easy entry into the production.

Small pins are usually made of tool steel, hardened and ground. Large pins may be made of cold-rolled steel, pack-hardened and ground. The shoulder of the pin is pressed against a finished surface or into a light spot face or counterbore to a suitable depth.

Bushings serve as locators in certain designs, as illustrated in Fig. 15.4. This jig is to serve in drilling and reaming holes in a gear case, on which the out-to-out distance between bosses is an accurate dimension with limits; hence the surfaces of these bosses provide good points for location, and the accurately

located shoulder bushings are designed to come to contact with them. Location of the subject in the other directions is by using finished surfaces, against which it is clamped by screws and a bar clamp.

V blocks are often used in jig design, both as locators and as clamps. An example was seen in Fig. 15.3. The jig in Fig. 15.5 employs a V whose purpose is mainly for location, though it also serves as a "backstop" in clamping, while the setscrews are the clamps proper. A V block is more easily made as a separate piece, secured to the body of the jig by screws and dowel pins. Fastening the V block without dowel pins, by using slotted holes for the cap screws, might be necessary in case the circular boss on the production varied considerably in diameter with different castings.

Accurate holes for pins.   A small plate jig is often used to drill a recurring series of holes in making a large jig, as shown in Fig. 15.6, or in a production itself. The small jig in the figure carries two locating pins, one round and the other flattened (for reasons already mentioned in paragraph 15.4). On the large jig the holes marked *A* have been previously drilled and reamed, with the jig borer or

FIG. 15.7. Drill and ream jig. The center locator (detail shown) locates the production through the accurate central hole in the production. The product, in red on the drawing, reproduces in gray lines on a print—and in this illustration.

Item	Name	Quan.	Mat'l.	Description
	BILL OF MATERIAL			
1	Jig Body	1	C.I.	
2	Bushing Plate	1	C.I.	
3	Quarter Turn Screw	1	M.S.	
4	Pin	1	C.R.S.	$\frac{3}{8}D \times 8\frac{5}{8}$ SF in ① RF in ②
5	Pin	1	C.R.S.	$\frac{1}{2}D \times 1\frac{1}{4}$ Drive Fit in ① and ②
6	Hex Nut	1	Stl.	$\frac{7}{8}-9$ NC-2 Std.
7	Locator	1		See Detail
8	Bushing	4	"	Liner, 1$\frac{1}{16}$O.D.x1"lg.x1"I.D.
9	"	1	"	Rem.ble slip, 1"O.D.x1"lg. for $\frac{7}{8}$ Drill
10	"	1	"	" 1"O.D.x1"lg. for $\frac{29}{32}$ Ream
11	Lockscrew	4	"	No. 2A A.S.A. Std.
12	C-Washer	1	C.R.S.	

DETAIL OF LOCATOR

on a radial boring machine, to match the pins of the small jig; by using the small jig, the series of holes *B* can then be drilled with far more accuracy and speed than if each hole had to be located individually.

Center locators. The jig in Fig. 15.7 uses a center locator. If the hole in the production is of such size that it has been bored on a lathe and the piece faced at the same time, this method of locating is indicated. The shank for locating is of such diameter that the hole is a slip fit over it.

Keyways serve as locators in cases where it is necessary to drill holes that must be in a particular position. In a jig designed for a coupling where the holes must be in the center of the bosses and at the

same time located with respect to the keyway, the center locator would include a key to slip into the keyway of the subject.

15.5. CLAMPS AND CLAMPING. Some of the more commonly used clamps for fastening the subject securely in the jig are the following:

1. Bar clamp
2. Slotted clamp
3. Setscrews and studs
4. C washer
5. V slide
6. Spiral-rise cam
7. Star knob and stud
8. Adjustable pins
9. Hydraulic piston

The jigs illustrated in this chapter show several of these methods of clamping. The important point to observe is that *the clamp must not distort the production, as such distortion introduces inaccuracy in the drilled holes upon release of the clamping pressure. Clamping must be applied at a point on the production that will withstand the strain introduced* and as close as possi-

FIG. 15.8. Spiral-rise cam clamps. These are quickly operated and clamp securely.

ble to the point drilled. It is not always possible to apply clamping close to the point drilled, but this is an important consideration.

Clamps suffer the most wear of any part of a jig, and cyanide hardening is advisable. When there is a possibility of marring a finished surface, a soft-nosed clamp should be employed.

Slotted clamps are widely used. To get proper action, they should have the stud at the center or closer to the production than to the tail of the clamp. Studs and nuts are preferred to cap screws, as they do not wear out the body of the jig and are cheap to replace.

Setscrews are cheap and highly efficient as a means of holding the production securely (Fig. 15.5). In clamping four sides of an object, the setscrews on two sides will have lock nuts, and those on the other two sides will be used for locking and unlocking the piece.

Use may be made of a stud and nut in combination with a C washer in cases where the production slips over the stud or a locating pin (Fig. 15.7).

V slide. In using the V slide in clamping, take care to see that its length is at least equal to its width, to avoid having an unstable action. Its thickness depends upon the production and whether the V is fixed or movable. In the latter case the size of the control screw will have a bearing on the thickness.

Spiral-rise cam clamps are useful in quantity production where quick clamping and unclamping with little thought required from the operator are the prime requisites. The maximum variation in the production pieces at the point of clamping must be known—the rise of the cam is computed from this point—in order that the cam face will clamp the production with a 90° turn of the

handle. Figure 15.8 shows two types of locking cams that give locking action in either of two directions from the axis.

Star knobs and studs are an adaptation of the setscrew principle for hand operation.

Adjustable pins are used to support fragile sections of the production. Correct designs are shown in Fig. 15.9. They should be locked into position by a setscrew.

Hydraulic pistons are for heavy work and work requiring special clamping. Their design is of too specialized a nature to include here.

FIG. 15.9. Three methods of supporting fragile sections. (*A*) adjustable pin and clamp; (*B*) adjustable screw; (*C*) spring-backed pin and clamp. The product, in red on the drawing, reproduces in gray lines on a print—and in this illustration.

15.6. AMERICAN STANDARD BUSHINGS.

Drill bushings are standardized items, made in five different styles (Fig. 15.10). They are available in from six to eight lengths in each style for use with all the numbered, lettered, and fractional drill sizes up to 2 in.

Plain, stationary press-fit bushings, used when the bushing is expected to last during the life of the jig, are made in two types: the *headless* and the *head* types.

LINER

RENEWABLE FIXED TYPE

REMOVABLE SLIP TYPE

HEADLESS TYPE

HEAD TYPE

FIG. 15.10. ASA jig bushings. See the Appendix.

The headless type is used when the center distance of holes is too close for a bushing with a head and when it is desirable to have the top of the bushing flush with the top of the jig plate. Both types are used without liners.

Renewable bushings, with liners, are used in cases where the bushing will wear enough for replacement or where it is necessary to interchange bushings in one hole. They are of two types: the *renewable fixed* and the *renewable-slip*[1] types. Renewable fixed bushings are used for one operation only. Renewable slip bushings are used where two or more operations, requiring different inside diameters, are performed in a single jig without removing the production from the jig, for example, when drilling is followed by reaming, spot-facing, counterboring, tapping, etc. They should be used in combination with a liner and lock screw unless the design cannot possibly allow the additional space required by the liner.

Bushings are specified by giving, in order, (1) type, (2) outside diameter, (3) length, (4) drill size.

For correct installation, design drawings should show clearly the bell-mouthed end of the bushing as the entry end for the drill. For accurate drilling, the other end should be not more than one drill diameter from the production. The thickness of the production, type of material being drilled, and design of the jig will all influence the minimum distance between the end of the bushing and the production. Chip clearance must be considered to avoid drill binding and the creation of unusual pressures. Sometimes the bushing is designed to touch the production, and the chips are carried up and out at the top.

[1] Also called *removable-slip* type.

Some shops prefer to use the type of bushings that have 1/64-in. grinding stock on the outside diameter, for fitting the bushing to the hole.

Bushings for special work should be described by following the tables of standard wall thicknesses, size of head, etc., and specifying the proper finish and heat-treatment.

Standard drill bushings are listed in the Appendix.

15.7. THE JIG BODY. Jig bodies are of two general classes: the open body and the closed or box type. In general, open jigs have drill bushings in the same plane, parallel to one another. Closed or box-shaped jigs are for drilling holes from various planes and directions. Occasionally there may be an overlap in the nomenclature of the two general types.

Because of the rigidity required, cast iron has been the usual material for jig bodies, but welded steel is now being used successfully.

The weight of the body should be considered. For ease of handling, it should have no excess weight, but it must not be lightened at the expense of the stiffness and rigidity needed for accuracy. It is often possible, however, to core out metal in various places without decreasing strength. For the comfort and safety of the operator, corners should be rounded and all burrs and sharp edges removed by filing. For convenience in moving, small jigs can be equipped with handles, and large ones with hooks for handling with a crane.

Finished feet should be provided on the sides opposite the drill bushings. For proper machining, small lugs are often placed on other sides to act as stops. The jig feet are generally part of the casting but in some cases are inserts.

Four should always be used in preference to three, because with four feet any unevenness in setting, such as a chip under one foot, will at once draw the attention of the operator, by rocking.

On the inside of the jig and at other places where machining is to be done, particular care should be taken to allow proper clearance for the machining tools. Points of location should, if possible, be visible to the operator.

Small jigs do not need to be clamped to the table, but large jigs and all fixtures (see paragraph 15.10) should be provided with means of clamping securely to the machine on which they are used.

15.8. SUMMARY. POINTS IN JIG DESIGN.

1. Provide the best method of locating.

2. Provide the best method of clamping.

3. Select correct types of bushings.

4. Have bushings accessible to the operator.

5. Design for quick loading and unloading.

6. Design for ability to withstand abuse without affecting accuracy.

7. Keep in mind the safety of the operator.

8. Provide clearance for drills after passing through the work.

9. Provide for chip clearance and easy removal of chips.

10. Design so that cheaper parts wear out first.

11. See that finished surfaces will not be marred by clamping devices.

12. Provide means for lifting heavy jigs.

13. If loose parts are unavoidable, chain them to the body of the jig.

14. Consider the cost of materials and labor, but do not attempt to cut the cost of the jig at the expense of efficiency.

15.9. MAKING A JIG DRAWING. The procedure in designing a jig or fixture should follow approximately this order:

1. Sketch the design freehand to get the proper choice of views and an idea of space requirements. This original sketch will take into account previously finished surfaces of the production.

2. Allowing ample space between views, carefully draw the production in *red* in its several views. When the jig drawing is reproduced, the red lines print gray, so the production remains distinguishable from the jig.

3. Build the jig around the production, following the correct principles of location, clamping, bushings, and body design. As to visibility, draw the jig as though the production were not in place.

4. Dimension the drawing of the jig, using decimal dimensions for all locators and bushings, following the system of base-line dimensioning, from zero coordinate axes.

5. Give each part an item number.

6. Prepare a bill of material of all items in sequence.

7. Check the drawing.

15.10. FIXTURES. A fixture is a device that holds and locates a production so that some machining operation can be performed. Fixtures are used on machine tools that have their own (built-in) guiding and controlling mechanism for the tool. Thus, on a lathe the fixture may be for facing, turning, or boring; on a milling machine, for milling one or more surfaces; on a grinder, for grinding cylindrical or flat surfaces.

Figure 15.11 is a photograph of a

FIG. 15.11. A turning fixture. The production (A) is located over pins on the fixture (B) and is held in place by the clamp (C). The tool (D) then makes the required cut.

FIG. 15.12. A milling fixture. The production (A) is located in the fixture (B) against the finished surfaces and over a pin. The clamp (C) holds the production in position as the milling cutter (D) makes the required cut.

PC.NO	NAME	MATL.
1	Face Plate	C.I.
2	Locating Pin	T.S.
3	"	"
4	Clamp	C.R.S.
5	Stud	"
6	Hex. Nut	St'd.
7	Clamp Seat	M.S.
8	Fil. Hd. Cap Scr.	St'd.
9	Centering Stud	C.R.S.
10	Hex. Nut	St'd.
11	C-Washer	C.R.S.
12	Spring	St'l.

FIG. 15.13.   Lathe fixture for boring and facing. This fixture is for Prob. 8.1.18.

turning fixture; Fig. 15.12, of a milling fixture.

Two examples are given in Figs. 15.13 and 15.14 to illustrate the principles of fixture construction. Figure 15.13 is a lathe fixture to aid in boring the hole and facing the projection and bottom of the flange of Prob. 8.1.18. The flange locates over the pins. The center clamp is removed, and slotted clamps are used while the hole and projection are being machined. To complete the finishing of the bottom, the clamps are slid back and the center clamp is put in place.

FIG. 15.14.   Counterbalanced boring-and-facing fixture. This fixture is for Prob. 5.6.4. The product, in red on the drawing, reproduces in gray lines on a print—and in this illustration.

Figure 15.14 is a fixture for holding the toggle-shaft support of Prob. 5.6.4 in boring the hole and facing the end. The bracket locates over two pins and is held in place by the clamp.

Both these fixtures clamp to the face-plate of the lathe, the entire fixture and production rotating. Being unbalanced, the offset bracket fixture requires a counterbalance to reduce vibration and aid in accuracy of work. To compute the size of the counterbalance, the center of gravity and the moment of the fixture and production together about the working center must be found. From this, the area and thickness of counterbalance and its working distance from the center may be calculated to find an equivalent moment to balance that on the opposite side of center. Common practice is to provide a slightly oversize counterbalance thickness, which allows the shop to complete the balance by removal of metal. This is a timesaver and permits slight changes that may take place in some parts used in the fixture.

In designing fixtures for milling, slotting, saw cutting, and similar operations, the same principles of location and clamping as those given for jig designing are followed. To obtain secure clamping, finished bases should be provided with two square keys for aligning the fixture with the T slots in the milling table, as well as with slots at each end for T bolts.

If a previous operation has been performed on the subject, a gaging surface should be provided, if at all possible, to which the cutter may be set, thus obtaining accurately the required distance between the two finished surfaces.

15.11. ASSEMBLY JIGS AND FIXTURES. Sometimes it is necessary to perform some machining operation at the time of assembly of parts. Thus, an assembly jig locates two (or more) parts and provides bushings for drilling, etc. Or an assembly fixture may locate two (or more) parts for a machining operation. In some cases a device is used *only* to *locate* one part, relative to another, at assembly. This is termed (*a*) an assembly fixture, (*b*) a locating fixture, or (*c*) an adjusting fixture.

15.12. STANDARDS. The scope of this book allows only an introduction to the very broad field of tooling and toolmaking. For further information, consult the standards of the ASA and SAE. Textbooks are listed in the bibliography. Especially pertinent are the standards on small tools and machine-tool elements.

PROBLEMS

15.1.1. Design a drill-and-ream jig for Fig. 11.23. Locate on a finished pad the lug in a finished slot and the finished end of the cylinder, 4 in. long, against a finished boss of the jig. Clamp from the top and back with one setscrew each. Provide plain bushings for the base holes in the pad and two liners with removable drill-and-ream bushings for the larger holes. Two lengths of removable bushings will be required, the longer being to reach into within a drill diameter of the cylinder 2¾ in. long. Design a box-type body with feet opposite the sides in which bushings are placed. The right side of the body will be open to permit loading. Spot-face the holes outside the jig.

15.1.2. Design a drill jig for special nut (Fig. 11.85*A*). Locate over a center locator on a finished pad through the 1⅛-in. hole, the locator reducing in size sufficiently to use a nut and

C washer for clamping on the 1¾-in.-diameter end. Nut should be small enough to clear the hole when loading and unloading. Provide bushings in an open-type body.

Alternative method. Use the same method of locating but provide only one drill bushing and an index pin 90° from the bushing. Drill one hole, index this hole to the pin, drill the next hole, etc.

15.1.3. Design a drill jig for the ¼-in. oil hole in the bracket of Prob. 13.3.3. Locate on a horizontal locator through the large center hole of the production, using a nut and C washer for removal. Index the production with a pin through one of the capscrew holes, so that the drill will enter the oil reservoir in the casting at the proper place.

15.1.4. Design a boring-and-facing fixture for flange, Prob. 8.1.18. Refer to the design shown in Fig. 15.13. Assume that the top flat surface has been finished and the ¾-in. holes reamed prior to the operation of boring and facing in this fixture. For boring the 2⅝ and 2-in.-diameter holes, use the two clamps, the center stud and washer being removed. For facing, remove or slip the clamps out of place and use the centering stud with washer and nut. On a production line, two fixtures could be made using the parts necessary for successive operations in each fixture.

15.1.5. Design a boring-and-facing fixture for plunger bracket, Prob. 5.6.2. Refer to the design shown in Fig. 15.14. Assume that the base is finished and that the base holes are reamed to size. Use these for locating over two pins, one flat and one round, and clamp down to the projecting shelf with a clamp as shown, or equivalent. This fixture should be counterbalanced to reduce vibration and obtain greater accuracy.

16

Drawings of Welded Parts

16.1. The subject of welding is of particular interest to the engineer and draftsman for two reasons. First, welding is used extensively for permanent fastenings of the components of machines and structures. Second, the production of machine parts by fabricating and welding instead of by casting or forging is a method that, for many purposes, forms a lighter and stronger part, often at an economy of cost.

16.2. WELDING PROCESSES. These are classified according to the manner in which the welded joint· is completed: (1) pressure welding (forging) and (2) nonpressure welding (fusion and brazing). Actually all welding is a fusion process, but by long usage, fusion weld-ing is understood to include the arc, gas, and thermit processes.

In arc welding, pieces of metal to be welded are brought to the proper welding temperature at point of contact by the heat liberated at the arc terminals so that the metals are completely fused into each other.

In gas or oxyacetylene welding a high-temperature flame is produced by igniting a mixture of two gases, usually oxygen and acetylene.

Resistance welding is a heat and squeeze process. The parts that are to be welded, while being forced together by mechanical pressure, are raised to the temperature of fusion by the passage of a heavy electrical current through the junction.

FIG. 16.1. Basic types of joints. The applicable welds for each type are listed.

	BUTT JOINT	LAP JOINT	TEE JOINT	CORNER JOINT	EDGE JOINT
APPLI-CABLE WELDS	SQUARE-GROOVE V-GROOVE BEVEL-GROOVE U-GROOVE J-GROOVE FLASH UPSET	FILLET BEVEL-GROOVE J-GROOVE SLOT PLUG SPOT PROJECTION SEAM	BEVEL-GROOVE J-GROOVE FILLET SLOT PLUG	SQUARE-GROOVE V-GROOVE BEVEL-GROOVE U-GROOVE J-GROOVE FILLET FLASH	SQUARE-GROOVE BEVEL-GROOVE V-GROOVE U-GROOVE J-GROOVE SPOT SEAM PROJECTION

FIG. 16.2. Fundamental welds. These can be applied to many different joints. See Fig. 16.1.

FIG. 16.3. Fundamental welds and individual basic symbols. Note that the symbols are pictorially descriptive of weld shapes.

16.3. CLASSIFICATION OF WELDED JOINTS. Figure 16.1 shows the basic types of joints, which are classified by the method of assembly of the parts. The applicable welds for each type are listed under each joint.

16.4. TYPES OF WELDS. Figure 16.2 shows in cross section the fundamental types of welds. For bead and fillet welds, the pieces are not prepared by cutting before making the weld, and the essential difference between V, bevel, U, and J welds is in the preparation of the parts joined. Pairs of the fundamental welds such as double V, double bevel, etc., make a further variety. Almost any combination is possible for complicated connections.

16.5. INDIVIDUAL BASIC WELD SYMBOLS. These are derived from the preparation of the pieces making up the joint or, where no preparation is necessary, from the section shape of the weld. Figure 16.3 shows the fundamental welds and the basic symbols that are used in specifying them.

Figure 16.4 shows the American Standard basic arc, gas, and resistance weld symbols, including supplementary symbols.

16.6. SIZES OF WELDS. In addition to specifying the type of weld to be made, a description of the size is also necessary. Thus, the *basic weld symbol* plus *size speci-*

ARC AND GAS WELD SYMBOLS											
TYPE OF WELD								SUPPLEMENTARY			
BEAD	FILLET	PLUG OR SLOT	GROOVE					WELD ALL AROUND	FIELD WELD	CONTOUR	
			SQUARE	V	BEVEL	U	J			FLUSH	CONVEX
⌒	◺	▽	‖	∨	⌵	⌈⌉	⌈⌉	○	●	—	⌒

RESISTANCE WELD SYMBOLS							
TYPE OF WELD				SUPPLEMENTARY			
SPOT	PROJECTION	SEAM	FLASH OR UPSET	WELD ALL AROUND	FIELD WELD	CONTOUR	
						FLUSH	CONVEX
✳	✕	XXX	│	○	●	—	⌒

FIG. 16.4. American Standard weld symbols.

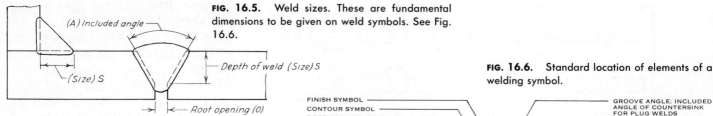

FIG. 16.5. Weld sizes. These are fundamental dimensions to be given on weld symbols. See Fig. 16.6.

fications are the elements included in a complete welding symbol. Figure 16.5 shows weld sizes. The dimensions of root opening, depth of preparation, and included angle are the important sizes to specify for grooved welds. The size of a 45° fillet weld is the dimension shown. Unequal-leg fillet welds are specified by giving the size of both legs, as described in paragraph 16.9, Art. B-2*b;* sizes of plug and slot welds are given as specified in Arts. E and F.

16.7. THE COMPLETE WELDING SYMBOL.

Figure 16.6 shows the basic form of the welding symbol and gives the position of the various marks and dimensions. There is a distinction between the terms *weld symbol* (paragraph 16.5) and *welding symbol.*

The *weld symbol* is the ideograph (Fig. 16.4) used to indicate the desired type of weld. The assembled *welding symbol* consists of the following eight elements, or such of these elements as are necessary: (1) reference line, (2) arrow, (3) basic weld symbols, (4) dimensions and other data, (5) supplementary symbols, (6) finish symbols, (7) tail, (8) specification process or other references.

Figure 16.7 summarizes the important points dealing with the specification of welds and the location of weld symbols. It also gives some general directions for drawing the symbols and shows the completed symbols.

FIG. 16.7. Location of weld symbols and specifications.

FIG. 16.6. Standard location of elements of a welding symbol.

1. THE SIDE OF THE JOINT TO WHICH THE ARROW POINTS IS THE ARROW SIDE.
2. BOTH-SIDES WELDS OF SAME TYPE ARE OF SAME SIZE UNLESS OTHERWISE SHOWN.
3. SYMBOLS APPLY BETWEEN ABRUPT CHANGES IN DIRECTION OF JOINT OR AS DIMENSIONED (EXCEPT WHERE ALL AROUND SYMBOL IS USED).
4. ALL WELDS ARE CONTINUOUS AND OF USER'S STANDARD PROPORTIONS. UNLESS OTHERWISE SHOWN.
5. TAIL OF ARROW USED FOR SPECIFICATION REFERENCE (TAIL MAY BE OMITTED WHEN REFERENCE NOT USED).
6. DIMENSIONS OF WELD SIZE. INCREMENT LENGTHS AND SPACINGS IN INCHES.

FIG. 16.8. Classification of welded joints.

Figure 16.8 classifies welded joints and shows the symbols for each. The arrow points to the grooved member at a point near the weld. The side of the weld pointed to is always called the arrow side. For nonsymmetrical welds (bevel and J), in order to show *which* piece is to be prepared, the leader must be made with a definite break pointing toward the piece to be prepared, as shown by the bevel and J welds in Fig. 16.8 and described in Art. A-15. The tail of the arrow is used to hold a reference only when specification of strength, type of rod, etc., is to be given. The individual basic symbols are placed on the basic form to describe any possible combination of welds for a complete joint. Every simple weld that is a part of the complete joint must be specified.

16.8. WELDING DRAWINGS. A welding drawing shows a unit or part made of several pieces of metal, with each welded joint described and specified. Figure 16.9 shows the detail drawing of a part made of cast iron, and Fig. 16.10 shows a part identical in function but made up by welding. Comparison of the two drawings shows the essential differences both in construction and in drawing technique. Note the absence of fillets and rounds in the welding drawing. Note also that all the pieces making up the welded part are dimensioned so that they can be cut easily from standard stock.

All joints between the individual pieces of the welded part must be shown, even though the joint would not appear as a line on the completed part. The lines marked *A* in Fig. 16.11 illustrate this principle. Each individual piece should be identified by number (Fig. 16.10).

FIG. 16.9.   Detail drawing of a casting. Compare with welded part, Fig. 16.10.

FIG. 16.10.   Detail drawing of a welded part. Compare with cast part, Fig. 16.9.

FIG. 16.11.   Joint lines. These are shown on drawings of welded parts.

16.9.   USE OF THE SYMBOLS.

The following instructions for the placement and form of welding symbols are adapted from ASA Z32.2.1—1949.

A. GENERAL PROVISIONS

1. Location Significance of Arrow

   a. In the case of groove, fillet, and flash or upset welding symbols, the arrow connects the welding symbol reference line to one side of the joint, and this side is considered the *arrow side* of the joint. The side opposite the arrow side of the joint is considered the *other side* of the joint (Fig. 16.6).

   b. In the case of plug, slot, spot, seam, and projection welding symbols, the arrow connects the welding symbol reference line to the outer surface of one of the members of the joint at the center line of the desired weld. The member to which the arrow points is considered the *arrow-side* member; the other member, the *other-side* member (Art. E-1a).

   c. When a joint is depicted by a single line on the drawing and the arrow of a welding symbol is directed to this line, the arrow side of the joint is considered the near side of the joint in accordance with the usual conventions of drafting (Fig. 16.8).

   d. When a joint is depicted as an area parallel to the plane of projection in a drawing and the arrow of a welding symbol is directed to near area, the *arrow-side* member of the joint is considered the near side of the joint in accordance with the usual conventions of drafting (Fig. 16.8).

2. Location of Weld with Respect to Joint

   a. Welds on the arrow side of the joint are shown by placing the weld symbol on the side of the reference line toward the reader.

   b. Welds on the other side of the joint are shown by placing the weld symbol on the side of the reference line away from the reader.

   c. Welds on both sides of the joint are shown by placing weld symbols on both sides of the reference line, toward and away from the reader.

d. Spot, seam, flash, and upset weld symbols have no arrow-side or other-side significance in themselves, although supplementary symbols used in conjunction with them may have such significance. Spot, seam, flash, and upset weld symbols are centered on the reference line.

3. Method of Drawing Symbols

a. Symbols may be drawn mechanically or freehand.

4. Use of Inch, Degree, and Pound Marks

a. Inch, degree, and pound marks may be used on welding symbols or not, as desired, except that inch marks must be used for indicating the diameter of spot and projection welds and the width of seam welds when such welds are specified by linear dimension.

5. Location of Specification, Process, or Other References

a. When a specification, process, or other reference is used with a welding symbol, the reference is placed in the tail.

6. Use of Symbols without References

a. When desired, weld symbols may be used without specification, process, or other references in the following instances:

(1) When a note such as the following is included on the drawing: "Unless otherwise designated, all welds are to be made in accordance with Specification No.___."

(2) When the welding procedure to be used is prescribed elsewhere.

7. Use of General Notes

a. When desired, general notes such as the following may be placed on a drawing to provide detailed information pertaining to the predominating welds, and this information need not be repeated on the symbols.

"Unless otherwise indicated, all fillet welds are 5/16 inch size."

"Unless otherwise indicated, root openings for all groove welds are 3/16 inch."

8. Use of Weld-all-around Symbol

a. Welds extending completely around a joint are indicated on the drawing by means of the weld-all-around symbol.

9. Use of Field-weld Symbol

a. Field welds (welds not made in a shop or at the place of initial construction) are indicated by means of the field-weld symbol.

10. Extent of Welding Denoted by Symbols

a. Symbols apply between abrupt changes in the direction of the welding or to the extent of hatching or dimension lines, except when the weld is indicated by means of the weld-all-around symbol.

11. Weld Proportions

a. All welds are continuous and of user's standard proportions unless otherwise indicated.

12. Finishing of Welds

a. Finishing of welds, other than cleaning, is indicated by suitable contour and finish symbols (Art. B-9).

13. Location of Weld Symbols

a. Weld symbols, except spot and seam, are shown only on the welding symbol reference line and not on the lines of the drawing.

b. Spot and seam weld symbols may be placed directly on drawings at the locations of the desired welds.

14. Construction of Fillet, and Bevel- and J-groove Welding Symbols

a. Fillet and bevel- and J-groove weld symbols are shown with the perpendicular leg *always* to the left.

15. Use of Break in Arrow of Bevel- and J-groove Welding Symbols

a. When a bevel- or J-groove weld symbol is used, the arrow points with a definite break toward the member that is to be chamfered, as shown. In cases where the member to be chamfered is obvious, the break in the arrow may be omitted.

16. Reading of Information on Welding Symbols

a. Information on welding symbols is placed to read from left to right along the reference line in accordance with the usual conventions of drafting.

17. Combined Weld Symbols

a. For joints having more than one weld, a symbol is shown for each weld.

18. Designation of Special Types of Welds

a. When the basic weld symbols are inadequate to indicate the desired weld, the weld is shown by a cross section, detail, or other data, with a reference to it on the welding symbol, observing the usual location significance.

B. FILLET WELDS

1. General

a. Dimensions of fillet welds are shown on the same side of the reference line as the weld symbol.

b. When no general note on the drawing governs the dimensions of fillet welds, the dimensions of fillet welds on both sides of the joint are shown:

(1) When both welds have the same dimensions, one or both may be dimensioned.

(2) When the welds differ in dimensions, both are dimensioned.

c. When there appears on the drawing a general note governing the dimensions of fillet welds, such as "All fillet welds ⁵⁄₁₆ in. size unless otherwise noted," the dimensions of fillet welds on both sides of the joint are indicated as follows:

(1) When both welds have dimensions governed by the note, neither need be dimensioned.

(2) When the dimensions of one or both welds differ from the dimensions given in the general note, both welds are dimensioned.

2. Size of Fillet Welds

a. The size of a fillet weld is shown to the left of the weld symbol.

b. The size of a fillet weld with unequal legs is shown in parentheses to the left of the weld symbol, as shown. Weld orientation is not shown by the symbol and is shown on the drawing when necessary.

3. Length of Fillet Welds

a. The length of a fillet weld, when indicated on the welding symbol, is shown to the right of the weld symbol.

b. When fillet welding extends for the full distance between abrupt changes in the direction of the welding, no length dimension need be shown on the welding symbol.

c. Specific lengths of fillet welding may be indicated by symbols in conjunction with dimension lines.

4. Extent of Fillet Welding

a. When it is desired to show the extent of fillet welding graphically, one type of hatching with definite end lines is used.

b. Fillet welding extending beyond abrupt changes in the direction of the welding is indicated by means of additional arrows pointing to each section of the joint to be welded, as shown in Art. A-10, except when the weld is indicated by means of the weld-all-around symbol.

5. Dimensioning of Intermittent Fillet Welding

a. The pitch (center-to-center spacing) of intermittent fillet welding is indicated as the distance between centers of increments on *one* side of the joint.

b. The pitch (center-to-center spacing) of intermittent fillet welding is shown to the right of the length dimension.

c. Chain intermittent fillet welding is shown thus:

d. Staggered intermittent fillet welding is shown thus:

6. Termination of Intermittent Fillet Welding

a. When intermittent fillet welding is used by itself, the symbol indicates that increments are located at the ends of the dimensioned length.

b. When intermittent fillet welding is used between continuous fillet welding, the symbol indicates that spaces equal to the pitch minus the length of one increment are to be left at the ends of the dimensioned length (Art. B-3).

7. Combination of Intermittent and Continuous Fillet Welding

a. Separate symbols are used for intermittent and continuous fillet welding when the two are used in combination (Art. B-3*c*).

8. Fillet Welds in Holes and Slots

a. Fillet welds in holes and slots are indicated by means of fillet-weld symbols.

9. Surface Contour of Fillet Welds

a. Fillet welds that are to be welded approximately flat-faced without recourse to any method of finishing are shown by adding the flush-contour symbol to the weld symbol, observing the usual location significance.

b. Fillet welds that are to be made flat-faced by mechanical means are shown by adding both the flush-contour symbol and the user's standard finish symbol[1] to the weld symbol, observing the usual location significance.

c. Fillet welds that are to be mechanically finished to a convex contour are shown by adding both the convex-contour symbol and the user's standard finish symbol[1] to the weld symbol, observing the usual location significance.

C. GROOVE WELDS

1. General

a. Dimensions of groove welds are shown on the same side of the reference line as the weld symbol.

b. When no general note governing the dimensions of groove welds appears

[1] Finish symbols used here indicate the method of finishing (C, chipping; G, grinding; M, machining) and not the degree of finish.

on the drawing, the dimensions of double-groove welds are shown as follows:

(1) When both welds have the same dimensions, one or both may be dimensioned.

(2) When the welds differ in dimensions, both are dimensioned.

c. When there appears on the drawing a general note governing the dimensions of groove welds, such as "All V-groove welds shall have a 60° groove angle unless otherwise noted," the dimensions of double-groove welds are indicated as follows:

(1) When both welds have dimensions governed by the note, neither need be dimensioned.

(2) When the dimensions of one or both welds differ from the dimensions given in the general note, both welds are dimensioned.

2. Size of Groove Welds

a. The size of groove welds is shown to the left of the weld symbol (groove depth plus root penetration).

b. The size of groove welds with no specified root penetration is shown as follows:

(1) The size of single-groove and symmetrical double-groove welds that extend completely through the member or members being joined need not be shown on the welding symbol.

(2) The size of groove welds that extend only partly through the member or members being joined is shown on the welding symbol.

c. The size of groove welds with specified root penetration is indicated by showing both the depth of chamfering and the root penetration, separated by a plus mark and placed to the left of the weld symbol. The depth of chamfering and the root penetration is read in that order from left to right along the reference line.

3. Groove Dimensions

a. Root opening of groove welds is the user's standard unless otherwise indicated. Root opening of groove welds, when not the user's standard, is shown inside the weld symbol.

b. Groove angle of groove welds is the user's standard, unless otherwise indicated. Groove angle of groove welds, when not the user's standard, is shown thus:

c. Groove radii and root faces of U- and J-groove welds are the user's standard unless otherwise indicated. When groove radii and root faces of U- and J-groove welds are not the user's standard, the weld is shown by a cross section, detail, or other data, with a reference to it on the weld-

ing symbol, observing the usual location significance.

4. Designation of Back and Backing Welds

Bead-type back and backing welds of single-groove welds are shown by means of the bead weld symbol (Art. D-2).

5. Surface Contour of Groove Welds

a. Groove welds that are to be welded approximately flush without recourse to any method of finishing are shown by adding the flush-contour symbol to the weld symbol, observing the usual location significance.

b. Groove welds that are to be made flush by mechanical means are shown by adding both the flush-contour symbol and the user's standard finish symbol[1] to the weld symbol, observing the usual location significance.

c. Groove welds that are to be mechanically finished to a convex contour are shown by adding both the convex-contour symbol and the user's standard finish symbol[1] to the weld symbol, observing the usual location significance.

D. BEAD WELDS

1. General

a. The single bead weld symbol is used to indicate bead-type back or backing welds of single-groove welds.

b. The dual bead weld symbol is used to indicate surfaces to be built up by welding.

DWG. 234

2. Use of Bead Weld Symbol to Indicate Bead-type Back or Backing Welds

a. Bead welds used as back or backing welds of single-groove welds are shown by placing a single bead weld symbol on the side of the reference line opposite the groove weld symbol.

b. Dimensions of bead welds used as back or backing welds are not shown on the welding symbol. If it is desired to specify these dimensions, they are shown on the drawing.

3. Surface Contour of Back or Backing Welds

a. Back or backing welds that are to be welded approximately flush without recourse to any method of finishing are shown by adding the flush-contour symbol to the bead weld symbol.

b. Back or backing welds that are to be made flush by mechanical means are shown by adding both the flush-contour symbol and the user's standard finish symbol[1] to the bead weld symbol.

c. Back or backing welds that are to be mechanically finished to a convex contour are shown by adding both the convex-contour symbol and the user's standard finish symbol[1] to the bead weld symbol.

4. Use of Bead Weld Symbol to Indicate Surfaces Built up by Welding

a. Surfaces built up by welding, whether by single- or multiple-pass bead

welds, are shown by the dual bead weld symbol.

b. The dual bead weld symbol does not indicate the welding of a joint, and hence has no arrow- or other-side significance. This symbol is drawn on the side of the reference line toward the reader, and the arrow must point clearly to the surface on which the weld is to be deposited.

c. Dimensions used in conjunction with the dual bead weld symbol are shown on the same side of the reference line as the weld symbol.

5. Size (Height) of Surfaces Built up by Welding

a. The size of a surface built up by welding is indicated by showing the minimum height of the weld deposit to the left of the weld symbol.

b. When no specific height of weld deposit is desired, no size dimension need be shown on the welding symbol.

6. Extent, Location, and Orientation of Surfaces Built up by Welding

a. When the entire area of a plane or curved surface is to be built up by welding, no dimension other than size (height of deposit) need be shown on the welding symbol.

b. When a portion of the area of a plane or curved surface is to be built up by welding, the extent, location and orientation of the area to be built up is indicated on the drawing.

E. PLUG WELDS

1. General

a. Holes in the arrow-side member of a joint for plug welding are indicated by placing the weld symbol on the side of the reference line toward the reader.

b. Holes in the other-side member of a joint for plug welding are indicated by placing the weld symbol on the side of the reference line away from the reader.

c. Dimensions of plug welds are shown on the same side of the reference line as the weld symbol.

d. The plug weld symbol is not used to designate fillet welds in holes (Art. B-8).

2. Size of Plug Welds

a. The size of a plug weld is shown to the left of the weld symbol.

3. Angle of Countersink

a. Included angle of countersink of plug welds is the user's standard unless otherwise indicated. Included angle of

countersink, when not the user's standard, is shown thus:

4. Depth of Filling

a. Depth of filling of plug welds is complete unless otherwise indicated. When the depth of filling is less than complete, the depth of filling, in inches, is shown inside the weld symbol.

5. Spacing of Plug Welds

a. Pitch (center-to-center spacing) of plug welds is shown to the right of the weld symbol.

6. Surface Contour of Plug Welds

a. Plug welds that are to be welded approximately flush without recourse to any method of finishing are shown by adding the flush-contour symbol to the weld symbol.

b. Plug welds that are to be made flush by mechanical means are shown by adding both the flush-contour symbol and the user's standard finish symbol[1] to the weld symbol.

F. SLOT WELDS

1. General

a. Slots in the arrow-side member of a joint for slot welding are indicated by placing the weld symbol on the side of the reference line toward the reader.

b. Slots in the other-side member of a joint for slot welding are indicated by placing the weld symbol on the side of the reference line away from the reader.

DESIRED   SYMBOL

c. Dimensions of slot welds are shown on the same side of the reference line as the weld symbol.

DWG. 23

d. The slot weld symbol is not used to designate fillet welds in slots (Art. B-8).

2. *Depth of Filling*

a. Depth of filling of slot welds is complete unless otherwise indicated. When the depth of filling is less than complete, the depth of filling, in inches, is shown inside the weld symbol.

1/2

3. *Details of Slot Welds*

a. The length, width, spacing, included angle of countersink, orientation, and location of slot welds cannot be shown on the welding symbol. These data are shown on the drawing or by a detail with a reference to it on the welding symbol, observing the usual location significance.

DWG. 233

4. *Surface Contour of Slot Welds*

a. Slot welds that are to be welded approximately flush without any method of finishing are shown by adding the flush-contour symbol to the weld symbol.

b. Slot welds that are to be made flush by mechanical means are shown by adding both the flush-contour symbol and the user's standard finish symbol[1] to the weld symbol.

c

G. SPOT WELDS

1. *General*

a. Spot weld symbols have no arrow- or other-side significance in themselves, although supplementary symbols used with them may have such significance (Art. G-6). Spot weld symbols are centered on the reference line (Art. G-4).

b. Dimensions of spot welds may be shown on either side of the reference line.

2. *Size of Spot Welds*

a. Spot welds are dimensioned by size or strength, as follows:

(1) The size of spot welds is designated as the diameter of the weld expressed decimally in hundredths of an inch, and is shown, with inch marks, to the left of the weld symbol.

.30"

(2) The strength of spot welds is designated as the minimum acceptable shear strength in pounds per spot, and is shown to the left of the weld symbol.

800

3. *Spacing of Spot Welds*

a. The pitch (center-to-center spacing) of spot welds is shown to the right of the weld symbol.

2

b. When spot weld symbols are shown directly on the drawing, spacing is shown by dimensions.

4. Extent of Spot Welding

a. When spot welding extends less than the distance between abrupt changes in the direction of the welding, or less than the full length of the joint (Art. A-10), the extent is dimensioned, thus:

5. Number of Spot Welds

a. When a definite number of spot welds is desired in a certain joint, the number is shown in parentheses above or below the weld symbol.

6. Flush Spot-welded Joints

a. When the exposed surface of one member of a spot-welded joint is to be flush, that surface is indicated by adding the flush-contour symbol to the weld symbol, observing the usual location significance.

H. SEAM WELDS

1. General

a. Seam weld symbols have no arrow- or other-side significance in themselves, although supplementary symbols used in conjunction with them may have such significance (Art. H-7). Seam weld symbols are centered on the reference line.

b. Dimensions of seam welds may be shown on either side of the reference line.

2. Size of Seam Welds

a. Seam welds are dimensioned by size or strength as follows:

(1) The size of seam welds is designated as the width of the weld expressed decimally in hundredths of an inch, and is shown, with inch marks, to the left of the weld symbol.

(2) The strength of seam welds is designated as the minimum acceptable shear strength in pounds per linear inch, and is shown to the left of the weld symbol.

3. Length of Seam Welds

a. The length of a seam weld, when indicated on the welding symbol, is shown to the right of the weld symbol.

b. When seam welding extends for the full distance between abrupt changes in the direction of the welding (Art. A-10), no length dimension need be shown on the welding symbol.

c. When seam welding extends less than the distance between abrupt changes in the direction of the welding, or less than the full length of the joint (Art. A-10), the extent is dimensioned in the same manner as for spot welds (Art. G-4).

4. Dimensioning of Intermittent Seam Welding

a. The pitch (center-to-center spacing) of intermittent seam welding is shown as the distance between centers of the weld increments.

b. The pitch (center-to-center spacing) of intermittent seam welding is shown to the right of the length dimension.

5. *Termination of Intermittent Seam Welding*

a. When intermittent seam welding is used by itself, the symbol indicates that increments are located at the ends of the dimensioned length.

b. When intermittent seam welding is used between continuous seam welding, the symbol indicates that spaces equal to the pitch minus the length of one increment are to be left at the ends of the dimensioned length.

6. *Combination of Intermittent and Continuous Seam Welding*

a. Separate symbols are used for intermittent and continuous seam welding when the two are used in combination.

7. *Flush Seam-welded Joints*

a. When the exposed surface of one member of a seam-welded joint is to be flush, that surface is indicated by adding the flush-contour symbol to the weld symbol, observing the usual location significance.

I. PROJECTION WELDS

1. *General*

a. Embossments on the arrow-side member of a joint for projection welding is indicated by placing the weld symbol on the side of the reference line toward the reader.

DESIRED   SECTION OR END VIEW   PLAN OR ELEVATION

SYMBOLS

b. Embossments on the other-side member of a joint for projection welding is indicated by placing the weld symbol on the side of the reference line away from the reader.

DESIRED   SECTION OR END VIEW   PLAN OR ELEVATION

SYMBOLS

c. Proportions of projections are shown by a detail or other suitable means.

d. Dimensions of projection welds are shown on the same side of the reference line as the weld symbol.

2. *Size of Projection Welds*

a. Projection welds are dimensioned by size or strength, as follows:

(1) The size of projection welds is designated as the diameter of the weld expressed decimally in hundredths of an inch, and is shown, with inch marks, to the left of the weld symbol.

(2) The strength of projection welds is designated as the minimum acceptable shear strength in pounds per weld, and is shown to the left of the weld symbol.

3. *Spacing of Projection Welds*

a. The pitch (center-to-center spacing) of projection welds is shown to the right of the weld symbol.

4. *Extent of Projection Welding*

a. When projection welding extends less than the distance between abrupt changes in the direction of the welding, or less than the full length of the joint, the extent is dimensioned in the same manner as for spot welds (Art. G-4).

5. Number of Projection Welds

  a. When a definite number of projection welds is desired in a certain joint, the number is shown in parentheses.

6. Flush Projection-welded Joints

  a. When the exposed surface of one member of a projection welded joint is to be made flush, that surface is indicated by adding the flush-contour symbol to the weld symbol, observing the usual location significance.

J. FLASH AND UPSET WELDS

1. General

  a. Flash and upset weld symbols have no arrow-side or other-side significance

in themselves although supplementary symbols used in conjunction with them may have such significance (Art. J-2). Flash or upset weld symbols are centered in the reference line.

  b. The dimensions of flash and upset welds are not shown on the welding symbol.

2. Surface Contour of Flash and Upset Welds

  a. Flash and upset welds that are to be made flush by mechanical means are shown by adding both the flush-contour symbol and the user's standard finish symbol[1] to the weld symbol, observing the usual location significance.

  b. Flash and upset welds that are to be mechanically finished to a convex contour are shown by adding both the convex-contour symbol and the user's standard finish symbol[1] to the weld symbol, observing the usual location significance.

PROBLEMS

Study the welding symbols so that you will be able to write and read them without hesitation. Problems 16.1.1 and 16.1.2 give practice in reading, Probs. 16.1.3 and 16.1.4 in writing. Problems 16.1.5 to 16.1.9 give practice in use of the symbols on working drawings.

16.1.1 and 16.1.2. Make full-size cross-sectional sketches of the joints indicated. Dimension each sketch.

16.1.3 and 16.1.4. Sketch members and show welding symbol for each complete joint. Estimate weld size from plate thickness.

PROB. 16.1.1. Butt joints.

PROB. 16.1.2. Tee and corner joints.

PROB. 16.1.3. Butt joints.

PROB. 16.1.4. Tee, corner, and edge joints.

PROB. 16.1.6.   Hinge clip.

PROB. 16.1.5.   Base.

16.1.5 and 16.1.6.   Make a complete welding drawing for each object. These problems are printed quarter size. Draw full size by scaling or transferring with dividers.

16.1.7.   Draw the views given, add welding symbols, dashed numbers for identification of the individual pieces, and complete the materials list.

16.1.8.   Draw the views given and add welding symbols and dashed numbers. Make a materials list similar to the one used in Prob. 16.1.7.

16.1.9.   Draw the views given and add welding symbols and dashed numbers. Make a materials list. Determine length of material for rim.

DASH NO.	MAT'L	STOCK SIZE

PROB. 16.1.7.   Pivoted spacer.

PROB. 16.1.8.   Belt-tightener bracket.

PROB. 16.1.9.   Ribbed-disk wheel.

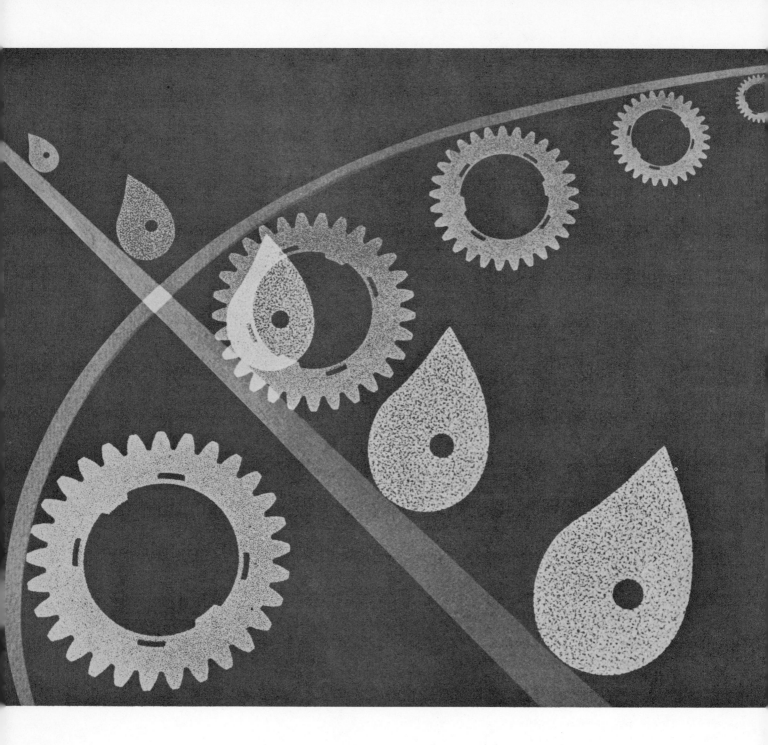

17

Drawings of Gears and Cams

17.1. GEARS. The representation and specification of gears are of such common occurrence that it is important to become familiar with the nomenclature, basic proportions, and formulas for calculation.

Gears are an adaptation of rolling cylinders and cones, designed to ensure positive motion. There are numerous variations, but the basic forms (Fig. 17.1) are *spur gears,* for transmitting power from one shaft to a parallel shaft; *spur gear* and *rack,* for changing rotary motion to linear motion; *bevel gears,* for shafts whose axes intersect; and *worm gears,* for nonintersecting shafts at right angles to each other.

17.2. GEAR TEETH. The teeth of gears are projections designed to fit into the tooth spaces of the mating gear and contact mating teeth along a common line

FIG. 17.1. Basic gear forms: (*A*) spur gears, (*B*) spur gear and rack, (*C*) bevel gears, (*D*) worm and worm gear.

449

FIG. 17.2. Mating gear teeth. The tooth faces are involute surfaces that "roll" on each other.

FIG. 17.3. Gear nomenclature.

known as the "pressure line" (Fig. 17.2). The most common form for the tooth flank is the *involute,* and when it is made in this form the gears are known as involute gears. The angle of the pressure line determines the particular involute the flank will have. The ASA has standardized two pressure angles, $14\frac{1}{2}°$ and $20°$. A composite $14\frac{1}{2}°$ tooth and a $20°$ stub tooth are also used (see ASA B6.1).

17.3. LETTER SYMBOLS AND FORMULAS FOR SPUR GEARING. The names of the various portions of a spur gear and the teeth are given in Fig. 17.3. The ASA standard letter symbols and formulas for calculation are as follows:

$N =$ number of teeth $= P_d \times D$

$P_d =$ diametral pitch $=$ number of teeth on the gear for each inch of pitch diameter $= N/D$

$D =$ pitch diameter $= N/P_d$

$p =$ circular pitch $=$ length of the arc of the pitch-diameter circle subtended by a tooth and a tooth space $= \pi D/N = \pi/P_d$

$t =$ circular (tooth) thickness $=$ length of the arc of the pitch-diameter circle subtended by a tooth $= p/2 = \pi D/2N = \pi/2P_d$

$t_c =$ chordal thickness $=$ length of the chord subtended by the circular thickness arc $= D \sin (90°/N)$

$a =$ addendum $=$ radial distance between the pitch-diameter circle and the top of a tooth $=$ a constant$/P_d =$ for standard $14\frac{1}{2}°$ or $20°$ involute teeth, $1/P_d$

$b =$ dedendum $=$ radial distance between the pitch-diameter circle and the bottom of a tooth space $=$ a constant$/P_d =$ for standard $14\frac{1}{2}°$ or $20°$ involute teeth, $1.157/P_d$

$c =$ clearance $=$ radial distance between the top of a tooth and the bottom of a mating tooth space $=$ a constant$/P_d =$ for standard $14\frac{1}{2}°$ or $20°$ involute teeth, $0.157/P_d$

$h_t =$ whole depth $=$ radial distance between the top and bottom of a tooth $= a + b =$ for standard $14\frac{1}{2}°$ or $20°$ involute teeth, $2.157/P_d$

$h_k =$ working depth $=$ greatest depth a tooth of one gear extends into a tooth space of a mating gear $= 2a =$ for standard $14\frac{1}{2}°$ or $20°$ involute teeth, $2/P_d$

$D_o =$ outside diameter $=$ diameter of the circle containing the top surfaces of the teeth $= D + 2a = (N + 2)/P_d$

$D_R =$ root diameter $=$ diameter of the circle containing the bottom surfaces of the tooth spaces $= D - 2b = (N - 2.314)/P_d$

$F =$ face width $=$ width of the tooth flank

$f =$ tooth fillet $=$ fillet joining the tooth flank and the bottom of the tooth space $= 0.157/P_d$ max

$r =$ edge round $=$ radius of the circumferential edge of a gear tooth (to break the sharp corner)

$n =$ revolutions per unit of time

In addition to the above basic letter symbols, subscripts G and P are used to denote gear and pinion, respectively. (When one of two mating gears is smaller than the other, it is known as the pinion.)

$m =$ gear ratio $= m_G$ for the gear $= N_G/N_P = n_P/n_G = D_G/D_P$

$m =$ gear ratio $= m_P$ for the pinion $= N_P/N_G = n_G/n_P = D_P/D_G$

Outside Circle
Pitch Point
Circular Pitch
Circular Thickness
$75\frac{1}{2}°$ or $70°$
Pressure line
$R = \frac{1}{4}$ of Pitch Radius
R
Tangent Point of Pressure
line and Base Circle
Pitch Circle
Root Circle
Base Circle

FIG. 17.4.   Method of drawing spur gear teeth. The involutes are approximated with circle arcs. This method is used only on assembly drawings.

(The pitch diameter and number of teeth are inversely proportional to speed.)

17.4.   SPUR-GEAR CALCULATIONS.   There are many different combinations producing various individual problems, but the following is typical and will illustrate the procedure:

Assume that the center distance and
   speeds are known.
Center distance = 7 in.
Speed of gear 500 rpm, speed of pinion
   1,500 rpm
Then $m_G = n_P/n_G = 1,500/500 = 3/1$
   $= D_G/D_P$
Therefore, $3D_P = D_G$
From the center distance, $D_P + D_G = 14$ in.
Substituting for D_G in terms of D_P,
$D_P + 3D_P = 14$. Solving, $D_P = 3\frac{1}{2}$ in.
Solving for $D_G = 3D_P = 3 \times 3\frac{1}{2} = 10\frac{1}{2}$ in.
At this time, the diametral pitch will
   have to be assumed.
Assume $P_d = 5$.
Then, $N_P = P_d \times D_P = 5 \times 3\frac{1}{2} = 17\frac{1}{2}$,
   which is obviously impossible since a
   gear could not have a half tooth.
Assuming $P_d = 6$,
$N_P = 6 \times 3\frac{1}{2} = 21$
$N_G = 6 \times 10\frac{1}{2} = 63$
   Now all the values such as adden-
dum, dedendum, outside diameter, can

be calculated from the equations in paragraph 17.3. Note that if, in a given problem, the two pitch diameters are known, the center distance must be found; if one pitch diameter is known and the center distance given, the second pitch diameter must be found, etc.

17.5.   TO DRAW A SPUR GEAR (FIG. 17.4). To draw the teeth of a standard involute-toothed spur gear by an approximate circle-arc method, lay off the pitch circle, root circle, and outside circle. Start with the pitch point and divide the pitch circle into distances equal to the circular thickness. Through the pitch point draw a line of 75½° with the center line for a 14½° involute tooth (for convenience, draftsmen use 75°), or 70° for a 20° tooth. Draw the basic circle tangent to the pressure line. With compass set to a radius equal to one-fourth the radius of the pitch circle, describe arcs through the division points on the pitch circle, keeping the needle point on the base circle. Darken the arcs for the tops of the teeth and bottoms of the spaces and add the tooth fillets. For 16 or fewer teeth, the radius value of one-fourth pitch radius *must be increased* to suit, in order to avoid the appearance of excessive undercut. For a small number of teeth, the radius may be as large as or equal to the pitch radius.

SPUR GEAR DATA	
NUMBER OF TEETH	56
DIAMETRAL PITCH	8
PITCH DIAMETER (THEOR.)	7.000
PRESSURE ANGLE	20°
ADDENDUM	.125
WHOLE DEPTH	.294
CHORDAL ADDENDUM	.126
FIN CHORDAL THICKNESS	.1915 / .1905
BASE CIRCLE DIAMETER	6.5779
BACKLASH WITH MATE	.012 / .010
PIN DIAMETER	.216
DIAMETER OVER PINS	7.291 7.289
CENTER DISTANCE	6.875
NO OF TEETH IN MATE	.54
MATING GEAR PART NO	6134 D 282
RATIO	1.037 : 1
METHOD	HOB & SHAVE

NOTES

MATERIAL SHALL CONFORM TO MIL-S-890
(SHIPS) CLASS B AS APPLICABLE TO
A.I.S.I. 4140 STEEL

ALL FINISHES NOT NOTED TO BE 125/

HEAT TREAT TO 30-36 ROCKWELL "C"
BEFORE CUTTING GEAR TEETH

DYNAMICALLY BALANCE FINISHED PART
TO WITHIN 0.3 INCH-OUNCES - GRIND
MATERIAL FROM LIGHTENING HOLES

FIG. 17.5. Working drawing of a spur gear.
Note that complete specifications include tooth
details (tabular), surface roughness, form tolerances, and special notes.

FIG. 17.6. Method of drawing
an involute rack. Circular pitch
and thickness are linear because
the pitch diameter is infinite.

This method of drawing gear teeth is
useful on display drawings, but on working drawings the tooth outlines are not
drawn. Figure 17.5 illustrates the method
of indicating the teeth and dimensioning
a spur gear on a working drawing.

Gears must be precisely made in
order to prevent noisy and faulty running characteristics. Thus, the dimensioning almost always includes surface
roughness and form tolerance specifications as shown on Fig. 17.5. The tabular
information given is for shop use in cutting and checking the teeth and as a
record of tooth dimensions for checking
with the mating gear.

17.6. TO DRAW A RACK (FIG. 17.6). A
rack is, theoretically, a spur gear having
an infinite pitch diameter. Therefore,
compared with the mating gear, all circular dimensions become linear. To draw
the teeth of a standard involute rack by
an approximate method, draw the pitch
line and lay off the addendum and dedendum distances. Divide the pitch line
into spaces equal to the circular thickness of the mating gear. Through these
points of division draw the tooth faces
at 14½° (15° is used by draftsmen).
Draw tops and bottoms and add the
tooth fillets. For standard 20° full-
depth or stub teeth, use 20° instead of
14½°. Specifications of rack teeth (to be
given on a detail drawing) are axial
(linear) pitch (equal to circular pitch of
the mating gear), number of teeth, diametral pitch, whole depth.

17.7. BEVEL GEARS. For bevel gears
the theoretical rolling surfaces become
cones. The pitch diameter D of the gear,

as shown in Fig. 17.7*A*, is the base diameter of the cone. The addendum and dedendum are calculated in the same way as for a spur gear and are measured on a cone, called the "back cone," whose elements are normal to the face-cone elements (Fig. 17.7*A*). The diametral pitch, circular pitch, etc., are the same as for a spur gear.

In addition to the letter symbols and calculations for spur gears, the dimensions shown in Fig. 17.7*B*, with formulas for calculating, are needed:

$\Gamma =$ pitch-cone angle = angle between a pitch-cone element and the cone axis. $\tan \Gamma = D_G/D_P = N_G/N_P$ (gear) $= D_P/D_G = N_P/N_G$ (pinion)

$R_{PC} =$ pitch-cone radius = length of an element of the pitch cone. $R_{PC} = D/2 \sin \Gamma$

$\alpha =$ addendum angle = angle between the pitch cone and the outside of a tooth. $\tan \alpha = a/R_{PC}$

$\delta =$ dedendum angle = angle between the pitch cone and the bottom of a tooth space. $\tan \delta = b/R_{PC}$

$\Gamma_o =$ face angle = angle between a line *normal* to the gear axis and the outside (face) of the teeth. $\Gamma_o = 90° - (\Gamma + \alpha)$. (Note that this angle is the complement of the angle an element of the outside cone makes with the axis.)

$\Gamma_R =$ root-cone angle = cutting angle = angle between the axis and an element of the root cone. $\Gamma_R = \Gamma - \delta$

$a_N =$ angular addendum = addendum distance measured *normal* to the gear axis. $a_N = a \cos \Gamma$

$D_o =$ outside diameter = outside diameter at the base of the teeth. $D_o = D + 2a_N$

$A =$ apex distance = altitude of the outside-diameter cone. $A = (D_o/2) \tan \Gamma$

17.8.   TO DRAW A BEVEL GEAR (FIG. 17.8).

To draw the teeth of an involute-toothed bevel gear by an approximate method (the Tredgold method), draw the center lines, intersecting at *O*. Across the center lines lay off the pitch diameters, and project them parallel to the center lines until the projectors intersect at the pitch point *P*. From the pitch point, draw the pitch-circle diameters for each gear, and from their extremities, draw the "pitch cones" to the vertex or "cone center" *O*. Lay off the addendum and dedendum distances for each gear on lines through the pitch points perpendicular to the cone elements. Extend one of these normals for each gear to intersect the axis, as at *B* and *C*, making the "back cones." With *B* as center, swing arcs 1, 2, and 3 for the top, pitch line, and bottom, respectively, of a developed tooth. On a radial center line *AB*, draw a tooth, by

FIG. 17.7.   Fundamental values and letter symbols for bevel-gear calculations.

FIG. 17.8.   Method of drawing the teeth of bevel gears. This is used only on assembly drawings.

the method of Fig. 17.4. Start the plan view of the gear by projecting points 1, 2, and 3 across to its vertical center line and drawing circles through the points. Lay off the radial center lines for each tooth. With dividers take the circular thickness distances from *A* and transfer them to each tooth. This will give three points on each side of each tooth through which a circle arc, found by trial, will pass, giving the foreshortened contour of the large end of the teeth in this view. From this point the drawing becomes a problem in projection drawing. Note that in every view the lines converge at the cone center *O* and that, by finding three points on the contour of each tooth, circle arcs can be found by trial which will be sufficiently close approximations to give the desired effect.

This method is used for finished display drawings. Working drawings for cut bevel gears are drawn without tooth outlines and are dimensioned as shown in Fig. 17.9, from the calculations given in paragraph 17.7. Tabular information on the drawing gives details for cutting and checking the teeth. The drawing proper is dimensioned with limits where required. Surface roughness and form tolerance specifications are necessary because of the degree of precision required.

17.9. WORM GEARS. Worm gears are used primarily to get great reductions in relative speed and to obtain a large increase in effective power. The worm is similar to a screw thread, and the computing of pitch diameter, etc., is also similar. On a section taken through the axis of the worm, the worm gear and worm have the same relationship as a spur gear and rack. Therefore, the tooth shape, addendum, dedendum, etc., will be the same as for a spur gear and rack.

In addition to the calculations necessary for a spur gear and rack (addendum, dedendum, etc.), the following are needed:

FIG. 17.9. Working drawing of a bevel gear. Note that complete specifications include tooth details (tabular), surface roughness, form tolerances, and special notes.

BEVEL GEAR DATA	
NUMBER OF TEETH	81
DIAMETRAL PITCH	10.4516
PITCH DIAMETER (THEOR)	7.750
PITCH ANGLE	82° 58'
ROOT ANGLE (BASIC)	80° 56'
PRESSURE ANGLE	20°
ADDENDUM (THEOR)	.042
WHOLE DEPTH (APPROX)	.181
CONE CENTER TO CROWN	.437
CONE DISTANCE	3.9044
BACKLASH WITH MATE	.010/.014
NO OF TEETH IN MATE	10
MATING GEAR PART NO	1620 D 10
DRIVING MEMBER	PINION

NOTES

(B) CARBURIZE AND HARDEN ENCLOSED ZONE TO ROCKWELL "C" 58 MIN - FINISHED CASE DEPTH .020-.025 DP - CORE AND UNCARBURIZED AREAS TO BE ROCKWELL "C" 27 MIN

FINISH UNLESS NOTED TO 100/ ALL OVER

GEAR AND PINION TO BE MATCHED AND LAPPED AS A SET - ETCH GEAR WITH SET NO, MOUNTING DIST, AND BACKLASH

MAGNETIC INSPECT PER MIL-I-6868

STATICALLY BALANCE TO WITHIN 0.06 INCH-OUNCES

PITCH DIAMETER OF GEAR CONCENTRIC TO A WITHIN .002 FIR

Worm

l = lead of worm threads
N_w = multiplicity of worm threads
p_{xw} = axial pitch = l/N_w
D_w = pitch diameter of worm
λ = lead angle. $\tan \lambda = l/\pi D$

Worm Gear

C = center distance between worm and wheel
D_G = pitch diameter of worm gear
D_{tp} = pitch throat diameter = pitch diameter of wheel = D_G
D_{to} = outer throat diameter = pitch diameter plus twice the addendum = $D_G + 2a$
D_{ti} = inner throat diameter = pitch diameter minus twice the dedendum = $D_G - 2b$
R_{tp} = pitch throat radius = pitch radius of worm = $D_w/2$
R_{to} = outer throat radius = $(D_w/2) - a$
R_{ti} = inner throat radius = $(D_w/2) + b$
C_{Rt} = center of throat radius = $C = (D_G/2) + (D_w/2)$

17.10.   TO DRAW WORM GEARS.   In assembly, a worm and worm gear are generally shown with the worm in section and the worm gear drawn as a conventional end view like the end view in Fig. 17.11. Detail drawings are made up as in Figs. 17.10 and 17.11. The calculated dimensions described in paragraph 17.9 are given as shown in the figures.

When tooth information is tabulated and given on drawings, as in Figs. 17.5 and 17.9, it should include:

For the Worm Wheel

1. Number of teeth
2. Addendum
3. Whole depth
4. Pitch diameter

WORM – LH AlO
Single Thread to Match Worm Wheel A9. 24:1 Ratio. 3.921 Centers. Helix Angle 6°-27'.
Material AISI 3120. Heat Treatment SAE $\mathrm{III}\frac{1}{16}$ Case.   Scleroscope 75-90.

FIG. 17.10.   Working drawing of a worm. This mates with the worm gear of Fig. 17.11.

FIG. 17.11.   Working drawing of a worm gear. This mates with the worm of Fig. 17.10.

WORM WHEEL–L.H. A9
24 Teeth , $\frac{3}{4}$ Cir. Pitch for Single Thread Worm Left Hand
to Match Worm A10. Material–15A Lumen Chill Cast Bronze.

5. Center distance between worm and wheel
6. Helix angle
7. Radius of throat
8. Face angle

For the Worm

1. Linear pitch
2. Addendum
3. Whole depth
4. Pitch diameter
5. Outside diameter
6. Root diameter
7. Helix angle
8. Minimum length of worm for complete action
9. Center distance between worm and wheel

17.11. CAMS. A cam is a machine element with surface or groove formed to produce special or irregular motion in a second part, called a "follower." The shape of the cam is dependent upon the motion that is required and the type of follower that is used. The type of cam is dictated by the required relationship of the parts and the motions of both.

17.12. TYPES OF CAMS. The direction of motion of the follower with respect to the cam axis determines two general types of cams: (1) radial or disk cams, in which the follower moves in a direction perpendicular to the cam axis; and (2) cylindrical or end cams, in which the follower moves in a direction parallel to the cam axis.

Figure 17.12 shows at (*A*) a *radial cam,* with a roller follower held against the cam by gravity or by a spring. As the cam revolves, the follower is raised and lowered. Followers are also made with pointed ends and with flat ends. At (*B*) is shown a *face cam,* with a roller follower

at the end of an arm or link, the follower oscillating as the cam revolves. When the cam itself oscillates, the *toe* and *wiper* are used, as at (*C*). The toe, or follower, may also be made in the form of a swinging arm. A *yoke* or *positive-motion cam* is shown at (*D*), the enclosed follower making possible the application of force in either direction. The sum of the two distances from the center of the cam to the points of contact must always be equal to the distance between the follower surfaces. The cylindrical *groove cam* at (*E*) and the *end cam* at (*F*) both move the follower parallel to the cam axis, force being applied to the follower in both directions with the groove cam, and in only one direction with the end cam.

17.13. KINDS OF MOTION. Cams can be designed to move the follower with constant velocity, acceleration, or harmonic motion. In many cases combinations of these motions, together with surfaces arranged for sudden rise or fall, or to hold the follower stationary, make up the complete cam surface.

17.14. CAM DIAGRAMS. In studying the motion of the follower, a diagram showing the height of the follower for successive cam positions is useful and is frequently employed. The cam position is shown on the abscissa, the full 360° rotation of the cam being divided, generally, every 30° (intermediate points may be used if necessary). The follower positions are shown on the ordinate, divided into the same number of parts as the abscissa. These diagrams are generally made to actual size.

Constant velocity gives a uniform rise and fall and can be plotted, as at (*A*) in Fig. 17.13, by laying off the cam positions on the abscissa, measuring the total follower movement on the ordinate

FIG. **17.12.** Types of cams. (A) radial, (B) face, (C) toe and wiper, (D) yoke, (E) cylindrical groove, (F) cylindrical end.

FIG. **17.13.** Methods of plotting cam diagrams. (A) constant velocity, (B) constant acceleration, (C) harmonic motion.

FIG. 17.14. A cam diagram. This is for the cam in Fig. 17.16.

and dividing it into the same number of parts as the abscissa. As the cam moves one unit of its rotation, the follower likewise moves one unit, producing the straight line of motion shown.

With constant acceleration, the distance traveled is proportional to the square of the time, or the total distance traveled is proportional to 1, 4, 9, 16, 25, etc., and if the increments of follower distance are made proportional to 1, 3, 5, 7, etc., the curve can be plotted as shown at (*B*). Using a scale, divide the follower rise into the same number of parts as the abscissa, making the first part one unit, the second three units, and so on. Plot points at the intersection of the coordinate lines, as shown. The curve at (*B*) accelerates and then decelerates to slow up the follower at the top of its rise.

Harmonic motion (sine curve) can be plotted as at (*C*) by measuring the rise

and drawing a semicircle, dividing it into the same number of parts as the abscissa, and projecting the points on the semicircle as ordinate lines. Points are plotted at the intersection of the coordinate lines, as shown.

Figure 17.14 is the cam diagram for the cam in Fig. 17.16. The follower rises with harmonic motion in 180°, drops halfway down instantly, and then returns with uniform motion to the point of beginning.

17.15. TIMING DIAGRAMS. When two or more cams are used on the same machine and their functions are dependent on each other, the "timing" and relative motions of each can be studied by means of a diagram showing each follower curve. The curves can be superimposed, but it is better to place one above the other as in Fig. 17.15.

17.16. TO DRAW A PLATE CAM. The same principle is involved in drawing all types of cams. The cam in Fig. 17.16, for which the diagram in Fig. 17.14 was made, will serve as an example. The point *C* is the center of the shaft, and *A* is the lowest and *B* the highest position of the center of the roller follower. Divide the rise into six parts harmonically proportional. Divide the semicircle *ADE* into as many equal parts as there are spaces in the rise, and draw radial lines. With *C* as center and radius *C*1, draw an arc intersecting the first radial line at 1′. In the same way locate points 2′, 3′, etc., and draw a smooth curve through them. If the cam is revolved in the direction of the arrow, it will raise the follower with the desired harmonic motion. Draw *B′F* equal to one-half *AB*. Divide *A*3 into six equal parts and the arc *EGA* into six equal parts. Then for equal

FIG. 17.15. A timing diagram. This is made to study the characteristics of two separate but related motions.

angles the follower must fall equal distances. Circle arcs drawn as indicated will locate the required points on the cam outline.

This outline is for the center of the roller; allowance for the roller size can be made by drawing the roller in its successive positions and then drawing a tangent curve as shown in the auxiliary figure.

17.17. TO DRAW A CYLINDRICAL CAM.
A drawing of a cylindrical cam differs somewhat from that of a plate cam, as in addition to the regular views it generally includes a developed view, from which a template is made. Assume that the follower is to move upward 1½ in. with harmonic motion in 180°, and then return with uniform acceleration. Top and front views of the cylinder are drawn (Fig. 17.17) and the development of the surface is laid out. Divide the surface as shown, also the top view to show the positions of points plotted. Divide the rise for harmonic motion by drawing the semicircle and projecting the points (refer to Fig. 17.13C). Divide the return for acceleration as shown (refer to Fig. 17.13B). The curve thus obtained is for the center of the follower. Curves drawn tangent to circles representing positions of the follower will locate the working surfaces of the cam. The development made as described is the drawing used to make the cam.

17.18. DIMENSIONING A CAM DRAWING.
In general, two practices are followed, depending upon the function of the cam: (1) For cams where follower position is not critical, full-size layouts, as in Fig. 17.16, with necessary fractional or decimal dimensions suffice. Cams of this type can be made by profiling the

FIG. 17.16. Method of drawing a plate cam. Layout of harmonic motion and constant velocity are illustrated.

surface by such methods as sawing, nibbling and finishing, and torch cutting. (2) For cams where the follower position and relative motion is critical, limit dimensioning from datum features is necessary. The dimensioning in Prob. 3.2.21 is an example. Where the degree of precision requires, surface roughness and form tolerances are needed.

FIG. 17.17. Method of drawing a cylindrical cam. Development of the cylinder is employed.

PROBLEMS

Gear	Speed	D	P_d	N	a	b	p	t_c	F
A									
B									

PROB. 17.1.2.   Spur-gear speed reducer.

17.1.1.   Make an assembly drawing of a pair of spur gears, from the following information: On an 11- by 17-in. sheet locate centers for front view of gear *B* 4½ in. from right border and 3½ in. from bottom border. Gear *A* is to the left of gear *B*. Center distances between gears are 5.250 in. Gear *A* revolves at 300 rpm and has four spokes, elliptical in cross section, 1-in. major and ½-in. minor axes; inside flange diameter, 4⅜ in.; hub 2 in. diameter, 1½ in. long. Gear *B* revolves at 400 rpm and is disk type with ½-in. web; inside flange diameter, 3¼ in.; hub, 2 in. diameter, 1½ in. long. Material is cast steel; face width, 1 in.; diametral pitch, 4; shaft diameters, 1 in.; ¼-in. Woodruff keys. Draw front view and sectional top view.

17.1.2.   The figure shows a gear box for a reducing mechanism using spur gears. Using the scale shown on the drawing, transfer the necessary distances to obtain the net available space for the gears and design gears as follows: center distance, 4 in.; gear *A* revolves at 900 rpm, gear *B* at 1,500 rpm; diametral pitch, 4; face width, 1 in. Use standard 14½° involute teeth. Calculate the necessary values (shown in table in Prob. 17.1.2). Draw the top view in section. Show four teeth on each gear on front view and complete the view with conventional lines.

17.1.3.   Same as Prob. 17.1.2 but for *A* = 525 rpm, *B* = 675 rpm. Use 20° involute teeth.

17.1.4.   Make working drawings for the gears in Prob. 17.1.2.

17.1.5.   Make working drawings for the gears in Prob. 17.1.3.

17.1.6.   A broken spur gear has been measured and the following information obtained: number of teeth, 33; outside diameter, 4⅜ in.; width of face, 1 in.; diameter of shaft, ⅞ in.; length of hub, 1¼ in. Make a drawing of a gear blank with all dimensions and information necessary for making a new gear.

The dimensions that are not specified here may be made to suit as the drawing is developed.

17.1.7. Make a drawing of a spur gear. The only information available is as follows: root diameter, 7.3372 in.; outside diameter, 8.200 in.; width of face, 1⅞ in.; diameter of shaft, 1⅜ in.; length of hub, 2 in.

GROUP 2. RACKS

17.2.1. Draw a spur gear and rack as follows: gear, 4-in. pitch diameter, 20 teeth, face width, 1 in.; standard 14½° involute teeth. Rack is to move laterally 5 in. Compute axial pitch, addendum and dedendum for rack and draw the rack and gear in assembly showing all teeth on rack and four teeth on gear.

17.2.2. Same as Prob. 17.2.1 but gear is 5-in. pitch diameter, has 25 teeth and ⅞-in. face width, with 20° standard involute teeth.

GROUP 3. BEVEL GEARS

17.3.1. The figure shows a gear box for a reducing mechanism using bevel gears. Using the scale shown on the drawing, transfer the necessary distances to obtain net available space for the gears and design gears as follows: gear *A* has 6-in. pitch diameter, diametral pitch, 4; speed, 350 rpm; face width, 1 in. Gear *B* has a speed of 600 rpm. Use standard 14½° involute teeth. Compute the necessary values (shown in table in Prob. 17.3.1). Draw top view in section and front view as an external view which shows all teeth.

17.3.2. Same as Prob. 17.3.1 but gear *A* has 5½-in. pitch diameter and 22 teeth; speed, 750 rpm. Gear *B* has a speed of 1,100 rpm. Use standard 20° involute teeth. Face width is 1 in.

17.3.3. Make working drawings for the bevel gears in Prob. 17.3.1; refer to paragraph 17.7 to compute values needed.

17.3.4. Make working drawings for the bevel gears in Prob. 17.3.2; refer to paragraph 17.7 to compute values needed.

Gear	A	B
Speed		
D		
P_d		
N		
a		
b		
p		
t_c		
F		

PROB. 17.3.1. Bevel-gear speed reducer.

GROUP 4. SPUR- AND BEVEL-GEAR TRAINS

17.4.1. Make an assembly drawing of gear train, as follows: *A* and *B* are bevel gears, with ⅞-in. face width and 6-in. pitch diameter. *A* is 3-in. pitch diameter, revolves at 150 rpm. *B* revolves at 100 rpm. *C* and *D* are spur gears with 8-in. pitch diameter, 1-in. face width. *C* engages *D*, which revolves at 40 rpm. All shafts are 1 in. Draw *A* in full section, *B* with lower half in section, *C* and *D* in full section, quarter-end view of gear *B* in space indicated, and end views of *C* and *D*.

17.4.2. A 3-in. diameter, 3 diametral pitch bevel gear *R* on shaft *AB* running 1,120 rpm drives another bevel gear *S* on shaft *AC* at 840 rpm. On shaft *AC* centered at *P,* an 8-in. diameter, 4 diametral pitch spur gear *T* drives a pinion *U* at 1,680 rpm. All shaft diameters are 1 in.; face widths, 1 in. Hub diameters of *R* and *S* are 1¾ in. Gear *C* has four spokes, elliptical, ⅝ by 1 in.; hub, 1⅞-in. diameter; thickness of flange, ½ in. Draw gear *R* with upper half in section; *S, T,* and *U* in full section. Put quarter-end view of *R* in space indicated and end views of *T* and *U* on center line *MN.*

PROB. 17.4.1. Spur-and-bevel-gear train.

PROB. 17.4.2. Bevel-and-spur-gear train.

GROUP 5. WORM GEARS

17.5.1. Make an assembly drawing of a pair of worm gears, as follows: center distance, 6 in.; pitch diameter of worm gear, 8½ in.; face width of worm gear, 1⅞ in.; pitch diameter of worm, 3½ in.; standard 14½° involute worm teeth. Single-threaded worm, left hand 4 in. long, 1 in. lead. Show appropriate spindle ends for worm and suitable hub for worm gear. Make assembly drawing as a half section through axis of worm.

17.5.2. Make detail drawings of the worm gear and worm of Prob. 17.5.1. Refer to paragraph 17.9 and Figs. 17.10 and 17.11 for calculation of necessary dimensions.

GROUP 6. CAMS

17.6.1. Make a drawing for a plate cam to satisfy the following conditions: On a vertical center line, a point *A* is ⅞ in. above a point *O,* and a point *B* is 1¾ in. above *A.* With center at *O,* revolution clockwise, the follower starts at *A* and rises to *B* with uniform motion during one-third revolution, remains at rest one-third revolution, and drops with uniform motion the last one-third revolution to the starting point. Diameter of shaft, ¾ in.; diameter of hub, 1¼ in.; thickness of plate, ½ in.; length of hub, 1¼ in.; diameter of roller, ½ in.

17.6.2. Make a drawing for a face cam using the data of Prob. 17.6.1.

17.6.3. Make a drawing for a toe-and-wiper

cam. The toe shaft is vertical, ¾ in. in diameter. Starting at a point 1 in. directly above center of wiper shaft, the toe is to move upward 2 in. with simple harmonic motion, with 135° turn of the shaft. Wiper has 1¼-in.-diameter hub; is 1¼ in. long; has ¾-in.-diameter shaft. Design toe to suit.

17.6.4. Make a drawing for a positive-motion cam. Starting at a point 1 in. above center of cam shaft, upper follower surface is to move upward 1 in. with simple harmonic motion in 180° turn of cam. Return is governed by necessary shape of cam. Follower is ½ in. thick on ½-in. vertical shaft. Cam is ½ in. thick on ¾-in.-diameter shaft; hub, 1¼-in. diameter, 1¼ in. long.

17.6.5. Make a drawing, with development, for a cylindrical cam. The ½-in.-diameter roller follower is to move 2 in. leftward with constant velocity in 180° turn of cylinder and return with simple harmonic motion. Cam axis is horizontal; cylinder, 4-in. diameter, 4 in. long on 1-in. shaft. Follower is pinned to ⅝-in. shaft 3 in. center to center from cylinder.

18

Drawings of Piping

18.1. A knowledge of pipe and pipe fittings is necessary not only for making piping drawings but because pipe is often used as a construction material. An understanding of pipe threads is also essential, because in making machine drawings it it frequently necessary to represent and specify tapped holes to receive pipe for liquid or gas supply lines.

18.2. METAL PIPE. Standard pipe of steel or wrought iron up to 12 in. in diameter is designated by its nominal inside diameter, which differs somewhat from the actual inside diameter. Early pipe manufacturers made the walls in the smaller sizes much too thick and in

correcting this error in design took the excess from the inside to avoid changing the sizes of fittings. Three weights of pipe —standard, extra strong, and double extra strong—are in common use. In the same nominal size all three have the same outside diameter, that of standard-weight pipe, the added thickness for the extra and double extra (XX) strong being on the inside. Thus the outside diameter of 1-in. pipe in all three weights is 1.315 in. The inside diameter of standard 1-in. pipe is 1.05 in.; of 1-in. extra strong, 0.951 in.; and of XX, 0.587 in. The ASA in B36.10—1950 gives a means of specifying wall thicknesses by a series of schedule numbers which indicate approximate values for the ex-

SCREWED JOINT

SCREWED FLANGE

WELDED JOINT

FIG. 18.1. Pipe joints. These are used for metal pipe.

RING JOINT
WELDED FLANGE

BELL-AND-SPIGOT
JOINT

FLARE

INVERTED FLARE

COMPRESSION

FIG. 18.2. Tube joints. These are used for metal tubing.

pression $1,000 \times (P/S)$, where P is pressure and S the allowable stress. Recommended values for S can be obtained from the ASME Boiler Code, the American Standard Code for Pressure Piping (ASA, B31.1), etc. The designer computes the exact value of wall thickness as required for a given condition and selects from the schedule numbers the one nearest to the computed values. In the ASA system, pipe is designated by giving nominal pipe size and wall thickness, or nominal pipe size and weight per foot.

All pipe over 12 in. in diameter is designated as OD (outside-diameter) pipe and is specified by its outside diameter and thickness of metal. Boiler tubes in all sizes are known by their outside diameters.

Brass, copper, stainless steel, and aluminum pipe has the same nominal diameters as iron pipe but some has thinner wall sections. There are two standard weights: regular and extra strong. Commercial lengths are 12 ft, with longer lengths made to order.

Lead pipe and lead-lined pipe are used in chemical work. Cast-iron pipe is used for water and gas in under-

ground mains and for drains in buildings.

Many other kinds of pipe are in more or less general use and are known by trade names, such as hydraulic pipe, merchant casing, API (American Petroleum Institute) pipe, etc. Details are given in manufacturers' catalogues.

Most small-line plumbing in homes, buildings, and industries, for hot and cold water installations, employ copper pipe with soldered-joint fittings.

18.3. TUBING. Seamless flexible metal tubing is used for conveying steam, gases, and liquids in all types of equipment such as locomotives, diesel engines, hydraulic presses, etc., where vibration is present, where outlets are not in alignment, and where there are moving parts.

Copper tubing is available in nominal diameters of 1/8 to 12 in. and in four weights known as classes K, L, M, and O. Class K is extra-heavy hard; class L is heavy hard; class M is standard hard; and class O is light hard. Boiler tubes in all sizes are designated by their outside diameters.

Tubing is made in a variety of materials—glass, steel, aluminum, copper, brass, aluminum bronze, asbestos, fiber, lead, and others. The mechanical catalogue of the American Society of Mechanical Engineers, New York 18, N. Y., lists manufacturers.

18.4. PLASTIC PIPE. Since plastic pipe does not corrode and has high resistance to a broad group of industrial chemicals, it is used extensively in place of metal pipe. Polyvinyl chloride, polyethelyne, and styrene are basic plastic materials. Of these, polyvinyl chloride (PVC) is the most widely used. It does not support combustion, is nonmagnetic and nonsparking, imparts no odor or taste to contents, is light (½ the weight of aluminum), has low flow resistance, resists weathering, and is easily bent and fabricated by solvent cementing or, in heavy weights, by threading. Its chief limitations are higher cost (partially off-set by lower installation cost), low temperature limit (150°F in continuous service), and low pressure limits. Also, it does not resist all solvents; and it re-quires more supports, and contracts and expands more (about 5 times) than steel.

Metal pipe lined with plastic has the advantage of combining the strength of metal with the chemical resistance of plastic. Seran rubber is also used for lining metal pipe.

The mechanical catalogue of the American Society of Mechanical Engi-neers, New York 18, N.Y., lists manu-facturers from whom catalogues and special information are available.

18.5. PIPE JOINTS. Pipe is connected by methods dependent upon the ma-terial and the demands of service. Steel, wrought-iron, brass, or bronze pipe is normally threaded and screwed into a coupling (or a fitting), as shown in Fig. 18.1 at (*A*). At (*B*) a screwed flange is illustrated; this joint is easily disas-sembled for cleaning or repair. At (*C*) a permanent welded joint is shown. When welded pipe must be disassembled periodically, ring joints (*D*) are used, where necessary, in the system; these joints are bolted together. Cast-iron pipe cannot be successfully welded or threaded; thus, a bell-and-spigot joint, caulked and leaded, as at (*E*) is used.

18.6. TUBE JOINTS. Tubing is com-monly employed to connect small com-

ponents for liquid or gas service. Figure 18.2 illustrates three common methods of connection. The *flare* and *inverted flare* can both be disassembled without serious injury to the joint, and can be used for fairly high pressures. The com-pression joint is used for lower pres-sures and when the joint is not expected to be taken apart and reassembled.

18.7. PIPE FITTINGS. Pipe fittings are the components used in connecting and "making up" pipe systems. Cast-iron or malleable-iron fittings (Fig. 18.3) are commonly used with threaded wrought-iron pipe. Brass and other alloys are employed for special purposes. Steel butt-welding fittings (Fig. 18.4) are used with steel pipe. Soldered-joint fittings (Fig. 18.5) are used with copper

FIG. 18.3. Screwed fittings. See the Appendix for detailed dimensions of malleable and cast-iron fittings.

FIG. 18.4. Butt-welding fittings. See the Appendix for detailed dimensions.

FIG. 18.5. Soldered-joint fittings. These are used principally for small-line plumbing. See the Appendix for detailed sizes.

FIG. 18.6. Screwed unions and union fittings. These are used to "close" a pipe system.

Ground joint Female — Gasket joint Male and Female — *Union*

Female — Male — *Tee Union on Run*

Female — Male — *90° Ell*

pipe. Cast-iron bell-and-spigot fittings are used with cast-iron pipe.

Elbows are used to change the direction of a pipe line either 90° or 45°. The *street elbow* has male threads on one end, thus eliminating one pipe joint if used at a fitting. *Tees* connect three pipes, and *crosses* connect four. *Laterals* are made with the third opening at 45° or 60° to the straight run.

Straight sections of pipe are made in 12- to 20-ft lengths and are connected by *couplings*. These are short cylinders, threaded on the inside. A right-hand coupling has right-hand threads at both ends. To close a system of piping, although a union is preferable, a *right-and-left coupling* is sometimes used. A *reducer* is similar to a coupling but has the two ends threaded for different-sized pipe. Pipes are also connected by screwing them into cast-iron flanges and bolting the flanges together. Unless the pressures are very low, flanged fittings are recommended for all systems requiring pipe over 4 in. in diameter.

Nipples are short pieces of pipe threaded on both ends. If the threaded portions meet, the fitting is a *close nipple;* if there is a short unthreaded portion, it is a *short nipple.* Long and extra-long nipples range in length up to 24 in.

A *cap* is used to close the end of a pipe. A *plug* is used to close an opening in a fitting. A *bushing* is used to reduce the size of an opening. *Unions* are used to close systems and to connect pipes that are to be disassembled occasionally. A screwed union (Fig. 18.6) is composed of three pieces, two of which, *A* and *B,* are screwed firmly on the ends of the pipes to be connected. The third piece *C* draws them together, the gasket *D* forming a tight joint. Unions are also made with ground joints or with special metallic joints instead of gaskets. Several forms of screwed unions and union fittings are shown in Fig. 18.6. Flange unions in a variety of forms are used for large sizes of pipe.

18.8. VALVES. Figure 18.7 shows a few types of valves used in piping. (*A*) is a gate valve, used for water and other liquids, as it allows a straight flow. (*B*) is a plug valve, opened and closed with a quarter turn; (*C*), a ball-check valve; and (*E*), a swing-check valve permitting flow in one direction. For heavy liquids the ball-check valve is preferred. (*D*) is a globe valve, used for throttling steam

FIG. 18.7. Valves. The sectional drawings show their construction.

$4\times4\times2$	$4\times3\times2$	$4\times4\times2$	$4\times3\times2$	$4\times4\times2\times2$	$4\times4\times3\times2$	$4\times3\times2\times1\frac{1}{2}$
Tee	Tee	Lateral	Lateral	Cross	Cross	Cross

FIG. 18.8. Order of specifying the openings of reducing fittings.

or fluids; (F) is a butterfly valve, opened and closed with a quarter turn, but not steamtight, and used only as a check or damper.

18.9. SPECIFICATION OF FITTINGS. Fittings are specified by giving the nominal pipe size, material, and name, for example,

2″ M.I. Elbow   1½″ Brass Tee

When a fitting connects more than one size of pipe, the size of the largest run opening is given first, followed by the size at the opposite end of the run. Figure 18.8 shows the order of specifying reducing fittings. The word "male" must follow the size of the opening if an external thread is wanted, for example,

2 × 1 (male) × ¾ M.I. Tee

Valves are specified by giving the nominal size, material, and type, for example,

1″ Iron Body Brass-mounted Globe Valve. (If a particular valve is required it is best to give, in addition, "Manufacturer's No.— or equal.")

18.10. PIPE THREADS. When screwed fittings are used or when a connection must be made to a tapped hole, pipe is threaded on the ends for the purpose. The ASA provides two types of pipe thread: tapered and straight. The normal type employs a taper internal

and taper external thread. This thread (originated in 1882 as the Briggs Standard) is illustrated in Fig. 18.9. The threads are cut on a taper of 1⁄16 in. per inch, measured on the diameter, thus fixing the distance a pipe enters a fitting and ensuring a tight joint. Taper threads are recommended by the ASA for all uses with the exception of the following five types of joints: type 1, pressure-tight joints for pipe couplings; type 2, pressure-tight joints for grease-cup, fuel, and oil fittings; type 3, free-fitting mechanical joints for fixtures; type 4, loose-fitting mechanical joints with lock nuts; type 5, loose-fitting mechanical joints for hose coupling. For these joints straight pipe threads can be used. The number of threads per inch is the same in taper and straight pipe threads. Actual diameters vary for the different types of joints. When needed they can be obtained from the ASA bulletins. A common practice is to use a taper external thread with a straight internal thread, on the assumption that the materials are sufficiently ductile to allow the threads to adjust themselves to the taper thread. All pipe threads are assumed to be tapered unless otherwise specified.

$$A = D - (0.05D + 1.1)P$$
$$B = A + 0.0625 F$$
$$E = (0.80D + 6.8)P$$
$$\text{Depth of thread} = 0.80 P$$

FIG. 18.9. American Standard taper pipe thread. "Wedging" action of the taper produces a tight seal.

FIG. 18.10. Conventional methods of drawing pipe threads. (*A*) regular method, (*B*) simplified method, (*C*) hole tapped for pipe.

Pipe threads are represented by the same conventional symbols as bolt threads. The taper is so slight that it shows only if exaggerated. It need not be indicated unless it is desired to call attention to it, as in Fig. 18.10. In plan view (*C*), the dashed circle should be the actual outside diameter of the pipe specified. The length of effective thread is $E = (0.80D + 6.8)P$ (Fig. 18.9).

18.11. SPECIFICATION OF THREADS. Pipe threads are specified by giving the nominal pipe diameter, number of threads per inch, and the standard letter symbol to denote the type of thread. The following ASA symbols are used:

NPT = taper pipe thread
NPTF = taper pipe thread (dryseal)
NPS = straight pipe thread
NPSC = straight pipe thread in couplings

NPSI = intermediate internal straight pipe thread (dryseal)
NPSF = internal straight pipe thread (dryseal)
NPSM = straight pipe thread for mechanical joints
NPSL = straight pipe thread for locknuts and locknut pipe threads
NPSH = straight pipe thread for hose couplings and nipples
NPTR = taper pipe thread for railing fittings

Examples: ½-14NPT   2½-8NPTR

The specification for a tapped (pipe-thread) hole must include the tap drill size, for example,

⁵⁹⁄₆₄ Drill, ¾-14NPT

Dimensions of ASA taper pipe threads (NPT) are given in the Appendix. Dimensions of other pipe threads are given in ASA B2.1 and in manufacturers' catalogues.

18.12. PIPING DRAWINGS. Two general systems are used: (1) *scale layout* and (2) *diagrammatic*. Scale layouts are used principally for large pipe (usually flanged), as in boiler and power-plant work where lengths are critical and especially when the pipe is not cut and fitted in the field. Also, smaller pipe can be thus detailed when the parts are cut and threaded and then shipped to the job. Figure 18.11 is an example of a scale layout. The fittings can be specified on the drawing, as in Fig. 18.11, or on a bill of material. On small-scale drawings such as architectural plans, plant layouts, etc., or on sketches, the diagrammatic system is used. According to this system the fittings are shown by symbols (see Appendix) and the runs of pipe are shown by a single line,

Note: All fittings 2" M.I. unless otherwise noted. All valves 2" Iron body.

FIG. 18.11. Scale layout of piping. Pipe and fittings are drawn from dimensional specifications (see Appendix).

regardless of the pipe diameters, as shown in Fig. 18.12. When lines carry different liquids or different states of a liquid, they are identified by coded line symbols. The standard code for hot water, steam, cold water, etc., is given in the Appendix. The single line should be made heavier than the other lines of the drawing.

The arrangement of views is generally in orthographic projection (Fig. 18.13*A*). Sometimes, however, it is clearer to rotate all the piping into one plane and make only one "developed view" as at (*B*). Isometric and oblique diagrams, used alone or in conjunction with orthographic or developed drawings, are often employed in representing piping. The representation at (*C*) is drawn in oblique. Problem 18.3.7 is an example of an isometric layout.

18.13. DIMENSIONING A PIPE DRAWING.

The dimensions on a piping drawing are principally *location* dimensions, all of which are made to center lines, both in single-line diagrams and in scale layouts, as shown in Figs. 18.11 and 18.12. Valves and fittings are located by measurements to their centers, and the allowances for make-up are left to the pipe fitter. In designing a piping layout, take care to locate valves so that they are easily accessible and have ample clearance at the handwheels. The *sizes* of pipe should be specified by notes telling the nominal diameters, never by dimension lines on the drawing of the pipes. The fittings are specified by note, as described in paragraph 18.9. Very complete notes are an essential of all piping drawings and sketches.

When it is necessary to dimension the actual length of a piece of pipe, the distance can be calculated by using the

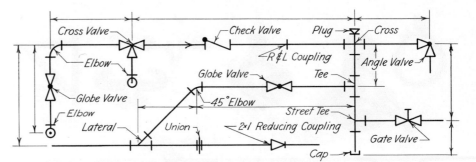

Note: All fittings 2"M.I. unless otherwise noted
All valves 2" Iron body.

FIG. 18.12. Diagrammatic drawing of piping. Fittings are indicated by standard symbols (see Appendix).

over-all fitting dimensions and accounting for the entrance length of the pipe threads.

Dimensions for standard pipe and for various fittings are given in the Appendix.

18.14. PIPE HANGERS AND SUPPORTS.

Small pipe and light tubing in short runs can be supported by connections to various machines or fittings. Straps of various types are used to tie pipe to posts, columns, walls, ceilings, etc. Pipe hangers and supports are available for almost any size and type of installation. In accordance with ASA B30.1—1955, Code for Pressure Piping, all piping systems require sway braces, guides,

FIG. 18.13. Diagrammatic methods. (*A*) orthographic, (*B*) developed, (*C*) pictorial.

Plan

Elevation

SPLIT RING (A)

DOUBLE BOLT CLAMP (B)

I-BEAM CLAMP (C)

BRACKET (D)

CLIP (E)

SINGLE PIPE ROLL

PIPE ROLL ON STAND (F)

SWIVEL PIPE ROLL

VARIABLE SPRING HANGER (G)

FIG. 18.14.   Pipe hangers and supports.

and supports. In Figure 18.14 a few commonly used hangers and supports are shown. A split ring (*A*) is used with a threaded rod attached to the building proper. The locking device prevents change of adjustment due to vibration and assures proper pitch of the line. A double bolt clamp, shown at (*B*), is for service where it is desirable to have the yoke extend outside of pipe covering. The I-beam clamp, two styles shown at (*C*), is suitable for clamping on flanges ranging in width from 2 to 6½ inches. The steel bracket (*D*) can be bolted to a wall and pipes can be supported on, as well as hung from, the horizontal member. The strap or clip (*E*) can be used for small pipe; this type is used when pipe is to be flush with a ceiling or wall. Pipe rolls (*F*) are designed to support piping so that longitudinal movement resulting from expansion and contraction can take place. Three types are shown for varying support conditions. The variable spring hanger (*G*) can be obtained in several different sizes and arrangements.

PROBLEMS

GROUP 1.   PIPE FITTINGS

18.1.1.   In the upper left-hand corner of one sheet draw a 2-in. tee (full size). Plug one outlet. In the second outlet place a 2- by 1½-in. bushing; in the remaining outlet use a 2-in. close nipple and on it screw a 2- by 1½-in. reducing coupling. Lay out the remainder of the sheet so as to include the following 1½-in. fittings: coupling, globe valve, R&L coupling, angle valve, 45° ell, 90° ell, 45° Y, cross, cap, three-part union, flange

union. Add extra pipe, nipples, and fittings so that the system will close at the reducing fitting first drawn.

18.1.2.   Make a one-view drawing of a 1½-in. globe valve. Use an 8½- by 11-in. sheet. See Appendix for proportions.

18.1.3.   Same as Prob. 18.1.2 for a 1½-in. angle globe valve.

18.1.4.   Same as Prob. 18.1.2 for a 1¼-in. gate valve.

GROUP 2.   PIPING LAYOUTS TO SCALE

18.2.1.   (*a*) Make a scale layout of the sodium hydroxide, NaOH + H$_2$O, lines of the hydro-

gen generator. Show cross section of the headers, one cylinder of the pump, a portion of the sodium hydroxide tank, and a portion of the top of one generator. (*b*) Make a scale layout of the hydrogen (H_2) line of the hydrogen generator. Show a portion of each generator with the lines in place. Use 11- by 17-in. paper. Scale, $3'' = 1'-0''$. Use standard pipe, malleable fittings, brass valves. Make a bill of material listing all pipe, valves, and fittings needed.

The operation of the unit is as follows: After the generators have been charged with ferrosilicon (Fe + Si), a mixture of sodium hydroxide (NaOH) and water (H_2O) is pumped into the generators. When the ferrosilicon, sodium hydroxide, and water are together in the generator, they react to form hydrogen (H_2) and a sludge (Fe, Na_2SiO_2 and H_2O). As the hydrogen gas forms, the internal pressure of the generator is built up. To keep the reaction going, additional water and sodium hydroxide solution has to be pumped into the generators against this pressure. As the hydrogen gas is formed, it is piped to a storage tank. The sludge is siphoned off periodically to prevent excessive accumulation that might retard the reaction.

A four-cylinder pump is used to provide a more uniform flow of fluid than would be obtained if a large single-cylinder pump were used. The four cylinders of the pump are connected to one intake line and to one exhaust line through headers (manifolds). Instead of building an intake and an exhaust valve into the cylinders of the pump, standard ball-type check valves are used and are connected as near as possible to the pump cylinders by means of standard pipe and fittings.

18.2.2. Make a scale layout of the gas-burner installation. Specify fittings and give center-line dimensions. Use 11- by 17-in. paper. Scale, $3'' = 1'-0''$.

18.2.3. Make a scale layout of a Grinell industrial heating unit, closed return, gravity system. Use center-line distances and placement of fittings as shown in the diagram. Use 3-in. supply main, 2-in. pipe and fittings to unit, ¾-in. pipe and fittings from unit to 2-in. return main. Add all necessary notes and dimensions. Use an 11- by 17-in. sheet. Scale, $3'' = 1'-0''$.

PROB. 18.2.1. Hydrogen generator.

PROB. 18.2.2. Gas-burner installation.

PROB. 18.2.3. Grinell industrial heating unit.

GROUP 3.   PIPING LAYOUTS, DIAGRAMMATIC

PROB. 18.3.1.   Storage and mixing tanks.

18.3.1.   *A* is a storage tank for supplying the mixing tanks *B, C,* and *D* and is located directly above them. The capacities of the mixers are in the ratios of 1, 2, and 3. Design (in one view) a piping system with sizes such that, neglecting frictional losses, the three tanks will fill in approximately the same time. So arrange the piping that any one of the tanks can be cut out or removed for repairs without disturbing the others. Use single-line conven-

should not be less than ¾ in. Dimension and specify all pipe and fittings.

18.3.3.   Make a drawing of the system of Prob. 18.3.2. Show the layout in a developed view. Dimension from center to center and specify all pipe and fittings.

18.3.4.   Make a list of the pipe and fittings to be ordered for the system of Prob. 18.3.2. Arrange the list in a table, heading the columns as below:

Size	Pipe lengths	Valves		Fittings		Material	Remarks (make, kind of threads, etc.)
		Number	Kind	Number	Kind		

tional representation. Dimension to center lines and specify the fittings.

18.3.2.   The figure shows the arrangement of a set of mixing tanks. Make an isometric drawing of an overhead piping system to supply water to each tank. Water supply enters the building through a 2½-in. main at point *A,* 3 ft below floor level. Place all pipe 10 ft above floor level, except riser from water main and drops to tanks, which are to end with globe valves 5 ft above floor level. Arrange the system to use as little pipe and as few fittings as possible. Neglecting frictional losses, sizes of pipe used should be such that they will deliver approximately an equal volume of water to each tank if all were being filled at the same time. The pipe size at the tank

PROB. 18.3.2.   Mixing tanks.

18.3.5.   Make an oblique drawing of a system of piping to supply the tanks in Prob. 18.3.2. All piping except risers is to be in a trench 1 ft below floor level. Risers should not run higher than 6 ft above floor level. Other conditions as in Prob. 18.3.2.

18.3.6.   The figure shows the outline of the right-hand half of a bank of eight heat-treating furnaces. *X* and *Y* are the leadins from the compressed-air and fuel mains. Draw the piping layout, using single-line representation, to distribute the air and fuel to the furnaces. The pipe sizes should be reduced proportionately as the oven leads are taken off. Each tail pipe should be removable without disturbing the other leads or closing down the other furnaces. Dimension the piping layout and make a bill of material for the pipe and fittings.

18.3.7.   The figure is the diagrammatic isometric layout of an industrial heater system. Using the basic layout as shown, assume positions for the preheating and reheating coils and make a complete, dimensioned, isometric diagrammatic layout.

18.3.8.   Make an orthographic diagrammatic layout for Prob. 18.3.7.

18.3.9.   Make a developed diagrammatic layout for Prob. 18.3.7.

18.3.10.   Shown is a scale layout of a meter and valve enclosure for an industrial plant. Make a scale drawing of the enclosure and show all piping diagrammatically.

PROB. 18.3.6.   Heat-treating furnaces.

PROB. 18.3.7. Industrial heater system.

Note: All 1½" Traps to Handle 800 lbs. Condensate per Hour at 2 psi.

PROB. 18.3.10. Meter and valve enclosure.

12" To City Water Main - For Cont. See Plot Plan, This Sheet

SECTION "A-A"

ELEVATION

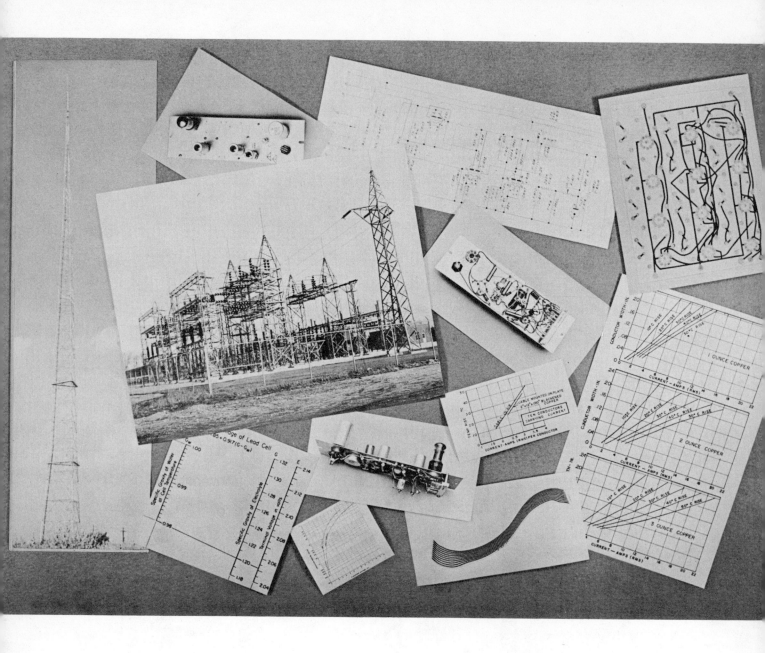

19

Drawings of Electrical Systems

19.1. Almost all engineering projects include mechanical and electrical components. The electrical components consist of items such as power supply, motors, generators, controls, heating and cooling devices, and lighting for industry; energy conversion, control apparatus, guidance systems and other devices for transportation in the air, on land, and in water; wired and wireless systems for communication; and home electrical and electronic appliances for everyday comfort and convenience. Thus, a knowledge of electrical systems is important for every engineer. Our purpose here is to show the kinds of drawings required for electrical systems, give the special drafting practices in electrical engineering, and point out the importance of graphics in this field.

Drafting for electrical equipment such as machinery, switchgear, and component circuitry is based upon the same principles as that for mechanical equipment. Because of the complex devices used in electrical circuits, graphic symbols are necessary to simplify representation. Graphic symbols for electrical diagrams have been standardized by the ASA in bulletin Y32.2—1954. "American Drafting Standards Manual," Y14.15 (tentative), gives drafting details for electrical diagrams.

19.2. DIAGRAMS. Many different types of diagrams are employed to show arrangements of components and wiring connections. Figure 19.1 is an example.

The following definitions for electrical diagrams have been adopted as standard by the ASA and are quoted from Y14.15 (tentative).

Single-line or One-line Diagram. "A diagram which shows, by means of single lines and graphical symbols, the course of an electric circuit or system of circuits and the component devices or parts used therein." See paragraph 19.21 and Fig. 19.20.

Schematic or Elementary Diagram. "A diagram which shows, by means of graphical symbols, the electrical connections and functions of a specific circuit arrangement. The schematic diagram facilitates tracing the circuit and its functions without regard to the actual physical size, shape, or location of the component device or parts." See paragraph 19.22 and Figs. 19.1 and 19.21.

Connection or Wiring Diagram. "A diagram which shows the connections of an installation or its component devices or parts. It may cover internal or external connections, or both, and contains such detail as is needed to make or trace connections that are involved. The connection diagram usually shows general physical arrangement of the component devices or parts."

Interconnection Diagram. "A form of connection or wiring diagram which shows only external connections between unit assemblies or equipment. The internal connections of the unit assemblies or equipment are usually omitted."

The text material and illustrations in paragraphs 19.3 to 19.22 are adapted from ASA Y14.15 (tentative), Section 15, Electrical Diagrams, by special permission by the ASME. The material given here is intended for educational purposes only. For commercial use, follow the latest issue of ASA or other national-level standards.

19.3. DIAGRAM TITLES. The title of a diagram is given to state the type of diagram and the system or component for which the diagram is made. Examples are: single-line diagram—audio circuit; schematic diagram—vertical oscillator.

19.4. COMBINED DIAGRAMS. Diagrams that combine features of more than one type are often more useful than those in the pure forms, defined in paragraph 19.2. For example, a schematic diagram may include wiring information or interconnection details, especially when the diagram is made for only a portion of a complete circuit. Note in Fig. 19.49 that connections to other parts of the circuit are shown and identified. The title for a combined diagram conforms to the *principal* purpose of the diagram.

19.5. DRAWING SIZE AND FORMAT. Drawing sizes and formats for electrical drawings conform to the standards of the ASA. See paragraph 13.12 and Fig. 13.8.

FIG. 19.1. A schematic diagram. This is for a small transistorized radio receiver. The symbols show the components; the notes give values and identifications.

19.6. LINE CONVENTIONS AND LETTERING.
A line of medium thickness, as shown in Fig. 19.2, is recommended for general use on electrical diagrams. Thin lines are used for brackets and leaders. A heavy line is used to emphasize a special feature. However, the thickness of a line has no significance in meaning—the line thickness is chosen solely for readability of the diagram. When a drawing for reproduction is to be reduced in size, for example, for a manual, the line weights are made heavier to give good readability. See paragraph 22.22 on drawing for reproduction.

Lettering on electrical drawings and diagrams should be done in capital letters. For drawings made for direct reproduction (same size), the smallest letters should be not less than 1/8 in. high. Drawings reduced for manuals should be lettered in a size that will be not less than 1/16 in. high when reduced.

19.7. GRAPHIC SYMBOLS. Graphic symbols on electrical diagrams conform to "American Standard Graphical Symbols for Electrical Diagrams," Y32.2, or other national-level standards if the symbol is not covered in the American Standard. A selection of symbols, adapted from Y32.2, is given in the Appendix. For special components, if no suitable symbol exists, an appropriate symbol may be made, but must be explained in a note. Symbols that can be reversed or rotated without affecting their meaning may be so drawn to simplify the circuit layout. Symbols may be drawn to any convenient size that suits the diagram and produces good readability.

19.8. LAYOUT OF ELECTRICAL DIAGRAMS.
The best way to start an electrical dia-

LINE APPLICATION	LINE THICKNESS
FOR GENERAL USE	MEDIUM
MECHANICAL-CONNECTING & SHIELDING LINE FUTURE CIRCUITS	MEDIUM
BRACKET-CONNECTING DASH LINE	MEDIUM
BRACKETS, LEADER LINES, ETC.	THIN
BOUNDARY OF MECHANICAL GROUPING	THIN
FOR EMPHASIS	THICK

USE OF THESE LINE THICK-NESSES OP-TIONAL

FIG. 19.2. Line conventions for electrical diagrams. Medium and thin lines are used for all lines normally needed on electrical diagrams. Thick lines are used only for emphasis.

gram is to make a freehand sketch of the proposed arrangement. While doing this, place the symbols—remembered or obtained from the Standard (Appendix)—in the best position to eliminate long connecting lines and require as few crossovers as possible. In making the drawing proper, use the sketch as a guide. The layout should prominently show the main features. Space the symbols and lines so that there is sufficient area for notes and reference information. However, avoid large blank spaces except when an area is needed for circuits or information to be added later. In general, electrical diagrams are drawn to follow the circuit, signal, or transmission path, from input to output, source to load, or in the order of functional sequence.

Connecting lines are drawn horizontally or vertically and with as few bends and crossovers as possible. No more than three lines should be shown connected at one point when an alternate arrangement is possible. Parallel lines are arranged in groups, preferably three to a group, with double space between groups. In grouping parallel lines, lines representing related functions are grouped together. Parallel lines should

CONNECTOR INPUT   CIRCUIT ARRANGEMENT

FIG. 19.3. Identification of interrupted lines. Left side of figure: a group of lines interrupted on the diagram. Right side of figure: single lines interrupted on the diagram.

FIG. 19.4. Typical arrangement of line identifications and destinations.

FIG. 19.5. Typical interrupted lines interconnected by dashed lines. The dashed line shows the interrupted paths that are to be connected. Individual line identifications indicate matching connections.

never be closer than $\frac{1}{16}$ in. in final reduced size.

Interrupted paths are used as needed in a diagram, but each path must be identified and the destination shown. Letters, numbers, or abbreviations used for identification should be placed as close as possible to the point of interruption. Figure 19.3 shows two examples of interrupted paths, multiple paths on the left and single paths on the right.

Interrupted grouped lines are employed in a diagram as needed. The destination of the group is shown by bracketing and identifying as in Fig. 19.4, or by using a dashed line connecting the brackets as in Fig. 19.5. The dashed line is drawn so that it will not form a continuation of one of the lines of the interrupted group.

Abbreviations used on electrical diagrams should conform to "American Standard Abbreviations for Use on Drawings," Z32.13, or other national-level standard if the abbreviation is not covered in the American Standard. If no suitable abbreviation exists, a special abbreviation may be used but must be explained by a note on the diagram.

19.9. REPRESENTATION OF ELECTRICAL CONTACTS. Switch symbols (see Appendix and ASA Y32.2) should be shown in the position of no applied operating force. For switches that may be in any of two or more positions with no operating force applied, or for switches actuated by mechanical or electrical means, a drawing note should identify the functional phase shown on the diagram. Relay contacts should be shown in the unenergized position.

19.10. IDENTIFICATION OF TERMINALS. Terminal identifications are added to graphic symbols to show actual physical markings on or near part terminations;

SYMBOL ON
SCHEMATIC
DIAGRAM

TERMINAL
ORIENTATION
DIAGRAM
IN NOTE

FIG. 19.6. Terminal identification.
Upper half: toggle switch. Lower half:
rotary switch.

SYMBOL ON
SCHEMATIC DIAGRAM

TERMINAL
ORIENTATION
DIAGRAM IN NOTE

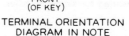

SYMBOL ON
SCHEMATIC DIAGRAM

TERMINAL ORIENTATION
DIAGRAM IN NOTE

FIG. 19.7. Terminal identification. This
example shows identifications necessary
for a multicontact lever-type key
switch.

also, when no markings exist on a part,
arbitrary number or letter designations
may be assigned. Figures 19.6 and 19.7
show terminal identifications on the
symbols of schematic diagrams and on
orientation diagrams for the actual part.
When terminal designations are arbi-
trarily assigned, the orientation diagram
must be included in order to relate the
designation to actual physical locations
on the part. Pictorial drawings of a part,
such as Fig. 19.8, are used when identification on a symbol and a simple terminal orientation note are insufficient.
Pictorial drawings are often used in
service manuals.

When terminals or leads are identified
on the part by color code, letter, number, or geometric symbol, this identification is shown on or near the connecting
line adjacent to the symbol.

19.11. TERMINAL IDENTIFICATION OF ADJUSTABLE RESISTORS.

If it is necessary
to indicate direction of rotation, it is
customary to refer to rotary motion as
clockwise or counterclockwise when
rotation is viewed from the knob or ac-

FIG. 19.8. Pictorial explanatory
drawing of an electrical part. This
shows the relationship and orientation
of elements and gives the identification sequence to be used on a diagram.

FIG. 19.9. Terminal identification. This example illustrates identifications on a variable resistor for (*A*) tap (CW) nearest variable contact in extreme clockwise position; (*B*) all taps (no. 2 assigned to variable contact); (*C*) additional fixed taps (4 and 5).

(A)   (B)   (C)

FIG. 19.10. Position and function identification for a rotary switch. The choice of method—diagram (left) or table (right)—is optional. These methods are recommended for simple switches.

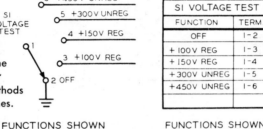

FUNCTIONS SHOWN AT SYMBOL

S1 VOLTAGE TEST	
FUNCTION	TERM.
OFF	1-2
+ 100 V REG	1-3
+ 150 V REG	1-4
+300 V UNREG	1-5
+450 V UNREG	1-6

FUNCTIONS SHOWN IN TABULAR FORM

Rotary switches that perform involved functions, as illustrated in Fig. 19.11, should be explained by using the tabular form shown. In tabular listings, dashes link the terminals that are connected.

19.13. ELECTRON TUBE-PIN IDENTIFICATION. Tube-pin numbers are shown outside the tube envelope and directly above or at one side of the connecting line, as in Fig. 19.12*A*. An alternative method is shown at (*B*), where the circles correspond to approximate physical locations of the pins when the tube is viewed from the bottom. Starting with the pin adjacent to the tube-base key or similar point of reference, the circles are numbered consecutively in clockwise order.

19.14. IDENTIFICATION OF PARTS BY SUFFIX NUMBER. Subdivisions of parts are indicated by adding a suffix letter to the reference designation. For example, C1A and C1B will designate electrically separate sections of a dual capacitor C1.

Suffix letters are also used to identify subdivisions of a complete part when the individual parts are shown enclosed or associated in a unit, as shown in Fig. 19.13.

19.15. IDENTIFICATION OF ROTARY-SWITCH PARTS. When parts or rotary switches are designated S1A, S1B, S1C, etc., the suffix letters start with *A* at the knob or actuator end and are assigned sequentially away from this position. Each section of the switch is shown

S1 REAR

(SWITCH VIEWED FROM REAR)

SYMBOL ON SCHEMATIC DIAGRAM

S1		
POS	FUNCTION	TERM.
1	OFF(SHOWN)	1-2,5-6,9-10
2	STANDBY	1-3,5-7,9-11
3	OPERATE	1-4,5-8,9-12

FUNCTIONS SHOWN IN TABULAR FORM

FIG. 19.11. Position and function identification for a rotary switch. Position and contact identification (only) are shown on the diagram proper. The tabular information then supplements by giving functional information. This method is recommended for complex switches.

tuator end of the control. The preferred method of terminal identification is to designate with the letters CW the terminal adjacent to the movable contact when it is in the extreme clockwise position, as shown in Fig. 19.9*A*. Numbers may also be used with the resistor symbol in which no. 2 is assigned to the adjustable contact as shown at (*B*). Additional fixed taps are numbered sequentially, 4, 5, as at (*C*).

19.12. SWITCH TERMINALS AND CIRCUIT FUNCTIONS. The relation of switch position to circuit function is shown on a schematic diagram by notation near the terminals as at the left in Fig. 19.10, or in tabular form as shown at the right. For simple toggle switches, the notations ON and OFF are usually sufficient.

(A)   (B)

FIG. 19.12. Terminal identification for electron tube pins. (*A*) arbitrary numbers are assigned; (*B*) physical location is shown when the tube is viewed from the bottom.

FIG. 19.13. Identification of parts by suffix letters. A and B are subdivisions of part Y1. Identifications are Y1A and Y1B.

FIG. 19.14. Typical development of a graphic symbol (complex rotary switch). Portions of the part are oriented relative to each other for identification on the graphic symbols.

(A) TYPICAL SWITCH SECTION

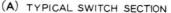

(B) GRAPHICAL SYMBOL

viewed from the same end, as in Fig. 19.14A. When both sides of a rotary switch are used for separate functions, the front (actuator end) and rear symbols should be differentiated by modifying the reference designation, for example, S1A FRONT and S1A REAR as at (B).

19.16. IDENTIFICATION OF PARTS BY "PART OF" PREFIX. When parts of connectors, terminal boards, or rotary-switch sections are functionally separated on the diagram, the words PART OF are used to precede the reference designation as in Fig. 19.15.

19.17. IDENTIFICATION OF PARTS AS INDIVIDUAL TERMINALS. When the separation of parts of connectors or terminal boards on the same drawing becomes extensive, the separated parts may be identified as individual terminals, as shown in Fig. 19.16.

FIG. 19.15. Identification of parts by "part of" prefix. All "part of" portions (separated on the diagram) form a single unit on the actual connector or terminal board.

FIG. 19.16. Identification of parts as individual terminals.

HIGHEST REFERENCE DESIGNATIONS	
R65	C35
REFERENCE DESIGNATIONS NOT USED	
R 7, R 9 R60, R62	C11, C14 C19, C23

FIG. 19.17. Typical table indicating highest and omitted numerical reference designations.

FIG. 19.18. Reference designations for electron tubes. The reference designation is given on the top, the tube type number next, and then function.

19.18. REFERENCE DESIGNATIONS. These are combinations of letters and numbers which identify parts shown on single-line and schematic diagrams and also on related drawings such as the assembly drawing and connection diagram.

The number portion of the designation follows the letter or letters without a space or hyphen and is of the same size as the letter(s), for example, S4, MG5, T6A, etc.

The assignment of numbers should start with the lowest numbers in the upper left-hand corner of the diagram and proceed consecutively from left to right throughout the drawing. When parts are eliminated as a result of a drawing revision, the remaining parts should not be renumbered. As an aid in accounting for all reference designations, a table, as in Fig. 19.17, may be included showing the highest reference designations and the reference designations not used.

Electron tubes are identified by tube type number in addition to the reference designation. The circuit function may also be given below the tube type number, as in Fig. 19.18.

19.19. NUMERICAL VALUES FOR RESISTANCE, CAPACITANCE, INDUCTANCE. The guiding principle is to use expressions that require the fewest ciphers.

Resistance. In expressing resistances, alternative methods of expression may be used depending on the range of values expressed.

(*a*) For the entire range of values of 1 to and including 99,999, *ohms* may be used. For example, 15,000Ω. For the range of 100,000 ohms and above, the expression *megohm* (equivalent to 1,000,000 ohms) may be used. For example, 200,000 ohms may be expressed as .2 MEG (megohms).

(*b*) For the range of values from 1,000 to 999,000, the abbreviation K (*kilohm*) may be used instead of ohms. For example, 56K instead of 56,000. This method of expression is preferable to the method described in (*a*) when the last three places of the value are ciphers.

(*c*) For resistance values less than 1 ohm, the value of resistance is expressed as a decimal. For example, 0.031Ω.

Capacitance. Capacitance up to and including 9,999 *micromicrofarads* should be expressed in micromicrofarads. Capacitance of 10,000 micromicrofarads and above should be expressed as microfarads (equivalent to 1,000,000 micromicrofads). For example, 92,000 UUF (micromicrofarads) should be expressed as 0.092 UF (microfarads).

Inductance. Inductance may be expressed in *henries* (H), *millihenries* (MH), or *microhenries* (UH). For example, 2UH instead of 0.002MH, and 5MH instead of either 0.005H or 5000UH.

Commas. In numerical values of four digits, the comma is omitted.

Value Placement. Numerical values of components are located as near as practical to the symbol. Preferred arrangements are shown in Fig. 19.19.

19.20. NOTES. To eliminate giving units of measurement which are applicable throughout the diagram, a general note can be used and only the numerical value given on the diagram. A recommended form is: "Unless otherwise specified: resistance values are in ohms. Capacitance values are in microfarads."

FIG. 19.19. Recommended placement of numerical values.

19.21. SINGLE-LINE DIAGRAMS. A single-line diagram conveys basic information about the operation of a circuit or system of circuits. Much of the detailed information such as reference designations, tube numbers, and part values is omitted. Also, a single-line diagram is a simplification of multiconductor circuits, such as communication and power systems, in which a single line represents a multiconductor group. Figure 19.20 is an example of a single-line diagram.

19.22. SCHEMATIC DIAGRAMS. A schematic diagram shows the electrical functions and connections of a circuit. Electrical components are shown by symbols (Appendix and ASA Y32.2). Components are identified by reference designations (paragraph 19.18). Values

of components are given by numerical value of resistance, capacitance, inductance (paragraph 19.19). Paragraphs 19.3 to 19.20 give details for the preparation of schematic diagrams. Figure 19.21 is an example.

FIG. 19.20. A typical single-line diagram. This type of diagram conveys basic functional information but does not give detailed information. The one illustrated is for a complex audio system.

FIG. 19.21. A typical schematic diagram. This type of diagram shows all components by graphic symbols and gives details of all electrical connections.

parent material. The backing is peeled off and the stanpat stuck in place on the drawing or sketch. Templates such as those shown in Fig. 22.10 save much time in drawing symbols. These are available from drawing-instrument manufacturers (see Bibliography).

19.23. SPECIAL DRAFTING PRACTICES. Most of the commercial practices and economies described in Chap. 22 are applicable to the making of electrical diagrams and drawings. Of particular value in electrical drafting are templates and overlays (paragraphs 22.11 and 22.12), special uses of reproduction (paragraph 22.13), photo drawing (paragraph 22.14), and the use of illustrated drawings (paragraph 22.19). An example of a gummed overlay is shown in Fig. 19.22. Many standard circuits, portions of circuits, and graphic symbols are available. The Stanpat Co. manufactures a variety printed on trans-

When the accuracy of an instrument drawing is not necessary, drafting time can be saved by making electrical diagrams freehand. Coordinate paper with divisions printed on the back (see paragraph 5.33) promotes economy. The coordinate lines aid in keeping lines straight—particularly the long parallel connecting lines. The symbol sizes are not important but should be kept to proportions that look well and read easily on the diagram.

19.24. MODELS. When models of plants are used, the conduit is included with other details in a full representation, to scale, of all conductors. These are added to the model after machines, process piping, plumbing, special equipment, etc., are in place. Figure 22.36 shows a plant model in which the conduit for lighting, power, and control circuits is included. Giving the conduit on the model has the advantage that it simplifies the arrangement, develops a true scale for installation, allows tagging of all lines for size and circuits included, and reduces the number of drawings required. The tagging of power and control lines on models is sometimes supplemented or replaced by a conduit schedule.

FIG. 19.23. A photo drawing. Photo drawings are used principally for service manuals. This one shows component and tube locations in a color-television chassis.

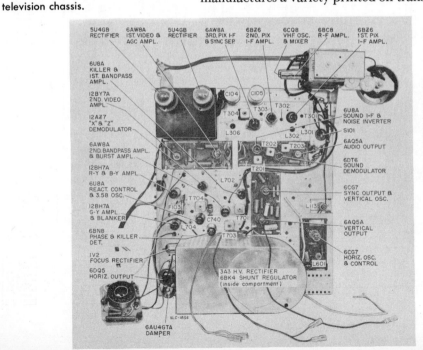

To speed up connection and tagging of wiring, or for service use, photo drawings such as Fig. 19.23 are sometimes prepared. A photograph of the actual equipment is made, and the connections, instructions, or identifications are added to the screened positive.

19.25.   DRAWINGS OF PRINTED CIRCUITS. Printed circuits can be obtained from very accurately drawn layouts. The method employs efficient laminated wiring on a wide variety of permanently bonded insulating plastics, from low cost vinyls and polyethylenes to fluorocarbons. Printed circuits allow miniaturization and the elimination of circuit errors—advantages that cannot be ob-

tained by other methods. Once a pattern or suitable design is established, preparation of a black and white drawing can start. Scales for reduction, for example, 4 to 1, 3 to 1, or 2 to 1, are used. To insure sufficient bonding area of the metal laminate during soldering operations, lines should not be less than $\frac{1}{32}$ inch in width when reduced. Line separation should never be closer than $\frac{1}{32}$ inch on the final circuit. Figure 19.24 illustrates the drawing of printed circuits.

To produce the circuit, a sheet of copper foil is bonded to a plastic board. The copper foil is processed by printing photographically from the layout and then etching to leave the circuits as originally drawn. Holes are punched (or drilled)

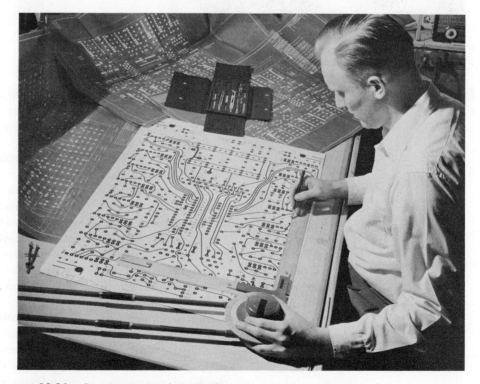

FIG. 19.24.   Drawing a printed circuit. The drawing is carefully planned and executed for photographic reproduction on the circuit board.

FIG. 19.25.   Punching holes in a circuit board.
The holes are to receive component wires.

in the board (Fig. 19.25) and various components inserted through them. The leads of the various components are cut and bent over the copper-foil wiring. The wiring side of the board is then dipped in molten solder to make all solder connections at once, and all copper-foil wiring becomes covered, thus increasing its ability to carry current. A coat of silicone resin varnish is applied to the wiring side of the board; this prevents short circuits caused by dust or moisture. The method is known as the etched-wiring method, and results in uniformity of wiring, compactness, and freedom from wiring errors. It is used more widely than other methods, such as embossed wiring, stamped wiring, and pressed powdered wiring, because of its reliability, its great flexibility, and low set-up cost. Figure 19.26 is a photographic reproduction of a printed circuit board; the caption explains several details of printed circuitry.

19.26.   INSTALLATION DRAWINGS AND DIAGRAMS.   The electrical drawings required for an industrial plant are: (1) contractors' drawings, (2) system-design drawings, (3) component and special-equipment drawings. These vary considerably depending upon the industry because of the diversity of processes and equipment.

19.27.   CONTRACTORS' DRAWINGS.   To illustrate the types of drawings needed, we will describe briefly several contractors' electrical drawings for an industrial manufacturing plant in which the products are machine parts. The plant consists of several buildings. The greater

FIG. 19.26.   A "double" printed circuit board. This type of circuit board has the circuit integrated and printed on both sides. The upper illustration shows the resistor side of the board; the lower illustration shows the side used for other components. The opposite side can be seen in both illustrations—the fainter, diffused lines. By printing both sides of the board, circuit crossovers are easily handled. Note that this complicated circuit can be produced in quantity without circuit errors.

part of the manufacturing area is shown in the plot plan in Fig. 19.27. In laying out the underground distribution along with substations, manholes, and duct locations, it is necessary to know all the power and lighting requirements for the entire plant as well as all breakdowns for power and lighting for each area. From these data the power to be supplied is determined and the outdoor substation located. The master substation and the seven other substations are located on the basis of area power requirements. The 34,500-volt overhead

FIG. 19.27. Plot plan for electrical distribution in a factory. This shows the location of power supply, substations, and underground wiring.

FIG. 19.28. Plot plan and riser diagram for electrical service. This is for a parking lot of an industrial plant and shows details of overhead and underground wiring.

transmission line is shown in the figure where it enters the plant. All substations are shown on the plot plan except substation no. 7, which controls the power requirements for the engineering and office area. The underground distribution is shown in the figure by dashed lines.

Figure 19.28 shows the parking-lot plot plan (upper right) for this plant and a riser diagram (left and lower portion) indicating the power distribution for this system. Each rectangle (X) on the riser diagram represents a waterproof cabinet housing two fused safety switches and two single-phase dry-type transformers, shown on the detail of the lighting pole in Fig. 19.29. The feeder conduits are brought up through the concrete piers into each of these cabinets. As shown on the plot plan, there are three rows of lights. Each pair is mounted on a pole supported from a square reinforced-concrete pier that projects above the ground.

Figure 19.30 is a plan view of the outdoor substation enlarged from the plot plan (Fig. 19.27). The incoming power line enters the outdoor substation

FIG. 19.29. Details of a lighting pole. This is one of the detail drawings to accompany the plot plan in Fig. 19.28.

FIG. 19.30. Plan of a substation. This is an enlarged detail to accompany the plot plan in Fig. 19.27.

PLAN
SCALE 1/4"=1'-0"

from the north and attaches to the super-structure with strain insulators and strain clamps. All major transmission lines are 1¼-in. copper tubing.

Figure 19.31 gives three sectional views, *A-A, B-B,* and *C-C,* which show how the transformers, lightning arrestors, circuit breakers, metering, and outlet are related to the master substation.

The power ducts run from the master

FIG. 19.31. Sections of a substation. These include *A-A* and *B-B,* taken from the plan in Fig. 19.30, and *C-C* identified on section *B-B.*

FIG. 19.32. Plan and sectional views of a manhole. These drawings show details of construction and wiring.

PLAN

SECTION C-C

SECTION D-D

MANHOLE No. 9
SCALE 1½"-1'-0"

FIG. 19.33. A portion of a single-line wiring diagram. This type of drawing shows the fundamentals of power distribution. Supplementary drawings show further details.

substation to the various substations shown in Fig. 19.27. Spare ducts are added so that additional circuits may be pulled when expansion or changes require more wiring. All circles in the dashed lines on Fig. 19.27 marked MH are manholes from which circuits are pulled and cable splices made. A detail of manhole no. 9 is shown in Fig. 19.32. This is a typical manhole although many are rectangular in shape rather than triangular. Shown in Fig. 19.32 are ten ducts with cables entering from the south from manhole no. 3. Some of these ducts are for spare cables. The distribution from this area is north with eight ducts to substation no. 2 and six ducts to substation no. 8. Shown projecting from the side walls are steel pulling eyes (used in pulling cables) and necessary cable supports. Other details sometimes necessary for duct layout are profile or elevation sheets showing variations in level to clear all obstructions such as footers, storm sewers, drains.

In addition to the plot-plan distribution shown in Fig. 19.27 a single-line wiring diagram is drawn for the entire power system. Separate single-line riser diagrams are then drawn to show the blocking distribution of the various circuits by floors and areas. Figure 19.33 is a portion of one of these drawings for substation no. 7, showing distribution circuits for lighting and power for the office building. The master lighting panel has three mains and three branches. All lighting panels have automatic circuit breakers. All power panels feed circuits in the underfloor ducts.

Figure 19.34 is an enlarged plan of

FIG. 19.34. Plan and sectional views of a substation. These are details of substation no. 5, which is indicated on the plot plan in Fig. 19.27. Cable locations, switchgear, and panels are shown.

ELEVATION "D-D"

PLAN OF SUBSTATION "5"

SECTION A-A

PLAN OF FIRST FLOOR UNDER MEZZANINE

substation no. 5 with a sectional elevation. It shows cable distribution with switchgear and panels. The lighting layout is also given with lights, fixtures, and switches.

Typical lighting layouts are indicated in Figs. 19.35 and 19.36. Figure 19.35 shows fluorescent fixtures with two tubes. Figure 19.36 shows holophane lights with switching arrangement. The power requirements are specified on Fig. 19.36.

Figure 19.37 gives a detail for mounting lighting fixtures from a messenger wire supported from purlins. This is a typical mounting for holophane lights when a cable hanger is used. The wiring diagram shows the usual circuit through an autotransformer. The lights are mounted so that the bottom of the fixtures are at the same elevation as the bottom chords of the trusses in low bays.

There are many more drawings and detailed specifications necessary in a complete set of electrical drawings for a plant of this size. These include a lighting layout for each factory and office area, an emergency-power layout, riser diagrams and lighting-panel layouts, power-transmission-duct layouts, night- and emergency-lighting layouts, telephone system and details, public-address

PLAN OF NORTH ENGINEERING BUILDING FAN ROOM #4

FIG. 19.36. Lighting details. This drawing shows power panel, wiring, and fixture locations.

19.28. System-design Drawings

system, and other miscellaneous services. Figures 19.27 to 19.37 show typical drawings from a complete set.

19.28. SYSTEM-DESIGN DRAWINGS. The starting point in designing an electrical system for an industrial plant is generally the motor list together with devices and interlocks list. From these the number, size, and characteristics of components and the location by buildings and floors may be set forth in a bill of material. (A typed bill of material is shown in Fig. 19.38.) From it the equipment is procured. If a special item of equipment

FIG. 19.37. Fixture-mounting details. This type of drawing specifies fixtures and shows the mounting and wiring.

WIRING DIAGRAM

DETAIL of MOUNTING LIGHTING FIXTURES ON MESSENGER WIRE SUPPORTED from PURLINS

ITEM No.	DRAWING No.	DESCRIPTION	MANUFACTURER & CATALOG NO.	QUAN.	REMARKS
1	C-19678	Pushbutton with double throw contact block.	Sq. D, Class 9001, Type TR1B marked "UP".	2	P.B. Sta. #1
2	C-19678	Pushbutton with double throw contact block.	Sq. D., Class 9001, Type TR2B marked "DOWN"	2	P. B. Sta. #1
3	C-19678	ON-OFF Selector Switch	Sq. D., Class 9001, Type TS1A, marked "No. 1 CLAMP-ON OFF".	1	SW. 1, P. B. Sta. #1
4	C-19678	ON-OFF Selector Switch	Sq. D., Class 9001, Type TS1A, marked "VIB. #1 - MAN-AUTO.	1	SW. 3, P. B. Sta. #2
5	C-19678	Selector switch with double throw contact block.	SQ. D., Class 9001, Type TS1B, marked "DUMP - No. 1, No. 2"	1	SW. 5, P. B. Sta. #2
6	C19678	Control relay 2 N. O. contacts, 110 volt, 60 cycle coil, open type.	Allen-Bradley, Bulletin 700, Type No. BX-220, 110 V., 60 cycle coil.	2	R1, R2
7	C-19678	Control relay 4 N. O. contacts, 110 volt, 60 cycle coil, open type.	Allen-Bradley, Bulletin 700, Type No. BX-440, 110 V., 60 cycle coil.	1	R3
8	C-19678	Timing Relay 1 N.O. & 1 N.C. contact, 110 V. 60 cycle coil, Time delay on energization.	AGASTAT, Type NE-12.	1	TR1
9	C-19678	Reversing starter for 1 HP Motor, 440 V., 3 phase, 60 cycle.	Complete combination unit to accommodate 1 HP, 440 V., 60 cycle, 3 phase, reversing induction motor complete with door and external brk'r. operating handle for installation in existing MCC serial No. _____ purchased in _____. Starter coil voltage 110 V, 60 cycle, single phase with no control transf. required. 1 N. O. aux. contact on the breaker is required.	2	HC1U - HC1D HC2U - HC2D
10	C-19678	Alarm Horn, Projector-less type with grille front, for 110 V. operation	Benjamin, Type SNP, Cat. No. 8741-115 V.	1	
11	C-19678	NEMA 12 sheet steel enclosure for 6 units.	Sq. D., Class 9001, Type TYA-6	2	P. B. Sta. #1 & #2
12	C-19678	Closing plate for unused hole in P.B. Sta. #2	Sq. D., Class 9001, Type TO-1	1	
13	C-19678	Thermal O.L. relay elements to accommodate 1 1/2 HP, 440 V., 3 phase, induction motor. Suitable for mounting in existing M.C.C. Serial No. _____, Purchased in _____.	Square D, Class 9065, Hand reset type.	1	

FIG. 19.38. A bill of material for electrical equipment. This is needed for the purchase of equipment.

FIG. **19.39.** Illustration of special equipment. This type of supplementary drawing is used to specify unusual items.

is needed, for example the impulse timer in Fig. 19.39, a picture or pictorial may be shown with the wiring diagram.

The next division of field effort is to install equipment and conduit and pull wire. A conduit schedule such as is shown in Fig. 19.40 is common. Numbers refer to numbers on the drawings or model. Figure 19.41 is an example of a conduit layout where approximate physical location of conduit and electrical equipment is shown on a background of the equipment layout. Figure 19.42 is an example of a conduit block diagram. It shows the equipment as blocks (hence the term) and the connecting conduits but does not indicate the physical routing. Photo drawing

NO.	POWER SIZE	WIRES POWER TYPE	NO.	CONTROL SIZE	CONTROL TYPE	CND SIZE (Inches)	NOTES	CONDUIT No.	FROM	TO
3	2/10	RH-RW				2	Feeder Tap (FT)	C1	Junction Box	Feeder Disconnect
3	6	RH-RW				1	6FT1, 6FT2, 6FT3	C2	Feeder Disconnect	Conduit Fitting
3	6	RH-RW	4	14	TW	1 1/4	44,45,46,47,6FT1	C3	Conduit Fitting	Conduit Fitting
			4	14	TW	1/2	44,45,46,47	C4	Conduit Fitting	Control Station #737
3	2/0	RH-RW				2		C5	Feeder Disconnect	Wiring Trough
3	12	TW	3	12	TW	1	Eq. #733,35,65,67	C6	Circuit Brkr. #733	Alarm Relay Box
3	12	TW	2	12	TW	3/4	Eq. #733A, 61,62	C7	Alarm Relay Box	Starter #733A
3	12	TW	2	12	TW	3/4	Eq. #733B, 63, 64	C8	Alarm Relay Box	Starter #733B
3	12	TW				1 1/2	EQ.#709-3T1,3T2,3T3	C9	Wiring Trough	Conduit Fitting
3	2	RH-RW				1 1/4	2T1, 2T2, 2T3	C10	Conduit Fitting	Motor #707
3	12	TW				1/2	3T1, 3T2,3T3	C11	Conduit Fitting	Motor #709
3	8	RH-RW	2	14	TW	1	24, 24A,4T1,4T2,4T3	C12	C. T. Cabinet	Equipment #731
3	10	TW	2	14	TW	3/4	40,40A,5T1,5T2,5Ta	C13	Starter #715	Equipment #715
3	8	RH-RW				1 1/4	Eq. #705,1T1,1T2, 1T3	C14	Wiring Trough	Conduit Fitting
3	12	TW	2	14	TW	3/4	Eq. #877,9T1,9T2,9T3	C15	Conduit Fitting	Conduit Fitting
			2	14	TW	1/2	48,50	C16	Conduit Fitting	P.B. #14
			2	14	TW	1/2	49,50	C17	P.B. #14	Float Switch
3	12	TW				1/2	9T1,9T2, 9T3	C18	Conduit Fitting	Motor #877
3	8	RH-RW				3/4	1T1, 1T2, 1T3	C19	Conduit Fitting	Motor #705
			28	14	TW	2	1,3,4,5,6,10,11,13,14	C20	Wiring Trough	Control Station #737
2	12	TW				1/2	31,35	C21	Control Station #737	Weigh Hopper
			3	14	TW	1/2	6,14,15	C22	Control Station #737	P.B. #5
			2	14	TW	1/2	14,15	C23	P.B. #5	Solenoid Valve S-1
3	12	TW	8	14	TW	1 1/4 (#12 are 31,32,35)	7,8,17,18,25,26,31,32,35	C24	Control Station #737	Buggy Fill Control Station
			3	12	TW	1/2	35,38,39	C25	Buggy Fill Control Station	Conduit Fitting
			2	12	TW	1/2	35,39	C26	Conduit Fitting	Solenoid Valve S-3
			2	12	TW	1/2	35,38	C27	Conduit Fitting	Solenoid Valve S-2
3	12	TW	3	12	TW	1	Eq. #733, 35,65,67	C28	Wiring Trough	Circuit Brkr. #733
6	12	TW	4	14	TW	1 1/4	16,20,22,23, 3FT1,3FT2	C29	Wiring Trough	Starter #709
2	12	TW				1/2		C30	Wiring Trough	Control Transformer
3	10	TW				3/4		C31	Control Transformer	110/220V Panel
3	12	TW				1/2	31,35,65	C32	110/220V Panel	Wiring Trough
6	2	RH-RW	4	14	TW	2 1/2	6,10,13,14,2FT1,2FT2,	C33	Wiring Trough	Starter #707
2	2	RH-RW				1 1/4	2T1, 2T1	C34	Starter #707	C. T. Cabinet
6	8	RH-RW	4	14	TW	1 1/4	1,3,4,5,1FT1,1FT2	C35	Wiring Trough	Starter #705

FIG. **19.40.** A conduit schedule. This is used to specify conduit details. Letters and numbers refer to a master layout.

FIG. 19.41. A conduit layout. This shows conduit location on a drawing showing equipment location.

FIG. 19.42. A conduit block diagram. This shows fundamentals of conduit wiring but does not show physical locations.

NEW FEEDER, 3-350 MCM-RH-RW-3"C.
RATING: 310 A., LOAD: 100 H.P.

220/110 V. PANEL   NEW MOTOR CONTROL CENTER   4TH FLOOR (P.O. LS 1943-6)

440 V. BUS - 3 PHASE - 60 CYCLE - 600 A.

5 KVA TRANSFORMER 440/220/110 V.

FIG. 19.43. A single-line power-flow diagram. This shows the necessary power supply to equipment but does not show physical details.

FIG. 19.44. A schematic diagram, also called an elementary wiring diagram. This one is made freehand, a common drawing practice for original planning.

lends itself well to this type of job involving long routes in *existing* buildings (see paragraph 22.14). Figure 19.43 shows a single-line power-flow diagram. Figure 19.44 is a freehand schematic diagram, also known as an elementary wiring diagram. This type of drawing is normally accompanied by a description-of-operation sheet and a devices list, typed either on a separate sheet (Fig. 19.45) or on stanpat paper and applied directly to the drawing.

DESCRIPTION OF OPERATION
ZEST PREMILLING

Purpose
    To provide necessary electrical control for Zest premilling equipment.

Operation
    Amalgamator 705
        When start button PB2 is depressed to start motor, timer TDR1 closes contact TDR1-1a and starts timing period. At the end of the timing period, contact TDR1-1a opens and stops the Amalgamator. When timer is de-energized, it resets to the zero position. Jog button PB3 will also operate the amalgamator.

    Four Roll Mill 707, Elevator 709, Premill Plodder 731
    Manual Operation (Selector Switch #1 in MANUAL position)
        Push button PB4 starts the Four Roll Mill and energizes relay R1. Contact R1-1a closes and energizes solenoid S1 which admits water to the mill. Push button PB7 starts the Bucket Elevator. Jog button PB10 will also operate the elevator. Push button PB6 starts the Premill Plodder.

    Automatic Operation (Selector Switch #1 in AUTO position)
        Elevator must be started before the Premill Plodder and the Four Roll Mill. Depressing start button PB7 starts Elevator and energizes relay R3. Contact R3-1a closes in Premill Plodder circuit. Relay R2 is energized and starts the Four Roll Mill. Contact R1-1a closes to energize solenoid S1. It the Elevator is stopped, contact R3-1a opens to stop Premill Plodder. Contact R2-1a opens to stop Four Roll Mill, and R1-1a opens to de-energize colenoid S1.

    Manual or Automatic Operation (Selector Switch #1 in AUTO or MANUAL position)
        Bypass push button PB5 can be used to energize solenoid S1 when the Four Roll Mill is not running. The Four Roll Mill, Elevator and Premill Plodder can be stopped by means of stop buttons. In case of an emergency, all three motors may be stopped simultaneously by means of stop button PB1, or PB11.

    Diverter Gats
        The purpose of this circuit is to provide a means of shifting a diverter gate after approximately twenty minutes of running time of the Four Roll Mill. Whenever contact R1-2a from relay R1 in the Four Roll Hill circuit is closed, timer TDR-3 will time. At the end of the timing period, contact M closes and energizes relays R4, R5, and TDR2. Contact R4-1a closes and resets timer. Ratchet relay contact R5-1a closes and contact R5-2b opens. Energization of solenoid S4 shifts the diverter gate. At the end of the next timing period the contacts will return to the position shown and energization of solenoid S5 will cause the diverter gate to return to its initial position. After timer has had sufficient time to reset, contact TDR2-1b opens and de-energizes relays R4, R5, and TDR2. Timer can be reset at any time by means of the reset push button PB8. The diverter gate can be operated manually and the timer reset by means of push button PB9.

    Weigh Hopper Slide Gate Control
        A 110 volt circuit is supplied for the Weigh Hopper slide gate control.

DEVICES LIST

(Bill of Materials are Drawings #2A-14047 and #2A-14048)

Notation	Description	Remarks
PB #1-11	Push Button	B/M Items #1-6, 16
SW #1	Selector Switch	B/M Item #7
PL #1-4	Pilot Light	B/M Items 8, 9
R1-5	Relay	B/M Items 14, 15, 18
TDR1-3	Time Delay Relay	B/M Items 11-13
S1	Solenoid Valve	Asco #81210A47, 2", 440V
S2, 3	Slide Gate Solenoid	Westinghouse Type D Pilotair Valve #PD-4-41-01-14, 110V
S4, 5	Diverter Gate Solenoid	Westinghouse Type D Pilotair Valve #PD-2-41-13-13, 110V
M1	Ammeter	B/M Item #10
CT 1	Current Transformer	B/M Item #17

FIG. 19.45. Description of operation and devices list. These accompany the schematic diagram in Fig. 19.44. The schematic diagram and the description of operation and devices list, together, give fundamental information for the production of more detailed drawings.

19.29. ARCHITECTURAL LAYOUTS. Figure 20.12 is a typical architectural drawing which shows, among other details, the electrical outlets, switches, lights, and wall receptacles. Exact dimensions for location of the components are not given but are maintained within reasonable proximity to the position shown on the drawing. The listing of details for switch boxes, wiring, fixtures, and the procedures and acceptable standards of installation are given in the specifications.

19.30. SPECIAL EQUIPMENT. Figures 19.46 and 19.47 show a regulated power-supply chassis assembly—a representative example of modular construction of electronic equipment. The schematic wiring diagram is shown in Fig. 19.46. The signal input is a direct current supply from an a-c to d-c rectifier circuit. The output is a direct current regulated to within 0.1 per cent and supplied to other components of the system. This unit is a part of an AccuRay Density Measuring System manufactured by Industrial Nucleonics Corporation. The system employs a radioactive source and detector for measuring the density of materials flowing inside a pipe or tube. Parts used in this chassis are shown and identified in Fig. 19.47, a drawing showing two views of the wiring side of the unit. The connecting wires to all parts are identified by color on this drawing. The three

FIG. 19.47. Wiring diagrams of electronic equipment. These specify the components, their location, and the details of wiring.

FIG. 19.48. Pictures of electronic equipment. These represent the electronic device in Figs. 19.46 and 19.47, and may be used for presentation to a customer or for service-manual illustration.

FIG. 19.49. Schematic diagram for a service manual. This gives the circuit and also specifies some details.

FIG. 19.50. Drawing of a printed circuit board for a service manual. This is produced from the original drawing of the circuit board.

FIG. 19.51. Overlay drawing for a service manual. This mates with the circuit-board drawing in Fig. 19.50 and shows the components.

photographs shown in Fig. 19.48 illustrate the finished production chassis from the top, the side, and the bottom (wiring side).

Transistors, because of their small size, lend themselves to compact lightweight assemblies such as portable radios. As an example of the drawings needed in a service manual, a schematic diagram of a small transistorized portable radio receiver is shown in Fig. 19.49. In this set the line-up of stages includes a converter, two intermediate-frequency amplifier stages, second detector, audio driver, and a matched pair of audio amplifiers. Further examples of the drawings required for this type of equipment are given in Fig. 19.50, the drawing of the printed circuit board, and Fig. 19.51, the drawing for identification of components. These two drawings are made to the same scale with register marks so that they can be combined and printed together (photo-

C9 IS ACROSS RI2, THE VOL. CONT.
R2I IS ACROSS J1, THE PHONE JACK.
SYMBOL # C10 OMITTED.

FIG. 19.52. Completed drawing for a service manual. The screened circuit-board drawing (Fig. 19.50) is printed with the overlay (Fig. 19.51) to give the final photocopy for reproduction.

graphically) to produce the drawing needed for a service manual (Fig. 19.52). Figure 19.53 is a photograph of the finished product.

19.31. ELECTRICAL CHARTS. Many charts, graphs, and diagrams are used

in electrical work to plot and determine the design and operating characteristics of components and of complete electrical devices. Chapter 14 describes and illustrates fundamental charts, graphs, and diagrams. These are used in electrical practice as well as in other fields.

FIG. 19.53. Picture of electronic equipment for a service manual. This accompanies the drawings showing details of wiring and construction.

PROBLEMS

GROUP 1. CIRCUITS

19.1.1. The drawing shows the arrangement of a circuit devised by an electrical engineer for testing the diode characteristics of a type-80 electronic tube. Draw the schematic diagram of this circuit. Include a voltmeter in parallel for measuring the voltage across the tube. It should be noted that the oscilloscope is a testing device which will trace a curve proportional to the voltages applied to the vertical and horizontal axes and that the electrical circuit will operate without this piece of equipment.

19.1.2. The drawing is a block diagram of the circuit for a simple regenerative radio. Draw the schematic diagram of this circuit on an 8½- by 11-in. sheet of drawing paper.

19.1.3. The block diagram of a simple electrical servo system is shown. In this system the voltage across the load is maintained almost constant when the load or the supply voltage is changed. For instance, if R_L or E would decrease, the voltage drop across R_1 would decrease. This decrease would in turn make the grid more positive and the current i_L would be increased back to (or near) the original value. Draw a schematic diagram of this circuit, making sure that the polarity is correct.

PROB. 19.1.1. A pictorial schematic diagram.

PROB. 19.1.2. Block diagram of a radio circuit.

PROB. 19.1.3. Block diagram of a servo system.

GROUP 2.   COMBINED ELECTRICAL AND MECHANICAL COMPONENTS

PROB. 19.2.1.   Data for determination of valve characteristics.

19.2.1.   The upper graph describes the flow of liquid raw materials necessary for a certain chemical process. These materials are forced to flow through a single solenoid-actuated automatic valve. In order to obtain the correct actuating mechanism, it is necessary to obtain the maximum dynamic requirements of the valve, that is the maximum change in valve opening per unit of time. A manufacturer of automatic valves has supplied a curve of valve-flow rate capacity versus valve opening for the valve size required (lower graph). Draw the curve of valve opening versus time, and find the point on the curve where maximum change in valve opening occurs (the point where the slope of the curve is a maximum).

19.2.1*A.*   Calculate the maximum change in valve opening per unit of time for Prob. 19.2.1. (Draw the slope of the curve and obtain $\dfrac{dy}{dx}\text{(max)} = \dfrac{\text{in.}}{\text{sec}}$). Show graphically how the solution was obtained.

19.2.1*B.*   Draw a block diagram showing the combined mechanical and electrical system for Prob. 19.2.1. A pressure-operated metering switch actuates a relay that in turn actuates the valve solenoid.

19.2.1*C.*   Draw a wiring diagram for the electrical system of Prob. 19.2.1*B.*

19.2.2.   This problem illustrates combined electrical and mechanical components. An industrial furnace is to be carried through a prescribed temperature cycle. This is to be done by adjusting the gas valve that supplies fuel to the furnace. It has been determined by calculation and tests that a synchronous, electrically controlled, cam-operated valve can be designed to give the desired time-temperature relationship. The cam turns at a constant speed and is so geared that it takes 90 minutes for a complete revolution. This time is equal to the length of the heat-treating cycle. From the curves shown, design the shape of the cam that will give the desired valve openings and thus the desired furnace temperature. See Chap. 17 for drawing the cam.

19.2.2*A*. Draw a block diagram for the system of Prob. 19.2.2. Include a temperature recorder, automatic "closed" and "open" warning lights on the furnace door, and a solenoid-operated door lock to prevent opening the door during the heating cycle.

19.2.2*B*. Draw a wiring diagram showing operation of the system in Prob. 19.2.2. List the required components.

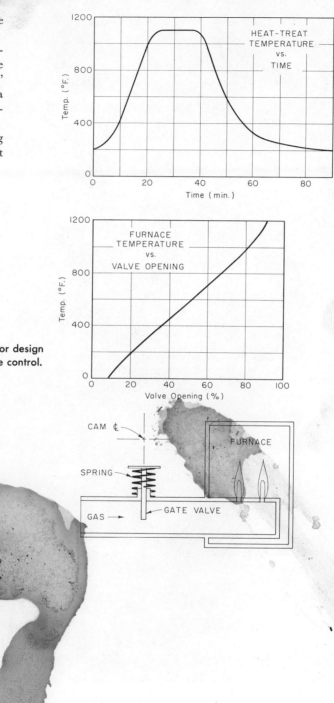

PROB. 19.2.2. Data for design of heat-treating-furnace control.

20

Drawings of Structures

20.1. The combined art and science of building structures, especially the art of building houses, churches, bridges, and the like, for the purposes of civil life, is properly placed, professionally, between engineering and the fine arts. Architectural designing is that phase of architecture based primarily upon study of the fine arts, but architects must understand structural engineering requirements. Conversely, engineers often work with architects in building structures and should therefore understand some of the procedures followed in an architectural drafting room. Structural engineers design columns, beams, floor slabs, etc.; mechanical engineers design heating and ventilating equipment; electrical engineers determine power requirements and design the electrical system of a structure to meet the requirements of the client; other engineers are often concerned with structures to house manufacturing and processing equipment.

ARCHITECTURAL DRAWINGS

20.2. CHARACTERISTICS OF ARCHITECTURAL DRAWING. The architect uses certain expressions that are peculiar to the architectural field. Engineers should be familiar with these expressions as they are often required to read and work with architectural drawings. Presenta-

511

FIG. 20.1. Special techniques in an architectural detail. Distinctive features of this drawing are a profiled section and a superimposed plan view.

WOOD
IRON
SECTION THRU
HANDRAIL

DETAIL
of
STAIRWAY

shown by drawings in other fields of engineering. The preparation of preliminary studies, presentation drawings, building models, and architectural working drawings requires various techniques and drawing skills. Thus, an architect, even more than his fellow engineers, must be able to draw both freehand and with instruments, using all the materials and techniques at a draftsman's disposal.

20.3. PRELIMINARY STUDIES. The design for a building is initiated by the client, who presents his requirements to the architect. This may be done in conferences or through the use of written material; at times a combination of both procedures is used. If the building is for industrial purposes, the engineers of the industry present flow sheets of the manufacturing processes to be carried on in the proposed structure. Close cooperation between engineering and architectural personnel is absolutely necessary to ensure that the building will meet the needs of the industry. Similarly, for all types of buildings, a program of minimum requirements, maximum allowable costs, architectural style, building materials, etc., is determined through client-architect contacts.

tion techniques, as in a profiled section (Fig. 20.1), or unusual views, such as a reflected plan (Fig. 20.2), or even the occasional use of first and second angles of projection may be foreign to an engineer whose previous experience has not required collaboration with an architect. To prepare himself fully for such an association, an engineering student should make a careful study of architectural drawings, noting the reason for the differences between them and the more usual engineering drawings.

The general principles of drawing are the same for all kinds of technical work. However, architectural drawings usually reveal a more spontaneous approach to drawing problems than that

FIG. 20.2. Special techniques in an architectural detail. This drawing illustrates the use of a floor plan and a reflected plan of the ceiling.

Half Floor Plan   Half Ceiling Plan

The architect then establishes a structural grid (see paragraphs 20.8 to 20.10) in keeping with the function and structural requirements of the building.[1] With this grid as a background several solutions to the problem are developed, usually in rough sketches on tracing paper. Then a selection of the better solutions is made for further study in plan, elevation, and section.

Throughout this phase of the work sketches are kept relatively small, although care is taken to maintain proper proportions. The smallness of these "thumbnail sketches" forces the designer to consider the essential elements only, for a study of detail is impossible at a small scale. Preliminary plans, showing two schemes for a one-floor house, are reproduced in Fig. 20.3 at approximately one-half the original scale.

20.4. PRESENTATION DRAWINGS.

Presentation drawings are made to provide realistic and effective representations of proposed designs. They are used to illustrate proposed buildings for clients and in submitting designs in competition. They are usually drawn in perspective, then rendered in water color, ink, crayon, or pencil, giving the effect of color or light and shade. Such accessories as human figures, adjacent buildings, and foliage are introduced for scale, to give an idea of relative size. Should the presentation show one or more floor plans, the scale of the plan is indicated by including furniture and floor designs on the interior and walks, drives, and planting on the grounds immediately surrounding the building. Ex-

[1] Various modular dimensions for the grid may be employed, but in residential work a 4'-0" square is most adaptable, whereas in commercial work, with reinforced concrete or steel construction, 20'-0" or larger is advantageous.

amples of presentation drawings are given in Fig. 20.4.

20.5. MODELS.

The use of building models, for presentation purposes, is widespread throughout the architectural profession. They are made in the drafting room, using drawing paper, illustration board, balsa wood, etc. The different walls and roof surfaces are laid out in developed form, rendered, folded, and then mounted on a rigid base. It is important that all features, such as moldings, railings, and plantings, be kept to scale. The advantage of a build-

FIG. 20.3. Preliminary-plan studies. These are sketched on coordinate paper and are for studying space and arrangement.

FIG. 20.4. Presentation drawings. These are made to illustrate proposed buildings for the client.

FIG. 20.5. Symbols for building materials. These indicate types of materials. Complete details are given in notes and specifications.

Recommended

1   2

FIG. 20.6. Grid positioning of walls. Referencing difficulties are eliminated by symmetrical location as in (1) and (2).

ing model in showing the appearance of a completed building from any station point is of obvious value, when compared with a presentation drawing, showing it from a single station point.

For reproduction purposes a photograph of the model, superimposed on a photograph of the actual site, makes an effective presentation.

20.6. MATERIALS FOR CONSTRUCTION. The selection of building materials must be made at some time prior to the preparation of the working drawings and specifications. Items that influence the choice include appearance, initial cost, erection time, and maintenance.

Not Recommended

3   4   5   6

Conventional symbols for the more common building materials are shown in Fig. 20.5.

20.7. SIZE COORDINATION OF BUILDING MATERIALS AND EQUIPMENT. Size coordination of a building's many parts is accomplished by cutting and fitting during field operations or by shop fabrication. In actual practice a combination of both techniques is used. However, it is apparent that tighter fits and lower costs result when shop-fabrication methods replace the more wasteful procedures inherent in the majority of field operations.

After considerable study and research the ASA approved a 4-in. unit as the standard module for building materials. From a practical standpoint, it must be understood that not all manufacturers are producing materials sized in 4-in. increments, nor is such standardization ever likely to occur. *Standardization, for the purpose of size coordination of building materials and equipment, is achieved by a judicious selection from the available sizes, followed by a tying of the resulting details into the modular grid.*

20.8. GRID POSITION OF DETAILS. A symmetrical location of walls and openings, with respect to the horizontal grid, is desirable in order to effect standardization. In the instance of wall locations, Fig. 20.6 shows that only one reference to the grid is possible if the walls are (1) centered on the grid lines, or (2) centered between grid lines. Any other system of positioning walls results in numerous possibilities of grid referencings. There are four possible grid positions, as shown in (3) to (6), if one face of each wall is positioned on a grid line.

Vertical referencing is usually restricted to maintaining floor levels on grid lines. Openings need not be symmetrical in their vertical positioning, since head and sill details differ. However, different sized openings are usually positioned with all heads on the same grid line, for any one story. Necessary adjustments due to variations in floor thicknesses are made at the intersections of the walls and ceilings (Fig. 20.7).

20.9. NOMINAL AND ACTUAL SIZE. Two systems of dimension notation are currently in use in architectural offices. The majority of offices show actual values in nearly all instances. However, the more modern procedure of grid referencing allows, in fact makes preferable, the use of nominal values on all small-scale layout drawings.

Figure 20.8 illustrates the difference between nominal and actual sizes. Nominal thicknesses of walls are established by the nominal size of the structural members. Since 2- by 4-in. studding is used in both the exterior and partition frame walls shown, the 4-in. size is assigned as their nominal thickness. The actual size of a 2 by 4 is 1⅝ by 3⅝ in. The glazed tile in the masonry partition wall is actually 3⅝ by 11⅝ by 3⅝ in. and nominally 4 by 12 by 4 in. (allowance for a ⅜-in. mortar joint having been made in each of the three dimensions). A ⅜-in. mortar joint is again designed for in the sizing of modular brick; actual dimensions are 2⁵⁄₁₆ by 7⅝ by 3⅝ in., while nominally they are 2⅔ by 8 by 4 in. Note that interior and exterior treatment, or finish, is not considered in the assignment of the nominal size to any wall thickness; the structural members alone are considered.

FIG. 20.7. Vertical referencing to grid. See notes on the drawing for details.

FIG. 20.8. Nominal and actual sizes. See notes on the drawing for details.

Comparison of the line of actual dimensions with the line of nominal dimensions in Fig. 20.9 shows the comparative ease in determining total dimensions (such as X) when nominal values are used in preference to actual quantities. A detail, dimensioned with actual values and referenced to the grid, completes the information required for the proper use of nominal values, thus simplifying the arithmetic processes

FIG. 20.9. Nominal and actual dimension values. Nominal values are used on drawings. When necessary, nominal values are supplemented by detailed views with actual-value dimensions.

FIG. 20.10. Dimension-line terminals. Arrowheads indicate points on the grid; dots indicate points not on the grid.

FIG. 20.11. Arrowheads. The type shown at (2) is used on architectural drawings.

ever present in checking, estimating from, and field use of architectural drawings.

20.10. DIMENSIONING. The correct dimensioning of an architectural drawing requires a knowledge of building-construction methods. The dimensions are placed so as to be most convenient for the workman, given to and from accessible points, and selected so that commercial variation in the sizes of materials will not affect the principal dimensions. In general, dimensions are given to the faces of masonry walls, the outside face of the studs in an exterior wall, and the center of the studs in a partition wall. Columns and beams are located by dimensioning to their center lines, as are window and door openings in frame walls (in masonry walls the openings are dimensioned). Compared

with drawings dimensioned according to the techniques used in the other engineering fields, architectural working drawings appear overdimensioned. There is no attempt to avoid duplicating a dimension as there is in fields where parts are made for interchangeable assembly. No usable dimension should be omitted on an architectural drawing, and, as in other fields, care must be taken to see that every dimension that is needed is given even though that dimension could be determined by the addition and/or subtraction of other dimensions on the sheet.

Legibility is of prime importance in dimensioning. All numerals must be carefully lettered. If a dimension value is not clearly indicated, a crease in the paper, a smudge, or a poor print of the drawing may cause it to be misread. Watch particularly the numerals 3 and 5.

In dimensioning drawings that have been laid out in the modular system, it is essential that the grid referencings be clearly indicated since the grid will usually be omitted from small-scale drawings. *An arrowhead is used at the end of the dimension line when the dimension is to a point on a grid line, and a dot is used for all points not on grid lines* (Fig. 20.10). Regardless of whether actual or nominal values are shown, the architect does not find the graceful but slim arrowhead used by other engineers suitable for his

FIG. 20.12. Working drawing. This is the floor plan of a one-floor three-bedroom house.

FIG. 20.13. Working drawing. This is the room finish schedule for the house in Fig. 20.12. Numbers are referenced to the floor plan.

Rm. No.	Floor	Base	Walls	Ceiling	Trim	Remarks
ROOM FINISH SCHEDULE						
1	Concrete	Concrete	Sheetrock	Sheetrock	Poplar	Built-in bench w/dwrs.
2	Linoleum	Cove	Linowall	"	"	See cabinet details.
3	Concrete	Birch	Sheetrock	"	Birch	See details.
4	Linoleum	Cove	Linowall	"	Poplar	" "
5	Cer. Tile	Cer. Tile	cer. tile wnsct sheetrock	"	"	" "
6	Concrete	Birch	Sheetrock	"	Birch	" "
7	"	"	"	"	"	" "
8	"	"	"	"	"	" "
9	"	"	"	"	"	" "
10	"	"	"	"	"	" "
11	Slate	"	"	"	"	" "
12	Concrete	Concrete	"	"	Poplar	" "

FIG. 20.14. Working drawing. This is the right-side elevation for the house in Fig. 20.12.

FIG. 20.15. Working drawing. This is the front elevation for the house in Fig. 20.12.

use. It is clear in Fig. 20.11 (1) that the dimensions might be taken to the solid or the dashed line; in (2), where a more bulky arrowhead is used, there is no question regarding the line to which the dimensions refer.

20.11. WORKING DRAWINGS.

The general principles of Chap. 13 on working drawings are applicable to architectural working drawings. As a general rule, details that are related should be shown together, and information should be grouped by craft whenever feasible. Many present-day buildings are so complicated that it is advantageous to draw several sets of plans, a set for each of the several crafts—structural, plumbing, electrical, heating and ventilating —in addition to the architectural set.

Architectural handbooks, American Institute of Architects' files, Sweet's Catalogues, and other literature should be freely consulted during the preparation of all working drawings. From them, sizes for building materials and equipment are determined, together with other factual data necessary for the proper selection and specification of such items. In preparing working drawings, publications such as local and state building codes must also be studied and their provisions adhered to. Legal requirements as to approval of the plans and specifications, securement of building permits, etc., must also be met.

Figures 20.12 to 20.18 are selections from a set of working drawings for a one-floor three-bedroom house. Omitted from reproduction here are the following

FIG. 20.16. Working drawing. This is the roof truss detail and cutting schedule for the house in Fig. 20.12.

FIG. 20.17. Working drawing. This is the wall detail for the house in Fig. 20.12.

FIG. 20.18. Working drawing. This is the trim detail for woodwork in the house in Fig. 20.12.

FIG. 20.19. Plot plan. This shows data pertinent to the building and its site.

working drawings: plot plan, left-side elevation, rear elevation, foundation details, radiant-heating layout, roof-framing plan, door and window schedules, doorway details, kitchen and bath elevations, fireplace details, cabinet detail, etc.

20.12. PLOT PLAN. Before designing any structure of importance, a plot plan is made giving the property line, contours, available utilities, location of trees, building lines, and other pertinent data. The building is then designed to fit the site. The plot plan is completed as one of the working drawings by locating on it the building, approaches, and finished grade contours (Fig. 20.19).

20.13. FLOOR PLANS. A floor plan is a horizontal section taken at distances

above the floor that vary so as to show best all the features of the building between that floor and the one above. Because of their small scale, floor plans are largely made up of conventional symbols. Some of the symbols currently in use are shown in Figs. 20.20 and 20.21.

In drawing a floor plan, the large structural grid is drawn first to serve as a guide. The entrance front is placed at the bottom of the sheet without regard to compass directions. Columns and walls are then positioned on the grid. Axes of communication, or route lines between the several rooms, are established. Interior doorways, stairways, elevator and service shafts, etc., are located. Exterior wall openings, however, are positioned *only after elevation studies have been made.* A completely dimensioned floor plan of a warehouse is

Frame Wall

Brick Wall
Lug Sill shown

Concrete Block Wall
Slip Sill shown

Brick Veneer Wall

Stone on Concrete Wall

Brick on Tile Wall
with Furring

DOORWAYS IN EXTERIOR WALLS

FIG. 20.20.   Doorway symbols.

Frame Wall

Pair of Doors in Glazed Tile Wall

Double-Swing Door
in Frame Wall

DOORWAYS IN PARTITION WALLS

Frame Wall   Brick Veneer Wall   Brick Wall

FIG. 20.21.   Window symbols.

DOUBLE HUNG WINDOWS

Frame Wall   Stone Veneer Wall   Concrete Block Wall

CASEMENT WINDOWS

shown in Fig. 20.22 (because of the simplicity of the architectural design, this drawing gives both architectural and structural information).

20.14.   ELEVATIONS.   An elevation is a view seen looking in a horizontal direction. For practical purposes, the elevations drawn are those showing normal views of wall surfaces.

In drawing an elevation, a wall section (showing the grade line, floor heights, head, and sill of a typical

window in each story, cornice, and roof ridge) is placed to the side of where the elevation is to be drawn, and a floor plan is secured to the top of the drawing board. The elevation is then projected from the section and plan. Figure 20.23 shows an end elevation for a hospital building.

FIG. 20.22.   A floor plan. This is an upper floor of a warehouse. The letters and numbers are structural references for beams, columns, and floors.

FIG. 20.23.   An elevation. This is the end elevation for a hospital building. Note references to other drawings.

FIG. 20.24. A sectional elevation. This is for an addition to a municipal building. Note inclusion of elevations, notes, and references.

20.15. SECTIONAL ELEVATIONS (FIG. 20.24). Sectional elevations through the entire structure show interior construction and architectural treatment. Two such sections, called the longitudinal and transverse sections, at right angles to each other, are usually included in a set of working drawings. The cutting planes for these sections do not need to be continuous, but may be offset so as to include as much information as possible.

20.16. DETAIL DRAWINGS. A set of architectural drawings contains, in addition to plans and elevations, larger-scale drawings of parts not indicated with sufficient definiteness on the small-scale drawings. Details and detail sections of items such as footings, windows,

and framing are required to show details of both construction and architectural design. Details are best grouped so that each sheet contains the references that are made on one sheet of the general drawings (the floor plans and elevations).

As the construction progresses, drawings are made of full-size details of moldings, millwork, ornamental iron, etc. Such drawings are made *after* measurements of the building have been taken. Sections are used freely on these drawings.

Figures 20.25 and 20.26 illustrate typical detail drawings.

20.17. LETTERING. There are two distinct divisions in the use of lettering by an architect. The first, office lettering,

FIG. 20.25.   A detail drawing of a section. Note use of grid-referencing dimension-line terminals.

Section "H-H" through
LOADING PLATFORM

FIG. 20.26.   A detail drawing. This is of a double-hung, spring-balanced metal window. Note 4-in. grid and referencing.

includes all titles and notes put on drawings for information; the second, design lettering, covers the drawing of letters to be executed in stone, bronze, or some other material, in connection with the architectural design. Legibility is the primary consideration in both divisions. In design lettering appearance is as important as legibility; in office lettering speed of execution is the second factor to consider. Pleasant appearance results from uniformity regardless of the letter style; speed in drawing necessarily depends upon simplicity of the letter forms.

The Old Roman alphabet is generally employed in design work. Before attempting to use this letter, the designer should become thoroughly familiar with its construction, character, and beauty. If he realizes that the alphabet was designed for inscription in stone and if he knows how the work is done, he will develop a sympathetic understanding of how to use these classic forms. See the Appendix.

Single-stroke letters, illustrated in the Appendix, are excellent for use in office lettering.

20.18.   TITLES.   An architectural title may be hand lettered on each sheet; printed, or impressed with a rubber stamp. In the latter two instances some bits of information will necessarily be hand lettered to complete the title. Fig-

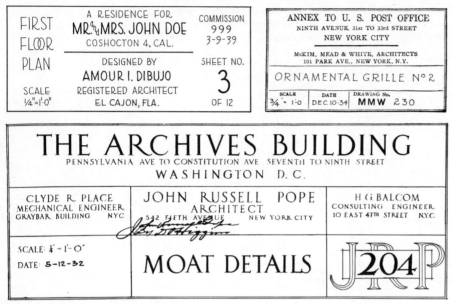

FIG. 20.27. Architectural titles.

20.20. SPECIFICATIONS, NOTES, AND SCHEDULES. Architectural drawings are amplified by a document called the "specifications," a detailed account of material and workmanship for the many parts of a structure. Since the workmen on a job seldom see these specifications, they should be briefed and given, as notes or schedules, on the working drawing sheets. An example of a schedule is given in Fig. 20.28, a partial door schedule taken from the working drawings for the municipal building whose sectional elevation is shown in Fig. 20.22.

20.21. CHECKING. As the architect develops the working drawings, he keeps a constant check for accuracy in his work. A tentatively final set of blueprints is then gone over by a responsible checker, who checks all correct items and marks, with red pencil, all mistakes. The drawings are then corrected, and another check set of blueprints is prepared.

All checking is done in a definite order with each item followed through separately and systematically. The order is dictated by the checker's preference or by conditions of the problem. The following is suggested as a guide:

1. Check over-all dimensions on the plans, seeing that all plans agree.

2. Check structural dimensions on the plans, seeing that column centers line up through the several stories.

3. Check location dimensions on the plans, seeing that openings line up vertically and that axes of communication are maintained by proper horizontal positioning of the openings.

4. See that detail drawings are dimensioned to correspond to the dimensions of the plan and will allow for

ure 20.27 shows several examples of architectural titles.

A complete title contains the following information:

1. Name and location of the building
2. Kind of view (as "First Floor Plan") and scale
3. Name and address of the client
4. Name and address of the architect
5. Sheet number
6. Office record, to include draftsman's and checker's initials and dates

20.19. SHOP DRAWINGS. The purchase of special items of equipment for installation in a building requires *shop drawings,* prepared by the equipment manufacturers. Such drawings show over-all sizes, details of construction, methods for securing the equipment to the structure, and any other pertinent data the architect needs for the final positioning of the equipment.

proper fitting with adjacent features.

5. Check all doors for proper size and swing.

6. Check design and notation for all structural members.

7. Check sizes and locations of all ducts and flues.

8. Check location and notation of electrical outlets and switching for same.

9. See that several items are not indicated for the same location. For example, wiring to a switch should not share wall space with a heat duct.

10. See that all notes are complete and accurate.

11. Check the specifications with the drawings, making sure that no discrepancy exists and that the specifications are complete in every detail.

12. Check for conformity with building codes and laws.

STRUCTURAL DRAWINGS

20.22. The term "structural drawings" means the drawings of steel, masonry, wood, concrete, etc., for structures such as buildings, bridges, and dams. Structural drawings differ from other drawings only in certain details and practices that have developed because of the materials worked with and the method of their fabrication. The differences are so well established that it is essential for every engineer to know something of the methods of representation used in structural work.

20.23. CLASSIFICATION OF STRUCTURAL DRAWINGS. Structural drawings are classified as follows:[2]

[2] From Milo S. Ketchum, "Structural Engineers' Handbook," McGraw-Hill, 1924.

	W.	H.	T.	TYPE	MATERIAL	GLASS	REMARKS
A	3'-0"	8'-4"	Std.	Solid	Steel	—	"Vulcan" Stor. Rm. Door
B	3'-6"	7'-6"	1¾	10 Pan.	Kalamein	—	
C	2'-6"	"	"	"	"	—	
D	3'-6"	"	"	Glaz.	"	Cl. Wr.	
E	2'-2"	7'-0"	1⅝	"	Hol. Met.	"	2 Speed Sliding
F	5'-4"	8'-4"	Std.	Tin Clad	Steel	—	
G	3'-6"	7'-6"	1¾	Glaz.	Hol. Met.	Cl. Wr.	
H	2'-8"	6'-8"	"	1 Pan.	Kalamein	—	Stock
I	4'-0"	9'-0"	2¼	10 Pan.	Wh. Pine	Plate	2 Sp. Bi-Part. Sl.
J	2'-10"	7'-0"	"	Glaz.	"	"	
K	3'-0"	"	1¾	10 Pan.	Wood	—	
L	"	"	"	Glaz.	"	Tap.	

Table title: DOOR SCHEDULE

FIG. 20.28. A door schedule. Note that sizes and materials are given.

(1) *General plan.* This will include a profile of the ground; location of the structure; elevations of ruling points in the structure; clearances; grades; direction of flow, high water, and low water (for a bridge); and all other data necessary for designing the substructure and superstructure.

(2) *Stress diagram.* This will give the main dimensions of the structure, the loading, stresses in all members for the dead loads, live loads, wind loads, etc., itemized separately; total maximum stresses and minimum stresses; sizes of members; typical sections of all built members showing arrangement of material; and all information necessary for detailing the various parts of the structure.

(3) *Shop drawings.* Shop detail drawings should be made of all steel and ironwork, and detail drawings should be made of all timber, masonry, and concrete work.

(4) *Foundation or masonry plan.* The foundation or masonry plan should contain detail drawings of all foundations, walls, piers, etc., that support the structure. The plans should show the loads on the foundations, the depth of footings, the spacing of piles where used, the proportions for the concrete, the quality of masonry and mortar, the allowable bearing on the soil, and all data necessary for accurately locating and constructing the foundations.

(5) *Erection diagram.* The erection diagram should show the relative location of every part of the structure, shipping marks for the various members, all main dimensions, number of pieces in a member, packing of pins,

size and grip of pins, and any special feature or information that may assist the erector in the field. The approximate weight of heavy pieces will materially assist the erector in designing his falsework and derricks.

(6) *Falsework plans.* For ordinary structures it is not common to prepare falsework plans in the office, this important detail being left to the erector in the field. For difficult or important work, erection plans should be worked out in the office and should show in detail all members and connections of the falsework and also give instructions for the successive steps in carrying out the work. Falsework plans are especially important for concrete and masonry arches and other concrete structures and for forms for all walls, piers, etc. Detail plans of travelers, derricks, etc., should also be furnished the erector.

(7) *Bills of material.* Complete bills of material showing the different parts of the structure with their marks and shipping weights should be prepared. This is necessary to permit checking of shipping weights and shipment and arrival of materials.

(8) *Rivet list.* The rivet list should show the dimensions and number of all field rivets, field bolts, spikes, etc., used in the erection of the structure.

(9) *List of drawings.* A list should be made showing the contents of all drawings belonging to the structure.

20.24. STRUCTURAL-STEEL SHAPES. Steel structures are made up of "rolled shapes" fastened together with rivets, bolts, or welds. The function of structural-steel drawings is to show how these shapes are to be fabricated in the shop and then erected to form the various members of bridges, buildings, etc. Sections of the common shapes are shown in Fig. 20.29. Dimensions for detailing these and other less common shapes are shown in the American Institute of Steel Construction handbook. Dimensions for detailing common sizes of channels, I beams, wide flange sections, and angles are given in the Appendix.

In designating rolled-steel shapes on drawings, the AISC standard abbreviations and order of specifications are used, as follows:

Plates. Pl 18 × ½ × 4'-2 (width × thickness × length)

Equal angles. L3 × 3 × ¼ × 7'-6 (size of legs × thickness × length)

Unequal angles. L6 × 4 × ⁵⁄₁₆ × 10'-0 (size of long leg × size of short leg × thickness × length)

Standard channels. 9 ⎿ 13.4 × 12'-4 (depth of section × weight per foot × length)

Standard I beams. 12 I 31.8 × 14'-6 (depth of section × weight per foot × length)

Wide flange sections. 14 W̄F 48 × 16'-3 (nominal depth of section × weight per foot × length)

Tees. T5 × 3 × 11.5 × 8'-0 (width of flange × depth × weight per foot × length)

Structural tees. Cut from W̄F section: ST 5 W̄F 10.5 × 4'-7 (depth × weight per foot × length)

Cut from I beam: ST 5 I 12.5 × 5'-4 (depth × weight per foot × length)

FIG. 20.29. Structural-steel shapes.

Angle (L)   Plate (P̄)   Tee (T)   Zee (Z)

Channel (⎿⎽)   Beam (I)   Wide Flange Shape (W̄F)

Zees. Z6 × 3½ × 15.7 × 9'-10 (depth × width of flange × weight per foot × length)

20.25. DRAWINGS OF STEEL STRUCTURES.

The general drawings include the general plan, the stress diagram, and the erection diagram and correspond in many respects to the design drawings of the mechanical engineer. In some cases the design is worked out completely by the engineer, who gives the sizes and weights of members and the number and spacing of all rivets, but in most cases the general dimensions, positions, and sizes of the members and the number of rivets are shown, leaving the details to be worked out in the shop or

to be given on separate complete shop drawings.

In order to show the details clearly, the structural draftsman often uses two scales in the same view, one for the center lines or skeleton of the structure, showing the shape, and a larger one for the parts composing it. The scale used for the skeleton is determined by the size of the structure as compared with the sheet; ¼", ⅜", and ½" to 1'-0" are commonly used. Figure 20.30 is a typical shop drawing of a small roof truss, giving complete details. Such drawings are made about the stress-diagram lines (used in calculating the stresses and sizes of the members), which are then employed as the gravity lines of the

FIG. 20.30. A structural shop drawing. This is of a roof truss. The design diagram is included in the upper left corner.

FIG. 20.31. A structural shop drawing. This is a detail of two beams, C3 and D3, which differ only in length.

ONE-BEAM-C3
ONE- do -D3

Note:
$\frac{7}{8}$ Rivets, $\frac{15}{16}$ Holes
except as noted

members and form the skeleton, as illustrated separately to small scale in the box on the figure. The intersections of these lines are called "working points" and are the points from which all distances are figured. The length of each working line is computed accurately, and from it the intermediate dimensions are obtained.

The design diagram is often put on the same sheet as the shop drawing, as in the drawing of the truss.

FIG. 20.32. A structural shop drawing. This is a detail of two beams, A3 and B3, which differ only in spacing of web holes.

ONE-BEAM-A3
Two- do -B3

20.26. DETAILING PRACTICE FOR STRUCTURAL STEEL. Separate drawings made to a sufficiently large scale to carry complete information are called "shop detail drawings" (Fig. 20.31). When possible, the drawings of all members are shown in the same relative position that they will occupy in the completed structure: vertical, horizontal, or inclined. Long vertical or inclined members may be drawn in a horizontal position, a vertical member always having its lower end at the left, and an inclined member drawn in the direction it would fall. Except in plain building work, a diagram to small scale (showing by a heavy line the relative position of the member in the structure) should be drawn on every detail sheet.

In steel construction a member is composed of either a single rolled shape or a combination of two or more rolled shapes. Figure 20.31 is a shop detail drawing of a member made from a single rolled shape. Figures 20.30, 20.32, and 20.33 are shop detail drawings of members made up of several rolled shapes. These figures illustrate detailing practice. Note in Fig. 20.30 that only one-half of the truss is shown. When thus drawn it is always the left end, looking toward the side on which the principal connections are made.

The scale of shop drawings ranges from ¼″ = 1′-0 to 1″ = 1′-0. Often, for long members, the cross section is drawn to a larger scale than the length. Sometimes it is even advantageous to pay no attention to scaled length but to draw the member as though there were breaks in the length (but not shown on the drawing, as in Fig. 20.33) so that rivet spacings at the ends (and intermediately) can be drawn to the same scale as the cross section.

Dimensions are always placed above the dimension line, and the dimension lines are not broken but continuous. Length dimensions are expressed in feet and inches. All inch symbols are omitted unless there is the possibility of misunderstanding, thus 1 bolt should be 1″ bolt to distinguish between size and number. Inch symbols are omitted even though the dimensions are in feet and inches, and dimensions should be hyphenated thus: 7′-0, 7′-0½, 7′-4. Plate widths and section depths of rolled shapes are given in inches. Dimensions are given to commercial sizes of materials.

Rolled shapes are specified by abbreviated notes, as described in paragraph 20.24. The specification is given either with the length dimension as in Fig. 20.31 or near and parallel to the shape as in Fig. 20.32.

Erection marks are necessary in order to identify the member. These are indicated on the drawing by letters and numbers in the subtitle. The erection

diagram then carries these marking numbers and identifies the position of the member. Problem 20.2.6 shows an example of an erection diagram with marking numbers.

The erection mark also identifies the member in the shop and serves as a shipping mark. The mark is composed of a letter and number. Capital letters are used, *B* for beam, *C* for column, *T* for truss, etc. The number gives the specific member in an assembly.

Assembly marks are used when the same shape is used in more than one place on a member. The member is completely specified *once* followed by the assembly mark (lower-case letters, to distinguish from erection marks). Then the complete specification is not repeated; only the assembly mark is given. As an example, see the angles "2 ∠ 4 × 3½ × ⅜ × 8½(a)" in Fig. 20.32.

Different members may be detailed together on the same drawing when they differ only in length or spacing of rivets

FIG. 20.33. A structural shop drawing. This is a detail of a column.

ONE COLUMN C4 – Mark Face A "North"

or holes, or when one member has special holes or an extra piece added. Figures 20.31 and 20.32 both show two beams detailed on the same drawing. Note that the different lengths are given with the erection mark at the end of the dimension line.

When one of two similar members has a hole or other feature on one member only, the special feature is indicated by drawing a freehand circle around the detail with a leader to a note such as, "on A-3 only."

Distances to center lines of another connecting member are given, as in Figs. 20.31 and 20.32, by placing the distance, preceded by a minus sign ($-$), at the end of the length dimension. These distances to center are a great aid in checking the details with an assembly or layout drawing.

Inclinations of members and inclined center lines, cuts, etc., are indicated by their tangents. As in Figs. 20.30 and 20.31, a small right triangle is drawn with its hypotenuse parallel to the line or on the line whose inclination is to be specified. The long leg of the triangle is always specified as 12.

Rivets and holes are dimensioned in the view that shows them as circles. Dimensions pertaining to a row of rivets are given in a single line as in Fig. 20.30. Gage dimensions, even though standard, are always given. The size of rivets and of holes is given in a general note, as in Fig. 20.31.

The length of rivets is not usually given on the drawing; the workman picks a rivet length long enough to go through the members and protrude far enough so that the head can be formed.

Common practice is to make rivet holes $\frac{1}{16}$ in. larger than the rivets (see Figs. 20.31 to 20.33).

If some of the rivets or holes for a member are of a different size, these are indicated by the size in a diamond, as in Figs. 20.31 and 20.32.

Rivet symbols are used because it is impossible to show the details of head form on a small-scale drawing. The ASA symbols for indicating various kinds of heads are given in Fig. 20.34.

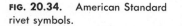

FIG. 20.34. American Standard rivet symbols.

The size of most structures prevents their being completely fabricated in the shop. Therefore, portions as large as transportation facilities or ease of handling will allow are assembled and then connected to other portions in the field. Shop rivets are indicated by an open circle, the size of the rivet head. Holes for field rivets are indicated by "blacked-in" circles the diameter of the hole (see Figs. 20.31 to 20.34). Rivets are drawn to scale. Figure 20.35 shows the proportions of rivet heads with respect to the diameter.

Rivet spacing is an important item in detailing, and there are a number of conditions that control the placement. Rivets spaced too close together or too close to a projecting part cannot be properly driven. Rivets placed too close to the edge or end of a member may weaken the member.

Rivets are spaced along "gage" lines, parallel to the axis of the member and at certain "pitch" distances along the gage line (Fig. 20.36). The minimum distance between rivets in any direction is three rivet diameters. The minimum edge distance (e, Fig. 20.37), from sheared edges of a member is 1½ rivet diameters. Distance to a rolled edge may be slightly less than 1½ diameters and is usually controlled by the location of the gage line. Whenever possible the same edge distance is used on all members, and the distance is then given in a general note such as "edge distance 1¼ except as noted."

Gage-line distances and minimum driving clearances for common rolled shapes are given in the Appendix.

Standard beam connections are also given in the Appendix.

Clearances between various members of a structure are necessary so that there will be no interferences, because of manufacturing inaccuracies. More clearance should be allowed for field erection than for shop fabrication. Field clearance (C_1, Fig. 20.37) should be approximately ½ in., and shop clearance (C) should be about ¼ in. Note the clearances shown between the angles (fastened with a gusset plate) in Fig. 20.37.

Elevations, sections, and other views are placed in relation to each other by the rules of third-angle projection, except that when a view is given under a front view, as in Fig. 20.30, it is made as a section taken above the lower flange, looking down, instead of as a regular bottom view looking up. Large sections of materials are shown with uniform crosshatching. Small-scale sections are blacked-in solid, with white spaces left between adjacent parts (see paragraph 8.11).

Bent plates should be developed and the "stretchout" length of bent forged bars given. The length of a bent plate may be taken as the inside length of the bend plus half the thickness of the plate for each bend.

A *bill of material* always accompanies a structural drawing. This can be put on the drawing, but the best practice is to attach it as a separate "bill sheet," generally on 8½- by 11-in. paper.

Lettering is done in rapid single stroke, inclined or vertical.

Checking is usually indicated by a red-pencil check mark placed under the dimension, note, or specification.

General notes either accompany the general drawing or appear in the title of the shop drawing. Items included are painting, shipping instructions, etc.

20.27. TIMBER STRUCTURES.

The representation of timber-framed structures

FIG. **20.35.** Proportions of structural rivets.

FIG. **20.36.** Hole spacings. These are: gage (g), pitch (p) and edge (e) distances.

FIG. **20.37.** Spacings on built-up members. These are edge (e) and clearance (c) distances.

FIG. 20.38. A structural shop drawing. This is a detail of a timber truss.

involves no new principles but requires particular attention to details. Timber members are generally rectangular in section and are specified to nominal sizes in even inches as 8″ × 12″. The general drawing must give center and other important distances accurately. Details drawn to larger scale give specific information as to separate parts. The particulars of joints, splices, methods of fastening, etc., are detailed.

Two scales are sometimes used to advantage on the general drawing, as is done in Fig. 20.38. Complete notes are an essential part of such drawings, especially when an attempt at dimensioning the smaller details results in confusion.

Joints in timber structures are fastened with nails or spikes, wood screws, bolts, or ring-shaped or flat *connectors*, similar in action to a dowel or key. Some common types are shown in Fig. 20.39. A split ring, shown at (*A*), is assembled in

grooves in each piece and held together with a bolt, as indicated at (*B*). The sharp projections on the alligator connector (*C*) are forced into the members by pressure. The claw-plate connector (*D*) is used either in pairs, back to back, for timber-to-timber connections; or single for timber to metal. A typical assembly is shown at (*E*). The Kubler wood dowel connector (*F*) fits into a bored hole in each timber face, and a bolt holds the parts together.

The Forest Products Laboratory publication, "Wood Handbook," gives basic information on wood as a material of construction, including the connectors, and is available at small cost from the Superintendent of Documents, Washington, D.C.

20.28. MASONRY STRUCTURES. In drawing masonry, the symbols used bear some resemblance to the material repre-

FIG. 20.39. Timber connectors. These are used for joints in wooden structures.

sented. Figure 20.40 gives those in common use and shows the stages followed to secure uniformity of effect in rendering earth and concrete. Drawings for piers, foundations for machines, and other masonry structures occur in all kinds of engineering work. Grade levels, floor levels, and other fixed heights are always given, together with accurate location dimensions for foundation bolts. All materials are marked plainly with name or notes.

20.29. REINFORCED CONCRETE. This is an important division of masonry construction and requires care in representation and specification. It is almost impossible to show the shape and location of reinforcing bars in concrete by the usual orthographic views without using a systematic scheme of conventional symbols and marking.

Figure 20.41 shows a portion of the general structural plan for the first floor of a building. By means of the plan, the tabular data, the general notes, and the specifications, the engineer has completely specified the reinforced-concrete floor of the building. The location of the reinforced beams is given on the plan; the size of the beam and reinforcing to be used are indicated in the beam schedule; and the typical beam sections give the basic information for bending the reinforcing bars. The type of floor slab used is shown on the plan and in the slab schedule by the letters *A, B,* etc. The slab schedule, in conjunction with the typical slab plan, indicates the direction and spacing of reinforcing.

General notes on the drawing or in the specifications cover items such as maximum strength of concrete, grade of steel, and minimum cover.

Coursed Rubble

Uncoursed Rubble

Stratified Rock

Cut Stone in Section

Cut Stone in Elevation

Stages in making earth

Stages in making Concrete

Reinforced Concrete

Cyclopean Concrete

FIG. 20.40. Symbols for masonry.

The general drawing in Fig. 20.41, although completely specifying the reinforced-concrete construction, does not give the exact details of how the bars are to be bent and placed. The contractor supplying the steel makes another drawing (Fig. 20.42), showing in detail the bending, spacing, etc., for all the steel.

Walls, columns, and other portions of reinforced structures are represented similarly to the beams and floor slabs illustrated.

SECOND FLOOR FRAMING PLAN

BEAM SCHEDULE											
BEAM MARK	SIZE		STRAIGHT		TRUSS		STIRRUPS				REMARKS
	W	D	No	Size	No	Size	No	Size	SPACING		
2B1	14	20	2	7/8	2	1φ	18	3/8	2@3, 3@6, 4@9		1-3/4 Top of E. end
2B2	14	20	2	3/4	2	1φ	18	3/8	2@3, 3@6, 4@9		
2B21	11	27	2	5/8	2	7/8	6	1/4	1@9, 2@12		
2B22	11	27	2	5/8	2	3/4	6	1/4	1@9, 2@12		

SLAB SCHEDULE							
SLAB MARK	DEPTH	DIREC-TION	BAR SIZE	BAR SPACING			REMARKS
				BAND "a"	BAND "b"	BAND "c"	
A	6	N-S	1/2	8½W	8½	11	"W" Wall band
		E-W	1/2	11	8½	8½W	
B	6	N-S	1/2	10W	10	13	
		E-W	1/2	11	8½	11	
C	6	N-S	1/2	11	8½	8½W	
		E-W	1/2	11	8½	8½W	
D	6	N-S	1/2	13	10	13	
		E-W	1/2	13	10	13	

TYPICAL BEAM & SLAB BENDING

Bend 2 bars out of 3 in all bands except as noted.

TYPICAL SLAB PLAN

FIG. 20.41. A general reinforced-concrete plan. The framing plan identifies beams and slabs by letter and number. Beam and slab schedules show the number, size, and spacing of reinforcing steel. Details show typical bending and location of reinforcing.

FIG. 20.42. A detail reinforced-concrete plan. The framing plan identifies all beams and slabs by letter and number. The slab, beam, and bend schedules give all details for preparation and placement of the reinforcing steel.

PROBLEMS

GROUP 1.   ARCHITECTURAL DRAWINGS

20.1.1. Prepare a preliminary sketch plan for a vacation cottage to meet the following requirements: kitchen-dining area (approximately 140 sq ft of floor space); living-recreation area (approximately 280 sq ft); two bunk rooms (approximately 70 sq ft each); bathroom; four closets (one for each bunk room, one for outer garments, and one for linens); and a porch. Scale: 1/16″ = 1′-0″. It is recommended that the plan be developed on 1/4-in. coordinate paper using sketch technique.

20.1.2. Prepare a preliminary sketch plan for a gasoline service station to be located on a corner lot (100 × 175 ft). Scale: 1/16″ = 1′-0″. Requirements: office-salesroom; one lubrication rack; one wash rack; work space for battery charging, tire repair, etc.; two rest rooms (women's rest room to be entered from the outside); two air stations; and two gasoline islands, each with three pumps.

20.1.3. Prepare a presentation perspective drawing of the house shown in Figs. 20.12 to 20.18. Scale ¼″ = 1′-0″. Picture plane to make an angle of 30° with the front wall and to contain the left front corner of the house. Perspective to show the front and left-side walls. Horizon: 5′-6″ above the finished grade.

20.1.4. Make a paper model of the house shown in block form. Scale of model: ⅛″ = 1′-0″. Mount on cardboard base.

Optional requirement: Draw windows and doors on all walls, after the instructor has approved preliminary first- and second-floor plans.

PROB. 20.1.4. House, in block form.

20.1.5. Prepare the working drawing details for a fireplace with a 40 in. wide by 29 in. high opening. Scale of drawings: ¾″ = 1′-0″. Refer to fireplace-equipment manufacturers' catalogues and architectural handbooks for necessary data.

20.1.6. Make an isometric drawing of the piping for the house shown in Figs. 20.12 to

20.18. Scale: ½″ = 1′-0″. Determine pipe sizes from published laws governing plumbing and drainage and from architectural handbooks; note pipe sizes on the isometric. (See Chap. 18, Drawings of Piping.)

20.1.7. Draw a completed plot plan showing the house of scheme *A*, Fig. 20.3, positioned on the lot shown in Prob. 20.1.7. Scale ⅛″ = 1′-0″.

20.1.8. Complete the working drawings for the garage shown.

20.1.9. Prepare the working drawings for the week-end cottage shown. Scale of elevation and plan: ¼″ = 1′-0″. Scale of wall section and fireplace details: ¾″ = 1′-0″. Scale of cornice, door, and window details: 1½″ = 1′-0″.

PROB. 20.1.7. Building lot.

FLOOR PLAN
1/16" = 1'-0"

4" Concrete Floor Slab Reinforced with #6 Ga. Welded Wire Fabric.

Provide: Fluorescent Lights over Workbench; Plugmold Multi-Outlet Strip on face of Window Stool; Gen. Illumination.

16'-0"x7'-0"x1/8" Overhead Door

Workbench with Storage Under

25'-4"

SEC. A-A   SEC. B-B   SEC. C-C

TRELLIS DETAILS

5" Galv. Iron Gutter

Commercial Projected Windows
(Actual Size: 3'-8 7/8" x 4'-1")

PROB. 20.1.8. Garage: a partial working drawing, to be completed.

SIDE ELEVATION
1/16" = 1'-0"

Louvre in Gable End

Pressed Standing Seam Roofing

3 Concrete Block Courses

END ELEVATION
1/16" = 1'-0"

3" Plain Round Leader

2 x 6 16"o.c.
2 x 8
2 x 10
Flashing
8" Conc. Block
Bench Top
7'-0"
1'-10"
6"
1'-4"

WALL SECTION
1/4" = 1'-0"

NORTH ELEVATION   EAST ELEVATION

NORTH
W   E
SOUTH

LIVING
BED
KITCHEN

ROOF PLAN
SCALE
5   0   10   20 ft.

PROB. 20.1.9. Week-end cottage.

WEST ELEVATION   SOUTH ELEVATION
SCALE 5 0 5 10 15 20 FEET

20.1.10. (*a*) Prepare preliminary plan and elevations for a shelter with a floor area approximately 24 by 40 ft. One end of the shelter is to have a large fireplace. Materials of construction: stone and heavy timbers. (*b*) After preliminary drawings have been approved by the instructor, prepare the working drawings for the shelter.

20.1.11. Complete the set of working drawings for the house shown in Figs. 20.12 to 20.18. Required views are listed in paragraph 20.11.

GROUP 2.   STRUCTURAL DRAWINGS

20.2.1.   Make a shop drawing of the triple-effect evaporator support. Assume complete shop fabrication. Use ⅜-in. rivets.

20.2.1*A.*   Make a shop drawing of the triple-effect evaporator support. Assume shop fabri-

cation of all parts except the long channels and the 3- by 3- by ¼-in. angle brace; use ⅜-in. shop rivets and ⅜-in. field bolts.

20.2.1*B.*   Same as Prob. 20.2.1*A*, but redesign for welded construction.

20.2.2.   Make a shop drawing of the column base. Assume complete assembly in the shop. Use ¾-in. rivets. Open holes are for 1-in. anchor bolts.

20.2.2*A.*   Make a shop bill of material listing all parts used in Prob. 20.2.4.

20.2.3.   Make a shop drawing for the crane trolley. Assume fabrication as indicated in the figure. One end is shown; the other end is similar. Use ⅜-in. rivets wherever possible.

20.2.3*A.*   Make a shop bill of material listing all parts used in Prob. 20.2.3.

20.2.4.   Redesign Fig. 20.38, using (wherever possible) fasteners shown in Fig. 20.39.

20.2.5.   Make a shop drawing for the motor support. Assume shop fabrication as follows: (*a*) 8-in. channels, 4- by 4- by ½-in. angles, ½-in. plate, and 6- by 4- by ⅜-in. beam connectors (angles), two members required, one

PROB. 20.2.1.   Triple-effect evaporator support.

PROB. 20.2.2.   Column base.

PROB. 20.2.3. Crane trolley.

right hand, one left hand; (b) 21 by ¾ by 2'-4 plate; (c) 12-in. I beam, two required with 4- by 4- by ⅜-in. beam connectors temporarily bolted in place. Assume columns to be part of the existing structure. Use ¾-in. rivets and ¾-in. bolts.

20.2.5A. Make an erection drawing for the motor support. Assume columns to be part of the existing structure.

20.2.6. Make a shop drawing of roof truss T1 for the steel-frame mill building. This drawing is to be similar to the drawing shown in Fig. 20.30. For truss T1, use the same size members and the same roof pitch as is used for truss T8, Fig. 20.30. Detail only the left half of the truss to a scale suitable for 11- by 17-in. paper.

20.2.6A. Prepare shop drawings for the following steel members used in fabricating the steel mill building: (a) bracket M1; (b) beams B1 and B3 (one detail for both); (c) beam B5 (assume ⅜-in. plate to be shop fabricated to column); and (d) beam B6. Assume shop and field fabrication indicated. Use ¾-in. rivets. These details, along with the shipping list and general notes, may be drawn on 11- by 17-in. paper to a scale of $1'' = 1'-0$.

PROB. 20.2.5. Motor support.

20.2.6B. Prepare shop drawings for the following steel members used in fabricating the steel mill building: (a) bracket M1, and (b) column C4. Assume shop and field fabrication indicated. Use ¾-in. rivets. Three faces of the column will have to be shown.

20.2.6C. Make a shop drawing of column D4. Assume shop and field fabrication as indicated. Use ¾-in. rivets.

20.2.6D. Make a shop drawing of beam B7.

20.2.6E. Make a shop drawing of rafter *R*1.
20.2.6F. Make a general structural plan, similar to Fig. 20.41, of the concrete floor at elevation 266'-0. Use ½-in. round reinforcing bars spaced 9 in. on centers, alternate bars

are bent for the floor. In 6-in. wall, use 3½-in. round bars in bottom and ⅜-in. round vertical bars at 18 in. hooked 18 in. into floor slab.
20.2.6G. Make a reinforcing detail drawing, similar to Fig. 20.42, for Prob. 20.2.6*F*.

PROB. 20.2.6. Steel-frame mill building.

20.2.7. Make a detailed shop drawing of the structural members in a section of the pipe bridge. Do not include the bents.

20.2.7A. Make a detailed drawing of the base section of bent A including the two bottom diagonal braces.

20.2.7B. Make a detailed shop drawing of the entire bent A.

20.2.7C. Make a detailed drawing of the pier support for bent A.

20.2.7D. Make a detail of a typical con-nection to the 10-in. channel using the hori-zontal members as $2 \angle 3 \times 2\frac{1}{2} \times \frac{1}{4}$ and each of the two diagonal members coming to this connection as $3 \times 3 \times \frac{1}{4}$ angles.

20.2.7E. The pipe bridge carries 10-in., 7-in., 4-in., and 3-in. insulated pipe lines sus-pended from the 8 in. 23 lb I beams on each bent. Keep the pipes in the order indicated from left to right and show a detail of the strap supports and their connection to the bent.

BENT A

DETAIL -BENT TOP

PIPE BRIDGE
PLAN

BASE M'T'L

DETAIL B

PROB. 20.2.7. Pipe bridge.

21

Map and Topographic Drawing

21.1. Thus far in our consideration of drawing as a graphic language we have had to represent the three dimensions of an object pictorially or, in the usual case, by drawing two or more views of it. In map drawing, that is, in representing features on parts of the earth's surface, there is the distinct difference that the drawing is complete with two dimensions given in one view; the third dimension, the height, is either represented in this view or omitted as not required for the purpose for which the particular map was made.

Surveying and mapping the site is the first preliminary in engineering projects, and all engineers should be familiar with the methods and symbols used in map and topographic drawing. Without considering the practice of surveying and plotting or the various methods used by cartographers in projecting the curved surface of the earth on a plane, we are interested in the use and details of execution of plats and topographic maps.

21.2. CLASSIFICATION. The content or information on maps is in general classified under three divisions:

1. The representation of boundaries, bearings, and distances, such as divisions between areas subject to different authority or ownership, either public or private; or lines indicating geometric measurements on land, on sea, and in

the air. This division includes plats or land maps, farm surveys, city subdivisions, plats of mineral claims, and nautical and aeronautical charts.

2. The representation of real or material features or objects within the limits of the tract, showing their relative location or size and location, depending upon the purpose of the map. When relative location only is required, the scale may be small, and symbols may be employed to represent objects, such as houses, bridges, or even towns. When the size of the objects is an important consideration, the scale must be large and the map becomes a real orthographic top view.

3. The representation of the relative elevations of the surface of the ground. Maps with this feature are called "relief maps" or, if contours are used with elevations marked on them, "contour maps." Hydrographic maps show fathom-line depth curves.

Various combinations of these three divisions are required for different purposes. Maps are classified according to purpose, as follows:

1. *Geographical maps* include large areas and consequently must be to small scale. They show important towns and cities, streams and bodies of water, political boundaries, and relief.

2. *Topographic maps* are complete descriptions of certain areas and show to larger scale the geographical positions of the natural features and the works of man. The relief is usually represented by contours.

3. *Hydrographic maps* deal with information concerning bodies of water, such as shore lines, sounding depths, subaqueous contours, navigation aids, and water control.

4. *Nautical maps* or charts are show aids to water navigation, such as buoys, beacons, lighthouses, lanes of traffic, sounding depths, shoals, and radio compass stations.

5. *Aeronautical maps* or charts give prominent landmarks of the terrain and accentuate the relief by layer tints, hachures, and 500- or 1,000-ft contours as aids to air navigation.

6. *Cadastral maps* are very accurate control maps for cities and towns, made to large scale with all features drawn to size. They are used to control city development and operation, particularly taxation.

7. *Engineering maps* are working maps for engineering projects and are designed for specific purposes to aid construction. They provide accurate horizontal and vertical control data and show objects on the site or along the right of way.

8. *Photogrammetric maps* represent features on the earth's surface from terrestrial and aerial photographs. These photographs are perspectives from which orthographic views are obtained by stereoscopic instruments. Ground-control stations are necessary to bring the photographs to a required datum.

9. *Military maps* contain information of military importance in the area represented.

21.3.   PLATS. A map plotted from a plane survey and having the third dimension omitted is called a "plat" or "land map." It is used in the description of any tract of land when it is not necessary to show relief, as in a farm survey or a city plat.

The plotting is done from field notes by (1) latitudes and departures, (2) bearings and distances, (3) azimuths and distances, (4) deflection angles and distances, or (5) rectangular coordinates. Or the plotting is done by the total latitude and departure from some fixed origin for each separate point; this method is necessary to distribute plotting errors over the entire survey. Angles are laid off from bearing or azimuth lines by plotting ·the tangent of the angle or the sine of half the angle, by sine-and-cosine method, or by an accurate protractor.

Simplicity is of first importance in the execution of this kind of drawing. Information should be clear, concise, and direct. The lettering should be done in single stroke, and the north point and border should be of the simplest character. The day of the intricate border corner, elaborate north point, and ornamental title is, happily, past, and all such embellishments are rightly considered to be a waste of time and in bad taste.

21.4. PLAT OF A SURVEY. The plat of a survey should give clearly all the information necessary for the legal description of a parcel of land. It should contain:

1. Direction and length of each line
2. Acreage
3. Location and description of monuments found and set
4. Location of highways, streams, rights of way, and any appurtenances required
5. Official division lines within the tract
6. Names of owners of abutting property
7. Title, scale, date
8. North point with certification of horizontal control
9. Plat certification properly executed

10. Reference to state plane-coordinate system

Figure 21.1 illustrates the general treatment of this kind of drawing. It is almost always traced and blueprinted, and no water-lining of streams or other elaboration should be attempted. The size of the lettering used for the several features must be in proportion to their importance.

FIG. 21.1. Plat of a survey. This type of map includes the information listed in paragraph 21.4.

FIG. 21.2. Part of an industrial map. This is a railroad property map.

FIG. 21.3. Plat of a city subdivision. This type of map shows the size and location of lots and streets.

21.5. INDUSTRIAL PLATS. Of the many kinds of plats used in industrial work only one is illustrated here, a portion of a railway situation or station map (Fig. 21.2). This might represent also a plant-valuation map, a type of plat often required. The information on such maps varies to meet the requirements of particular cases. In addition to the items in the preceding list, the map might include pipe lines, fire hydrants, location and description of buildings, railroads and switch points, outdoor crane runways, etc.

21.6. PLATS OF SUBDIVISIONS. The plats of subdivisions and allotments in cities are filed with the county recorder for record and must be complete in their information concerning the location and size of the various lots and parcels composing the subdivisions (Fig. 21.3). All monuments set should be shown and all directions and distances recorded, so that it will be possible to locate any lot with precision.

Sometimes landowners use these maps in display to prospective buyers and often include a blueprint or black-line print bound with the deed. Some degree of embellishment is allowable, but care must be taken not to overdo the ornamentation. Figure 21.4 is an example showing an acceptable style of execution and finish.

FIG. 21.4. A real-estate display map. This type of map shows the size of lots and streets but does not include the details given in a survey.

21.7. CITY PLATS. Under this head are included chiefly maps or plats drawn from subdivision plats or other sources for the record of city improvements. These plats are used to record a variety of information, such as the location of sewers, water mains, gas, power and steam lines, telephone installations, and street improvements.

The records maintained on these maps provide valuable data for assessments and constitute progress reports on the growth of a city. These maps are made for a definite purpose and should contain only the information needed for that purpose; hence they will not include all the details as to sizes of lots, which are given on subdivision plats, but they should carry both horizontal and vertical control points for proper location of utilities. They are usually made on mounted paper and should be to a scale large enough to show clearly the features required; 100 and 200 ft to the inch are common scales, and as large as 50 ft is sometimes used. For small cities the entire area may be covered by one map; for large cities the maps are made in sections that can be conveniently filed.

A study of Fig. 21.5, a sewer map, will show the general treatment of city plats. The appearance of the drawing is improved by adding shade lines on the lower and right-hand side of the blocks, that is, treating the streets and water features as depressions. A few of the more important public buildings are shown, to facilitate reading. The various wards, subdivisions, or districts may be shown by large outline letters or numerals as illustrated in the figure. Contours are often put on these maps in red or brown ink, either on the original or on a positive print from it. Figure 21.6 shows a modern system of horizontal control used by the city of

Cleveland for a geodetic and underground survey.

21.8. TOPOGRAPHIC DRAWING. A complete topographic map will contain

1. The lines establishing the divisions of authority or ownership.

2. The geographical position of both the natural features and the works of man. It may also include information on the vegetation.

3. The relief, or indication of the relative elevations and depressions. The relief, which is the third dimension, is represented in general by contours or by hill shading.

These are represented on the drawing

FIG. 21.5. A city plat. This is a sewer map.

FIG. 21.6. Horizontal control. This locates accurate points of reference for surveys.

FIG. 21.8. A perspective view. This is a pictorial map in which relief is indicated by line shading. Maps of this type are used only for illustrative purposes.

FIG. 21.7. Contours. These are theoretical lines of constant elevation.

by lines, symbols, and lettered information, as explained in the paragraphs that follow.

21.9. CONTOURS. A contour is a theoretical line on the surface of the ground which at every point passes through the same elevation; thus the shore line of a body of water represents a contour. If the water should rise 1 ft, the new shore line would be another contour, with 1-ft "contour interval." A series of contours may be illustrated approximately as in Fig. 21.7.

Figure 21.8 is a perspective view of a tract of land. Figure 21.9 is a contour map of the same area, and Fig. 21.10 shows the same surface with hill shading by hachures. Contours are drawn as fine full lines, with every fifth one of heavier weight and with the elevations in feet marked on them at intervals, usually with the sea level as datum. They may be drawn with a swivel pen, or a fine pen such as Gillott's 170 or Esterbrook's 356. On paper drawings they are usually made in brown.

FIG. 21.9. A contour map. This is a map of the area shown in Fig. 21.8. The relief is read by noting the elevation, position, and spacing of the contours.

FIG. 21.10. A relief map. In this map of the area given in Fig. 21.8 the relief is shown by hachures. High areas are light, low areas dark. This type of map shows only relative and approximate relief and is therefore not used for scientific purposes.

Figure 21.11 is a topographic map of the site of a proposed filtration plant and illustrates the use of the contour map as the necessary preliminary drawing for engineering projects. Often the same drawing shows, by lines of different character, both the existing contours and the required finished grades.

21.10.   HILL SHADING.

Showing relief by means of hill shading gives a pleasing effect but is difficult to execute, does not give exact elevations, and would not be applied on maps to be used for engineering purposes. Hill shading is sometimes used to advantage in reconnaissance maps or in small-scale maps for illustration. There are several systems, of which hachuring, as shown in Fig. 21.10, is the commonest. This is done by sketching the contours lightly in pencil and drawing the hachures perpendicular to them, starting at the summit and grading the weight of line to the degree of slope. A scale of hachures, graded from black for 45° to white for horizontal, is often made to use for reference. The rows of strokes should touch the pencil line to avoid white streaks along the contours. Two other systems in use are the horizontal, or English system, using graded hachure lines parallel to the contours; and the oblique illumination, or French system, using hachures graded to give sunlight effect as well as the degree of slope.

21.11.   WATER LINING.

On topographic maps made for display or reproduction, the water features are usually finished by "water lining," that is, by running a system of fine lines parallel to the shore lines, either in black or in blue (it must be remembered that blue will not photograph for reproduction or print

well from a tracing). Poor water lining will ruin the appearance of an otherwise well-executed map, and it is better to omit it rather than do it hastily. The shore line is drawn first, and the water lining done with a fine mapping pen, the draftsman always drawing toward his body, with the preceding line to his left. The first line should follow the shore line closely; the distances between the succeeding lines should be gradually increased and the irregularities lessened. Sometimes the weight of lines is graded as well as the intervals, but this is a difficult operation and not necessary for the effect. A common mistake is to make the lines excessively wavy or rippled.

In water lining a stream of varying width, the lines are not crowded so as to be carried through the narrower portions; corresponding lines are brought together in the middle of the stream, as illustrated in Fig. 21.10. Avoid spots of sudden increase or decrease in spacing.

FIG. 21.11. A contour map of an engineering project. This type of map shows relief by contours and includes other physical features such as buildings, roadways, and streams.

FIG. 21.12. Culture symbols. These are used to indicate the works of man.

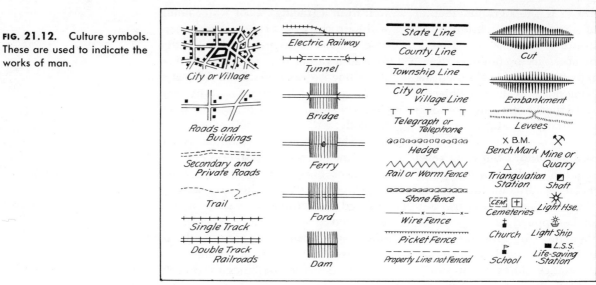

Military post or headquarters _____

Arsenal or shop _____

Embarkation or debarkation point ____

General hospital _____

Laboratory _____

Observation point _____

Reception center _____

Replacement center _____

Supply depot _____

Troop unit _____

Cemetery _____

School _____

Mobilization point _____

Wire entanglement _____

Artillery _____

Cavalry _____

Coast artillery or antiaircraft ____

Tanks _____

FIG. 21.13. Military symbols. These are used on military maps.

21.12. TOPOGRAPHIC SYMBOLS. The various symbols used in topographic drawing can be grouped under four heads:

1. Culture, or the works of man
2. Relief—relative elevations and depressions
3. Water features
4. Vegetation

When color is used the culture is done in black, the relief in brown, the water features in blue, and the vegetation in black or green.

Army, Navy or Marine Corps Field _____

Commercial or Municipal Airport _____

Dep't. of Commerce Intermediate Field _____

Marked Auxiliary Field _____

Seaplane Anchorage _____

Airway Light Beacon, rotating (Arrows indicate course lights)

Auxiliary Airway Light Beacon, flashing ____

*Airport Light Beacon, rotating, with Code Light ____

*Airport Light Beacon, rotating, without Code Light ____

*Place in center of field symbol

Landmark Light Beacon, rotating, with bearing projector ____

Landmark Light Beacon, rotating, without bearing projector ____

High Explosive Area { Marked _____ HI○×
                      Unmarked _____ }

Obstruction (Numerals indicate height above ground in feet) _____ 384

Lighting facilities at the field _____ LF

Marker Beacon _____

Prohibited Area _____

*Mooring Mast _____

‡When at a field attach to top of field symbol

Radio Range, Bearings are magnetic
(All the above symbols to be drawn in red)

FIG. 21.14. Aviation symbols. These are used on navigation maps for aircraft.

Wreck (hull above low water)_____ ⋈
Wreck (depth unknown)_____ +++
Sunken wreck (dangerous to surface navigation)__ ⊞
Rock under water_____ +
Rock awash (any tide)_____ ✻
Breakers along shore_____ ⁀⁀⁀
Beacon__ ★, not lighted___ ▲ ⚓ ⚓ ⚓ ⚓ ⚓
Buoy of any kind (or red)_____ ◊
Buoy (black)_____ ❢

Life-saving station (in general)_____ ➤ L.S.S.
Life-saving station (Coast Guard)___ ➤ C.G.165
Lighthouse _____ ✿
Radio station_____ R.S. ⊙
Radio tower_____ R.T. ⊙
Radio beacon _____ R.Bn. ⊙
Anchorage (any kind)_____ ⚓
Anchorage (small vessels)_____ ⚓
Dry dock _____ ⊳▭

FIG. 21.15. Marine symbols. These are used on navigation maps for water craft.

Topographic symbols, used to represent characteristics on the earth's surface, are made, when possible, to resemble somewhat the features or objects represented as they would appear in plan or in elevation. No attempt is made here to give symbols for all the features that might occur in a map; indeed one may have to invent symbols for some particular condition.

Figure 21.12 illustrates a few of the conventional symbols used for culture or the works of man. When the scale used is large, houses, bridges, roads, and even tree trunks can be plotted so that their principal dimensions can be scaled. The landscape architect is interested not only in the size of the trunk of a tree but also in the spread of its branches. A small-scale map can give by its symbols only the relative locations.

Some military symbols are shown in Fig. 21.13, symbols for aerial navigation in Fig. 21.14, and aids to water navigation in Fig. 21.15—all as adopted by the U.S. Board of Surveys and Maps. Figure 21.16 gives the standard symbols used in the development of oil and gas fields, Fig. 21.17 the symbols used

Location__○, Rig__○, Drilling Well__⊙
Producing Oil Well_____●
Small Oil Well _____◑
Producing Gas Well_____☼
Symbol of Abandonment__∨, thus_____☼
Number of Well, thus_____☼³
Show Volumes, Depth, etc. thus_____☼² {B.750 {C.2900 {3 M.

Producing Oil and Gas Well__☀
Dry Hole with showing of Oil__◈
Dry Hole_____◇
Salt Well_____⊕

●   ☀   ☼
●⁷ ☀¹⁶ ◇⁵
●⁷{Sand{30B. ☀⁴{3M.{2B ◇⁹{Injun

FIG. 21.16.   Oil and gas symbols. These are used on contour and relief maps.

Contours

1200
1300
1400
1300
1200

Depression Contours
320
340

Hill-shading

FIG. 21.17. Relief symbols. These are used on contour and relief maps.

⊙
577.5
Determined Elevation

Sand

Sand Dunes

Mud Flat

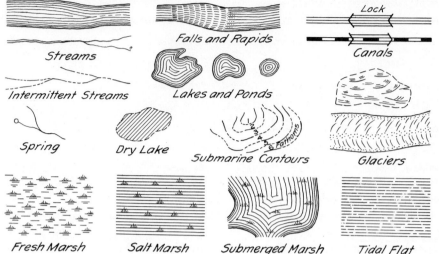

FIG. 21.18. Symbols for water features. These are used as needed on any map.

Streams

Intermittent Streams

Spring

Dry Lake

Falls and Rapids

Lakes and Ponds

Submarine Contours

Lock

Canals

Glaciers

Fresh Marsh   *Salt Marsh*   *Submerged Marsh*   *Tidal Flat*

to show relief, Fig. 21.18 water features, and Fig. 21.19 some of the common symbols for vegetation and cultivation.

Keep in mind the purpose of the map and in some measure indicate the relative importance of the features, varying their prominence by the weight of lines used or by varying the scale of the symbol. For instance, in a map made for military maneuvers a cornfield might be an important feature; or

in maps made to show the location of special features, such as fire hydrants, these objects would be plainly indicated. The map of an airport or a golf course would emphasize features significant for an airport or golf course. The principle calls for some originality in meeting various cases.

A beginner will often make symbols too large. The symbols for grass, shown under "meadow" (Fig. 21.19), must

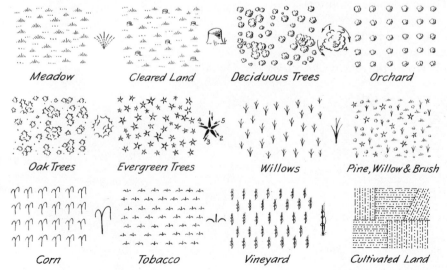

Meadow   *Cleared Land*   *Deciduous Trees*   *Orchard*

Oak Trees   *Evergreen Trees*   *Willows*   *Pine, Willow & Brush*

FIG. 21.19. Symbols for vegetation. These are used as needed on any map.

Corn   *Tobacco*   *Vineyard*   *Cultivated Land*

be made and spaced correctly or they will spoil an entire map. The symbol for grass is composed of five to seven short strokes radiating from a common center and starting along a horizontal line, as shown in the enlarged example, each tuft beginning and ending with a mere dot. Always place the tufts with the bottom parallel to the border and distribute them uniformly over the space, but not in rows. A few incomplete tufts or rows of dots improve the appearance. Grass-tuft symbols should never be as heavy as tree symbols. In drawing the symbol for deciduous trees, the sequence of strokes shown should be followed.

Figure 21.20 is a topographic map, given to illustrate the general execution and placing of symbols.

The well-known maps of the U.S. Coast and Geodetic Survey and the Geological Survey illustrate the application of topographic drawing. The *quadrangle sheets* issued by the topographic branch of the U.S. Geological Survey are excellent examples and so easily available that every engineer should be

FIG. 21.20. Part of a topographic map. This map shows the application of relief, water, and vegetation symbols.

familiar with them. These sheets represent 15 minutes of latitude and 15 minutes of longitude to the scale of 1 : 62,500 or approximately 1 in. to the mile. The entire United States is being mapped by the department in cooperation with the different states. This work is now greatly facilitated through the use of aerial photography. Much territory in the West and South has been mapped ½ in. to the mile, and earlier some in the West was mapped ¼ in. to the mile. These maps may be secured from The Director, U.S. Geological Survey, Washington, D.C., who will also give information as to the completion of any particular locality or the progress in any state.

21.13. LANDSCAPE MAPS. A topographic map made to a relatively large scale and showing all details is called a "landscape map." Such maps are required by architects and landscape gardeners for use in planning buildings to fit the natural topographic features and in landscaping parks, playgrounds, and private estates. These are generally maps of small areas, and a scale of 1″ = 20′ to 1″ = 50′, depending upon the amount of detail, is used.

The contour interval varies from 6 in. to 2 ft according to the ruggedness of the surface. The commonest interval is 1 ft. Landscape maps are often reproduced in black-line prints, upon which contours in different color are drawn to show the landscape treatment proposed. Natural features and culture are added in more detail than on ordinary topographic maps. Trees are designated as to size, species, and sometimes spread of branches and condition. It is often necessary to invent symbols suitable for a particular survey and to include a key or legend on the map. Roads, walks, streams, flower beds, houses, etc., should be plotted carefully to scale, so that measurements can be taken from them.

21.14. COLORS. Instead of using colored inks, which are thin and unsatisfactory to handle in the pen and do not photograph or blueprint well, it is better to use water colors for contours, streams, and other colored features in topographic mapping: for contours, burnt sienna, either straight or darkened with a drop of black, and mixed rather thick; for streams, Prussian blue; and for features in red, alizarin crimson. All work well in crow-quill or contour pen and make good blueprints. Colors in tubes are more convenient than those in cakes or pans.

21.15. LETTERING. The style of lettering on a topographic map will depend upon the purpose for which the map is made. If it is for construction purposes, such as a contour map for the study of municipal problems, street grades, plants, or railroads, the single-stroke Gothic and Reinhardt is preferred. For a finished map, vertical Modern Roman letters should be used, capitals for important land features and lower case for less important features, such as small towns and villages; for water features, inclined Roman and stump letters (see Appendix). The scale should always be drawn as well as stated.

21.16. TITLES. Modern Roman is the standard letter for finished map titles. The design should be symmetrical, with the height of the letters proportioned to the relative importance of the line. A map title should contain as many of the following items as are necessary.

1. Kind—"Map of," etc.
2. Name
3. Location of tract
4. Purpose, if special features are represented
5. For whom made
6. Engineer in charge
7. Date (of survey)
8. Scale—stated and drawn, contour interval, datum
9. Authorities
10. Legend or key to symbols
11. North point, with certification of horizontal control
12. Certification, properly executed
13. Reference to state plane-coordinate system

21.17. PROFILES. Perhaps no kind of drawing is used more by civil engineers than the ordinary profile, which is simply a vertical section taken along a given line, either straight or curved. Such drawings are indispensable in problems of railroad construction, highway and street improvements, sewer construction, and many other problems where a study of the surface of the ground is required. Frequently engineers other than civil engineers are called upon to make profile drawings. Several different types of profile and cross-section paper are in use; they are described in the catalogues of the various firms dealing in drawing materials. One type of profile paper in common use is known as "Plate A" and has 4 divisions to the inch horizontally and 20 to the inch vertically. Other divisions in use are 4×30 to the inch and 5×25 to the inch. At intervals, both horizontally and verti-

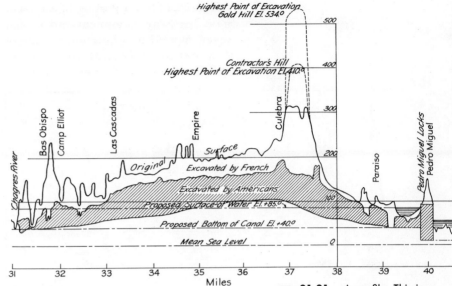

FIG. 21.21. A profile. This is used to study surface variations. In this profile the vertical scale is 50 times the horizontal scale.

cally, somewhat heavier lines are made to facilitate reading.

Horizontal distances are plotted as abscissas and elevations as ordinates. Since the vertical distances represent elevations and are plotted to larger scale, a vertical exaggeration is obtained that is useful in studying profiles that are to be used for establishing grades. The vertical exaggeration is sometimes confusing to the layman or inexperienced engineer, but ordinarily a profile will fail in the purpose for which it was intended if the horizontal and vertical scales are the same. Furthermore, if the profile were not distorted in this way, it would be a long and unwieldy affair, perhaps even impossible to make. The difference between profiles with and without vertical exaggeration is shown in Figs. 21.21 and 21.22.

FIG. 21.22. A profile. This is the same surface as in Fig. 21.21 but plotted on equal horizontal and vertical scales. Note the superiority of Fig. 21.21 for analysis.

Figure 21.23 is a portion of a typical State Highway Alignment and Profile Sheet, plotted to a horizontal scale of $1'' = 100'$ and a vertical scale of $1'' = 10'$. For this type of drawing, tracing cloth is available with the coordinates printed in red on the back so that any changes or erasures on the profile will not damage the coordinate lines. Lettering or other features are sometimes brought out by erasing the lines on the back. The alignment and profile sheet is one of a set of drawings used in the construction of a highway for estimating cost and as a working drawing, by the contractor, during construction. Other drawings in the set would consist of a title sheet showing the location plan with detours provided, a sheet indicating conventional signs, a sheet giving an index to bound sheets, and a sheet with space reserved for declarations of approval and signatures of proper officials.

There would also be sheets of cross sections taken at each 100-ft station and all necessary intermediate stations to estimate earthwork for grading; working drawings for drainage structures; site plans for bridges; specifications for guard rails and other safety devices; standard or typical road sections for cut and fill and various other conditions; and finally summary sheets for separate tables and quantities of materials for roadway, pavement, and structures.

FIG. 21.23. Part of a state highway alignment and profile sheet. This gives fundamental information needed for construction of a highway.

PROBLEMS

In Probs. 21.1 and 21.2, contour maps are needed. These can be obtained from local, county, state, or federal authorities.

GROUP 1. CONTOUR PROBLEMS

21.1.1. Obtain a contour map showing a river. Plot the watershed of the river. This is done by locating the series of highest points on each side of the river and drawing a watershed line connecting the points. Indicate the watershed area by crosshatching.

21.1.2. Obtain a contour map showing a river. At a point on the river where the banks are steep, or where there is a maximum rise above the river, locate a dam. Plot the lake formed by the dam. Represent the lake by crosshatching.

GROUP 2. PLATS OF SUBDIVISIONS

21.2.1. From Fig. 21.1, lay out the complete tract of land enclosed by the survey. Divide this tract into lots with (approximately) 70-foot frontage. Locate appropriate 30-foot roadways.

21.2.2. Lay out the tract of land in Fig. 21.3 and plan streets and lots as follows: Provide a park-type entrance on Main Street; use two curved roadways extending back to the former Walnut Alley; provide shorter streets as needed in the plan; use lots of approximately 100-foot frontage.

21.2.3. Make a sewer map for Prob. 21.2.1.

21.2.4. Make a gas supply map for Prob. 21.2.2. Scale to fit a 17 × 22 in. sheet.

GROUP 3. INDUSTRIAL PLATS

21.3.1. Lay out the complete tract of land in Fig. 21.1 on 17 × 22 in. paper. On the tract, locate an industrial building 175 feet × 100 feet. Locate a spur track from the LM and V railway to one side of the building. Provide a parking area and access street from Beaver Road.

21.3.2. Convert the city subdivision in Fig. 21.3 to an industrial site. Specifications of building are the same as in Prob. 22.3.1. Provide a large parking lot, with access road from Main Street.

GROUP 4. PROFILES

21.4.1. Plot the profile of Fig. 21.21 to suitable scale on a 17 × 22 in. sheet.

21.4.2. Plot the profile of a roadway similar to Fig. 21.23 but with these elevations:

Station Point and Elevation

Sta.	19	20	21	22	23	24	25	26	27	28	29	30
Elev.	511.0	511.0	511.0	511.0	511.2	511.5	513.5	516.0	518.5	520.5	520.9	519.8

Add a profile of ditch elevations deviating from the roadway as follows:

Station Point and Elevation

Sta.	19	20	21	22	23	24	25	26	27	28	29	30
Elev.	−1.0	−1.5	−1.5	−1.6	−1.4	−1.0	−0.5	+1.0	+1.5	+2.5	+3.5	+4.5

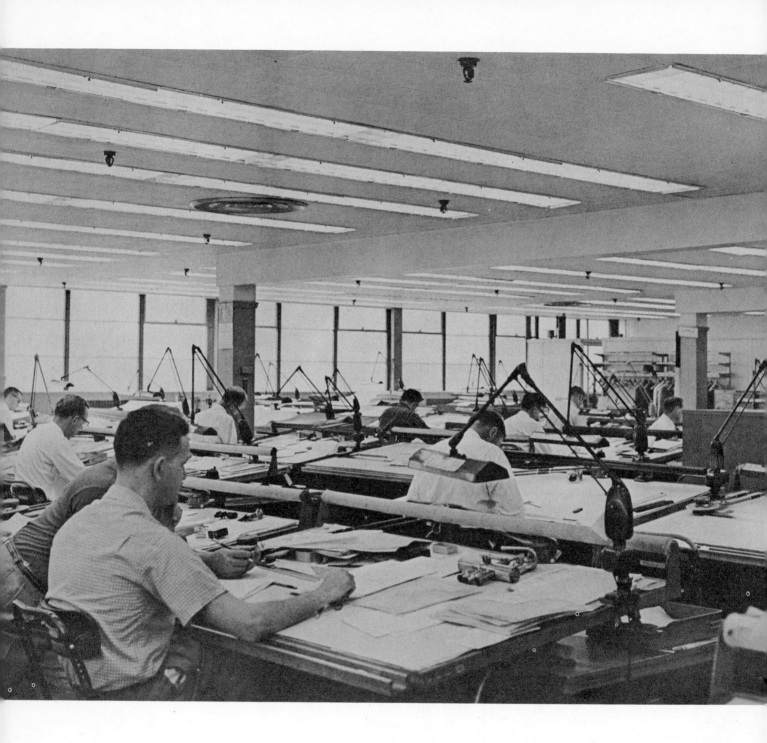

22

Commercial Practices and Economies

22.1. The bulk of commercial design and representation is done in the conventional manner, that is, by drawing orthographic or pictorial views and dimensioning them as described in the preceding chapters. However, there are many modifications of standard practice which result in economies both in making and in using drawings. These economies can be classified as (1) simplified practices, (2) elimination of drafting effort by the use of templates and overlays, (3) special uses of reproduction, (4) photo drawing,[1] (5) model-

making,[1] (6) illustrated drawings, and (7) use of special methods and equipment. The purpose in this chapter is to describe and illustrate modifications of standard practice and to suggest ways in which they can be applied.

SIMPLIFIED PRACTICES

22.2. "SIMPLIFIED" DRAWING: ECONOMICAL DRAFTING PRACTICES. The drafting of any engineering creation is generally considered by management to be an expensive part of the complete operation of producing a finished, salable product. Furthermore, the percentage of total cost relegated to research, development, drafting, tooling, factory,

---

[1] The material on photo drawing and model-making in this chapter is adapted from original subject matter and a selection of illustrations by G. P. Hammond of Procter & Gamble.

FIG. 22.1. Conventional drawing of a pulley. The two views represent the shape; the dimensions give size description (magnitudes).

FIG. 22.2. Simplified drawing of a pulley. The single view describes the cross-sectional shape and the letter *D* on the dimensions specifies that the shape is cylindrical. The figured dimensions give size description (magnitudes).

FIG. 22.3. A structural drawing. This drawing is "simplified" in that it is not drawn to scale; thus some drafting effort is eliminated.

labor, and other items of expense can be judged only on the economy of each individual department. Thus the drafting department comes under the same critical scrutiny as any other division of operation. Any saving in time and expense that can be made without injuring the effectiveness and efficiency of the department is true economy.

This question of thrift has been studied by many executives for years, but W. L. Healy and A. H. Rau,[2] of the General Electric Company, are credited with the first publication recommending and describing methods by which economies can be effected in the drafting room. There are a number of economical practices in making drawings and others that are important only to management. The principles on which economical drafting is based are discussed in the paragraphs that follow.

22.3. UNNECESSARY VIEWS. Any view that is not necessary for clear description is a waste of drafting time, paper, reproduction (area and cost), and filing space. Figure 22.1 is a conventional drawing of a pulley in which the top view is used to describe the cylindrical shapes. This pulley *can* be represented economically, as in Fig. 22.2, by eliminating the top view and using the

[2] "Simplified Drafting Practice" (New York: John Wiley & Sons, Inc., 1953).

letter *D* on the dimensions of the front view to show that the shapes represented are cylinders. Some drafting economists argue that even the letter *D* is not necessary because the title block will tell that the object is a pulley and therefore a combination of cylinders. Each drafting executive must judge the extent to which extra views, letters, etc., can be eliminated without making the interpretation of the drawing obscure or misleading. Nevertheless, the following principles should be observed: (1) Never draw more views than are necessary for clear description; (2) examine the object to see if a view can be eliminated by use of a descriptive title, note, symbols, letters, or numbers; (3) examine the object to determine whether a word statement can eliminate *all* views (this is usually possible only for very simple parts).

22.4. UNNECESSARY SCALE. The reader of the drawing does not establish distances by scaling the drawing, and most commercial drawings carry a note stating that the drawing is not to be scaled. Drafting time should not be used in drawing to scale *when it is not necessary*. A good example is given in Fig. 22.3, a structural detail *not to any scale* at all but just as effective and readable as if drawn carefully and meticulously to scale. The cardinal points are: (1) do not draw to scale unless it is necessary for proper layout and readability; (2)

do not cautiously draw to scale when approximations will suffice.

In sketching, *proportions* need not be meticulously maintained. Note in Fig. 22.4 that the two holes (⅞ and ⅜ in. diameter) are *not* in good proportion and that the two ½ in. radii for the bends are not shown centered according to the dimensioning. Nevertheless, the drawing is readable, and if the dimensions are followed—and of course they *must* be—the correct object will be manufactured. Figure 22.4 is not an extreme case—proportions could be *much* poorer than in Fig. 22.4 and the drawing still be perfectly usable.

FIG. 22.4. A simplified sketch. In this example, proportions have not been carefully maintained, thus saving time. The object is built by following the general shape shown and adhering to the dimensions; therefore, careful proportioning is not necessary.

22.5. UNNECESSARY LINES AND ELABORATION.

Every line made on a drawing costs in drafting time and the company's money. Therefore, any line that does not accomplish a useful purpose should be eliminated. Such lines will include extra lines (on any view) that are not necessary for describing the object. Meticulous crosshatching and embellishment, especially, can be omitted without seriously affecting readability. Compare the two drawings in Figs. 22.5 and 22.6. Painstaking and complete representation of sections such as is given in Fig. 22.5 is a waste of time and could be advantageously simplified as in Fig. 22.6. The drawing in Fig. 22.6 actually gives more structural information than the detailed representation in Fig. 22.5.

FIG. 22.5. A conventional drawing. Because of the drafting effort required to produce the detail and embellishment, this drawing is expensive.

FIG. 22.6. A simplified drawing. This drawing represents the same structure as in Fig. 22.5. Note the absence of extra detail and embellishment, which reduces drawing cost.

FIG. 22.7. Simplified base-line dimensioning. This system accomplishes the same purpose as standard dimensioning from datum, but eliminates all unnecessary lines and arrowheads, thus reducing drafting time.

FIG. 22.8. A simplified sketch. This drawing, made freehand, is economical, but economy is carried further by elimination of extra views, embellishment, and arrowheads on the dimensions.

22.6. ARROWLESS DIMENSIONING. Time can be saved by eliminating unnecessary arrows on dimension lines and leaders, as has been done in Figs. 22.2, 22.3, 22.4, 22.6, and 22.8. To the uninitiated, these drawings may appear to be unfinished, but careful examination will show that arrows are not really needed.

22.7. SIMPLIFIED BASE-LINE DIMENSIONING. If the base-line system of dimensioning (see paragraph 11.70) is used, even the dimension *lines* can be eliminated. As shown in Fig. 22.7, two base lines, one horizontal and the other vertical, are established. The location of base lines may be at the edge of the part, on the center of symmetry, or through some important feature. Distances are then given, as shown in the figure, *from* the base lines (corresponding to any coordinate system) and include all the information necessary for construction.

22.8. FREEHAND DRAWING. The greatest saving of drafting time can often be realized by using the methods just described and by making the drawing freehand. Compare the simplified sketch in Fig. 22.8 with the conventional sketch in Fig. 13.15. See also paragraph 22.4 and Fig. 22.4 where proportioning is discussed and illustrated.

22.9. CAUTIONS IN THE USE OF SIMPLIFIED PRACTICES. Simplified drafting practices are comparatively new and therefore may not be understood by some engineers and manufacturers. For example, for one unfamiliar with simplified practices, the drawing in Fig. 22.7 *may* be more difficult to read than a conventional drawing. Further, if mistakes occur in manufacture because of misreading a simplified drawing, the saving in drafting time is offset many times over in costly rejected parts. The common, and safest, use of simplified practices occurs *within an organization* where everyone concerned is thoroughly trained in all company practices. It is potentially dangerous to send a simplified drawing to a subcontractor or supplier *unless it is known* that *all* special drafting practices will be understood.

22.10. ABBREVIATIONS. Another economy results from using abbreviations where this does not detract from the readability of the drawing. American Standard abbreviations are given in the Appendix. Note the use of abbreviations in Figs. 22.2 to 22.8.

TEMPLATES AND OVERLAYS

22.11. TEMPLATES. Use of modern aids such as the drafting machine, pencil sharpener and pointer, and special instruments such as an ellipsograph (Fig. 22.52) conserves drafting time. For features such as circles, ellipses, boltheads, nuts, and symbols which must be drawn repeatedly, a template greatly shortens the time required for layout. Figure 22.9 shows several typical templates: (*A*) and (*B*), Rapidesign templates for ellipses and circles; (*C*), a Tilt-hex template for boltheads; (*D*), a Du-all template for a variety of operations; (*E*), a Holometer for boltheads and nuts; (*F*), a K & E thread template; and (*G*), a Rapidesign template for piping symbols.

A number of symbol templates are available for use with Leroy lettering equipment; Fig. 22.10 shows some of

FIG. 22.9. Templates. A wide variety are available for many purposes. Their use conserves drafting time.

MAP SYMBOLS

ALSO CAPITAL LETTERS & NUMBERS, SIZE 80

WELDING SYMBOLS

0123456789()"°#
0123456789   ALSO CAPS & NUMBERS, SIZE 100

ELECTRICAL SYMBOLS

FIG. 22.10. Leroy symbol templates (Keuffel & Esser Co.). A wide variety of these templates, for use with standard Leroy equipment, are available. Special templates of a user's design also can be obtained.

FIG. 22.11. A symbolic drawing. Components are shown by symbols. Magnitudes and other details are given by lettered information. *Courtesy of Radio Corporation of America.*

FIG. 22.12. An overlay sheet. This overlay is custom-made for a specific use. Portions needed are cut from the sheet and fastened to the drawing with transparent tape.

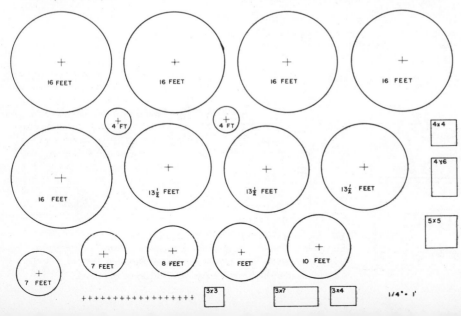

them. Figure 22.11 is an example of a symbolic drawing.

22.12. OVERLAYS. An overlay is typed or printed detail reproduced on tracing paper, Mylar, or some other translucent or transparent material. Overlays are fastened to a drawing by means of transparent tape or the adhesive backing on the overlay.

Most companies have standard items that must be repeated on drawings. The use of overlays eliminates the need for redrawing these items each time they appear. One prominent processing company, for example, is continually build-

ing new plants and expanding existing plants, and it must make plant layout drawings showing the location of equipment. The plan views of tanks, pumps, filters, and other items are drawn and identified for size and scale, and then reproduced on a suitable overlay material. Figure 22.12 shows the standard overlay sheet. Needed items are cut from this sheet and applied to the drawing with tape. Figure 22.13 gives the finished result. The outline of the overlays and the tape will show faintly on the reproduced drawing but will not impair its readability. Extra information is lettered on the overlays, as shown in Fig. 22.13.

Many standard items are available from companies that manufacture a general line of overlays. For details that are time-consuming to draw and that occur again and again, the use of an overlay such as the "north point" illustrated in Fig. 22.14 is a great economy. This north point is manufactured by the Stanpat Co., which makes a wide variety of overlays, all printed on a transparent material with gummed backing. See also paragraph 19.23 and Fig. 19.22.

Parts lists, tables, references, and specifications must often appear on drawings, and it is time-consuming to letter these. Laborious lettering can be eliminated by employing a standard overlay such as the one shown in Fig. 22.15. If a standard overlay cannot be used, information can be typed on blank stanpat or some other overlay material and applied to the drawing.

The use of overlays is not restricted to prepared details and lettering. Black tape is used to block out unwanted areas or in place of drawn material. It is especially useful for wide detail such

22.13. Reproduction Methods

as the building outline in Fig. 22.13. Tape can be cut with a sharp blade to any width needed. Tapes in widths from ⅟₃₂ in. to 1 in. for full, dashed, and special lines and for areas, and a "tape pen" for application are manufactured by Chart-Pac, Inc., Leeds, Massachusetts.

SPECIAL USES OF REPRODUCTION

22.13. REPRODUCTION METHODS. There are many reproduction methods by which drafting time can be saved. Whole drawings or portions can be reproduced, and alterations can be made by painting out previous detail with an eradicating solution and then drawing in the new feature. Several companies manufacture reproducible materials and machines. The materials of the Eastman Kodak Company are typical. The following information is adapted from their supplement to the Kodak data book on Kodagraph reproduction materials:

An intermediate printed on Kodagraph autopositive paper saves wear

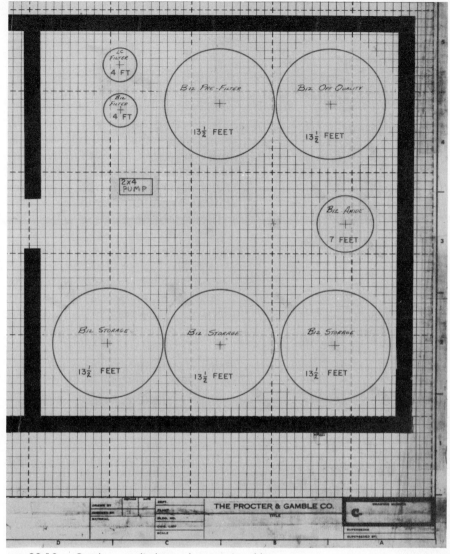

FIG. 22.13. Overlays applied to a drawing. In addition to saving drafting time, overlays can be moved around as the arrangement of elements is planned.

FIG. 22.14. A gummed overlay. This "north point" is typical of details that are often repeated. Such details are expensive to draw and an overlay saves practically all drafting time required for the detail. *Courtesy of Stanpat Co.*

FIG. 22.15. A gummed overlay for tabular information. This overlay is printed in reverse for application to the back of the drawing, thus preserving the front for any extra information that must be added. The illustration shows the overlay partially in place, to indicate how the overlay is applied. *Courtesy of Stanpat Co.*

and tear on original drawings. Prints are made from the autopositive, thus eliminating handling of the original.

A drawing that is unprintable because of age or hard use can be printed on Kodagraph autopositive paper and then printed from this intermediate. By this method its usefulness is restored without cost in drafting time.

Direct-process prints or white prints are often the only available record. A print of this record made on Kodagraph autopositive paper provides an intermediate from which copies can be made.

When a blueprint is the only available record, additional prints can be obtained by making an intermediate on Kodagraph autopositive paper or kodak repro-negative paper.

Portions of two or more drawings can be made into a new drawing by printing the portions on separate sheets of Kodagraph autopositive paper and then combining these to make prints.

Kodagraph contact materials, which must be handled in a safelighted darkroom, are used to produce printable copies of old drawings, blueprints, brownprints, or direct-process prints.

Kodalith film is often used to reproduce details for insertion in other drawings or reproducibles. A reproducible is any medium from which prints can be made.

Kodagraph projection and fast-projection materials provide enlarged- or reduced-scale prints from negatives made in a camera.

Reproducibles save much drafting time. The background of Fig. 22.13 is an intermediate printed on transparent material. Thus the standard grid drawing is available in quantity.

FIG. 22.16. Method of making a reproducible. A negative in the enlarger is projected through a contact screen onto a sensitized plastic sheet, held in a vacuum frame. The exposed sheet is then developed in conventional photographic trays. *Courtesy of Procter & Gamble.*

PHOTO DRAWING

22.14. A recent development in the field of engineering presentation is the use of photography to reduce drafting time or to replace conventional drawings. By recording engineering subjects, the camera has become an important aid.

Individual applications of photo-drawing technique vary widely in industry, depending on the type of business in which the company is engaged. There are two principal areas in which photo drawings are of value: (1) in revising and in adding to existing equipment, (2) in recording and in supplementing model designs. Many process companies constantly change their facilities, to make a new product or to improve and expand; photography can play a major role in such engineering changes. Some companies have manufacturing operations that call for adding completely new units. Photo-drawings of models are used to record the design, and aid in obtaining the best job on new-unit construction at the lowest cost.

Regardless of how they are used, photo drawings have two main advantages:

1. They lower engineering costs. The camera records information that would have to be drawn if photo drawings were not utilized.

2. They provide better visualization of the design intent than is obtained from a drawing. The camera records an image approximately as the eye sees it —in three dimensions. In contrast, when conventional plan and elevation drawings are made, the reader has to

mentally combine the various views to visualize the design intent.

22.15.   PHOTO DRAWINGS FOR REVISIONS OF EXISTING AREAS.   The cost of engineering revisions of existing facilities can be reduced one-third to one-half through the use of photo drawings. The original and main use of photo drawings is in the field of piping rework, but new applications are being found in the electrical, mechanical, structural, and site-clearance fields.

No matter what phase of rework is being engineered, preparation of a photo drawing is similar and involves four basic steps: (1) taking the photographs, (2) making the reproducible[3] (the transparent base for all drawing effort), (3) drawing on the reproducible to show the design intent of the revision, and (4) making prints from the photo drawing for distribution to the construction forces.

Arrangements for taking the photographs depend on the facilities at the disposal of the engineering personnel. The highest-quality reproducibles, and therefore the best photo drawings, are obtained when the picture is taken by a skilled photographer working in close association with the engineer or designer responsible for the project. The photographer knows the correct camera setting, lighting, etc., that will produce a negative which can be made into a good reproducible; the engineer or designer knows what changes are to be made and can direct the photographer so that the photo drawings will show clearly the work to be done.

A reproducible is made in several ways, depending on the company's

FIG. 22.17.   Illustration of screening on a reproducible. The drawing at the bottom shows a normal, screened positive image. The portion at the top is the small section enlarged ten times to show the screen pattern of dots. *Courtesy of Procter & Gamble.*

[3] See paragraph 22.13.

facilities. The procedure diagramed in Fig. 22.16 gives the highest-quality reproducible because it has less photographic steps than other methods. The resulting reproducible is a screened image on which highlights and shadows have been obtained by varying the concentration of white and black dots (see Fig. 22.17). Screened images, with their tonal characteristics, give much superior and more realistic prints than are available with printing processes that record only in solid black and pure white.

FIG. 22.18. Typical photo drawing of piping for the revision of an existing facility. Observe the extensive notes and directions added to the reproducible in pencil. *Courtesy of Procter & Gamble.*

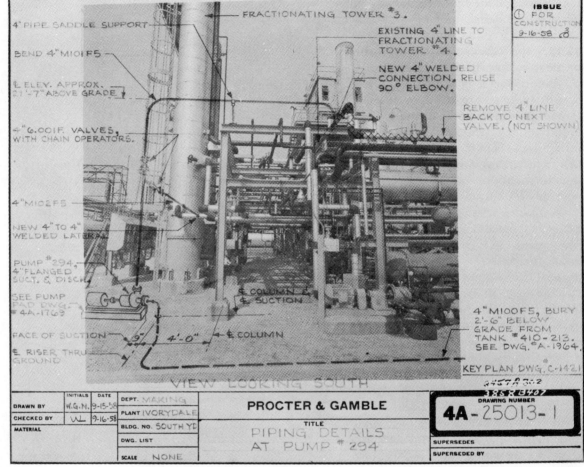

Several materials have been developed and are used as reproducible bases. The best ones are made of polyester resin-base plastics but some acetate-base material is used. The drawing technique is the same no matter what material is used to prepare the reproducible. There are no unusual mechanical problems in drawing on photo drawings. By using a soft pencil, which produces heavy black lines, and by controlling the printing speed, it is possible to make additions stand out in contrast to the existing photographic background, as shown in Fig. 22.18.

Frequently it is necessary to clear a site before new equipment can be installed. Instructions for site clearance are easily transmitted by crossing out on a photo drawing the items that are to be removed, as indicated in Fig. 22.19. A second photo drawing of the same area is then made with the existing equipment removed from the picture so that it does not interfere with the drawing of new equipment. Any part of the photographic image can be removed from a photo-drawing reproducible with a wet eraser or with chemicals. Note the removed and drawn-in portions in Fig. 22.20.

Perspective can cause difficulty when drawn material is added to a photograph. Since each photo drawing has a slightly different station point, it is important that the draftsman determine this point and draw the new information with a similar perspective; otherwise the drawing will have a peculiar appearance and may convey the wrong intent to the construction forces.

Usually photo drawings convey design intent with only the important control dimensions indicated. It would be difficult, but not impossible, to include all of the detailed dimensions normally shown on conventional drawings. Craftsmen are accustomed to revision work and to "field checking" the drawings they receive, so the lack of complete dimensioning is not critical if the design intent is clear. Note the di-

FIG. 22.19. Typical drafting-room scene when work is being done on a photo drawing.

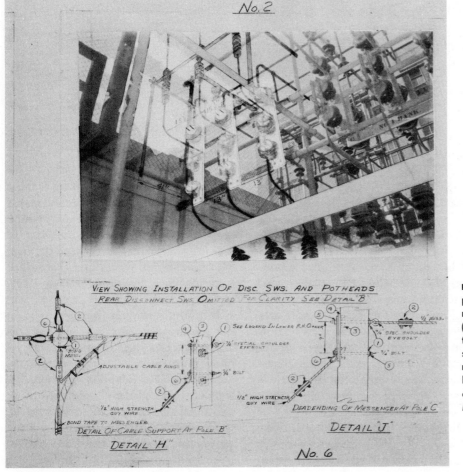

FIG. 22.20. Typical completed photo drawing for piping revision of an existing facility. (Compare with Fig. 22.18.) In this case the photo portion shows design intent, and the necessary details are given below in conventional orthographic views. *Courtesy of Procter & Gamble.*

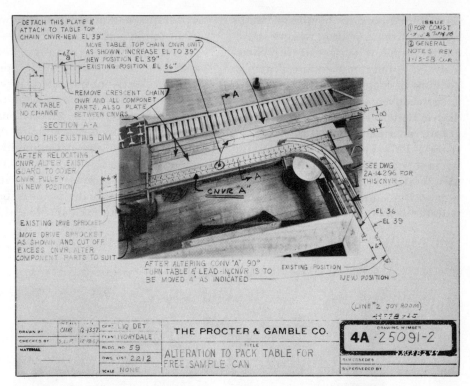

FIG. 22.21. Typical photo drawing for revision of mechanical equipment. Note that this drawing employs dimensioning and notes applied to the photo portion, and also uses small explanatory views. *Courtesy of Procter & Gamble.*

FIG. 22.22. Method for shadowless lighting. The model is placed in front of a light box, which eliminates back shadows. Shadowless front lighting is produced by a swinging fluorescent light. *Courtesy of Procter & Gamble.*

mensioning and extensive use of notes in Fig. 22.21.

When more than one photograph is required to portray a change, each photo drawing is referenced to the other. This is done when there are multiple images on one photo drawing as well as when there are several single-image photo drawings. When there are several photo drawings for a project, a key plan is made. The key plan is a simple sketch of the area involved on which are shown the numbers of the various photo drawings with an arrow indicating the direction in which each picture was taken.

22.16. MODEL PHOTO DRAWINGS. The camera can also record a design shown by a model, thus giving the engineer or designer a drawing base to which he can add information.

The basic steps followed in making photo drawings of existing areas (taking the picture, preparing the reproducible, drawing in the engineering information, making the prints) apply also in making model photo drawings. The principal difference between the two uses is in taking of the pictures.

Model photo drawings are used for (1) equipment layouts, (2) location drawings, (3) information for people remote from the model, and (4) permanent records of the job once the model is destroyed. All these applications require that the photo drawings be shadowless, so that the equipment and piping on the model stand out clearly.

One solution to the shadowless-lighting problem is shown in Fig. 22.22, where a swinging light is employed. There are other solutions, which vary from a simple "washing with light" technique to building a complete "tent" of lights around the model. A photo drawing produced with the equipment in Fig. 22.22 is shown in Fig. 22.23.

The problems of perspective are more difficult to solve. The ultimate in model photo drawings is a complete absence of perspective, that is, purely orthographic photo drawings, representing all dimensions to true scale. Most companies use the more easily attainable minimum perspective, which is obtained through use of a long-focal-length camera lens. Photo drawings in this perspective are not unreasonably difficult to dimension and understand, but are still not scalable. Development work has been done on equipment that will take orthographic photographs—devices that utilize segments of parabolic mirrors combined to form a telecentric optical system. Such devices can take

FIG. 22.23. A portion of a shadowless model photo drawing. The photographic portions were produced by the lighting method shown in Fig. 22.22. *Courtesy of Procter & Gamble.*

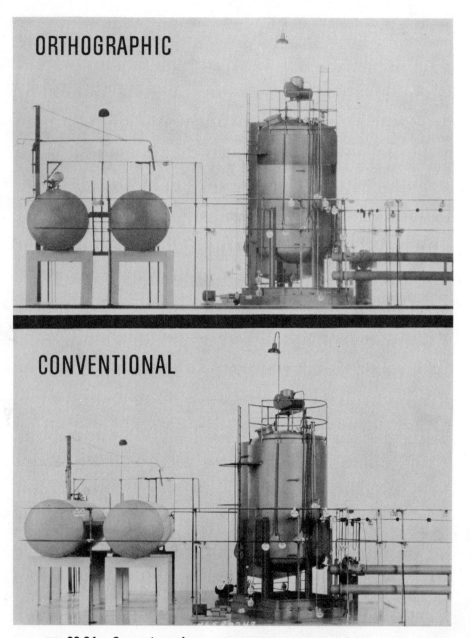

ORTHOGRAPHIC

CONVENTIONAL

FIG. 22.24. Comparison of methods of taking photographs of a model. The lower picture was taken with a conventional camera; the upper picture, with a device employing a telecentric system to produce an orthographic (nonperspective) view. *Courtesy of Procter & Gamble.*

perspective results, the reproducible, which is the base for the model photo drawing, is made in the same manner as previously outlined for existing-area photo drawings.

MODELS

22.17. SCALE MODELS. Three-dimensional models serve a purpose in design that normally cannot be achieved by two-dimensional drawings. Whereas almost anyone can look at a model for a short period of time and grasp the design intent, only those trained in reading and interpreting drawings can visualize what is portrayed by plans, elevations, sections, and details shown on drawings.

Models are used:

1. To provide study tools for engineers and designers

2. As a method of presentation and review

3. To communicate the designer's ideas to the construction forces, thus reducing the number of drawings required for some phases of construction.

22.18. MODEL TYPES. There are many different types of models which an engineer can use. They can be grouped into four general types: (1) architectural presentation, (2) equipment prototype, (3) equipment arrangement, and (4) process. The utilization of these types of models varies widely from one company to another, but there is increasingly wider acceptance of modeling as an aid in engineering.

Architectural Presentation. A model of this type is built strictly for approval of a proposed design. Models for presentation are usually built to a small scale

scalable photographs of a model or other three-dimensional subject. An example is shown in Fig. 22.24.

Once the picture has been taken, under conditions that will produce either orthographic or minimum-

FIG. 22.25.   Typical architectural model. This type of model is made for presentation of a design to the client. *Courtesy of Procter & Gamble.*

but with considerable detail and elaboration to achieve the realism desired. Some even have simulated lighting and working parts. All have miniature trees, bushes, sidewalks, and other landscaping details, in addition to detailed representation of the architectural treatment. A typical architectural model, which is relatively simple compared with many, is shown in Fig. 22.25.

Equipment Prototype. Prototype models are built to check the appearance or feasibility of a design and to assist in sales efforts. They are usually built to a large scale. Often they are full size, and for large pieces of equipment they are one-quarter or one-half size. Appliance manufacturers always build prototype models before setting up a production run. Several alternative designs for radios, clocks, etc., frequently are modeled and distributed to large buyers to check their preferences before a final design is settled upon. Car makers always make a full-size model of a new car to check the appearance before they proceed with the expensive tooling that leads to the new product. A typical prototype model is shown in Fig. 22.26.

Equipment Arrangement. The equipment-arrangement model has perhaps

had the widest acceptance and application. This is due to the ease with which it is constructed and straightforward methods of utilization. The modeling techniques vary slightly with the type of facility under study. There are three general applications of this type of model: (1) small-scale plot plan, (2) machine shop or factory, (3) process equipment.

The scale and the amount of detail

FIG. 22.26.   Typical prototype model of equipment. This kind of model is used to demonstrate a new device or design. *Courtesy of Industrial Models.*

FIG. 22.27. Typical plot-plan model. This model, built to a scale of ⅛″ = 1′-0″, is used to establish the over-all layout of a factory. *Courtesy of Procter & Gamble.*

on these models vary to suit individual requirements, but in general the scale ranges from ⅛ in. to the foot on plot-plan models to ¾ in. to the foot on some process-equipment models. Scale is an important consideration in planning a model. The size depends on how much detail must be shown for visualization of the problems to be solved.

Plot-plan models are usually built to a small scale for two reasons: (1) not much detail is needed to show the relationships between buildings and/or units of equipment; (2) the plot under study is frequently so big that a large scale would make the size of the model inconvenient to work with. A common scale is ⅛ in. to the foot. The model in Fig. 22.27 is built to this scale. As can be seen, the buildings and equipment are simple blocks. This type of model is used instead of drawing several alternative plot plans on paper. To study alternatives, an engineer or designer simply moves the blocks around on the study board until he finds the optimum arrangement, taking into account future planning as well as the current project.

FIG. 22.28. Typical factory layout model. This type of model shows equipment, route and assembly lines, raw and finished material, etc. *Courtesy of Visual Plant Layouts.*

After he has studied the arrangement, he invites other interested persons to review and approve the layout. With modeling, much more can be contributed by all levels of management than would normally be anticipated with drawings, and this usually results in the best over-all job for a company at the lowest total cost.

Figure 22.28 shows a typical machine-shop or factory layout model. This type of model is widely used to determine the most efficient manufacturing operations. It is commonly constructed to a scale of ¼ in. to the foot, and many companies have models of all the tools in their factory so that each time a manufacturing change is contemplated, its effect can be studied by modeling. This type of effort has become so common that die-cast and injection-molded models of the more common machine tools and factory accessories are available at low cost. On mass-produced models it is practical to have more detail than would normally be shown if a few units were made for a specific project. This increased detail adds to the realism without running up the cost of the modeling effort. Usually a grid background is used to facilitate the alternative placing of the model components.

Chemical process industries also use equipment-arrangement models to determine the most economical placing of equipment from a first-cost and operating standpoint. Whereas machine-shop or factory models are built to a ¼ in. to 1'-0" scale, the scale of process-equipment layout models varies widely with the physical size of the equipment and the size of the area under study. Models of large areas with large equipment, such as a petroleum refinery, commonly are

made to ¼ in. to the foot. Small processing units frequently are made to ¾ in. to the foot and in special cases even larger. The equipment is represented by wooden dowels or blocks on the smaller-scale models and by styrofoam or some other light-weight plastic on those of larger scales. A typical process-equipment layout model is shown in Fig. 22.29. Many modeling companies now supply special kits designed to facilitate layout study work. These kits include an assortment of equipment and basic material and usually provide some patented method of building a model with multistoried units. The application of such a kit is shown in Fig. 22.30. As with other layout models, the object is to find an arrangement that will give a unit of the lowest over-all cost, by having as many people as practicable make contributions.

FIG. 22.29. Typical equipment-arrangement model. This one is for processing units in a chemical plant. *Courtesy of Procter & Gamble.*

FIG. 22.30. Structural components of a modeling kit. These are used to facilitate the erection and use of a preliminary process-equipment model. *Courtesy of Industrial Models.*

FIG. 22.31. Examples of equipment models. These are made of plastic and are shown here prior to painting. *Courtesy of Procter & Gamble.*

One reason why layout models have been so effective is that once the model pieces are built, the engineer moves them around and studies the layout himself, instead of trying to solve the problem on paper.

Process Models. One important use of models is in portraying complete process systems. Full sets of drawings of modern piping systems which represent every detail of design and its relationship to equipment, structural steel, electrical conduit, etc., are time-consuming and expensive to prepare. Many man-hours are required to make the necessary checks between all phases—electrical, mechanical, piping—to assure no interferences and to show the piping in the most economical manner. After the drawings are completed, only trained people can read and visualize the piping systems. In view of this, the modern

construction practice is to make sketches of each pipe line, and carry out fabrication from these.

Even with the best designers and checkers, it is difficult to find all errors and interferences and to arrive at the minimum cost when stainless steel and other expensive materials are used. Costly mistakes in construction have lead many companies to use three-dimensional models of their piping systems. Use of these models varies from company to company, and in most instances the application of modeling as an engineering technique has evolved because of well-established habits and methods of operation. The application of piping models ranges from building a model *after* the design has been worked out on paper, thus making the model an instrument for confirmation and approval; to building a model without assembly piping drawings, thus using the model to communicate design information to the construction forces.

Piping models normally are built to a scale that varies from ¼ in. to the foot up to ¾ in. to the foot and occasionally to 1 in. to the foot. In general, the scale used depends upon the intended use of the model. If conventional drawings are prepared along with the model, a scale of ¼ in. or ⅜ in. to the foot is large enough. In this case the model is used for confirmation and approval, and detail and accuracy are not required since information is given on the drawings. If the model is used to the utmost—if the designs are worked out on it and it is then used by the construction forces without the aid of drawings—the scale should be ½ in. or ¾ in. to the foot. If the piping is large-size (6 in., 10 in., or 12 in., in diameter), such as in a paper mill, the ½ in. scale is adequate. If the average line size is 2 in. in diameter or less, the ¾ in. scale should be used. The ¾ in. scale has an added advantage in being easier to work, because with this scale $\frac{1}{16}$ in. on the model represents 1 in. actual, and this is the tolerance to which models can be made economically.

Regardless of scale and use, methods of building piping models are similar but of course vary between companies. The first step in building a model is to construct what is called the basic model. The basic model consists of a base board, models of all the equipment, and a replica of the structural design. All equipment is mounted in its appropriate location on the base or structure, and forms the background on which the piping and other systems are installed. It is interesting to note that this is the same way the actual plant will be constructed. Also, this method is similar to that used in making conventional piping assembly drawings— the equipment and structural background is drawn on the paper before the piping design is started. In modern practice plastics are used almost exclusively in building the basic model. Several different kinds of plastic meet the requirements for this purpose. They are easy to work, light in weight, not subject to deterioration from moisture and moderate temperature changes, easy to join with solvent cements, and easy to paint. Figure 22.31 illustrates some unpainted basic-equipment items made of plastic. Figure 22.32 shows a typical basic model that is ready for installation of the piping.

The piping may be installed on the model from conventional drawings or the design may be worked out on the model directly without making conventional piping assembly drawings. In either case the piping itself can be represented by using the "fine-wire" or the "true-scale" technique. The fine-wire technique normally uses a $\frac{1}{16}$ in.-diameter brass wire, which represents the pipe center line, with fiber disks or rubber sleeves of the appropriate diameter spaced along its length to indicate the outside diameter of the pipe. The true-scale technique uses plastic rod or

FIG. 22.32. Completed basic model. At this stage the model is ready for installation of the piping. *Courtesy of Procter & Gamble.*

tubing whose outside diameter is equal to the scale diameter of the various standard pipe sizes. A typical fine-wire model is shown in Fig. 22.33. Fine-wire models are sometimes unsuccessful because inaccuracies and faulty representation on the model result in a piping system that cannot be installed as shown on the model; this is especially true at the smaller scales. As a result many companies now build true-scale models. Several modeling companies market a complete line of true-scale piping components made from various types of plastic. These are quickly and easily assembled. It is anticipated that in the near future almost all piping models will be constructed by the true-scale

technique because this method gives superior representation and better visualization by all concerned. Figure 22.34 shows a typical true-scale modeling system developed for a scale of ¾ in. to the foot.

The installation of the piping on the basic model is straightforward when drawings have been prepared. When the model alone is used, the basic procedure is to design the piping on the model directly from the flow diagrams without any intermediate studies. Since there are no drawings, every pipe line, regardless of size, and each instrument and piping accessory (such as valves, steam traps, and strainers) is installed in its proper location. Before installation

FIG. 22.33. Typical fine-wire model. This one is for a process unit. *Courtesy of Procter & Gamble.*

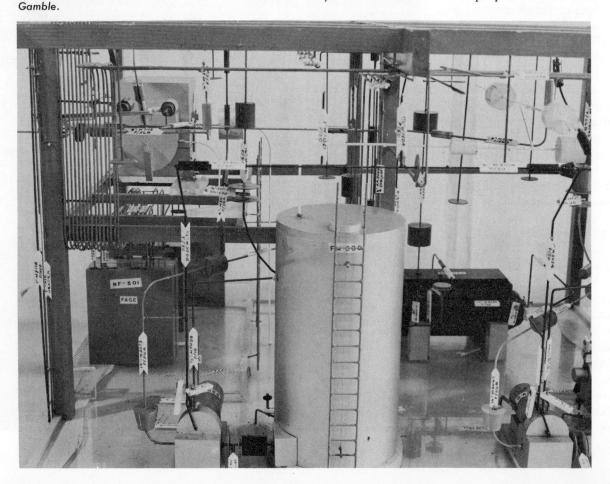

FIG. 22.34. True-scale modeling components. This illustration shows one of several systems that have been developed. *Courtesy of Procter & Gamble.*

of the piping is begun, some guiding rules are usually established by a model specification. One of these rules will establish the piping elevations. For example, it might be specified that all pipes running east to west will run at 8-ft elevation and those running north to south will run at 10-ft elevation. With a few guiding rules such as this, it is practical to install the piping directly on the model from the flow diagram. Figure 22.35 shows a typical true-scale model with most of the piping installed on it. When the model is nearly completed, it is carefully examined in a "model-review conference"

FIG. 22.35. True-scale model under construction. This illustration shows the model at the stage of construction before color-coding and pipe-line tagging. *Courtesy of Procter & Gamble.*

by all parties who have an interest in the project. At this review each pipe is traced out and examined critically to make sure that it fulfills the needs of the process in addition to representing the most economical design. After the review the model is revised to reflect the contribution of the reviewers and then color coded, tagged, and shipped to the field construction site.

Normally, model color coding can be carried out in one of two ways. If the model is a confirmation or approval model, the pipe lines are coded according to the system of which they are a part; for example, all water lines might be light blue. If the model illustrates a piping design for which there are no conventional drawings, each pipe line is coded to indicate its construction specification; for example, yellow might mean that a pipe is to be constructed of Sched. 10, type 304 stainless steel.

Piping is not the only phase that is shown on a process model. Since one of the difficult things to achieve in working out a design for a complicated piping system is the coordination with other phases, all other phases should be shown on the model with the piping. If all the phases go together on the model, they will fit in the actual construction. How much, and to what detail, other phases are shown varies widely. Many companies now expand the model approach used for piping to some of the other phases, such as electrical-conduit routing, lighting, chutes, ducts, and instrument location and mounting. Some companies show designs of minor structural items, such as ladders, handrails, small-equipment supports, and platforms on the model without making additional drawings. The construction forces then install these items directly from the design intent shown on the model. Figure 22.36 shows a completed true-scale piping model that has been

FIG. 22.36. Completed true-scale model. This one shows all phases—piping, electrical and mechanical—and is now ready for use by the construction forces. *Courtesy of Procter & Gamble.*

color coded and tagged, and is ready
for shipment to the construction site. It
is typical of a final piping model on
which all the piping, electrical conduit,
lights, chutes, ducts, instruments, and
minor structural items are shown. From
this model, the unit will be constructed
without conventional assembly drawings for the various phases.

All the modeling work mentioned in
this chapter has developed in answer to
the problems inherent in visualizing a
design when the information is presented solely by drawings. Models give
a realistic rendition that is not achieved
in drawings. However, drawings will
always be required because some details
that can *not* be shown on models *can* be
shown on drawings.

ILLUSTRATED DRAWINGS

22.19.   ILLUSTRATION.   Illustrated drawings are used in commercial practice
for many of the same reasons that
models are made. As applied to the
graphic language, illustration means
clarification in the readability of a
drawing by the use of shading and
special methods of projection and representation. Often a drawing can be
made so clear that a person unfamiliar
with graphic methods can read it as
readily as one experienced in them.
Any drawing—orthographic, diagrammatic, or pictorial—made freehand or
with instruments, in pencil or ink, may
be illustrated. Figure 22.37 is an example of an illustrated drawing.

22.20.   TYPES OF ILLUSTRATED DRAWINGS.
Illustrated drawings are used for many
purposes and in many different fields.
The following examples are typical:

FIG. 22.37.   An illustrated
drawing. This is an "exploded"
pictorial used to illustrate the
method of assembly of a number
of parts.

Advertising illustrations are usually
shaded pictorial drawings, often with
color added to make the presentation
as forceful as possible.

Catalogue illustrations, orthographic or
pictorial, are often shaded in pencil or
ink, by stippling, air brush, etc.

Operation, service, and repair charts are
drawings showing the working parts of
a machine with appropriate directions
for the purpose intended. These drawings are effective in shaded pictorial
form.

Piping, wiring, and installation diagrams
are easy to read when made in shaded
pictorial form.

*Architectural and engineering presentation
drawings,* sometimes shaded in pencil or
ink, often in water color, show the
building or structure as it will appear
when completed.

Textbook illustrations in pictorial form,
usually in black and white but sometimes in two colors or full color, add visual clarity and give emphasis not
achieved by words alone.

FIG. 22.38. A design illustration. This shows the breakdown of an airplane into basic components.

Patent drawings are usually shaded to bring out and clarify every feature of the invention.

Production drawings, from original design sketches to the final details, subassemblies, and assemblies, are frequently made in pictorial form, often shaded. Such drawings are particularly useful when persons not trained in reading orthographic drawings are employed for manufacturing.

22.21. ILLUSTRATED WORKING DRAWINGS. Modern mass-production methods demand simplification and breakdown of a multitude of manufacturing opera-

tions. Illustrated drawings bring complex and difficult jobs within the grasp of workers not trained in reading orthographic drawings. They are used in every phase of production, from the original design to the final operating instructions.

Actual practice varies somewhat within an industry and widely among industries, but, in general, illustrated drawings can be classified as (1) *design drawings,* (2) *manufacturing illustrations,* and (3) *operation and maintenance illustrations.*

Design drawings include a variety of pictorial illustrations that show the machine or structure broken down into small, workable units, and then give details of construction, location of equipment, structural features, function of parts and equipment, tooling methods, etc. These drawings are used to study the complete production job and to plan and correlate the work. As the design progresses they are altered, corrected, or redrawn. The preliminary production breakdown shown in Fig. 22.38 is an example of the type of illustration used in the design stage of the work.

Manufacturing illustrations give detailed information regarding the breakdown

FIG. 22.39. A manufacturing illustration. It specifies the parts and tools needed for an assembly. Drawings of this type are used for original manufacture and in service manuals. Compare this illustration with the orthographic drawing for Prob. 13.2.2.

JOB TICKET
CRANE HOOK ASSEMBLY
TOOL REQUIREMENTS
2-3¾" OPEN END WRENCHES
1-4½" OPEN END WRENCH
1-MACHINISTS VICE
1-12 OZ. BALL PEEN HAMMER
1-PAIR PLIERS

PROCEDURE
I TRUNION ASSEMBLY
    PART 5 CRANE HOOK   1 REQ.
    PART 9 WASHER   2 REQ.
    PART 6 HOOK TRUNION 1 REQ.
    PART 8 A.S. SLOTTED NUT 1 REQ.
    PART 4 NUT LOCK PIN   1 REQ.
    PART 10 COTTER PIN   2 REQ.
II PULLEY ASSEMBLY
    PART 3 PULLEY PIN   2 REQ.
    PART 2 PULLEY   2 REQ.
III PLATE ASSEMBLY
    PART 1 SIDE PLATE   2 REQ.
    INSTALL
        PULLEY PIN ASSEMBLY
        TRUNION ASSEMBLY
    PART 7 A.S. SEMI-FIN. NUT 6 REQ.

of the structure or machine from which a multitude of separate illustrations are made to show the location of sub-assemblies, parts, and equipment; give directions for performing operations; provide detailed information for the manufacture of parts; and furnish directions for assembly. Figure 22.39 is an example of a manufacturing illustration taken from the set of details given in Fig. 13.2.2.

Operation and maintenance illustrations give directions for disassembly, repair and replacement of parts, lubrication, inspection and care of equipment, etc. In many cases the drawings that were originally made for manufacturing can be used in a service manual. Figure 22.40 is an example.

22.22. DRAWING FOR REPRODUCTION.
Drawings for illustrations in books, periodicals, catalogues, or other printed materials must be made with an understanding of reproduction processes.

Preparation of the Drawings. The drawings are usually made larger than the final size of the illustration and reduced photographically in the reproduction process. Consequently the work must be done with visualization of the line weights, contrast, size of lettering, and general effect in reduced size. To preserve the hand-drawn character of the original, the reduction should be slight. For a very smooth effect, the drawing may be as much as three or four times larger than the reproduction. The best general size is one and a half (for one-third reduction) to two times (for one-half reduction) the linear size of the cut.

The reduction is usually an even proportion such as one-fourth, one-third,

FIG. 22.40. A maintenance illustration. This type of drawing is used in a service manual to illustrate repair by replacement of components.

FIG. 22.41. A drawing for reproduction. This drawing is made for reduction to half size. The reduced reproduction is shown in Fig. 22.42.

one-half, etc., although odd reductions may be used. For a drawing marked "Reduce ⅓," the reproduction will be two-thirds the linear size of the original. Figure 22.41 illustrates the appearance of an original drawing, and Fig. 22.42 shows the same drawing reduced one-half. The coarse appearance, open shading, and lettering size of the original

FIG. 22.42. The drawing shown in Fig. 22.41 reduced to half size and reproduced.

should be noted. The line work must be kept fairly "open," for if lines are drawn close together the space between them may choke in the reproduction and mar the effect. A reducing glass, a concave lens mounted like a reading glass, is sometimes used to aid in judging the appearance of a drawing on reduction.

Drawings for reproduction may be altered and corrected in ways not permissible in other work. Irregularities may be painted out with opaque white. A sharp blade or "scratcher" may be used to clean off small errors. If a figure that has been inked is to be shifted, it may be cut out and pasted in the required position. A piece of paper may be pasted over a portion of the drawing for blocking out or redrawing. Reference letters and numbers, notes, and other lettering are often cut out of a sheet printed from type of proper size, and pasted on the drawing. Marks made by edges of pasted pieces will not show on the final reproduction as they will be eliminated by the engraver when the plate is finished.

Methods of Reproduction. Drawings for illustrations are reproduced by one of the photomechanical processes, that is, by zinc or copper etching, halftone, or one of the methods of photolithography.

Line drawings are usually reproduced by zinc etching. By this process the drawing is photographed on a pre-pared zinc plate (when a particularly fine result is desired, a copper plate is used); then the plate is etched with acid, leaving the lines in relief and giving, when mounted, a block that can be printed along with type in an ordinary printing press. Drawings for zinc etching should be made on smooth white paper or tracing cloth in black drawing ink. The finest lines should be black and definite—weak thin lines will not reproduce well.

Wash drawings and photographs are reproduced in a similar way on copper by the halftone process. A ruled screen is placed in front of the camera lens, and it breaks up the tones into a series of dots. The fineness of the screen varies with the kind of paper used. Screens of 65 to 100 lines to the square inch are used for newspaper halftones, of 110 to 133 lines to the square inch for ordinary commercial and magazine halftones, of 133 to 175 lines to the square inch for fine half tones printed on very smooth coated paper.

The photolithographic processes may be used to reproduce line drawings, wash drawings, or photographs. The drawing is photographed on a thin sensitized sheet and chemically processed to use in a lithographic press in which the plate prints on a rubber blanket, which in turn prints on the paper. Paper, zinc, bimetal, and trimetal plates are used, depending upon the number of copies needed. This book is printed by photolithography.

22.23. SPECIAL SHADING METHODS. There are several methods of representing textures, in addition to the regular methods of shading in pencil and ink, given in Chap. 6.

FIG. 22.43. Smudge shading. This method gives an appearance similar to airbrush work and photography.

Smudge shading is a rapid method often used for smooth surfaces (Fig. 22.43). Graphite from a soft pencil, powdered graphite, charcoal, or crayon sauce is first rubbed on a piece of paper, then picked up with a piece of cotton or an artist's stump and applied to the drawing. High lights are easily brought out with a sharpened eraser. Be careful in shading an erased portion, however, as the abrading of the paper will cause the shading medium to "take" more heavily.

Stippling with pen, pencil, brush, or sponge is an effective method of indicating rough-texture surfaces. In pen and pencil stippling, a good effect of light and shade is achieved with a multitude of dots, widely spaced for light surfaces, more closely for dark surfaces. In brush and sponge stippling, printer's ink or artist's oil color (drier added) is first worked out smoothly on a palette; then the medium is picked up from the palette with a bristle brush or sponge and applied to the drawing with a dabbing motion. Sharp edges of shaded areas can be maintained by the use of masks.

Small areas are easily lightened with a razor blade or "scratcher." High lights are brought out with an eraser after the ink is dry. Figure 22.44 is an example of brush stippling with the smooth surfaces rendered by smudging.

Prepared papers are popular for a variety of commercial drawings. Craftint papers[4] have a shading pattern in the paper that is brought out by a special developer. They are of two types: single-tone and double-tone. When these papers are used, the drawing is penciled and the solid blacks are inked in with waterproof drawing ink. The shading

tones are then brought out by brushing on the developer in the areas where shading is wanted. These papers are available in many different shading patterns. Figure 22.38 is drawn on Craftint paper.

Shading screens of clear cellulose with printed line or dot patterns provide a simple and effective shading method. Craftint shading film is an overlay sheet containing a pattern printed in black or white. The shading pattern is easily rubbed off with a smooth wood stick wherever the shading is not wanted. Any part of the white pattern can be converted to black with a special developer.

Zip-a-tone screens[5] are of clear cellulose printed with a shading pattern and backed with a special adhesive. The screen is applied to the drawing and rubbed down lightly wherever shading is wanted. The shaded sections are then outlined with a cutting needle and the unwanted pieces stripped off. The portions left on the drawing are then rubbed down firmly with a burnisher. High lights can be painted out with opaque white if the area is too small to strip off in the regular way. A variety of shading patterns are available. Figure 2.60 is shaded with a Zip-a-tone screen.

Scratchboard. Drawing paper with a chalky surface is much used for commercial illustrations because of the ease with which white lines can be produced on a black background, as well as black lines on a white background. Rossboard,[6] available in many surface textures for both pencil and ink drawings, is popular among illustrators.

FIG. 22.44. Brush-stipple shading. This type of shading can also be done with a pen, pencil, or sponge.

[4] Craftint Manufacturing Co., Cleveland, Ohio.

[5] Para-tone Company, Chicago, Ill.

[6] Charles J. Ross Co., Philadelphia, Pa.

FIG. 22.45. A scratchboard drawing. The effect is similar to a woodcut.

For ink work, the drawing is penciled on the board in the usual way, and then inked by line-shading the lighter areas, working gradually to the darker areas. The darker areas are painted in with a brush, and when dry, white lines, dots, etc., are produced by scratching off the ink with a sharp-pointed knife, sharp stylus, or a needle point. Corrections are easily made by scratching off unwanted ink. Scratched areas can be reinked if necessary. Figure 22.45 is an example of scratchboard technique.

22.24. PATENT OFFICE DRAWINGS. In an application for letters patent on an invention or discovery a written description, called the "specification," is required, and for a machine or device a drawing showing every feature of the invention must also be supplied. A high standard of execution and conformity to the rules of the Patent Office must be observed. A pamphlet called "Rules of Practice," giving full information and rules governing Patent Office procedure in applying for a patent, can be obtained from the Commissioner of Patents, Washington, D.C.

The rules call for drawings made on smooth white paper, 10 by 15 in., with a border line 1 in. from the edges. A space not less than 1¼ in. inside the top border must be left blank for the printed title to be added by the Patent Office. Drawings must be made in India ink and drawn for reproduction to a reduced size. As many sheets as necessary may be used.

Patent Office drawings are not working drawings. They are descriptive and pictorial rather than structural, hence they have no center lines, dimensions, notes, or names of views. The views are lettered with figure numbers, and the parts are designated by reference numbers through which the invention is described in the specification.

The drawings may be made in orthographic, axonometric, oblique, or perspective projection. The pictorial system is used extensively, for all or part of the views. Surface shading is used whenever it will aid readability.

Figure 22.46 is an example of a Patent Office drawing.

SPECIAL METHODS AND EQUIPMENT

22.25. STRETCHING PAPER. If a drawing is to be tinted, the paper should be stretched on the board. First dampen it on both sides, with a sponge or under the faucet, until it is limp; then lay it on the drawing board face down, take up the excess water from the edges with a blotter, brush a strip of glue or paste about ½ in. wide around the edge, turn the paper over, and rub its edges down on the board until set. Allow it to dry horizontally.

Drawings or maps on which much work is to be done, even though they are not to be tinted, may be made advantageously on stretched paper; but Bristol or calendered paper should not be stretched.

22.26. TINTING. This is done with washes made with water colors. The drawing may be inked (with waterproof ink) before or preferably after tinting. It should be cleaned and unnecessary pencil marks removed with a very soft rubber. The tint is mixed in a saucer and applied with a camel's-hair or sable brush. Incline the board and flow the color with horizontal strokes, leading the pool of color down over the surface, taking up the surplus at the bottom by wiping the brush quickly and using it to pick up the excess color. Stir the color each time the brush is dipped into the saucer. Tints should be made in light washes; depth of color is obtained if necessary by repeating the wash. To get an even color, it is well to go over the surface first with a wash of clear water. Diluted colored inks may be used for washes instead of water color.

22.27. METHODS OF COPYING DRAWINGS —PRICKING.

Drawings are often copied on opaque paper by laying the drawing over the paper and pricking through with a needle point, turning the upper sheet back frequently, and connecting the points. Prickers may be purchased, or made by forcing a fine needle into a softwood handle. They can also be used in accurate drawing to transfer measurements from scale to paper.

22.28. TRANSFER BY RUBBING.

This method, known as *frotté*, is useful, particularly in architectural drawing, in transferring any kind of sketch or design to the paper on which it is to be rendered.

The original is made on any paper and may be worked over, changed, and marked up until the design is satisfactory. To transfer the drawing, lay a piece of tracing paper over the original and trace the outline carefully. Turn the tracing over and retrace the outline just as carefully on the other side, using a medium soft pencil with a *sharp* point. Turn back to first position and tack down smoothly over the paper on which the drawing is to be made, registering the tracing to proper position by center or reference lines on both tracing and

drawing. Now transfer the drawing by rubbing the tracing with the rounded edge of a knife handle or other instrument (a smooth-edged coin held between thumb and forefinger and scraped back and forth is commonly used), holding a small piece of tracing cloth with smooth side up between the rub-

FIG. 22.46. A Patent Office drawing. The illustration here is reduced one-half.

FIG. 22.47. A suspended pantograph. The illustration shows the instrument set up for enlarging: tracer point (*T*) following the points and lines of a drawing gives enlargement at marking point (*M*). For reduction, (*T*) and (*M*) are reversed in position.

bing instrument and the paper, to protect the paper. Do not rub too hard and be sure that neither the cloth nor the paper moves while rubbing. Transfers in ink instead of pencil, useful on wash drawings, may be made by tracing with *encre à poncer,* a rubbing ink made for this purpose.

If the drawing is symmetrical about any axis, the reversed tracing need not be made, as the rubbing can be done from the first tracing by reversing it about the axis of symmetry.

Several rubbings can be made from one tracing, and when the same figure or detail must be repeated several times on a drawing, much time can be saved by drawing it on tracing paper and rubbing it in the several positions.

22.29. GLASS DRAWING BOARD. Drawing tables with glass tops and with lights in reflecting boxes underneath are successful devices for copying drawings on opaque paper. Even pencil drawings can be copied readily on the heaviest paper or Bristol board by the use of a transparent drawing board.

22.30. PROPORTIONAL METHODS—THE PANTOGRAPH. The principle of the pantograph, used for reducing or enlarging drawings in any proportion, is well known. The instrument consists

essentially of four bars, which for any setting must form a parallelogram and have the pivot, tracing point, and marking point in a straight line. Any arrangement of four arms conforming to this requirement will work in true proportion. For reduction the tracing point and marking point are interchanged. A suspended pantograph with metal arms, for accurate engineering work, is shown in Fig. 22.47.

Drawings can be copied to reduced or enlarged scale by using proportional dividers, illustrated in Fig. 22.48. The divisions marked "lines" are linear proportions; those marked "circles" give the setting for dividing a circle into a desired number of equal parts when the large end is opened to the diameter of the circle.

The well-known method of *proportional squares* is often used for reduction or enlargement. The drawing to be copied is ruled in squares of convenient size, or if it is undesirable to mark the drawing, a sheet of ruled tracing cloth or celluloid is laid over it and the copy made freehand on the paper, which has been ruled in corresponding squares, larger or smaller (Fig. 22.49).

Reduction or enlargement of a drawing can of course be done photographically. Especially, for complicated drawings, photographic reproduction eliminates much drafting time.

22.31. SPECIAL INSTRUMENTS. There are some instruments not in the usual assortment that are occasionally needed. Beam compasses are used for circles larger than the capacity of ordinary compasses with lengthening bar. A

FIG. 22.48. Proportional dividers. The pivot is adjustable for different values of reduction or enlargement.

FIG. 22.49. Enlargement or reduction by squares. Points are plotted by inspection from one square grid to the other. This method is also known as graticulation.

FIG. 22.50. A beam compass. This one employs a wooden beam, obtainable in various lengths up to 6 feet.

good form is illustrated in Fig. 22.50. A metal-bar beam compass is shown in Fig. 2.18.

With the drop pen or rivet pen (Fig. 22.51) smaller circles can be made than with the bow pen, and they are made quickly. It is held as shown; the needle point is stationary, and the pen is revolved around it. This pen is particularly convenient in bridge and structural work and in topographic drawing.

Several instruments for drawing ellipses have been made. The ellipsograph (Fig. 22.52) is very satisfactory.

Three special pens are shown in Fig. 22.53. The *railroad pen* (*A*) is used for double lines. A better pen for double lines up to ¼ in. apart is the *border pen* (*B*), as it can be held down to the paper more satisfactorily. It can be used for very wide solid lines by inking the middle space as well as the two pens. The *contour pen* or curve pen (*C*), made with a swivel, is used in map work for freehand curves.

FIG. 22.51. A drop pen. This type of compass is particularly efficient for drawing a number of small circles of the same diameter. These are much used in structural drawing.

FIG. 22.52. An ellipsograph. Several styles are manufactured. This one is well-made and accurate.

FIG. 22.53. Special pens. (*A*) is a "railroad" pen for drawing double lines, (*B*) a border pen for wide lines, (*C*) a contour pen used in map drawing.

FIG. 22.54. An accurate protractor. This one (Brown and Sharpe) is readable to 5 minutes of angle.

FIG. 22.55. Combined triangle, scale, and protractor. Several different types are made. This one is the Tri-pro-scale.

FIG. 22.56. Alteneder bottle-holder. The design makes it possible to fill the pen with one hand.

A *protractor* is a necessity in map and topographic work. A semicircular brass or nickel-silver one, 6 in. in diameter, will read to half degrees. Protractors are available with an arm and vernier reading to minutes. Large circular paper protractors 8 and 14 in. in diameter reading to half and quarter degrees are used and preferred by some map draftsmen. Others prefer the Brown and Sharpe protractor (Fig. 22.54), which reads to 5 minutes.

A combination of triangle and protractor popular with architects and draftsmen is shown in Fig. 22.55. Numerous different combination "triangles" have been devised; several types are usually carried by dealers.

Vertical drawing boards with sliding parallel straightedges are found by some draftsmen to be most suitable for large work.

Figure 22.56 shows a special *bottle-holder* made by the Alteneder Company. The pen can be filled with one hand, saving time.

Some irregular *curves* were illustrated in Fig. 2.10. There are also many others on the market. Sometimes for special or recurring curves it is advisable for a draftsman to make his own template. Templates can be cut out of thin holly or basswood, sheet lead, celluloid, or even cardboard or pressboard. To make a paper curve, sketch the desired shape on paper, cut it out with scissors, and sandpaper the edge. For inking, use it over a triangle or another piece of paper. Flexible curves of different kinds are sold. A copper wire or piece of wire solder can be used as a homemade substitute.

The curve shown in Fig. 22.57 is particularly useful for engineering diagrams, steam curves, etc.

If the glaze is removed from a celluloid irregular curve, by rubbing with fine sandpaper, pencil marks that facilitate the drawing of symmetrical curves can be made on it.

Splines are flexible-curve rulers that are adjusted to the points of the curve to be drawn and held in place by lead weights, called "ducks" by draftsmen. They come in various lengths and are part of the regular equipment of all aircraft drawing rooms (Fig. 22.58).

FIG. 22.57. A diagram curve. Many special curves are available from manufacturers.

FIG. 22.58. A spline and "ducks." This flexible-curve ruler is used principally for drawing large curves, especially in lofting work.

FIG. 22.59. Rounded drawing-board edge. This prevents large drawings from being creased.

22.32. VARIOUS DEVICES. If a drawing or map is so large that it extends over the bottom edge of the board, a piece of half round should be fastened to the board, as in Fig. 22.59, to prevent creasing the paper.

A steel edge for a drawing board can be made of an angle iron planed straight and set flush with the edge. A well-liked adjustable metal edge is made by L. S. Starrett & Company (Fig. 22.60). With a steel edge and steel T square, very accurate plotting can be done. These are often used in bridge offices.

Section lining or crosshatching is a difficult operation for a beginner but is done almost automatically by an experienced draftsman. A number of instruments for mechanical spacing have been devised. *Section liners* are mechanical spacers for use in crosshatching or other evenly spaced line work. One type is shown in Fig. 22.61.

There are many other devices designed to save labor and for convenience in drafting rooms. The Bostich tacker is used instead of thumbtacks. Many draftsmen like to fasten paper to the board with Scotch tape. For this, *draft-ing tape* should be used in preference to masking tape or other varieties of Scotch tape. The Dexter "Draftsmen's Special" pencil sharpener removes the wood only, leaving a long exposure of lead. Electric erasing machines are popular.

22.33. LETTERING DEVICES. The Braddock-Rowe triangle and the Ames lettering instrument (Fig. 4.2*A* and *B*) are convenient devices used to draw guide lines for lettering.

Commercial drafting rooms regard mechanical lettering instruments as necessary for producing neat consistent lettering and symbols on inked drawings. The Leroy set (Figs. 22.62 and 22.63) is one of the most popular. It is available with a wide variety of letter styles and with many electrical, welding, mapping, geological, and mathematical symbols.

FIG. 22.60. A metal drawing-board edge. Some are fastened permanently to the board. This one (L. S. Starrett & Company) is particularly rugged.

FIG. 22.61. A section liner. Several designs are available. The spacing and angle of the blade are adjustable.

FIG. 22.62. Leroy lettering set (Keuffel & Esser Co.). Many different templates for lettering symbols, and special designs are available.

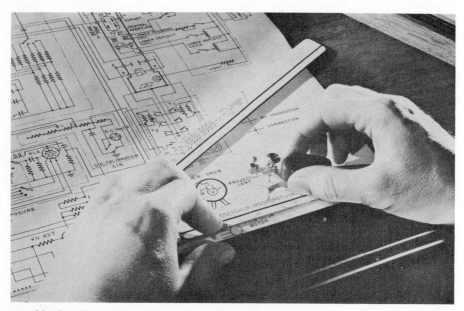

FIG. 22.63. The Leroy instrument in use. The scriber is guided by engraved grooves in the template. Many different pen sizes can be inserted in the scriber.

FIG. 22.64. A drafting machine. This combines T square, triangles, scales, and protractor in one instrument.

22.34. DRAFTING MACHINES. Since the expiration of the patent on the Universal drafting machine, several makers have come into competition with different designs of this important instrument, which combines the functions of T square, triangles, scale, and protractor and which is used extensively in commercial drafting rooms. It is estimated that 35 per cent of time in machine drawing and over 50 per cent in structural drawing is saved by the use of drafting machines. Figure 22.64 shows a band-type drafting machine. Special drafting machines are made for left-handed draftsmen.

22.35. THE SLIDE RULE. Although not a drawing instrument, the slide rule (see Appendix B) is an engineer's tool, and proficiency in its use is a requirement in every modern drafting room. A good way for a beginner to learn to use a slide rule is in connection with a drawing course. Its use facilitates the rapid calculation of volumes and weights, as an aid in reading drawings or later as an essential part of drafting work. Of the several varieties of slide rule, those recommended for prospective engineers are a Polyphase Duplex Trig,[7] a Polyphase Duplex Decitrig,[7] a Log Log Duplex Trig,[7] a Log Log Duplex Decitrig,[7] or a Versilog[7] in 10-in. size.

[7] Registered trade-mark.

Appendixes

Appendixes

Glossary

PART A. SHOP TERMS

anneal (*v.*) To soften a metal piece and remove internal stresses by heating to its critical temperature and allowing to cool very slowly.

arc-weld (*v.*) To weld by electric-arc process.

bore (*v.*) To enlarge a hole with a boring tool, as in a lathe or boring mill. Distinguished from *drill*.

boss (*n.*) A projection of circular cross section, as on a casting or forging.

braze (*v.*) To join by the use of hard solder.

broach (*v.*) To finish the inside of a hole to a shape usually other than round. (*n.*) A tool with serrated edges pushed or pulled through a hole to enlarge it to a required shape.

buff (*v.*) To polish with abrasive on a cloth wheel or other soft carrier.

burnish (*v.*) To smooth or polish by a rolling or sliding tool under pressure.

bushing (*n.*) A removable sleeve or liner for a bearing; also a guide for a tool in a jig or fixture.

carburize (*v.*) To prepare a low-carbon steel for heat-treatment by packing in a box with carbonizing material, such as wood charcoal, and heating to about 2000°F for several hours, then allowing to cool slowly.

caseharden (*v.*) To harden the surface of carburized steel by heating to critical temperature and quenching, as in an oil or lead bath.

castellate (*v.*) To form into a shape resembling a castle battlement, as castellated nut. Often applied to a shaft with multiple integral keys milled on it.

chamfer (*v.*) To bevel a sharp external edge. (*n.*) A beveled edge.

Boss

Bushing

Chamfer

A1

Counterbore

Countersink

Fillet

Flange

Kerf

chase (*v.*)   To cut threads in a lathe, as distinguished from cutting threads with a die. (*n.*) A slot or groove.

chill (*v.*)   To harden the surface of cast iron by sudden cooling against a metal mold.

chip (*v.*)   To cut or clean with a chisel.

coin (*v.*)   To stamp and form a metal piece in one operation, usually with a surface design.

cold-work (*v.*)   To deform metal stock by hammering, forming, drawing, etc., while the metal is at ordinary room temperature.

color-harden (*v.*)   To caseharden to a very shallow depth, chiefly for appearance.

core (*v.*)   To form the hollow part of a casting, using a solid form made of sand, shaped in a core box, baked, and placed in the mold. After cooling, the core is easily broken up, leaving the casting hollow.

counterbore (*v.*)   To enlarge a hole to a given depth. (*n.*) 1. The cylindrical enlargement of the end of a drilled or bored hole. 2. A cutting tool for counterboring, having a piloted end the size of the drilled hole.

countersink (*v.*)   To form a depression to fit the conic head of a screw or the thickness of a plate so that the face will be level with the surface. (*n.*) A conic tool for countersinking.

crown (*n.*)   Angular or rounded contour, as on the face of a pulley.

die (*n.*)   1. One of a pair of hardened metal blocks for forming, impressing, or cutting out a desired shape. 2 (thread). A tool for cutting external threads. Opposite of *tap*.

die casting (*n.*)   A very accurate and smooth casting made by pouring a molten alloy (or composition, as Bakelite) usually under pressure into a metal mold or die. Distinguished from a casting made in sand.

die stamping (*n.*)   A piece, usually of sheet metal, formed or cut out by a die.

draw (*v.*)   1. To form by a distorting or stretching process. 2. To temper steel by gradual or intermittent quenching.

drill (*v.*)   To sink a hole with a drill, usually a twist drill. (*n.*) A pointed cutting tool rotated under pressure.

drop forging (*n.*)   A wrought piece formed hot between dies under a drop hammer, or by pressure.

face (*v.*)   To machine a flat surface perpendicular to the axis of rotation on a lathe. Distinguished from *turn*.

feather (*n.*)   A flat sliding key, usually fastened to the hub.

fettle (*v.*)   To remove fins and smooth the corners on unfired ceramic products.

file (*v.*)   To finish or trim with a file.

fillet (*n.*)   A rounded filling of the internal angle between two surfaces.

fin (*n.*)   A thin projecting rib. Also, excess ridge of material.

fit (*n.*)   The kind of contact between two machined surfaces. 1. *Drive, force,* or *press:* When the shaft is slightly larger than the hole and must be forced in with sledge or power press. 2. *Shrink:* When the shaft is slightly larger than the hole, the piece containing the hole is heated, thereby expanding the hole sufficiently to slip over the shaft. On cooling, the shaft will be seized firmly if the fit allowances have been correctly proportioned. 3. *Running* or *sliding:* When sufficient allowance has been made between sizes of shaft and hole to allow free running without seizing or heating. 4. *Wringing:* When the allowance is smaller than a running fit and the shaft will enter the hole by twisting it by hand.

flange (*n.*)   A projecting rim or edge for fastening or stiffening.

forge (*v.*)   To shape metal while hot and plastic by a hammering or forcing process either by hand or by machine.

galvanize (*v.*)   To treat with a bath of lead and zinc to prevent rusting.

graduate (*v.*)   To divide a scale or dial into regular spaces.

grind (*v.*)   To finish or polish a surface by means of an abrasive wheel.

harden (*v.*)   To heat hardenable steel above critical temperature and quench in bath.

hot-work (*v.*)   To deform metal stock by hammering, forming, drawing, etc., while the metal is heated to a plastic state.

kerf (*n.*)   The channel or groove cut by a saw or other tool.

key (*n.*)   A small block or wedge inserted between shaft and hub to prevent circumferential movement.

keyway, key seat (*n.*)   A groove or slot cut to fit a key. A key fits into a key seat and slides in a keyway.

knurl (*v.*)   To roughen or indent a turned surface, as a knob or handle.

lap (*n.*)   A piece of soft metal, wood, or leather charged with abrasive material, used for obtaining an accurate finish. (*v.*) To finish by lapping.

lug (*n.*)   A projecting "ear," usually rectangular in cross section. Distinguished from *boss*.

malleable casting (*n.*)   An ordinary casting toughened by annealing. Applicable to small castings with uniform metal thicknesses.

mill (*v.*)   To machine with rotating toothed cutters on a milling machine.

neck (*v.*) To cut a groove around a shaft, usually near the end or at a change in diameter. (*n.*) A portion reduced in diameter between the ends of a shaft.

normalize (*v.*)   To remove internal stresses by heating a metal piece to its critical temperature and allowing to cool very slowly.

pack-harden (*v.*)   To carburize and case-harden.

pad (*n.*)   A shallow projection. Distinguished from *boss* by shape or size.

peen (*v.*)   To stretch, rivet, or clinch over by strokes with the peen of a hammer. (*n.*) The end of a hammer head opposite the face, as *ball peen*.

pickle (*v.*)   To clean castings or forgings in a hot weak sulfuric acid bath.

plane (*v.*)   To machine work on a planer having a fixed tool and reciprocating bed.

planish (*v.*)   To finish sheet metal by hammering with polished-faced hammers.

plate (*v.*)   The electrochemical coating of a metal piece with a different metal.

polish (*v.*)   To make smooth or lustrous by friction with a very fine abrasive.

profile (*v.*)   To machine an outline with a rotary cutter usually controlled by a master cam or die.

punch (*v.*)   To perforate by pressing a non-rotating tool through the work.

ream (*v.*)   To finish a drilled or punched hole very accurately with a rotating fluted tool of the required diameter.

relief (*n.*)   The amount one plane surface of a piece is set below or above another plane, usually for clearance or for economy in machining.

rivet (*v.*)   1. To fasten with rivets. 2. To batter or upset the headless end of a pin used as a permanent fastening.

round (*n.*)   A rounded exterior corner between two surfaces. Compare with *fillet*.

sandblast (*v.*)   To clean castings or forgings by means of sand driven through a nozzle by compressed air.

shape (*v.*)   To machine with a shaper, a machine tool differing from a planer in that the work is stationary and the tool reciprocating.

shear (*v.*)   To cut off sheet or bar metal between two blades.

sherardize (*v.*)   To galvanize with zinc by a dry heating process.

shim (*n.*)   A thin spacer of sheet metal used for adjusting.

shoulder (*n.*)   A plane surface on a shaft, normal to the axis and formed by a difference in diameter.

spin (*v.*)   To shape sheet metal by forcing it against a form as it revolves.

spline (*n.*)   A long keyway. Sometimes also a flat key.

spot-face (*v.*)   To finish a round spot on a rough surface, usually around a drilled hole, to give a good seat to a screw or bolthead, cut, usually 1/16 in. deep, by a rotating milling cutter.

spot-weld (*v.*)   To weld in spots by means of the heat of resistance to an electric current. Not applicable to sheet copper or brass.

steel casting (*n.*)   Material used in machine construction. It is ordinary cast iron into which varying amounts of scrap steel have been added in the melting.

swage (*v.*)   To shape metal by hammering or pressure with the aid of a form or anvil called a "swage block."

Keyway

Key and seat

Lug

Neck

Pad

Round

Spline

Spot-face

Trepan

Undercut

sweat (*v.*) To join metal pieces by clamping together with solder between and applying heat.

tack-weld (*v.*) To join at the edge by welding in short intermittent sections.

tap (*v.*) To cut threads in a hole with a rotating tool called a "tap," having threads on it and fluted to give cutting edges.

temper (*v.*) To change the physical characteristics of hardened steel by reheating to a temperature below the critical point and allowing to cool.

template, templet (*n.*) A flat pattern for laying out shapes, location of holes, etc.

trepan (*v.*) To cut an outside annular groove around a hole.

tumble (*v.*) To clean, smooth, or polish castings or forgings in a rotating barrel or drum by friction with each other, assisted by added mediums, as scraps, "jacks," balls, sawdust, etc.

turn (*v.*) To machine on a lathe. Distinguished from *face*.

undercut (*v.*) To cut, leaving an overhanging edge. (*n.*) A cut having inwardly sloping sides.

upset (*v.*) To forge a larger diameter or shoulder on a bar.

weld (*v.*) To join two pieces by heating them to the fusing point and pressing or hammering together.

PART B. STRUCTURAL TERMS

bar Square or round rod; also flat steel up to 6 in. in width.

batten plate A small plate used to hold two parts in their proper position when made up as one member.

batter A deviation from the vertical in upright members.

bay The distance between two trusses or transverse bents.

beam A horizontal member forming part of the frame of a building or structure.

bearing plate A steel plate, usually at the base of a column, used to distribute a load over a larger area.

bent A vertical framework usually consisting of a truss or beam supported at the ends on columns.

brace A diagonal member used to stiffen a framework.

buckle plate A flat plate with dished depression pressed into it to give transverse strength.

built-up member A member built from standard shapes to give one single stronger member.

camber Slight upward curve given to trusses and girders to avoid effect of sag.

cantilever A beam, girder, or truss overhanging one or both supports.

chord The principal member of a truss on either the top or bottom.

clearance Rivet driving clearance is distance from center of rivet to obstruction. Erection clearance is amount of space left between members for ease in assembly.

clevis U-shaped shackle for connecting a rod to a pin.

clip angle A small angle used for fastening various members together.

column A vertical compression member.

cope To cut out top or bottom of flanges and web so that one member will frame into another.

coping A projecting top course of concrete or stone.

counters Diagonal members in a truss to provide for reversal of shear due to live load.

cover plate A plate used in building up flanges, in a built-up member, to give greater strength and area or for protection.

crimp To offset the end of a stiffener to fit over the leg of an angle.

diagonals Diagonal members used for stiffening and wind bracing.

dowel An iron or wooden pin extending into, but not through, two timbers to connect them.

driftpin A tapered steel pin used to bring rivet holes fair in assembling steel work.

edge distance The distance from center of rivet to edge of plate or flange.

fabricate To cut, punch, and subassemble members in the shop.

fillers Either plate or ring fills used to take up space in riveting two members where a gusset is not used.

flange The projecting portion of a beam, channel, or column.

gage line The center line for rivet holes.

gin pole A guyed mast with block at the top for hoisting.

girder A horizontal member, either single or built up, acting as a principal beam.

girt A beam usually bolted to columns to support the side covering or serve as window lintels.

gusset plate A plate used to connect various members, such as in a truss.

hip The intersection between two sloping surfaces forming an exterior angle.

knee brace A corner brace used to prevent angular movement.

lacing or lattice bars Bars used diagonally to space and stiffen two parallel members, such as in a built-up column.

laterals Members used to prevent lateral deflection.

lintel A horizontal member used to carry a wall over an opening.

louvers Metal slats either movable or fixed, as in a monitor ventilator.

monitor ventilator A framework that carries fixed or movable louvers at the top of the roof.

panel The space between adjacent floor supports or purlins in a roof.

pitch Center distance between rivets parallel to axis of member. Also, for roofs, the ratio of rise to span.

plate Flat steel over 6 in. in width and ¼ in. or more in thickness.

purlins Horizontal members extending between trusses, used as beams for supporting the roof.

rafters Beams or truss members supporting the purlins.

sag ties Tie rods between purlins in the plane of the roof to carry the component of the roof load parallel to the roof.

separator Either a cast-iron spacer or wrought-iron pipe on a bolt for the purpose of holding members a fixed distance apart.

sheet Flat steel over 6 in. in width and less than ¼ in. in thickness.

shim A thin piece of wood or steel placed under a member to bring it to a desired elevation.

sleeve nut A long nut with right and left threads for connecting two rods to make an adjustable member.

span Distance between centers of supports of a truss, beam, or girder.

splice A longitudinal connection between the parts of a continuous member.

stiffener Angle, plate, or channel riveted to a member to prevent buckling.

stringer A longitudinal member used to support loads directly.

strut A compression member in a framework.

truss A rigid framework for carrying loads, formed in a series of triangles.

turnbuckle A coupling, threaded right and left or swiveled on one end, for adjustably connecting two rods.

valley The intersection between two sloping surfaces, forming a reentrant angle.

web The part of a channel, I beam, or girder between the flanges.

PART C. ARCHITECTURAL TERMS

apron The finished board placed against the wall surface, immediately below a window stool.

ashlar Thin, squared, and dressed stone facing of a masonry wall.

backing The inner portion of a wall; that which is used behind the facing.

batten A strip of wood used for nailing across two other pieces of wood to hold them together and cover a crack.

batter boards Boards set up at the corners of a proposed building from which the lines marking off the walls are stretched.

bearing wall A wall that supports loads other than its own weight.

bond The joining together of building materials to ensure solidity.

bridging The braces or system of bracing used between joists or other structural members to stiffen them and to distribute the load.

centering   A substructure of temporary nature, usually of timber or planks, on which a masonry arch or vault is built.

coffer   An ornamental panel deeply recessed, usually in a dome or portico ceiling.

corbel   A bracket formed on a wall by building out successive courses of masonry.

curtain wall   A wall that carries no building load other than its own weight.

fenestration   The arrangement and proportioning of window and door openings.

flashing   The sheet metal built into the joints of a wall, or covering the valleys, ridges, and hips of a roof for the purpose of preventing leakage.

footing   A course or series of courses projecting at the base of a wall for the purpose of distributing the load from above over a greater area, thereby preventing excessive settlement.

furring   The application of thin wood, metal, or other building material to a wall, beam, ceiling, or the like to level a surface for lathing, boarding, etc., or to make an air space within a wall.

glazing   The act of furnishing or fitting with glass.

ground   Strips of wood, flush with the plastering, to which moldings, etc., are attached. Grounds are usually installed first and the plastering floated flush with them.

grout   A thin mortar used for filling up spaces where heavier mortar will not penetrate.

head   The horizontal piece forming the top of a wall opening, as a door or window.

hip   The intersection of two roof surfaces, which form on the plan an external angle.

jamb   The vertical piece forming the side of a wall opening.

lintel   The horizontal structural member that supports the wall over an opening.

millwork   The finish woodwork, machined and in some cases partly assembled at the mill.

miter   To match together, as two pieces of

molding, on a line bisecting the angle of junction.

mullion   A vertical division of a window opening.

muntin   The thin members that separate the individual lights of glass in a window frame.

party wall   A division wall common to two adjacent pieces of property.

plate   A horizontal member that carries other structural members; usually the top timber of a wall that carries the roof trusses or rafters directly.

rail   A horizontal piece in a frame or paneling.

return   The continuation in a different direction, most often at right angles, of the face of a building or any member, as a colonnade or molding; applied to the shorter in contradistinction to the longer.

reveal   The side of a wall opening; the whole thickness of the wall; the jamb.

riser   The upright piece of a step, from tread to tread.

saddle   A small double-sloping roof to carry water away from behind chimneys, etc.

scratch coat   The first coat in plastering, roughened by scratching or scoring so that the next coat will firmly adhere to it.

screeds   A strip of plaster of the thickness proposed for the work, applied to the wall at intervals of 4 or 5 ft, to serve as guides.

shoring   A prop, as a timber, placed against the side of a structure; a prop placed beneath anything, as a beam, to prevent sinking or sagging.

sill   The horizontal piece, as a timber, which forms the lowest member of a frame.

sleepers   The timbers laid on a firm foundation to carry and secure the superstructure.

soffit   The underside of subordinate parts and members of buildings, such as staircases, beams, arches, etc.

stile   A vertical piece in a frame or paneling.

stool   The narrow shelf fitted on the inside of a window against the actual sill.

threshold   The stone, wood, or metal piece that lies directly under a door.

trap   A water seal in a sewage system to prevent sewer gas from entering the building.

tread   The upper horizontal piece of a step, on which the foot is placed.

valley   The intersection of two roof surfaces which form, on the plan, a reentrant angle.

PART D. WELDING TERMS

air-acetylene welding   A gas-welding process in which coalescence is produced by heating with a gas flame or flames obtained from the combustion of acetylene with air, without the application of pressure and with or without the use of filler metal.

arc cutting   A group of cutting processes in which the severing of metals is effected by melting with the heat of an arc between an electrode and the base metal.

arc welding   A group of welding processes in which coalescence is produced by heating with an electric arc or arcs, with or without the application of pressure and with or without the use of filler metal.

As-welded   The condition of weld metal, welded joints, and weldments after welding prior to any subsequent thermal or mechanical treatment.

atomic-hydrogen welding   An arc-welding process in which coalescence is produced by heating with an electric arc maintained between two metal electrodes in an atmosphere of hydrogen. Shielding is obtained from the hydrogen. Pressure may or may not be used, and filler metal may or may not be used.

automatic welding   Welding with equipment which performs the entire welding operation without constant observation and adjustment of the controls by an operator. The equipment may or may not perform the loading and unloading of the work.

axis of a weld   A line through the length of a weld, perpendicular to the cross section at its center of gravity.

backing   Material (metal, weld metal, asbestos, carbon, granular flux, etc.) backing up the joint during welding to facilitate obtaining a sound weld at the root.

bevel   A type of edge preparation.

braze   A weld in which coalescence is produced by heating to suitable temperatures above 800°F and by using a nonferrous filler metal having a melting point below that of the base metals. The filler metal is distributed between the closely fitted surfaces of the joint by capillary attraction.

butt joint   A joint between two members lying approximately in the same plane.

coalesce   To unite or merge into a single body or mass. Fusion.

die welding   A forge-welding process in which coalescence is produced by heating in a furnace and by applying pressure by means of dies.

edge joint   A joint between the edges of two or more parallel or nearly parallel members.

filler metal   Metal to be added in making a weld.

fillet weld   A weld of approximately triangular cross section joining two surfaces approximately at right angles to each other in a lap joint, tee joint, or corner joint.

forge welding   A group of welding processes in which coalescence is produced by heating in a forge or other furnace and by applying pressure or blows.

fusion   The melting together of filler metal and base metal, or of base metal only, which results in coalescence.

gas welding   A group of welding processes in which coalescence is produced by heating with a gas flame or flames, with or without the application of pressure, and with or without the use of filler metal.

groove weld   A weld made in the groove between two members to be joined. The standard types of groove welds are: square-groove weld; single-V-groove weld; single-bevel-groove weld; single-U-groove weld; single-J-groove weld; double-V-groove weld; double-bevel-groove weld; double-U-groove weld; double-J-groove weld.

hammer welding   A forge-welding process in which coalescence is produced by heating in a forge or other furnace and by applying pressure by means of hammer blows.

intermittent welding   Welding in which the

continuity is broken by recurring unwelded spaces.

joint penetration   The minimum depth a groove weld extends from its face into a joint, exclusive of reinforcement.

kerf   The space from which metal has been removed by a cutting process.

lap joint   A joint between two overlapping members.

oxy-acetylene welding   A gas-welding process in which coalescence is produced by heating with a gas flame or flames obtained from a combustion of acetylene with oxygen, with or without the application of pressure and with or without the use of filler metal.

peening   The mechanical working of metals by means of hammer blows.

plug weld   A circular weld made by either arc or gas welding through one member of a lap or tee joint joining that member to the other. The weld may or may not be made through a hole in the first member.

pressure welding   Any welding process or method in which pressure is used to complete the weld.

projection welding   A resistance-welding process in which coalescence is produced by the heat obtained from resistance to the flow of electric current through the work parts held together under pressure by electrodes.

root opening   The separation between the members to be joined, at the root of the joint.

seam weld   A weld consisting of a series of overlapping spot welds, made by seam welding or spot welding.

slot weld   A weld made in an elongated hole in one member of a lap or tee joint joining that member to the portion of the surface of the other member which is exposed through the hole.

spot welding   A resistance-welding process in which coalescence is produced by the heat obtained from resistance to the flow of electric current through the work parts, which are held together under pressure by electrodes.

tack weld   A weld made to hold parts of a weldment in proper alignment until the final welds are made.

tee joint   A joint between two members located approximately at right angles to each other in the form of a T.

upset welding   A resistance-welding process in which coalescence is produced, simultaneously over the entire area of abutting surfaces or progressively along a joint, by the heat obtained from resistance to the flow of electric current through the area of contact of those surfaces. Pressure is applied before heating is started and is maintained throughout the heating period.

Bibliography of Allied Subjects

The following classified list is given to supplement this book, whose scope as a general treatise on engineering drawing permits only the mention or brief explanation of some subjects.

AERONAUTICAL DRAFTING AND DESIGN

Anderson, Newton H.: "Aircraft Layout and Detail Design," 2d ed., McGraw-Hill, New York, 1946.

Apalategui, J. J., and J. J. Adams: "Aircraft Analytic Geometry," McGraw-Hill, New York, 1944.

Davis, D. J., and C. H. Goen: "Aircraft Mechanical Drawing," McGraw-Hill, New York, 1944.

Katz, H. H.: "Aircraft Drafting," Macmillan, New York, 1946.

Leavell, S., and S. Bungay: "Aircraft Production Standards," McGraw-Hill, New York, 1943.

Liston, Joseph: "Powerplants for Aircraft," McGraw-Hill, New York, 1953.

Svensen, C. L.: "A Manual of Aircraft Drafting," Van Nostrand, Princeton, N. J., 1941.

Tharratt, George: "Aircraft Production Illustration," McGraw-Hill, New York, 1944.

ARCHITECTURAL DRAWING

Crane, T.: "Architectural Construction," 2d ed., Wiley, New York, 1956.

Kenney, Joseph E., and John P. McGrail: "Architectural Drawing for the Building Trades," McGraw-Hill, New York, 1949.

Morgan, Sherley W.: "Architectural Drawing," McGraw-Hill, New York, 1950.

Ramsey, C. G., and H. R. Sleeper: "Architectural Graphic Standards," Wiley, New York, 1956.

Saylor, H. H.: "Dictionary of Architecture," Wiley, New York, 1952.

Sleeper, H. R.: "Architectural Specifications," Wiley, New York, 1940.

DESCRIPTIVE GEOMETRY

Bradley, H. C., and E. H. Uhler: "Descriptive Geometry for Engineers," International Textbook, Scranton, Pa., 1943.

Grant, Hiram E.: "Practical Descriptive Geometry," McGraw-Hill, New York, 1952.

Higbee, F. G.: "Drawing-board Geometry," Wiley, New York, 1938.

Hood, George J., and Albert S. Palmerlee: "Geometry of Engineering Drawing," 4th ed., McGraw-Hill, New York, 1946.

Johnson, L. O., and I. Wladaver: "Elements of Descriptive Geometry," Prentice-Hall, Englewood Cliffs, N.J., 1953.

Paré, E. G., R. O. Loving, and I. L. Hill: "Descriptive Geometry," Macmillan, New York, 1952.

Rowe, C. E., and James Dorr McFarland: "Engineering Descriptive Geometry," 2d ed., Van Nostrand, Princeton, N.J., 1953.

Shupe, Hollie W., and Paul E. Machovina: "A Manual of Engineering Geometry and Graphics for Students and Draftsmen," McGraw-Hill, New York, 1956.

Street, W. E.: "Technical Descriptive Geometry," Van Nostrand, Princeton, N.J., 1948.

Warner, Frank M., and Matthew McNeary, "Applied Descriptive Geometry," 5th ed., McGraw-Hill, New York, 1954.

Watts, Earle P., and John T. Rule: "Descriptive Geometry," Prentice-Hall, Englewood Cliffs, N.J., 1946.

Wellman, B. Leighton: "Technical Descriptive Geometry," McGraw-Hill, New York, 1957.

DRAWING-INSTRUMENT CATALOGUES

Theo. Alteneder and Sons, Philadelphia.
Eugene Dietzgen Co., Chicago.
Gramercy Guild Group, Inc., New York.
Keuffel & Esser Co., Hoboken, N.J.
The Frederick Post Co., Chicago.
V and E Manufacturing Co., Pasadena, Calif.

ELECTRICAL DRAFTING

Baer, C. J.: "Electrical and Electronic Drawing," McGraw-Hill, New York, 1960.

Bishop, Calvin C., C. T. Gilliam, and Associates: "Electrical Drafting and Design," 3d ed., McGraw-Hill, New York, 1952.

Carini, L. F. B.: "Drafting for Electronics," McGraw-Hill, New York, 1946.

Kocher, S. E.: "Electrical Drafting," International Textbook, Scranton, Pa., 1939.

Van Gieson, D. Walter: "Electrical Drafting," McGraw-Hill, New York, 1945.

ENGINEERING DRAWING

French, Thomas E., and Charles J. Vierck: "Fundamentals of Engineering Drawing," McGraw-Hill, New York, 1960.

French, Thomas E., and Charles J. Vierck: "Graphic Science," McGraw-Hill, New York, 1958.

French, Thomas E., and Charles J. Vierck: "A Manual of Engineering Drawing for Students and Draftsmen," 9th ed., McGraw-Hill, New York, 1960.

Giesecke, F. E., A. Mitchell, and H. C. Spencer: "Technical Drawing," Macmillan, New York, 1940.

Healy, W. L., and A. H. Rau: "Simplified Drafting Practice," Wiley, New York, 1953.

Hoelscher, R. P., and C. H. Springer: "Engineering Drawing and Geometry," Wiley, New York, 1956.

Luzadder, W. J.: "Graphics for Engineers," Prentice-Hall, Englewood Cliffs, N.J., 1957.

Zozzora, Frank: "Engineering Drawing," McGraw-Hill, New York, 1953.

ENGINEERING-DRAWING PROBLEM SHEETS

Cooper, Charles D., and Paul E. Machovina: "Engineering Drawing Problems," Series III, 11 × 17, McGraw-Hill, New York, 1960.

Higbee, F. G., and J. M. Russ: "Engineering Drawing Problems," 8½ × 11 in., Wiley, New York, 1955.

Levens, A. S., and A. E. Edstrom: "Problems in Engineering Drawing," Series V, 8½ × 11 in., McGraw-Hill, New York, 1960.

Vierck, Charles J., and R. I. Hang: "Elementary Engineering Drawing Problems," 8½ × 11 in., McGraw-Hill, New York, 1960.

Vierck, Charles J., and R. I. Hang: "Engineering Drawing Problems," 8½ × 11 in., McGraw-Hill, New York, 1960.

Vierck, Charles J., and R. I. Hang: "Graphic Science Problems," 11 × 11¼ in., McGraw-Hill, New York, 1958.

GRAPHIC SOLUTIONS

Davis, D. S.: "Empirical Equations and Nomography," McGraw-Hill, New York, 1943.

Douglass, Raymond D., and Douglas P. Adams: "Elements of Nomography," McGraw-Hill, New York, 1947.

Hoelscher, R. P., J. Norman Arnold, and S. H. Pierce: "Graphic Aids in Engineering Computation," McGraw-Hill, New York, 1952.

Kulmann, C. Albert: "Nomographic Charts," McGraw-Hill, New York, 1951.

Levens, A. S.: "Nomography," Wiley, New York, 1948.

Levens, A. S.: "Graphics in Engineering and Science," Wiley, New York, 1954.

Lipka, J.: "Graphical and Mechanical Computation," Wiley, New York, 1918.

Rule, John T., and Earle P. Watts: "Engineering Graphics," McGraw-Hill, New York, 1951.

HANDBOOKS

A great many handbooks, with tables, formulas, and information, are published for the different branches of the engineering profession, and are useful for ready reference. Handbook formulas and figures should of course be used only with an understanding of the principles upon which they are based. Among the best-known handbooks are the following, alphabetized by title:

"Chemical Engineers' Handbook," 3d ed., John H. Perry (ed.), McGraw-Hill, New York, 1950.

"Civil Engineering Handbook," 4th ed., by L. C. Urquhart, Porter, Urquhart, McCreary, and O'Brien, McGraw-Hill, New York, 1959.

"Cutting of Metals," American Society of Mechanical Engineers, New York, 1945.

"Definitions of Occupational Specialties in Engineering," American Society of Mechanical Engineers, New York, 1952.

"Design Data and Methods—Applied Mechanics," American Society of Mechanical Engineers, New York, 1953.

"Dynamics of Automatic Controls," American Society of Mechanical Engineers, New York, 1948.

"Engineering Tables," American Society of Mechanical Engineers, New York, 1956.

"Frequency Response," American Society of Mechanical Engineers, New York, 1956.

"General Engineering Handbook," 2d ed., Charles Edward O'Rourke (ed.), McGraw-Hill, New York, 1940.

"Glossary of Terms in Nuclear Science and Technology," American Society of Mechanical Engineers, New York, 1957.

"Machinery's Handbook," The Industrial Press, New York, 1956.

"Manual on Cutting Metals," American Society of Mechanical Engineers, New York, 1952.

"Manual of Standard Practice for Detailing Reinforced Concrete Structures," American Concrete Institute, Detroit, Mich., 1956.

"Mechanical Engineers' Handbook," 6th ed., Lionel S. Marks (ed.), McGraw-Hill, New York, 1958.

"Mechanical Engineers' Handbook," 12th ed., William Kent (ed.), Wiley, New York, 1950.

"Metals Engineering—Design," American Society of Mechanical Engineers, New York, 1953.

"Metals Properties," American Society of Mechanical Engineers, New York, 1954.

"New American Machinists' Handbook," Rupert Le Grand (ed.), McGraw-Hill, New York, 1955.

"Operation and Flow Process Charts," American Society of Mechanical Engineers, New York, 1947.

"Piping Handbook," 4th ed., by Sabin Crocker, McGraw-Hill, New York, 1945.

"Plant Layout Templates and Models," American Society of Mechanical Engineers, New York, 1949.

"Riveted Joints," American Society of Mechanical Engineers, New York, 1945.

"SAE Handbook," Society of Automotive Engineers, New York, yearly.

"Shock and Vibration Instrumentation," American Society of Mechanical Engineers, New York, 1956.

"Standard Handbook for Electrical Engineers," 9th ed., Archer E. Knowlton (ed.), McGraw-Hill, New York, 1957.

"Steel Castings Handbook," Steel Founders Society of America, Cleveland, Ohio, 1956.

"Steel Construction," American Institute of Steel Construction, New York, 1956.

"Structural Shop Drafting," American Institute of Steel Construction, New York, 1950.

"Tool Engineers' Handbook," 2d ed., Frank W. Wilson (ed.), McGraw-Hill, New York, 1959.

ILLUSTRATION

Hoelscher, Randolph Philip, Clifford Harry Springer, and Richard F. Pohle: "Industrial Production Illustration," 2d ed., McGraw-Hill, New York, 1946.

Tharratt, George: "Aircraft Production Illustration," McGraw-Hill, New York, 1944.

Treacy, John: "Production Illustration," Wiley, New York, 1945.

KINEMATICS AND MACHINE DESIGN

Albert, C. D.: "Machine Design Drawing Room Problems," 4th ed., Wiley, New York, 1951.

Black, Paul H.: "Machine Design," McGraw-Hill, New York, 1955.

Faires, V. M.: "Design of Machine Elements," Macmillan, New York, 1947.

Guillet, G. L.: "Kinematics of Machines," 5th ed., Wiley, New York, 1950.

Ham, C. W., E. J. Crane, and W. L. Rogers: "Mechanics of Machinery," 4th ed., McGraw-Hill, New York, 1958.

Hyland, P. H., and J. B. Kommers: "Machine Design," 3d ed., McGraw-Hill, New York, 1943.

Keown, Robert McArdle, and Virgil Moring Faires: "Mechanism," 4th ed., McGraw-Hill, New York, 1939.

Prageman, I. H.: "Mechanism," International Textbook, Scranton, Pa., 1943.

Sahag, L. M.: "Kinematics of Machines," Ronald, New York, 1948.

Schwamb, Peter, and others: "Elements of Mechanism," Wiley, New York, 1954.

Sloane, A.: "Engineering Kinematics," Macmillan, New York, 1947.

Vallance, Alex, and Venton L. Doughtie: "Design of Machine Members," 3d ed., McGraw-Hill, New York, 1951.

LETTERING

French, Thomas E., and W. D. Turnbull: "Lessons in Lettering," McGraw-Hill, New York, 1950.

Svensen, C. L.: "The Art of Lettering," Van Nostrand, Princeton, N.J., 1947.

MAP AND TOPOGRAPHIC DRAWING

Sloane, Roscoe C., and John M. Montz: "Elements of Topographic Drawing," 2d ed., McGraw-Hill, New York, 1943.

PERSPECTIVE

Lawson, Philip J.: "Practical Perspective Drawing," McGraw-Hill, New York, 1943.

Lubschez, B.: "Perspective," Van Nostrand, Princeton, N.J., 1926.

PIPING

See Handbooks, as well as the following:

"Catalogue," Crane & Co., Chicago.

"Catalogue," Walworth Company, Boston.

Crocker, Sabin: "Piping Handbook," 4th ed., McGraw-Hill, New York, 1945.

Plum, S.: "Plumbing Practice and Design," Wiley, New York, 1943.

SHOP PRACTICE AND TOOLS

See Handbooks, as well as the following:

Benedict, Otis J., Jr.: "Manual of Foundry and Pattern Shop Practice," McGraw-Hill, New York, 1947.

Boston, O. W.: "Metal Processing," Wiley, New York, 1951.

Burghardt, Henry D., and Aaron Axelrod: "Machine Tool Operation," McGraw-Hill, New York, 1953.

Campbell, James S., Jr.: "Casting and Forming Processes in Manufacturing," McGraw-Hill, New York, 1950.

Colvin, Fred H., and Lucian L. Haas: "Jigs and Fixtures," 5th ed., McGraw-Hill, New York, 1948.

Doe, E. W.: "Foundry Work," Wiley, New York, 1951.

Hine, Charles R.: "Machine Tools for Engineers," 2d ed., McGraw-Hill, New York, 1959.

Schaller, Gilbert S.: "Engineering Manufacturing Methods," McGraw-Hill, New York, 1953.

SLIDE RULE

Cajori, F.: "A History of the Logarithmic Slide Rule," Engineering News Publishing Co., New York, 1910.

Machovina, Paul E.: "A Manual for the Slide Rule," McGraw-Hill, New York, 1950.

STRUCTURAL DRAWING AND DESIGN

See Handbooks, as well as the following:

Bishop, C. T.: "Structural Drafting," Wiley, New York, 1941.

Shedd and Vawter: "Theory of Simple Structures," 2d ed., Wiley, New York, 1941.

Urquhart, L. C., and C. E. O'Rourke: "Design of Steel Structures," McGraw-Hill, New York, 1930.

Urquhart, Leonard C., Charles Edward O'Rourke, and George Winter: "Design of Concrete Structures," 6th ed., McGraw-Hill, New York, 1958.

AMERICAN STANDARDS

The ASA is working continually on standardization projects. Of its many publications, the following Standards relating to the subjects in this book are now available. A complete list of American Standards will be sent by the Association on application to its offices, 10 East 40th Street, New York 17.

AMERICAN STANDARD SAFETY CODES

Code for pressure piping, B31.1—1955

Gas-transmission and distribution piping systems, B31.1.8—1955

Jacks, B30.1—1952

Mechanical power-transmission apparatus, B15.1—1953

Scheme for identification of piping systems, A13.1—1956

ASME BOILER AND PRESSURE-VESSEL CODES

Material specifications, 1956–7

Power boilers, 1956–7

Welding qualifications, 1956–7

BOLTS, NUTS, RIVETS, AND SCREWS

Hexagonal- and slotted-head cap screws, square-head setscrews, slotted headless setscrews, B18.6.2—1956

High-strength, high-temperature internal wrenching bolts, B18.8—1950

Large rivets, B18.4—1957

Plow bolts, B18.9—1950

Round-head bolts, B18.5—1952

Slotted- and recessed-head wood screws, B18.6.1—1956

Small solid rivets, B18.1—1955

Socket-head cap screws and socket setscrews, B18.3—1954

Square and hexagonal bolts and nuts and lag bolts, B18.2—1955

Track bolts and nuts, B18.10—1952

DRAFTING, CHARTS, AND SYMBOLS

Abbreviations for scientific and engineering terms, Z10.1—1941

Abbreviations for use on drawings, Z32.13—1950

Drawings and drafting-room practice, Z14.1—1946

Graphical symbols for heating, ventilating, and air conditioning, Z32.2.4—1949

Graphical symbols for heat-power apparatus, Z32.2.6—1950

Graphical symbols for pipe fittings, valves, and piping, Z32.2.3—1953

Graphical symbols for plumbing, Y32.4—1955

Graphical symbols for railway use, Z32.2.5—1950

Graphical symbols for welding and instructions for their use, Z32.2.1—1949

A guide for preparing technical illustrations for publications and projections, 1954

Letter symbols for acoustics, Y10.11—1953

Letter symbols for aeronautical sciences, Y10.7—1954

Letter symbols for chemical engineering, Y10.12—1955

Letter symbols for heat and thermodynamics, including heat flow, Z10.4—1943

Letter symbols for hydraulics, Z10.2—1942

Letter symbols for mechanics of solid bodies, Z10.3—1948

Letter symbols for meteorology, Y10.10—1953

Letter symbols for physics, Z10.6—1948

Letter symbols for radio, Y10.9—1953

Letter symbols for structural analysis, Z10.8—1949

Time series charts, Z15.2—1947

ELECTRICAL DRAWING

Electrical Diagrams Y14.15—Tentative

Graphical Electrical Symbols for Architectural Plans, Y32.9—1943

Graphical Symbols for Electrical Diagrams, Y32.2—1954

Letter Symbols for Electrical Quantities, Z10.5–1949

GEAR DESIGN, DIMENSIONS, AND INSPECTION

Design for fine-pitch worm gearing, B6.9—1956

Fine-pitch straight bevel gears, B6.8—1950

Gear nomenclature, B6.10—1954

Gear tolerances and inspection, B6.6—1946

Inspection of fine-pitch gears, B6.11—1956

Letter symbols for gear engineering, B6.5—1954

Nomenclature for gear-tooth wear and failure, B6.12—1954

Spur-gear tooth form, B6.1—1932

System for straight bevel gears, B6.13—1955

Twenty-degree involute fine-pitch system for spur and helical gears, B6.7—1956

MISCELLANEOUS STANDARDS

Indicating pressure and vacuum gages, B40.1—1953

Lock washers, B27.1—1950

Plain washers, B27.2—1953

Preferred thickness for uncoated, thin, flat metals, B32.1—1952

Shaft coupling, B49.1—1947

Surface roughness, waviness, and lay, B46.1—1955

Woodruff keys, keyslots, and cutters, B17f—1955

PIPE, PIPE FITTINGS, AND THREADS

Brass fittings for flared copper tubes, A40.2—1936

Brass or bronze flanges and flanged fittings—150 and 300 lb, B16.24—1953

Brass or bronze screwed fittings—125 lb, B16.15—1952

Brass or bronze screwed fittings—250 lb, B16.17—1953

Butt-welding ends, B16.25—1955

Cast-brass solder-joint drainage fittings, B16.23—1955

Cast-brass solder-joint fittings, B16.18—1950

CI pipe flanges and flanged fittings, 25-psi, B16b2—1931; class 125, B16.1—1948; class 250, B16b—1944; 800-lb hydraulic pressure, B16b1—1952; class 300-lb refrigerant, B16.16—1952

CI screwed drainage fittings, B16.12—1953

CI screwed fittings, 125- and 250-lb, B16.4—1953

CI soil pipe and fittings, A40.1—1935

Face-to-face dimensions of ferrous flanged and welding end valves, B16.10—1947

Ferrous plugs, bushings, and locknuts with pipe threads, B16.14—1953

Malleable-iron screwed fittings, 150-lb, B16.3—1951

Malleable-iron screwed fittings, 300-lb, B16.19—1951

National plumbing code, A40.8—1955

Nonmetallic gaskets for pipe flanges, B16.21 1951

Pipe threads, B2.1—1945

Ring-joint gaskets and grooves for steel pipe flanges, B16.20—1956

Stainless-steel pipe, B36.19—1957

Steel butt-welding fittings, B16.9—1951

Steel pipe flanges and flanged fittings, 150-, 300-, 400-, 600-, 900-, 1,500-, and 2,500-lb, B16.5—1953

Steel-socket welding fittings, B16.11—1952

Threaded cast-iron pipe for drainage, vent, and waste services, A40.5—1943

Wrought-copper and wrought-bronze solder-joint fittings, B16.22—1951

Wrought-steel and wrought-iron pipe, B36.10—1950

SMALL TOOLS AND MACHINE-TOOL ELEMENTS

Acme screw threads, B1.5—1952
Buttress screw threads, B1.9—1953
Chucks and chuck jaws, B5.8—1954
Hose-coupling screw threads, B33.1—1947
Involute serrations, B5.26—1950
Involute splines, B5.15—1950
Jig bushings, B5.6—1949
Knurling, B5.30—1953
Machine tapers, B5.10—1953
Milling cutters, B5.3—1950
Nomenclature, definitions, and letter symbols for screw threads, B1.7—1953
Preferred limits and fits for cylindrical parts, B4.1—1955
Reamers, B5.14—1949
Screw thread gages and gaging, B1.2—1951
Stub Acme screw threads, B1.8—1952
Taps—cut and ground threads, B5.4—1948
T slots and their bolts, nuts, tongues, and cutters, B5.1—1949
Twist drills, B5.12—1950
Unified and American screw threads standard, B1.1—1951

STANDARDS UNDER DEVELOPMENT

Abbreviations—for use in text
Drafting standards manual—size and format, line conventions, lettering and sectioning, projections, pictorial drawings, dimensions and notes, castings, die castings, forgings, gears, splines and serrations, helical and flat springs, hydraulic and pneumatic diagrams, metal stampings, plastics, schematic wiring and diagrams, screw threads, structural drafting
Fluid meters—theory and application
Gears—inspection of coarse-pitch spur and helical gears
Screws and screw threads—microscope-objective threads, surveying-instrument mounting threads, national miniature screw threads, "trial" class 5 interference-fit thread
Small tools—inserted-blade milling-cutter bodies, driving and spindle ends for portable electric tools
Symbols—miscellaneous
Washers—precision

PUBLICATIONS OF NATIONAL SOCIETIES

The national engineering organizations publish a wide variety of manuals, standards, handbooks, and pamphlets. Information concerning these publications is available directly from the societies. The following is a selected list of American organizations:

Air Conditioning and Refrigeration Institute, 1346 Connecticut Ave. NW, Washington 6, D.C.
Aircraft Industries Association of America, Inc., 610 Shoreham Bldg., Washington 5, D.C.
American Association for the Advancement of Science (AAAS), 1515 Massachusetts Ave. NW, Washington 5, D.C.
American Association of Engineers (AAE), 8 South Michigan Ave., Chicago 3, Ill.
American Association of Petroleum Geologists, Inc. (AAPG), P.O. Box 979, Tulsa 1, Okla.
American Association of University Professors, 1785 Massachusetts Ave. NW, Washington 6, D.C.
American Ceramic Society (ACerS), 4055 North High St., Columbus 14, Ohio
American Chemical Society (ACS), ACS Bldg., 1155 16th St. NW, Washington 6, D.C.
American Concrete Institute (ACI), 22400 West 7 Mile Rd., Detroit 19, Mich.
American Concrete Pipe Association, 228 North LaSalle St., Chicago 1, Ill.
American Gas Association (AGA), 420 Lexington Ave., New York 17, N.Y.
American Institute of Chemical Engineers (AIChE), 25 West 45th St., New York 17, N.Y.
American Institute of Consulting Engineers (AICE), 33 West 39th St., New York, N.Y.
American Institute of Electrical Engineers (AIEE), 33 West 39th St., New York 18, N.Y.
American Institute of Mining and Metallurgical, and Petroleum Engineers, Inc. (AIME), 29 West 39th St., New York, N.Y.

American Institute of Steel Construction, Inc. (AISC), 101 Park Ave., New York 17, N.Y.

American Mining Congress, Ring Bldg., Washington 6, D.C.

American Petroleum Institute (API), Rm. 2040, 50 West 50th St., New York 20, N.Y.

American Society for Engineering Education (ASEE), University of Illinois, Urbana, Ill.

American Society for Metals (ASM), 7301 Euclid Ave., Cleveland, Ohio

American Society for Quality Control (ASQC), 161 West Wisconsin Ave., Milwaukee 3, Wis.

American Society for Testing Materials (ASTM), 1916 Race St., Philadelphia 3, Pa.

American Society of Agricultural Engineers (ASAE), St. Joseph, Mich.

American Society of Civil Engineers (ASCE), 33 West 39th St., New York 18, N.Y.

American Society of Heating, Refrigerating, and Air-conditioning Engineers (ASHRAE), 234 Fifth Ave., New York 1, N.Y.

American Society of Lubrication Engineers, 84 East Randolph St., Chicago 1, Ill.

American Society of Mechanical Engineers (ASME), 29 West 39th St., New York 18, N.Y.

American Society of Photogrammetry, 1515 Massachusetts Ave., Washington 5, D.C.

American Society of Refrigerating Engineers, 234 Fifth Ave., New York, N.Y.

American Society of Safety Engineers: National Safety Council Engineering Section, 425 North Michigan Ave., Chicago 11, Ill.

American Society of Tool Engineers (ASTE), 10700 Puritan Ave., Detroit 38, Mich.

American Standards Association (ASA), 10 East 40th St., New York 17, N.Y.

American Welding Society (AWS), 29 West 39th St., New York 18, N.Y.

Asphalt Institute, The, 1270 Sixth Ave., New York, N.Y.

Association of Iron and Steel Engineers (AISE), 1010 Empire Bldg., Pittsburgh 22, Pa.

Electrochemical Society, Inc., The, 1860 Broadway, New York 23, N.Y.

Federation of American Scientists (FAS), 1805 H St. NW, Washington 6, D.C.

Highway Research Board, 2101 Constitution Ave., Washington 25, D.C.

Illuminating Engineering Society, 1860 Broadway, New York 23, N.Y.

Industrial Management Society (IMS), 330 South Wells St., Chicago, Ill.

Industrial Research Institute, Inc., 100 Park Ave., New York 17, N.Y.

Institute of the Aeronautical Sciences (IAS), 2 East 64 St., New York, N.Y.

The Institute of Radio Engineers, Inc. (IRE), 1 East 79th St., New York 21, N.Y.

Mining and Metallurgical Society of America (MMSA), 11 Broadway, New York 4, N.Y.

National Aeronautic Association (NAA), 1025 Connecticut Ave. NW, Washington 6, D.C.

National Institute of Ceramic Engineers, The, 4055 North High St., Columbus 14, Ohio

National Society of Professional Engineers (NSPE), 2029 K St., NW, Washington 6, D.C.

Society of Automotive Engineers (SAE), 485 Lexington Ave., New York 17, N.Y.

ABCDEFGHIJ
KLMNOPQRS
TUVWXYZ &

APPENDIX A

Lettering

OUTLINED COMMERCIAL GOTHIC. In Chap. 4, the so-called "Gothic" letter was considered only as a single-stroke letter. For sizes larger than say ⅝ in., or for boldface letters, it is drawn in outline and filled in solid. For a given size, this letter is readable at a greater distance than any other style; hence it is used where legibility is the principal requirement. The stems may be one-tenth to one-fifth of the height, and care must be taken to keep them uniform in width at every point on the letter. In inking a penciled outline, keep the *outside* of the ink line on the pencil line (Fig. A-1) or the letter will be heavier than expected.

The general order and direction of penciling large commercial Gothic letters is similar to that for the single-stroke letter but with two strokes made in place of one, as shown in typical examples in Fig. A-2. Free ends, such as on *C, G,* and *S,* are cut off perpendicular to the stem. The stiffness of plain letters is sometimes relieved by finishing the ends with a slight spur, as in

FIG. A-1.

FIG. A-2. Typical construction for large commercial Gothic.

A17

ABCDEFGHIJ KLMNOPQRS TUVWXYZ &

FIG. A-3. Compressed commercial Gothic.

Fig. A-3. The complete alphabet in outline, with stems one-sixth of the height, is given in Fig. A-4. The same scale of widths may be used for drawing lighter-face letters. Figure A-3 illustrates a commercial Gothic alphabet compressed to two-thirds the normal width. In this figure the stems are drawn one-seventh of the height, but the scale is given in sixths, as in Fig. A-4.

THE ROMAN LETTER. The Roman letter is the parent of all the styles that are in use today. Although there are many variations of it, the three general forms

FIG. A-4. Large commercial Gothic construction.

are: (1) early or classic, (2) Renaissance, and (3) Modern. The first two are very similar in effect, and the general term "Old Roman" is used for both.

The Roman letter is composed of two weights of lines, corresponding to the downstroke and the upstroke of a broad reed pen, with which it was originally written. It is an inexcusable fault to shade a Roman letter on the wrong stroke.

Rule for shading. All horizontal strokes are light. All vertical strokes are heavy except in M, N, and U. To determine the heavy stroke in letters containing slanting sides, trace the shape of the letter from left to right in one stroke and note which lines were made downward. Figure A-5 is an Old Roman alphabet with the width of the body stroke one-tenth of the height of the letter and the light lines slightly over one-half this width. For inscriptions and

FIG. A-5. Old Roman capitals.

abcdefghijklmn
opqrstuvwxyz

FIG. A-6. Old Roman lower case.

titles, capitals are generally used, but sometimes lower case is needed; the examples given in Fig. A-6 are drawn with waist line six-tenths high and the width of the stems one-twelfth of capital height.

Old Roman is the architect's general-purpose letter. A single-stroke adaptation (Fig. A-7) is generally used on architectural drawings.

MODERN ROMAN. Civil engineers in particular must be familiar with Modern Roman, as it is the standard letter for titles of finished maps and the names of civil divisions, such as countries and cities. It is a difficult letter to draw and

can be mastered only by careful attention to details. The heavy or "body" strokes are one-sixth to one-eighth the height of the letter. Those in Fig. A-8 are one-seventh the height of the letter. A paper scale made by dividing the height into seven parts will aid in penciling.

Modern lower case (Fig. A-9) is used on maps for names of towns and villages. Notice the difference in the serifs of Figs. A-9 and A-6.

The order and direction of strokes used in drawing Modern Roman letters are illustrated in typical letters in Fig. A-10. The serifs on the ends of the strokes extend one space on each side

FIG. A-7. Single stroke Roman and italic.

ABCDEFGHIJKLMNOPQRS
TUVWXYZ& 1234567890
abcdefghijklmnopqrstuvwxyz
Compressed Italic for Limited Space
Sans-serif for Speed & Simplicity

A B C D E F G H I J K L
M N O P Q R S T U V W
X Y Z & 1 2 3 4 5 6 7 8
9 0

FIG. A-8. Modern Roman capitals.

FIG. A-9. Modern Roman lower case.

a b c d e f g h i j k l m
n o p q r s t u v w x y z

FIG. A-10. Modern Roman construction.

MAP SHOWING
IRON ORE DEPOSITS
IN THE
WESTERN STATES
SCALE—MILES 0 50 100   200   300   400

FIG. A-11. A Roman-letter title.

and are joined to the main stroke by small fillets. The curved letters are flattened slightly on their diagonals. A title in Roman letters is illustrated in Fig. A-11.

The Roman letter may be extended or compressed, as shown in Fig. A-12. For extended or compressed letters, a scale for widths would be longer or shorter than the normal scale. The compressed letters in Fig. A-12 are made with a scale three-fourths the height divided into sevenths.

INCLINED ROMAN. Inclined letters are used for water features on maps. An alphabet of inclined Roman made to the same proportions as the vertical in Fig. A-8 is shown in Fig. A-13. The slope may be 65° to 75°. Those shown are inclined 2 to 5. The lower-case letters in this figure are known as stump letters. For small sizes, lines are made with one stroke of a fine flexible pen;

for larger sizes they are drawn and filled in.

THE PROPORTIONAL METHOD. Because of the varying widths of Roman letters, it is sometimes difficult to space a word or line to a given length by counting letters. Figure A-14 illustrates the method of spacing by the principle of similar triangles. Suppose it is necessary to put the word "ROMAN" on the line to the length *ab*. Draw line *ac* from *a* at any angle, say 30°, and a second line *de* parallel to it; then sketch the word in this space, starting at *a* and spacing each letter with reference to the one before it, allowing the word to end where it will. Connect the end of the last letter, at *c*, with *b*, and draw lines parallel to *cb* from each letter, thus dividing *ab* proportionately. Obtain the height *bf* from *ce* by the construction shown. Then sketch the word in its final position.

THE GREEK ALPHABET. While Greek is not a required subject in most engineering curricula, the engineer often uses letters of the Greek alphabet, both capitals and lower case, as symbols and reference letters. He should therefore be able to draw them readily and to read them without hesitation.

FIG. A-12. Modern Roman, extended and compressed.

EXTENDED ROMAN
BCGHJKLPQSUVW
COMPRESSED ROMAN—BHKTWG

$$ABCDEFGHIJKLMN$$
$$OPQRSTUVWXYZ\&ab$$
$$cdefghijklmnopqrstu\,v_{or}v\,w_{or}w$$
$$x\,y_{or}yz\ 1234567890$$

FIG. A-13. Inclined Roman and stump letters.

There is variety in Greek alphabets, just as there is in Roman alphabets. The alphabet given in Fig. A-15 is clearly legible, and has accented and unaccented strokes in the capitals which follow closely the rules for shading Roman letters. The lower case has good historical precedent in form, shading, and comparative size.

When Greek letters are used in equations and formulas, the letters are made in a single stroke by simply following the letter shape without any attempt at shading. For display purposes and when shading is desirable for legibility, the letters are outlined and filled in by the method described for outlined commercial Gothic.

FIG. A-14. Proportional method.

$A\alpha$	$B\beta$	$\Gamma\gamma$	$\Delta\delta$	$E\epsilon$	$Z\zeta$	$H\eta$	$\Theta\vartheta$
ALPHA	BETA	GAMMA	DELTA	EPSILON	ZETA	ETA	THETA

$I\iota$	$K\kappa$	$\Lambda\lambda$	$M\mu$	$N\nu$	$\Xi\xi$	Oo	$\Pi\pi$
IOTA	KAPPA	LAMBDA	MU	NU	XI	OMICRON	PI

$P\rho$	$\Sigma\sigma$	$T\tau$	$Y\upsilon$	$\Phi\phi$	$X\chi$	$\Psi\psi$	$\Omega\omega$
RHO	SIGMA	TAU	UPSILON	PHI	CHI	PSI	OMEGA

FIG. A-15. The Greek alphabet.

The slide rule is a graphic instrument for making mathematical calculations. Because the instrument is *graphic,* and also because its use is common in all engineering work, the following pictorial guide to its use is given.

The slide rule is based on the well-known mathematical relationships of logarithms of numbers. For example, the equation for the multiplication of two factors, $A \times B = C$, when written logarithmically becomes: $\log A + \log B = \log C$. Thus, to multiply, logarithms are *added* and, conversely, to divide, logarithms are subtracted. Slide-rule scales are arranged in such a way that the addition and subtraction of logarithms is accomplished *graphically*.

It is beyond our scope here to give a complete discussion of slide-rule use. The pictorial examples are intended only for quick, easy visual reference. Complete discussions on the theory and use of slide rules are given in manuals prepared especially for the slide rule (see Bibliography).

Because slide-rule settings of values and the answers depend upon reading a graphic scale, results are not absolutely accurate. However, the instrument is unrivaled as an inexpensive, portable, and efficient device for calculation whenever absolute accuracy is not essential.

MULTIPLICATION OF TWO VALUES (C AND D SCALES)

$A \times B = R$

Set A on D scale with index of C scale (Fig. B-1). Set B on C scale with hairline of glass slide. Read answer R on D scale at hairline. Example shown:

$1.375 \times 1.962 = 2.697$

FIG. B-1.

DIVISION OF TWO VALUES (C AND D SCALES)

$\dfrac{A}{B} = C$

Set A on D scale with hairline (Fig. B-2). Set B on C scale under hairline.

Read answer R on D scale at index of C scale. Example shown:

$\dfrac{2.70}{1.962} = 1.375$

FIG. B-2.

PROPORTION (C AND D SCALES)

$$\frac{A}{B} = \frac{C}{D} = \frac{E}{F}$$

Set A on D scale and B on C scale opposite each other by using the hairline (Fig. B-3). Then any other combination in the same proportion is had by moving the hairline and reading both values on C and D scales. Example shown:

$$\frac{A}{B} = \frac{2.0}{1.5}, \frac{C}{D} = \frac{1.4}{1.05}, \frac{E}{F} = \frac{2.7}{2.025}$$

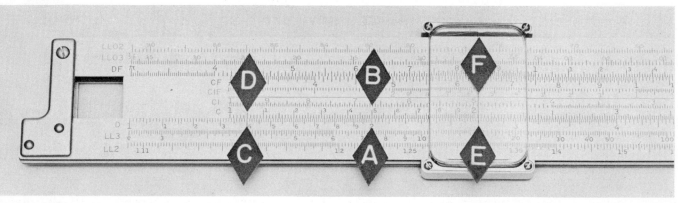

FIG. B-3.

SUCCESSIVE MULTIPLICATION OF ONE VALUE BY SEVERAL OTHERS (C AND D SCALES)

$A \times B = R$
$A \times C = S$
$A \times D = T$

Set A on D scale with index of C scale (Fig. B-4). Then set B, C, and D with hairline on C scale and read answers on D scale at R, S, and T under hairline. Example shown:

$2.4 \times 1.8 = 4.32\ (R)$
$2.4 \times 2.5 = 6.0\ (S)$
$2.4 \times 3.0 = 7.2\ (T)$

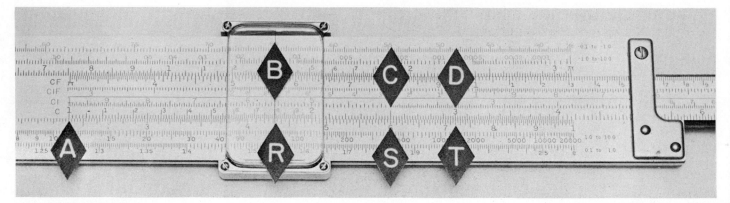

FIG. B-4.

SUCCESSIVE DIVISION OF ONE VALUE BY SEVERAL OTHERS (D AND CI SCALES)

$$\frac{A}{B} = R$$

$$\frac{A}{C} = S$$

$$\frac{A}{D} = T$$

Set A on D scale with index (right) of CI scale (Fig. B-5). The CI scale is the same as the C scale, but inverted. Then set B, C, and D with hairline on CI scale and read answers under hairline on D scale. Example shown:

$$\frac{7.0}{2} = 3.5 \ (R) \quad \frac{7.0}{3.0} = 2.33 \ (S)$$

$$\frac{7.0}{4.0} = 1.75 \ (T)$$

FIG. B-5.

MULTIPLICATION BY USING THE CF AND DF SCALES

The "folded" scales, CF and DF, are used whenever a value on the C scale falls beyond the D scale. In the example shown, value B on the C scale cannot be set. Therefore, using the CF and DF scales:

$$A \times C = R$$

Set A on D scale with index of C scale (Fig. B-6). CF and DF scales *have moved in exactly the same proportion as* C scale relative to D scale. Therefore, when value B falls off end of C scale, set C on CF scale and read answer on DF scale under hairline. Example shown:

$$3.1 \times 4.5 = 13.95$$

FIG. B-6.

DIVISION BY USING THE CIF SCALE

The "folded and inverted" scale, CIF, is a folded scale to augment the CI scale. In successive division, using the CI scale, some values will be off the end of the scale. The CIF scale can then be used:

$$\frac{A}{B} = R \text{ or } \frac{A}{C} = S$$

Set A on D scale with hairline (Fig. B-7). Set index of CIF scale under hairline. Then $\frac{A}{B} = R$, and $\frac{A}{C} = S$. Answer is read on D scale. Example shown:

$$\frac{2.0}{8.0} = 0.25 \ (R)$$

$$\frac{2.0}{5.0} = 0.40 \ (S)$$

FIG. B-7.

MULTIPLICATION OF THREE VALUES (D AND CI SCALES)

$$A \times B \times C = S$$

Set A on D scale, using hairline (Fig. B-8). Set B on CI scale under hairline. The answer of this operation ($A \times B$) can then be read at index of C scale at R on D scale. The third value C, now set on C scale, gives answer of $A \times B \times C$ at S on D scale. Example shown:

$$2.5 \times 2 \times 3.6 = 18.0$$

FIG. B-8.

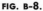

COMBINED MULTIPLICATION AND DIVISION (D AND CI SCALES)

$$\frac{A \times B}{C} = S$$

Set *A* on D scale with hairline (Fig. B-9). Set *B* on CI scale under hairline. The answer of $A \times B$ is at index of CI scale at *R* on D scale. Then the third value *C*, on CI scale, gives answer of $\frac{A \times B}{C}$ at *S* on D scale. Example shown:

$$\frac{1.5 \times 2.0}{15.0} = 0.20$$

FIG. B-9.

COMBINED MULTIPLICATION AND DIVISION (C, D, AND CI SCALES)

$$\frac{A}{B \times C} = S$$

Set *A* on D scale with hairline (Fig. B-10). Set *B* on C scale under hairline. The answer of $\frac{A}{B}$ is at index of CI scale at *R* on D scale. Then the third value *C*, on the CI scale, gives the answer of $\frac{A}{B \times C}$ at *S* on D scale. Example shown:

$$\frac{3.0}{2.0 \times 7.0} = 0.214$$

FIG. B-10.

COMBINED MULTIPLICATION AND DIVISION (C, D, CF, DF, AND CIF SCALES)

$$\frac{A}{B \times C} = S$$

Sometimes in combined multiplication and division, values needed will be inaccessible on a scale. To illustrate, set A on D scale with hairline (Fig. B-11). Set B on C scale under hairline. Then the answer of $\frac{A}{B}$ is at index of C scale at R on D scale. If C is a value that cannot be set on CI scale, set C on CIF scale and read answer at S on DF scale. To prove this, note that CF scale has moved in exactly the same relationship to DF scale as C scale has moved in relation to D scale. Example shown:

$$\frac{15.0}{4.0 \times 6.0} = 0.625$$

FIG. B-11.

SQUARES AND SQUARE ROOTS (D AND A SCALES)

$R^2 = A$ and $\sqrt{A} = R$

The A scale is plotted as the square of the D scale.

To determine $R^2 = A$, set R on D scale and read square on A scale (Fig. B-12). Example shown:

$2.0^2 = 4.0$

To determine $\sqrt{A} = R$, set A on A scale and read square root on D scale. Example shown:

$$\sqrt{4.0} = 2.0$$

FIG. B-12.

CUBES AND CUBE ROOTS (D AND K SCALES)

$A^3 = R$ and $\sqrt[3]{R} = A$

The K scale is plotted as the cube of the D scale.

To determine $A^3 = R$, set A on D scale and read cube on K scale (Fig. B-13). Example shown:

$2.0^3 = 8.0$

To determine $\sqrt[3]{R} = A$, set R on K scale and read cube root on D scale. Example shown:

$\sqrt[3]{8.0} = 2.0$

FIG. B-13.

USE OF THE A AND B SCALES

The A and B scales can be used to multiply and divide, and are useful for performing these operations *after* a square has been obtained, *or* if the square root is needed *after* multiplication or division.

$A^2 \times B = S$

Set A on D scale (Fig. B-14). A^2 can then be read on the A scale at R. Set B on B scale with hairline. The answer S is under hairline on A scale. Example shown:

$2.0^2 \times 4.0 = 16.0$

FIG. B-14.

MATHEMATICAL VALUE OF SINE OR TANGENT (ST SCALE)

$\sin A$ (or $\tan A$) $= R$

The values of sines and tangents from zero degrees up to about 5½ degrees are identical for the accuracy with which the scales can be read.

Index the ST scale with the D scale (Fig. B-15). Set angle (A) on ST scale with hairline and read mathematical value (R) on D scale under hairline. Example shown:

$\sin$ (or $\tan$) $1.5° = 0.0262$

FIG. B-15.

MATHEMATICAL VALUE OF SINE (S SCALE)

$\sin A = R$

Index S scale with D scale (Fig. B-16). Set angle (degrees) (A) on S scale with hairline and read mathematical value (R) on D scale under hairline. The cosine (degrees) is printed on most rules on the S scale in red. Example shown:

$\sin 15° = 0.2588$
$\cos 75° = 0.2588$

FIG. B-16.

ANGLE OF SINE, CORRESPONDING TO MATHEMATICAL VALUE (S SCALE)

A (sin) $= R$ (angle in degrees)

Index S scale with D scale (Fig. B-17). Set A on D scale with hairline. Read angle in degrees (R) on S scale under hairline. Example shown:

$$\sin = 0.176 = 10.16°$$

FIG. B-17.

MATHEMATICAL VALUE OF TANGENT (T SCALE) UP TO 45°

$\tan A = R$

Index T scale with D scale (Fig. B-18). Set A, angle in degrees, on T scale with hairline. Read mathematical value of tangent (R) on D scale under hairline. Example shown:

$$\tan 10° = 0.176$$

FIG. B-18.

MATHEMATICAL VALUE OF TANGENT (T SCALE) FROM 45° UP

tan $A = R$

Index T scale with DI scale—inverted D scale (Fig. B-19). On most rules, the T scale above 45° and the DI scale are printed in red. Set angle in degrees (A) on T scale with hairline. Read mathematical value (R) on DI scale under hairline. Example shown:

tan 75° = 3.74

FIG. B-19.

MULTIPLICATION WITH THE TRIGONOMETRIC SCALES (ST SCALE)

$A \sin B = R$

Set A on D scale with index of ST scale (Fig. B-20). Set angle in degrees (B), corresponding to mathematical value of a sine or tangent, with hairline on ST scale. Read answer at R on D scale. Example shown:

2 sin (tan) 1° = 0.0350

The S and T scales are employed for multiplication in the same manner.

FIG. B-20.

DIVISION WITH THE TRIGONOMETRIC SCALES (S SCALE)

$$\frac{A}{\sin B} = R$$

Set A on D scale with hairline (Fig. B-21). Set angle in degrees (B), corresponding to mathematical value of the sine, on S scale, under hairline. Read answer R, at index of S scale on D scale. Example shown:

$$\frac{3.24}{\sin 11°} = 17.0$$

The ST and T scales are employed for division in the same manner.

FIG. B-21.

LOGARITHMS (L SCALE)

$$\log A = R$$

Set A with hairline on D scale (Fig. B-22). Read logarithm, mantissa only, (R) under hairline on L scale. Example shown:

$$\log 2.10 = 0.322$$

FIG. B-22.

ANTILOGARITHMS (L SCALE)

$A = \log R$

Set logarithms, mantissa only, (A) with hairline on L scale (Fig. B-23).

Read antilog (R) under hairline on D scale. Example shown:

$0.330 = \log 2.14$

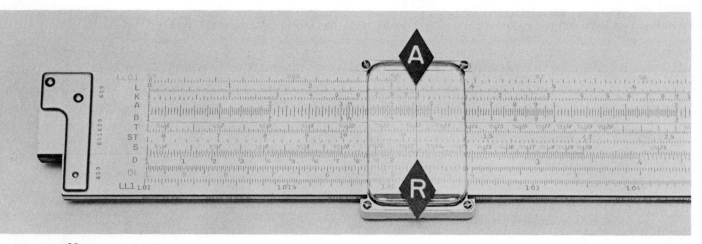

FIG. B-23.

POWERS (LL SCALES)

$A^B = R$

Set A with hairline on LL scale (depending upon the value) and match index of C scale under hairline (Fig.

B-24). Set power B with hairline on C scale. Read answer on LL scale at R. Example shown:

$6.0^{1.75} = 23.0$

FIG. B-24.

THE LL SCALES

The LL scales run continuously, for example, LL2 ends at e at the right index, and LL3 begins with e at the left index (Fig. B-25). Depending on the value set, and the power, the answer *may* be on the next scale in sequence.

$$A^B = R$$

Set as in previous example, but if left index of the C scale is used and value of the power is then beyond range of scale, change to right index and answer will appear on *next* LL scale. Example shown:

$$2.0^4 = 16.0$$

(The value 2.0 is set on LL2 and 16.0 is read on LL3.) The LL01, LL02 and LL03 scales are for numbers less than 1.0. Note that these scales are inverted.

FIG. B-25.

ROOTS (LL SCALES)

$$(A)^{1/B} = R$$

Set A with hairline on LL scale (depending upon the value) and set root (B), exponential denominator, on C scale under hairline (Fig. B-26). Read answer on LL scale at R. Example shown:

$$49.0^{1/2} = 7.0$$

FIG. B-26.

Mathematical Tables

Selected Mathematical Values

$\pi = 3.141593$	$\sqrt{\pi} = 1.772454$	$\sqrt{2} = 1.414214$
$2\pi = 6.283185$	$\sqrt[3]{\pi} = 1.464592$	$\sqrt{3} = 1.732055$
$3\pi = 9.424778$	$\log_e \pi* = 1.144730$	$\dfrac{\pi}{\sqrt{g}} = 0.55399$
$4\pi = 12.566371$	$\dfrac{1}{\pi} = 0.318310$	
$\dfrac{\pi}{2} = 1.570796$	$\dfrac{1}{\pi^2} = 0.101321$	$\dfrac{1}{\sqrt{g}} = 0.17634$
$\dfrac{\pi}{3} = 1.047198$	$\dfrac{1}{\sqrt{\pi}} = 0.564190$	$\sqrt{2g} = 8.01998$
		$\dfrac{1}{2g} = 0.01555$
$\dfrac{\pi}{4} = 0.785398$	$\log_{10} \pi = 0.497150$	$g^2 = 1034.266$
$\pi^2 = 9.869604$	$\dfrac{1}{e} = 0.367879$	$2g = 64.32$
$\pi^3 = 31.006277$		$g = 32.16$

*$e = 2.718282$

Decimal Equivalents of Inch Fractions

Fraction	Equiv.	Fraction	Equiv.	Fraction	Equiv.	Fraction	Equiv.
1/64	0.015625	17/64	0.265625	33/64	0.515625	49/64	0.765625
1/32	0.03125	9/32	0.28125	17/32	0.53125	25/32	0.78125
3/64	0.046875	19/64	0.296875	35/64	0.546875	51/64	0.796875
1/16	0.0625	5/16	0.3125	9/16	0.5625	13/16	0.8125
5/64	0.078125	21/64	0.328125	37/64	0.578125	53/64	0.828125
3/32	0.09375	11/32	0.34375	19/32	0.59375	27/32	0.84375
7/64	0.109375	23/64	0.359375	39/64	0.609375	55/64	0.859375
1/8	0.1250	3/8	0.3750	5/8	0.6250	7/8	0.8750
9/64	0.140625	25/64	0.390625	41/64	0.640625	57/64	0.890625
5/32	0.15625	13/32	0.40625	21/32	0.65625	29/32	0.90625
11/64	0.171875	27/64	0.421875	43/64	0.671875	59/64	0.921875
3/16	0.1875	7/16	0.4375	11/16	0.6875	15/16	0.9375
13/64	0.203125	29/64	0.453125	45/64	0.703125	61/64	0.953125
7/32	0.21875	15/32	0.46875	23/32	0.71875	31/32	0.96875
15/64	0.234375	31/64	0.484375	47/64	0.734375	63/64	0.984375
1/4	0.2500	1/2	0.5000	3/4	0.7500	1	1.0000

Metric Equivalents

Mm	In.*	Mm	In.	In.	Mm †	In.	Mm
1 = 0.0394		17 = 0.6693		1/32 = 0.794		17/32 = 13.493	
2 = 0.0787		18 = 0.7087		1/16 = 1.587		9/16 = 14.287	
3 = 0.1181		19 = 0.7480		3/32 = 2.381		19/32 = 15.081	
4 = 0.1575		20 = 0.7874		1/8 = 3.175		5/8 = 15.875	
5 = 0.1969		21 = 0.8268		5/32 = 3.968		21/32 = 16.668	
6 = 0.2362		22 = 0.8662		3/16 = 4.762		11/16 = 17.462	
7 = 0.2756		23 = 0.9055		7/32 = 5.556		23/32 = 18.256	
8 = 0.3150		24 = 0.9449		1/4 = 6.349		3/4 = 19.050	
9 = 0.3543		25 = 0.9843		9/32 = 7.144		25/32 = 19.843	
10 = 0.3937		26 = 1.0236		5/16 = 7.937		13/16 = 20.637	
11 = 0.4331		27 = 1.0630		11/32 = 8.731		27/32 = 21.431	
12 = 0.4724		28 = 1.1024		3/8 = 9.525		7/8 = 22.225	
13 = 0.5118		29 = 1.1418		13/32 = 10.319		29/32 = 23.018	
14 = 0.5512		30 = 1.1811		7/16 = 11.112		15/16 = 23.812	
15 = 0.5906		31 = 1.2205		15/32 = 11.906		31/32 = 24.606	
16 = 0.6299		32 = 1.2599		1/2 = 12.699		1 = 25.400	

* Calculated to *nearest* fourth decimal place.
† Calculated to *nearest* third decimal place.

Logarithms of Numbers

10	0	1	2	3	4	5	6	7	8	9
10	0000	0043	0086	0128	0170	0212	0253	0294	0334	0374
11	0414	0453	0492	0531	0569	0607	0645	0682	0719	0755
12	0792	0828	0864	0899	0934	0969	1004	1038	1072	1106
13	1139	1173	1206	1239	1271	1303	1335	1367	1399	1430
14	1461	1492	1523	1553	1584	1614	1644	1673	1703	1732
15	1761	1790	1818	1847	1875	1903	1931	1959	1987	2014
16	2041	2068	2095	2122	2148	2175	2201	2227	2253	2279
17	2304	2330	2355	2380	2405	2430	2455	2480	2504	2529
18	2553	2577	2601	2625	2648	2672	2695	2718	2742	2765
19	2788	2810	2833	2856	2878	2900	2923	2945	2967	2989
20	3010	3032	3054	3075	3096	3118	3139	3160	3181	3201
21	3222	3243	3263	3284	3304	3324	3345	3365	3385	3404
22	3424	3444	3464	3483	3502	3522	3541	3560	3579	3598
23	3617	3636	3655	3674	3692	3711	3729	3747	3766	3784
24	3802	3820	3838	3856	3874	3892	3909	3927	3945	3962
25	3979	3997	4014	4031	4048	4065	4082	4099	4116	4133
26	4150	4166	4183	4200	4216	4232	4249	4265	4281	4298
27	4314	4330	4346	4362	4378	4393	4409	4425	4440	4456
28	4472	4487	4502	4518	4533	4548	4564	4579	4594	4609
29	4624	4639	4654	4669	4683	4698	4713	4728	4742	4757
30	4771	4786	4800	4814	4829	4843	4857	4871	4886	4900
31	4914	4928	4942	4955	4969	4983	4997	5011	5024	5038
32	5051	5065	5079	5092	5105	5119	5132	5145	5159	5172
33	5185	5198	5211	5224	5237	5250	5263	5276	5289	5302
34	5315	5328	5340	5353	5366	5378	5391	5403	5416	5428
35	5441	5453	5465	5478	5490	5502	5514	5527	5539	5551
36	5563	5575	5587	5599	5611	5623	5635	5647	5658	5670
37	5682	5694	5705	5717	5729	5740	5752	5763	5775	5786
38	5798	5809	5821	5832	5843	5855	5866	5877	5888	5899
39	5911	5922	5933	5944	5955	5966	5977	5988	5999	6010
40	6021	6031	6042	6053	6064	6075	6085	6096	6107	6117
41	6128	6138	6149	6160	6170	6180	6191	6201	6212	6222
42	6232	6243	6253	6263	6274	6284	6294	6304	6314	6325
43	6335	6345	6355	6365	6375	6385	6395	6405	6415	6425
44	6435	6444	6454	6464	6474	6484	6493	6503	6513	6522
45	6532	6542	6551	6561	6571	6580	6590	6599	6609	6618
46	6628	6637	6646	6656	6665	6675	6684	6693	6702	6712
47	6721	6730	6739	6749	6758	6767	6776	6785	6794	6803
48	6812	6821	6830	6839	6848	6857	6866	6875	6884	6893
49	6902	6911	6920	6928	6937	6946	6955	6964	6972	6981
50	6990	6998	7007	7016	7024	7033	7042	7050	7059	7067
51	7076	7084	7093	7101	7110	7118	7126	7135	7143	7152
52	7160	7168	7177	7185	7193	7202	7210	7218	7226	7235
53	7243	7251	7259	7267	7275	7284	7292	7300	7308	7316
54	7324	7332	7340	7348	7356	7364	7372	7380	7388	7396

Logarithms of Numbers (Cont.)

55	0	1	2	3	4	5	6	7	8	9
55	7404	7412	7419	7427	7435	7443	7451	7459	7466	7474
56	7482	7490	7497	7505	7513	7520	7528	7536	7543	7551
57	7559	7566	7574	7582	7589	7597	7604	7612	7619	7627
58	7634	7642	7649	7657	7664	7672	7679	7686	7694	7701
59	7709	7716	7723	7731	7738	7745	7752	7760	7767	7774
60	7782	7789	7796	7803	7810	7818	7825	7832	7839	7846
61	7853	7860	7868	7875	7882	7889	7896	7903	7910	7917
62	7924	7931	7938	7945	7952	7959	7966	7973	7980	7987
63	7993	8000	8007	8014	8021	8028	8035	8041	8048	8055
64	8062	8069	8075	8082	8089	8096	8102	8109	8116	8122
65	8129	8136	8142	8149	8156	8162	8169	8176	8182	8189
66	8195	8202	8209	8215	8222	8228	8235	8241	8248	8254
67	8261	8267	8274	8280	8287	8293	8299	8306	8312	8319
68	8325	8331	8338	8344	8351	8357	8363	8370	8376	8382
69	8388	8395	8401	8407	8414	8420	8426	8432	8439	8445
70	8451	8457	8463	8470	8476	8482	8488	8494	8500	8506
71	8513	8519	8525	8531	8537	8543	8549	8555	8561	8567
72	8573	8579	8585	8591	8597	8603	8609	8615	8621	8627
73	8633	8639	8645	8651	8657	8663	8669	8675	8681	8686
74	8692	8698	8704	8710	8716	8722	8727	8733	8739	8745
75	8751	8756	8762	8768	8774	8779	8785	8791	8797	8802
76	8808	8814	8820	8825	8831	8837	8842	8848	8854	8859
77	8865	8871	8876	8882	8887	8893	8899	8904	8910	8915
78	8921	8927	8932	8938	8943	8949	8954	8960	8965	8971
79	8976	8982	8987	8993	8998	9004	9009	9015	9020	9025
80	9031	9036	9042	9047	9053	9058	9063	9069	9074	9079
81	9085	9090	9096	9101	9106	9112	9117	9122	9128	9133
82	9138	9143	9149	9154	9159	9165	9170	9175	9180	9186
83	9191	9196	9201	9206	9212	9217	9222	9227	9232	9238
84	9243	9248	9253	9258	9263	9269	9274	9279	9284	9289
85	9294	9299	9304	9309	9315	9320	9325	9330	9335	9340
86	9345	9350	9355	9360	9365	9370	9375	9380	9385	9390
87	9395	9400	9405	9410	9415	9420	9425	9430	9435	9440
88	9445	9450	9455	9460	9465	9469	9474	9479	9484	9489
89	9494	9499	9504	9509	9513	9518	9523	9528	9533	9538
90	9542	9547	9552	9557	9562	9566	9571	9576	9581	9586
91	9590	9595	9600	9605	9609	9614	9619	9624	9628	9633
92	9638	9643	9647	9652	9657	9661	9666	9671	9675	9680
93	9685	9689	9694	9699	9703	9708	9713	9717	9722	9727
94	9731	9736	9741	9745	9750	9754	9759	9763	9768	9773
95	9777	9782	9786	9791	9795	9800	9805	9809	9814	9818
96	9823	9827	9832	9836	9841	9845	9850	9854	9859	9863
97	9868	9872	9877	9881	9886	9890	9894	9899	9903	9908
98	9912	9917	9921	9926	9930	9934	9939	9943	9948	9952
99	9956	9961	9965	9969	9974	9978	9983	9987	9991	9996

Trigonometric Functions

Angle	Sine		Cosine		Tangent		Cotangent		Angle
	Nat.	Log.	Nat.	Log.	Nat.	Log.	Nat.	Log.	
0° 00′	.0000	∞	1.0000	0.0000	.0000	∞	∞	∞	90° 00′
10	.0029	7.4637	1.0000	0000	.0029	7.4637	343.77	2.5363	50
20	.0058	7648	1.0000	0000	.0058	7648	171.89	2352	40
30	.0087	9408	1.0000	0000	.0087	9409	114.59	0591	30
40	.0116	8.0658	.9999	0000	.0116	8.0658	85.940	1.9342	20
50	.0145	1627	.9999	0000	.0145	1627	68.750	8373	10
1° 00′	.0175	8.2419	.9998	9.9999	.0175	8.2419	57.290	1.7581	89° 00′
10	.0204	3088	.9998	9999	.0204	3089	49.104	6911	50
20	.0233	3668	.9997	9999	.0233	3669	42.964	6331	40
30	.0262	4179	.9997	9999	.0262	4181	38.188	5819	30
40	.0291	4637	.9996	9998	.0291	4638	34.368	5362	20
50	.0320	5050	.9995	9998	.0320	5053	31.242	4947	10
2° 00′	.0349	8.5428	.9994	9.9997	.0349	8.5431	28.636	1.4569	88° 00′
10	.0378	5776	.9993	9997	.0378	5779	26.432	4221	50
20	.0407	6097	.9992	9996	.0407	6101	24.542	3899	40
30	.0436	6397	.9990	9996	.0437	6401	22.904	3599	30
40	.0465	6677	.9989	9995	.0466	6682	21.470	3318	20
50	.0494	6940	.9988	9995	.0495	6945	20.206	3055	10
3° 00′	.0523	8.7188	.9986	9.9994	.0524	8.7194	19.081	1.2806	87° 00′
10	.0552	7423	.9985	9993	.0553	7429	18.075	2571	50
20	.0581	7645	.9983	9993	.0582	7652	17.169	2348	40
30	.0610	7857	.9981	9992	.0612	7865	16.350	2135	30
40	.0640	8059	.9980	9991	.0641	8067	15.605	1933	20
50	.0669	8251	.9978	9990	.0670	8261	14.924	1739	10
4° 00′	.0698	8.8436	.9976	9.9989	.0699	8.8446	14.301	1.1554	86° 00′
10	.0727	8613	.9974	9989	.0729	8624	13.727	1376	50
20	.0756	8783	.9971	9988	.0758	8795	13.197	1205	40
30	.0785	8946	.9969	9987	.0787	8960	12.706	1040	30
40	.0814	9104	.9967	9986	.0816	9118	12.251	0882	20
50	.0843	9256	.9964	9985	.0846	9272	11.826	0728	10
5° 00′	.0872	8.9403	.9962	9.9983	.0875	8.9420	11.430	1.0580	85° 00′
10	.0901	9545	.9959	9982	.0904	9563	11.059	0437	50
20	.0929	9682	.9957	9981	.0934	9701	10.712	0299	40
30	.0958	9816	.9954	9980	.0963	9836	10.385	0164	30
40	.0987	9945	.9951	9979	.0992	9966	10.078	0034	20
50	.1016	9.0070	.9948	9977	.1022	9.0093	9.7882	0.9907	10
6° 00′	.1045	9.0192	.9945	9.9976	.1051	9.0216	9.5144	0.9784	84° 00′
10	.1074	0311	.9942	9975	.1080	0336	9.2553	9664	50
20	.1103	0426	.9939	9973	.1110	0453	9.0098	9547	40
30	.1132	0539	.9936	9972	.1139	0567	8.7769	9433	30
40	.1161	0648	.9932	9971	.1169	0678	8.5555	9322	20
50	.1190	0755	.9929	9969	.1198	0786	8.3450	9214	10
7° 00′	.1219	9.0859	.9925	9.9968	.1228	9.0891	8.1443	0.9109	83° 00′
10	.1248	0961	.9922	9966	.1257	0995	7.9530	9005	50
20	.1276	1060	.9918	9964	.1287	1096	7.7704	8904	40
	Nat.	Log.	Nat.	Log.	Nat.	Log.	Nat.	Log.	
Angle	Cosine		Sine		Cotangent		Tangent		Angle

Trigonometric Functions (*Cont.*)

Angle	Sine		Cosine		Tangent		Cotangent		Angle
	Nat.	Log.	Nat.	Log.	Nat.	Log.	Nat.	Log.	
30	.1305	1157	.9914	9963	.1317	1194	7.5958	8806	30
40	.1334	1252	.9911	9961	.1346	1291	7.4287	8709	20
50	.1363	1345	.9907	9959	.1376	1385	7.2687	8615	10
8° 00′	.1392	9.1436	.9903	9.9958	.1405	9.1478	7.1154	0.8522	82° 00′
10	.1421	1525	.9899	9956	.1435	1569	6.9682	8431	50
20	.1449	1612	.9894	9954	.1465	1658	6.8269	8342	40
30	.1478	1697	.9890	9952	.1495	1745	6.6912	8255	30
40	.1507	1781	.9886	9950	.1524	1831	6.5606	8169	20
50	.1536	1863	.9881	9948	.1554	1915	6.4348	8085	10
9° 00′	.1564	9.1943	.9877	9.9946	.1584	9.1997	6.3138	0.8003	81° 00′
10	.1593	2022	.9872	9944	.1614	2078	6.1970	7922	50
20	.1622	2100	.9868	9942	.1644	2158	6.0844	7842	40
30	.1650	2176	.9863	9940	.1673	2236	5.9758	7764	30
40	.1679	2251	.9858	9938	.1703	2313	5.8708	7687	20
50	.1708	2324	.9853	9936	.1733	2389	5.7694	7611	10
10° 00′	.1736	9.2397	.9848	9.9934	.1763	9.2463	5.6713	0.7537	80° 00′
10	.1765	2468	.9843	9931	.1793	2536	5.5764	7464	50
20	.1794	2538	.9838	9929	.1823	2609	5.4845	7391	40
30	.1822	2606	.9833	9927	.1853	2680	5.3955	7320	30
40	.1851	2674	.9827	9924	.1883	2750	5.3093	7250	20
50	.1880	2740	.9822	9922	.1914	2819	5.2257	7181	10
11° 00′	.1908	9.2806	.9816	9.9919	.1944	9.2887	5.1446	0.7113	79° 00′
10	.1937	2870	.9811	9917	.1974	2953	5.0658	7047	50
20	.1965	2934	.9805	9914	.2004	3020	4.9894	6980	40
30	.1994	2997	.9799	9912	.2035	3085	4.9152	6915	30
40	.2022	3058	.9793	9909	.2065	3149	4.8430	6851	20
50	.2051	3119	.9787	9907	.2095	3212	4.7729	6788	10
12° 00′	.2079	9.3179	.9781	9.9904	.2126	9.3275	4.7046	0.6725	78° 00′
10	.2108	3238	.9775	9901	.2156	3336	4.6382	6664	50
20	.2136	3296	.9769	9899	.2186	3397	4.5736	6603	40
30	.2164	3353	.9763	9896	.2217	3458	4.5107	6542	30
40	.2193	3410	.9757	9893	.2247	3517	4.4494	6483	20
50	.2221	3466	.9750	9890	.2278	3576	4.3897	6424	10
13° 00′	.2250	9.3521	.9744	9.9887	.2309	9.3634	4.3315	0.6366	77° 00′
10	.2278	3575	.9737	9884	.2339	3691	4.2747	6309	50
20	.2306	3629	.9730	9881	.2370	3748	4.2193	6252	40
30	.2334	3682	.9724	9878	.2401	3804	4.1653	6196	30
40	.2363	3734	.9717	9875	.2432	3859	4.1126	6141	20
50	.2391	3786	.9710	9872	.2462	3914	4.0611	6086	10
14° 00′	.2419	9.3837	.9703	9.9869	.2493	9.3968	4.0108	0.6032	76° 00′
10	.2447	3887	.9696	9866	.2524	4021	3.9617	5979	50
20	.2476	3937	.9689	9863	.2555	4074	3.9136	5926	40
30	.2504	3986	.9681	9859	.2586	4127	3.8667	5873	30
40	.2532	4035	.9674	9856	.2617	4178	3.8208	5822	20
50	.2560	4083	.9667	9853	.2648	4230	3.7760	5770	10
	Nat.	Log.	Nat.	Log.	Nat.	Log.	Nat.	Log.	
Angle	Cosine		Sine		Cotangent		Tangent		Angle

Trigonometric Functions (*Cont.*)

Angle	Sine		Cosine		Tangent		Cotangent		Angle
	Nat.	Log.	Nat.	Log.	Nat.	Log.	Nat.	Log.	
15° 00′	.2588	9.4130	.9659	9.9849	.2679	9.4281	3.7321	0.5719	75° 00′
10	.2616	4177	.9652	9846	.2711	4331	3.6891	5669	50
20	.2644	4223	.9644	9843	.2742	4381	3.6470	5619	40
30	.2672	4269	.9636	9839	.2773	4430	3.6059	5570	30
40	.2700	4314	.9628	9836	.2805	4479	3.5656	5521	20
50	.2728	4359	.9621	9832	.2836	4527	3.5261	5473	10
16° 00′	.2756	9.4403	.9613	9.9828	.2867	9.4575	3.4874	0.5425	74° 00′
10	.2784	4447	.9605	9825	.2899	4622	3.4495	5378	50
20	.2812	4491	.9596	9821	.2931	4669	3.4124	5331	40
30	.2840	4533	.9588	9817	.2962	4716	3.3759	5284	30
40	.2868	4576	.9580	9814	.2994	4762	3.3402	5238	20
50	.2896	4618	.9572	9810	.3026	4808	3.3052	5192	10
17° 00′	.2924	9.4659	.9563	9.9806	.3057	9.4853	3.2709	0.5147	73° 00′
10	.2952	4700	.9555	9802	.3089	4898	3.2371	5102	50
20	.2979	4741	.9546	9798	.3121	4943	3.2041	5057	40
30	.3007	4781	.9537	9794	.3153	4987	3.1716	5013	30
40	.3035	4821	.9528	9790	.3185	5031	3.1397	4969	20
50	.3062	4861	.9520	9786	.3217	5075	3.1084	4925	10
18° 00′	.3090	9.4900	.9511	9.9782	.3249	9.5118	3.0777	0.4882	72° 00′
10	.3118	4939	.9502	9778	.3281	5161	3.0475	4839	50
20	.3145	4977	.9492	9774	.3314	5203	3.0178	4797	40
30	.3173	5015	.9483	9770	.3346	5245	2.9887	4755	30
40	.3201	5052	.9474	9765	.3378	5287	2.9600	4713	20
50	.3228	5090	.9465	9761	.3411	5329	2.9319	4671	10
19° 00′	.3256	9.5126	.9455	9.9757	.3443	9.5370	2.9042	0.4630	71° 00′
10	.3283	5163	.9446	9752	.3476	5411	2.8770	4589	50
20	.3311	5199	.9436	9748	.3508	5451	2.8502	4549	40
30	.3338	5235	.9426	9743	.3541	5491	2.8239	4509	30
40	.3365	5270	.9417	9739	.3574	5531	2.7980	4469	20
50	.3393	5306	.9407	9734	.3607	5571	2.7725	4429	10
20° 00′	.3420	9.5341	.9397	9.9730	.3640	9.5611	2.7475	0.4389	70° 00′
10	.3448	5375	.9387	9725	.3673	5650	2.7228	4350	50
20	.3475	5409	.9377	9721	.3706	5689	2.6985	4311	40
30	.3502	5443	.9367	9716	.3739	5727	2.6746	4273	30
40	.3529	5477	.9356	9711	.3772	5766	2.6511	4234	20
50	.3557	5510	.9346	9706	.3805	5804	2.6279	4196	10
21° 00′	.3584	9.5543	.9336	9.9702	.3839	9.5842	2.6051	0.4158	69° 00′
10	.3611	5576	.9325	9697	.3872	5879	2.5826	4121	50
20	.3638	5609	.9315	9692	.3906	5917	2.5605	4083	40
30	.3665	5641	.9304	9687	.3939	5954	2.5386	4046	30
40	.3692	5673	.9293	9682	.3973	5991	2.5172	4009	20
50	.3719	5704	.9283	9677	.4006	6028	2.4960	3972	10
22° 00′	.3746	9.5736	.9272	9.9672	.4040	9.6064	2.4751	0.3936	68° 00′
10	.3773	5767	.9261	9667	.4074	6100	2.4545	3900	50
20	.3800	5798	.9250	9661	.4108	6136	2.4342	3864	40
	Nat.	Log.	Nat.	Log.	Nat.	Log.	Nat.	Log.	
Angle	Cosine		Sine		Cotangent		Tangent		Angle

Trigonometric Functions (*Cont.*)

Angle	Sine		Cosine		Tangent		Cotangent		Angle
	Nat.	Log.	Nat.	Log.	Nat.	Log.	Nat.	Log.	
30	.3827	5828	.9239	9656	.4142	6172	2.4142	3828	30
40	.3854	5859	.9228	9651	.4176	6208	2.3945	3792	20
50	.3881	5889	.9216	9646	.4210	6243	2.3750	3757	10
23° 00'	.3907	9.5919	.9205	9.9640	4245	9.6279	2.3559	0.3721	67° 00'
10	.3934	5948	.9194	9635	.4279	6314	2.3369	3686	50
20	.3961	5978	.9182	9629	.4314	6348	2.3183	3652	40
30	.3987	6007	.9171	9624	.4348	6383	2.2998	3617	30
40	.4014	6036	.9159	9618	.4383	6417	2.2817	3583	20
50	.4041	6065	.9147	9613	.4417	6452	2.2637	3548	10
24° 00'	.4067	9.6093	.9135	9.9607	.4452	9.6486	2.2460	0.3514	66° 00'
10	.4094	6121	.9124	9602	.4487	6520	2.2286	3480	50
20	.4120	6149	.9112	9596	.4522	6553	2.2113	3447	40
30	.4147	6177	.9100	9590	.4557	6587	2.1943	3413	30
40	.4173	6205	.9088	9584	.4592	6620	2.1775	3380	20
50	.4200	6232	.9075	9579	.4628	6654	2.1609	3346	10
25° 00'	.4226	9.6259	.9063	9.9573	.4663	9.6687	2.1445	0.3313	65° 00'
10	.4253	6286	.9051	9567	.4699	6720	2.1283	3280	50
20	.4279	6313	.9038	9561	.4734	6752	2.1123	3248	40
30	.4305	6340	.9026	9555	.4770	6785	2.0965	3215	30
40	.4331	6366	.9013	9549	.4806	6817	2.0809	3183	20
50	.4358	6392	.9001	9543	.4841	6850	2.0655	3150	10
26° 00'	.4384	9.6418	.8988	9.9537	.4877	9.6882	2.0503	0.3118	64° 00'
10	.4410	6444	.8975	9530	.4913	6914	2.0353	3086	50
20	.4436	6470	.8962	9524	.4950	6946	2.0204	3054	40
30	.4462	6495	.8949	9518	.4986	6977	2.0057	3023	30
40	.4488	6521	.8936	9512	.5022	7009	1.9912	2991	20
50	.4514	6546	.8923	9505	.5059	7040	1.9768	2960	10
27° 00'	.4540	9.6570	.8910	9.9499	.5095	9.7072	1.9626	0.2928	63° 00'
10	.4566	6595	.8897	9492	.5132	7103	1.9486	2897	50
20	.4592	6620	.8884	9486	.5169	7134	1.9347	2866	40
30	.4617	6644	.8870	9479	.5206	7165	1.9210	2835	30
40	.4643	6668	.8857	9473	.5243	7196	1.9074	2804	20
50	.4669	6692	.8843	9466	.5280	7226	1.8940	2774	10
28° 00'	.4695	9.6716	.8829	9.9459	.5317	9.7257	1.8807	0.2743	62° 00'
10	.4720	6740	.8816	9453	.5354	7287	1.8676	2713	50
20	.4746	6763	.8802	9446	.5392	7317	1.8546	2683	40
30	.4772	6787	.8788	9439	.5430	7348	1.8418	2652	30
40	.4797	6810	.8774	9432	.5467	7378	1.8291	2622	20
50	.4823	6833	.8760	9425	.5505	7408	1.8165	2592	10
29° 00'	.4848	9.6856	.8746	9.9418	.5543	9.7438	1.8040	0.2562	61° 00'
10	.4874	6878	.8732	9411	.5581	7467	1.7917	2533	50
20	.4899	6901	.8718	9404	.5619	7497	1.7796	2503	40
30	.4924	6923	.8704	9397	.5658	7526	1.7675	2474	30
40	.4950	6946	.8689	9390	.5696	7556	1.7556	2444	20
50	.4975	6968	.8675	9383	.5735	7585	1.7437	2415	10
	Nat.	Log.	Nat.	Log.	Nat.	Log.	Nat.	Log.	
Angle	Cosine		Sine		Cotangent		Tangent		Angle

Trigonometric Functions (*Cont.*)

Angle	Sine		Cosine		Tangent		Cotangent		Angle
	Nat.	Log.	Nat.	Log.	Nat.	Log.	Nat.	Log.	
30° 00′	.5000	9.6990	.8660	9.9375	.5774	9.7614	1.7321	0.2386	60° 00′
10	.5025	7012	.8646	9368	.5812	7644	1.7205	2356	50
20	.5050	7033	.8631	9361	.5851	7673	1.7090	2327	40
30	.5075	7055	.8616	9353	.5890	7701	1.6977	2299	30
40	.5100	7076	.8601	9346	.5930	7730	1.6864	2270	20
50	.5125	7097	.8587	9338	.5969	7759	1.6753	2241	10
31° 00′	.5150	9.7118	.8572	9.9331	.6009	9.7788	1.6643	0.2212	59° 00′
10	.5175	7139	.8557	9323	.6048	7816	1.6534	2184	50
20	.5200	7160	.8542	9315	.6088	7845	1.6426	2155	40
30	.5225	7181	.8526	9308	.6128	7873	1.6319	2127	30
40	.5250	7201	.8511	9300	.6168	7902	1.6212	2098	20
50	.5275	7222	.8496	9292	.6208	7930	1.6107	2070	10
32° 00′	.5299	9.7242	.8480	9.9284	.6249	9.7958	1.6003	0.2042	58° 00′
10	.5324	7262	.8465	9276	.6289	7986	1.5900	2014	50
20	.5348	7282	.8450	9268	.6330	8014	1.5798	1986	40
30	.5373	7302	.8434	9260	.6371	8042	1.5697	1958	30
40	.5398	7322	.8418	9252	.6412	8070	1.5597	1930	20
50	.5422	7342	.8403	9244	.6453	8097	1.5497	1903	10
33° 00′	.5446	9.7361	.8387	9.9236	.6494	9.8125	1.5399	0.1875	57° 00′
10	.5471	7380	.8371	9228	.6536	8153	1.5301	1847	50
20	.5495	7400	.8355	9219	.6577	8180	1.5204	1820	40
30	.5519	7419	.8339	9211	.6619	8208	1.5108	1792	30
40	.5544	7438	.8323	9203	.6661	8235	1.5013	1765	20
50	.5568	7457	.8307	9194	.6703	8263	1.4919	1737	10
34° 00′	.5592	9.7476	.8290	9.9186	.6745	9.8290	1.4826	0.1710	56° 00′
10	.5616	7494	.8274	9177	.6787	8317	1.4733	1683	50
20	.5640	7513	.8258	9169	.6830	8344	1.4641	1656	40
30	.5664	7531	.8241	9160	.6873	8371	1.4550	1629	30
40	.5688	7550	.8225	9151	.6916	8398	1.4460	1602	20
50	.5712	7568	.8208	9142	.6959	8425	1.4370	1575	10
35° 00′	.5736	9.7586	.8192	9.9134	.7002	9.8452	1.4281	0.1548	55° 00′
10	.5760	7604	.8175	9125	.7046	8479	1.4193	1521	50
20	.5783	7622	.8158	9116	.7089	8506	1.4106	1494	40
30	.5807	7640	.8141	9107	.7133	8533	1.4019	1467	30
40	.5831	7657	.8124	9098	.7177	8559	1.3934	1441	20
50	.5854	7675	.8107	9089	.7221	8586	1.3848	1414	10
36° 00′	.5878	9.7692	.8090	9.9080	.7265	9.8613	1.3764	0.1387	54° 00′
10	.5901	7710	.8073	9070	.7310	8639	1.3680	1361	50
20	.5925	7727	.8056	9061	.7355	8666	1.3597	1334	40
30	.5948	7744	.8039	9052	.7400	8692	1.3514	1308	30
40	.5972	7761	.8021	9042	.7445	8718	1.3432	1282	20
50	.5995	7778	.8004	9033	.7490	8745	1.3351	1255	10
37° 00′	.6018	9.7795	.7986	9.9023	.7536	9.8771	1.3270	0.1229	53° 00′
10	.6041	7811	.7969	9014	.7581	8797	1.3190	1203	50
20	.6065	7828	.7951	9004	.7627	8824	1.3111	1176	40
	Nat.	Log.	Nat.	Log.	Nat.	Log.	Nat.	Log.	
Angle	Cosine		Sine		Cotangent		Tangent		Angle

Trigonometric Functions (Cont.)

Angle	Sine		Cosine		Tangent		Cotangent		Angle
	Nat.	Log.	Nat.	Log.	Nat.	Log.	Nat.	Log.	
30	.6088	7844	.7934	8995	.7673	8850	1.3032	1150	30
40	.6111	7861	.7916	8985	.7720	8876	1.2954	1124	20
50	.6134	7877	.7898	8975	.7766	8902	1.2876	1098	10
38° 00′	.6157	9.7893	.7880	9.8965	.7813	9.8928	1.2799	0.1072	52° 00′
10	.6180	7910	.7862	8955	.7860	8954	1.2723	1046	50
20	.6202	7926	.7844	8945	.7907	8980	1.2647	1020	40
30	.6225	7941	.7826	8935	.7954	9006	1.2572	0994	30
40	.6248	7957	.7808	8925	.8002	9032	1.2497	0968	20
50	.6271	7973	.7790	8915	.8050	9058	1.2423	0942	10
39° 00′	.6293	9.7989	.7771	9.8905	.8098	9.9084	1.2349	0.0916	51° 00′
10	.6316	8004	.7753	8895	.8146	9110	1.2276	0890	50
20	.6338	8020	.7735	8884	.8195	9135	1.2203	0865	40
30	.6361	8035	.7716	8874	.8243	9161	1.2131	0839	30
40	.6383	8050	.7698	8864	.8292	9187	1.2059	0813	20
50	.6406	8066	.7679	8853	.8342	9212	1.1988	0788	10
40° 00′	.6428	9.8081	.7660	9.8843	.8391	9.9238	1.1918	0.0762	50° 00′
10	.6450	8096	.7642	8832	.8441	9264	1.1847	0736	50
20	.6472	8111	.7623	8821	.8491	9289	1.1778	0711	40
30	.6494	8125	.7604	8810	.8541	9315	1.1708	0685	30
40	.6517	8140	.7585	8800	.8591	9341	1.1640	0659	20
50	.6539	8155	.7566	8789	.8642	9366	1.1571	0634	10
41° 00′	.6561	9.8169	.7547	9.8778	.8693	9.9392	1.1504	0.0608	49° 00′
10	.6583	8184	.7528	8767	.8744	9417	1.1436	0583	50
20	.6604	8198	.7509	8756	.8796	9443	1.1369	0557	40
30	.6626	8213	.7490	8745	.8847	9468	1.1303	0532	30
40	.6648	8227	.7470	8733	.8899	9494	1.1237	0506	20
50	.6670	8241	.7451	8722	.8952	9519	1.1171	0481	10
42° 00′	.6691	9.8255	.7431	9.8711	.9004	9.9544	1.1106	0.0456	48° 00′
10	.6713	8269	.7412	8699	.9057	9570	1.1041	0430	50
20	.6734	8283	.7392	8688	.9110	9595	1.0977	0405	40
30	.6756	8297	.7373	8676	.9163	9621	1.0913	0379	30
40	.6777	8311	.7353	8665	.9217	9646	1.0850	0354	20
50	.6799	8324	.7333	8653	.9271	9671	1.0786	0329	10
43° 00′	.6820	9.8338	.7314	9.8641	.9325	9.9697	1.0724	0.0303	47° 00′
10	.6841	8351	.7294	8629	.9380	9722	1.0661	0278	50
20	.6862	8365	.7274	8618	.9435	9747	1.0599	0253	40
30	.6884	8378	.7254	8606	.9490	9772	1.0538	0228	30
40	.6905	8391	.7234	8594	.9545	9798	1.0477	0202	20
50	.6926	8405	.7214	8582	.9601	9823	1.0416	0177	10
44° 00′	.6947	9.8418	.7193	9.8569	.9657	9.9848	1.0355	0.0152	46° 00′
10	.6967	8431	.7173	8557	.9713	9874	1.0295	0126	50
20	.6988	8444	.7153	8545	.9770	9899	1.0235	0101	40
30	.7009	8457	.7133	8532	.9827	9924	1.0176	0076	30
40	.7030	8469	.7112	8520	.9884	9949	1.0117	0051	20
50	.7050	8482	.7092	8507	.9942	9975	1.0058	0025	10
45° 00′	.7071	9.8495	.7071	9.8495	1.0000	0.0000	1.0000	0.0000	45° 00′
	Nat.	Log.	Nat.	Log.	Nat.	Log.	Nat.	Log	
Angle	Cosine		Sine		Cotangent		Tangent		Angle

Length of Chord for Circle Arcs of 1-in. Radius

°	0′	10′	20′	30′	40′	50′
0	0.0000	0.0029	0.0058	0.0087	0.0116	0.0145
1	0.0175	0.0204	0.0233	0.0262	0.0291	0.0320
2	0.0349	0.0378	0.0407	0.0436	0.0465	0.0494
3	0.0524	0.0553	0.0582	0.0611	0.0640	0.0669
4	0.0698	0.0727	0.0756	0.0785	0.0814	0.0843
5	0.0872	0.0901	0.0931	0.0960	0.0989	0.1018
6	0.1047	0.1076	0.1105	0.1134	0.1163	0.1192
7	0.1221	0.1250	0.1279	0.1308	0.1337	0.1366
8	0.1395	0.1424	0.1453	0.1482	0.1511	0.1540
9	0.1569	0.1598	0.1627	0.1656	0.1685	0.1714
10	0.1743	0.1772	0.1801	0.1830	0.1859	0.1888
11	0.1917	0.1946	0.1975	0.2004	0.2033	0.2062
12	0.2091	0.2119	0.2148	0.2177	0.2206	0.2235
13	0.2264	0.2293	0.2322	0.2351	0.2380	0.2409
14	0.2437	0.2466	0.2495	0.2524	0.2553	0.2582
15	0.2611	0.2639	0.2668	0.2697	0.2726	0.2755
16	0.2783	0.2812	0.2841	0.2870	0.2899	0.2927
17	0.2956	0.2985	0.3014	0.3042	0.3071	0.3100
18	0.3129	0.3157	0.3186	0.3215	0.3244	0.3272
19	0.3301	0.3330	0.3358	0.3387	0.3416	0.3444
20	0.3473	0.3502	0.3530	0.3559	0.3587	0.3616
21	0.3645	0.3673	0.3702	0.3730	0.3759	0.3788
22	0.3816	0.3845	0.3873	0.3902	0.3930	0.3959
23	0.3987	0.4016	0.4044	0.4073	0.4101	0.4130
24	0.4158	0.4187	0.4215	0.4244	0.4272	0.4300
25	0.4329	0.4357	0.4386	0.4414	0.4442	0.4471
26	0.4499	0.4527	0.4556	0.4584	0.4612	0.4641
27	0.4669	0.4697	0.4725	0.4754	0.4782	0.4810
28	0.4838	0.4867	0.4895	0.4923	0.4951	0.4979
29	0.5008	0.5036	0.5064	0.5092	0.5120	0.5148
30	0.5176	0.5204	0.5233	0.5261	0.5289	0.5317
31	0.5345	0.5373	0.5401	0.5429	0.5457	0.5485
32	0.5513	0.5541	0.5569	0.5597	0.5625	0.5652
33	0.5680	0.5708	0.5736	0.5764	0.5792	0.5820
34	0.5847	0.5875	0.5903	0.5931	0.5959	0.5986
35	0.6014	0.6042	0.6070	0.6097	0.6125	0.6153
36	0.6180	0.6208	0.6236	0.6263	0.6291	0.6319
37	0.6346	0.6374	0.6401	0.6429	0.6456	0.6484
38	0.6511	0.6539	0.6566	0.6594	0.6621	0.6649
39	0.6676	0.6704	0.6731	0.6758	0.6786	0.6813
40	0.6840	0.6868	0.6895	0.6922	0.6950	0.6977
41	0.7004	0.7031	0.7059	0.7086	0.7113	0.7140
42	0.7167	0.7195	0.7222	0.7249	0.7276	0.7303
43	0.7330	0.7357	0.7384	0.7411	0.7438	0.7465
44	0.7492	0.7519	0.7546	0.7573	0.7600	0.7627
45*	0.7654	0.7681	0.7707	0.7734	0.7761	0.7788

* For angles between 45° and 90°, draw 90° angle and lay off complement from 90° line.

Conversions of Weights and Measures

Given	Multiply by	To obtain
Absolute temperature (abs temp), centigrade	1.0	degrees Centigrade $+273.160 \pm .010$
Absolute temperature, Fahrenheit	1.0	degrees Fahrenheit $+491.2$
Acceleration by gravity	980.665	centimeters per second
Acceleration by gravity	32.16	feet per second
Acres	0.4047	hectares
Acres	10.0	square chains
Acres	43,560.0	square feet
Acre	0.00156	square miles
Ares	100.0	centiares
Ares	119.6	square yards
Atmospheres (atm)	29.921	inches of mercury
Atmospheres	33.934	feet of water
Atmospheres	1.033228	kilograms per square centimeter
Atmospheres	14.6959	pounds per square inch
British thermal units (Btu)	0.252	calories
British thermal units	778.0	foot-pounds
British thermal units	1,054.86	watt-seconds
Bushels (bu), imperial	1.032	bushels, U.S.
Bushels, imperial	1.2837	cubic feet
Bushels, imperial	2,218.19	cubic inches
Bushels, imperial	8.0	gallons, imperial
Bushels, imperial	36.368	liters
Bushels, U.S.	0.968	bushels, imperial
Bushels, U.S.	1.2445	cubic feet
Bushels, U.S.	2,150.42	cubic inches
Bushels, U.S.	35.2393	liters
Bushels, U.S.	4.0	pecks
Bushels, U.S.	64.0	pints, dry
Bushels, U.S.	32.0	quarts, dry
Calories (cal)	3.9682	British thermal units
Calories	3,088.4	foot-pounds
Carats	3.086	grains
Carats	200.0	milligrams
Centiares	1,549.997	square inches
Centiares	1.0	square meters
Centigrade, degrees (°C)	$\frac{9}{5}\,°C + 32$	Fahrenheit, degrees
Centigrams (cg)	0.1543	grains
Centigrams	0.01	grams
Centiliters (cl)	0.01	liters
Centiliters	0.0338	ounces, fluid

Conversions of Weights and Measures (Cont.)

Given	Multiply by	To obtain
Centimeters (cm)	0.0328	feet
Centimeters	0.3937	inches
Centimeters	0.01	meters
Chains	0.10000	furlongs
Chains	0.01250	miles, statute
Chains	100.0	links
Circle (angular)	360.0	degrees
Circular inch (cir in.)	1.0	area of a 1-in.-diameter circle
Circular inches	1,000,000.0	circular mils
Circular inches	0.7854	square inches
Circular mil	1.0	area of a 0.001-in.-diameter circle
Circular mils	0.0000001	circular inches
Circumference of the earth at the equator	21,600.0	miles, nautical
Circumference of the earth at the equator	24,874.5	miles, statute
Cord (cd), of wood, (4 × 4 × 8)	128.0	cubic feet
Cubic centimeters (cu cm)	0.00003531	cubic feet
Cubic centimeters	0.06102	cubic inches
Cubic centimeters	0.0010	liters
Cubic centimeters	0.0000010	cubic meter
Cubic decimeters	1,000.0	cubic centimeters
Cubic decimeters	61.02	cubic inches
Cubic feet (cu ft)	0.7790	bushels, imperial
Cubic feet	0.80290	bushels, U.S.
Cubic feet	0.00781	cords, of wood
Cubic feet	28,317.08	cubic centimeters
Cubic feet	1,728.0	cubic inches
Cubic feet	0.0283	cubic meters
Cubic feet	0.0370	cubic yards
Cubic feet	7.4805	gallons, U.S.
Cubic feet	28.3163	liters
Cubic feet	0.04040	perch, of masonry
Cubic feet of water at 39.1 degrees Fahrenheit (°F)	28.3156	kilograms
Cubic feet of water at 39.1 degrees Fahrenheit	62.4245	pounds
Cubic inches (cu in.)	0.00045	bushels, imperial
Cubic inches	0.00046	bushels, U.S.
Cubic inches	16.3872	cubic centimeters
Cubic inches	0.00058	cubic feet
Cubic inches	0.000016	cubic meters
Cubic inches	0.0000214	cubic yards
Cubic inches	0.0036	gallons, imperial

Conversions of Weights and Measures (*Cont.*)

Given	Multiply by	To obtain
Cubic inches	0.00432	gallons, U.S.
Cubic inches	0.0164	liters
Cubic inches	0.00186	pecks
Cubic inches	0.02976	pints, dry
Cubic inches	0.0346	pints, liquid
Cubic inches	0.01488	quarts, dry
Cubic inches	0.0173	quarts, liquid
Cubic meters (cu m or m³)	1,000,000.0	cubic centimeters
Cubic meters	35.3133	cubic feet
Cubic meters	61,023.3753	cubic inches
Cubic meters	1.3079	cubic yards
Cubic meters	264.170	gallons, U.S.
Cubic millimeters (cu mm or mm³)	0.001	cubic centimeters
Cubic millimeters	0.00006	cubic inches
Cubic yards (cu yd)	27.0	cubic feet
Cubic yards	46,656.0	cubic inches
Cubic yards	0.7646	cubic meters
Decigrams	1.5432	grains
Decigrams	0.1	grams
Decimeters	3.937	inches
Decimeters	0.01	meters
Deciliter	0.338	ounces, fluid
Decagrams	10.0	grams
Decagrams	0.3527	ounces, avoirdupois
Decaliters	0.284	bushels, U.S.
Decaliters	2.64	gallons, U.S.
Decaliters	10.0	liters
Decameters	393.7	inches
Decameters	10.0	meters
Decileters	0.1	liters
Degrees (deg or °)	60.0	minutes
Degrees (arc)	0.0175	radians
Degrees (at the equator)	60.0	miles, nautical
Degrees (at the equator)	69.168	miles, statute
Dozens (doz)	12.0	units
Drams (dr), apothecaries	60.0	grains
Drams, apothecaries	3.543	grams
Drams, apothecaries	3.0	scruples
Drams, avoirdupois	27.344	grains
Drams, avoirdupois	1.772	grams
Drams, avoirdupois	0.0625	ounces, avoirdupois
Drams, fluid	0.2256	cubic inches
Drams, fluid	3.6966	milliliters

Conversions of Weights and Measures (*Cont.*)

Given	Multiply by	To obtain
Drams, fluid	60.0	minims
Drams, fluid	0.125	ounces, U.S. fluid
Dynes	0.00102	grams
Ergs	1.0	dyne-centimeters
Fahrenheit	$\dfrac{5(°F-32)}{9}$	centigrade, degrees
Fathoms	6.0	feet
Fathoms	1.8288	meters
Fathoms	2.0	yards
Feet (ft)	30.4801	centimeters
Feet	0.16667	fathom
Feet	12.0	inches
Feet	0.66000	links
Feet	0.3048	meters
Feet	0.000189	miles
Feet	0.0001645	miles, nautical
Feet	0.06061	rods
Feet	0.3333	yards
Feet of water at 62 degrees Fahrenheit	304.442	kilograms per square meter
Feet of water at 62 degrees Fahrenheit	62.355	pounds per square foot
Feet of water at 62 degrees Fahrenheit	0.4334	pounds per square inch
Feet per second (fps)	0.5921	knots
Feet per second	0.6816	miles per hour
Foot-pounds (ft-lb)	0.00129	British thermal units
Foot-pounds	0.00032	calories
Foot-pounds	0.13835	meter-kilograms
Foot-pounds per minute	0.000003	horsepower
Foot-pounds per second	0.000018	horsepower
Furlongs	10.0	chains
Furlongs	660.0	feet
Furlongs	201.17	meters
Furlongs	0.12500	miles, statute
Furlongs	220.0	yards
Gallons (gal), imperial	0.125	bushels, imperial
Gallons, imperial	277.4176	cubic inches
Gallons, imperial	1.2009	gallons, U.S.
Gallons, imperial	4.54607	liters
Gallons, U.S.	0.1337	cubic feet
Gallons, U.S.	231.0	cubic inches
Gallons, U.S.	0.0038	cubic meters
Gallons, U.S.	0.8327	gallons, imperial
Gallons, U.S.	3.7878	liters

Conversions of Weights and Measures (Cont.)

Given	Multiply by	To obtain
Gallons, U.S.	128.0	ounces, U.S. fluid
Gallons, U.S., water	8.5	pounds
Gills	0.25	pints, liquid
Grains	0.0366	drams, avoirdupois
Grains	0.0648	grams
Grains	64.7989	milligrams
Grains	0.00229	ounces, avoirdupois
Grains	0.00208	ounces, troy and apothecaries'
Grains	0.00014	pounds, avoirdupois
Grains	0.00017	pounds, troy and apothecaries'
Grams (g)	981	dynes
Grams	15.4475	grains
Grams	0.0010	kilograms
Grams	1,000.0	milligrams
Grams	0.0353	ounces, avoirdupois
Grams	0.0022	pounds, avoirdupois
Grams per cubic centimeter	1,000.0	kilograms per cubic meter
Grams per cubic centimeter	62.4	pounds per cubic foot
Grams per cubic centimeter	0.03613	pounds per cubic inch
Gross	12.0	dozen
Gross, great	12.0	gross
Hands	4.0	inches
Hectares (ha)	100.0	ares
Hectograms	100.0	grams
Hectograms	3.5274	ounces, avoirdupois
Hectoliters	26.417	gallons
Hectoliters	100.0	liters
Hectometers	328.083	feet
Hectometers	100.0	meters
Horsepower (hp)	76.042	kilogram-meters per second
Horsepower	550.0	foot-pounds per second
Horsepower	33,000.0	foot-pounds per minute
Horsepower	1.0139	metric horsepower
Horsepower	746.0	watts per minute
Horsepower, metric	0.9862	horsepower
Horsepower, metric	32,550.0	foot-pounds per minute
Horsepower, metric	542.5	foot-pounds per second
Horsepower, metric	75.0	kilogram meters per second
Inches (in.)	2.5400	centimeters
Inches	0.08333	feet
Inches	0.25000	hands
Inches	0.12626	links

Conversions of Weights and Measures (Cont.)

Given	Multiply by	To obtain
Inches	0.0254	meters
Inches	1,000.0	mils
Inches	0.11111	spans
Inches	0.02778	yards
Inches of mercury	1.1341	feet of water
Inches of mercury	34.542	grams per square centimeter
Inches of mercury	13.6092	inches of water
Inches of mercury	0.49115	pounds per square inch
Inches of water	2.537	grams per square centimeter
Inches of water	0.07347	inches of mercury
Inches of water	5.1052	pounds per square foot
Kilocycles	1,000.0	cycles per second
Kilogram-meters (kg-m)	7.2330	pound-feet
Kilogram-meters per second	0.01305	horsepower
Kilogram-meters per second	0.01333	horsepower, metric
Kilograms (kg)	15,432.36	grains
Kilograms	1,000.0	grams
Kilograms	35.2740	ounces, avoirdupois
Kilograms	2.2046	pounds, avoirdupois
Kilograms	0.00110	tons
Kilograms	0.00098	tons, long
Kilograms	0.001	tons, metric
Kilograms per cubic meter (kg per cu m or kg/m³)	0.06243	pounds per cubic foot
Kilograms per meter	0.6721	pounds per foot
Kilograms per square centimeter	14.22	pounds per square inch
Kilograms per square meter	0.2048	pounds per square inch
Kilograms per square meter	0.00142	pounds per square inch
Kiloliters (kl)	1,000.0	liters
Kilometers (km)	3,280.8330	feet
Kilometers	1,000.0	meters
Kilometers	0.5396	miles, nautical
Kilometers	0.6214	miles, statute
Kilometers per hour	0.5396	knots
Kilometers per hour	0.62138	miles per hour
Kilowatts (kw)	0.04426	foot-pounds per minute
Kilowatt-hours (kwhr)	3,412.75	British thermal units per hour
Kilowatt-hours	1.3414	horsepower hours
Knots	1.6889	feet per second
Knots	1.8532	kilometers per hour
Knots	0.5148	meters per second
Knots	1.1516	miles per hour
Knots	1.0	nautical miles per hour

Conversions of Weights and Measures (*Cont.*)

Given	Multiply by	To obtain
Leagues, land	4.83	kilometers
Leagues, land	2.6050	miles, nautical
Leagues, land	3.0	miles, statute
Leagues, marine	5.56	kilometers
Leagues, marine	3.0	miles, nautical
Leagues, marine	3.45	miles, statute
Links	0.01	chains
Links	0.66	feet
Links	7.92	inches
Links	0.04	rods
Links	0.22	yards
Liters (l)	0.0284	bushels, U.S.
Liters	1,000.0	cubic centimeters
Liters	0.035313	cubic feet
Liters	61.02398	cubic inches
Liters	0.2199	gallons, imperial
Liters	0.2641	gallons, U.S.
Liters	0.1135	pecks
Liters	0.9081	quarts, dry
Liters	1.0567	quarts, liquid
Long tons	2,240.0	pounds, avoirdupois
Megacycles	1,000,000.0	cycles per second
Megameters	100,000.0	meters
Meters (m)	0.5468	fathoms
Meters	3.2808	feet
Meters	39.370	inches
Meters	0.000541	miles, nautical
Meters	0.000622	miles, U.S.
Meters	1.0936	yards
Meter-kilograms (m-kg)	7.2330	foot-pounds
Meters per second	1.9425	knots
Meters per second	2.2369	miles per hour
Microns (μ)	0.000039	inches
Microns	0.000001	meters
Microns	0.03937	mils
Miles, nautical	6,080.20	feet
Miles, nautical	1.85325	kilometers
Miles, nautical	0.33333	leagues, marine
Miles, nautical	1,853.2486	meters
Miles, nautical	1.1516	miles, statute
Miles, statute	80.0	chains
Miles, statute	5,280.0	feet
Miles, statute	8.0	furlongs

Conversions of Weights and Measures (Cont.)

Given	Multiply by	To obtain
Miles, statute	1.6093	kilometers
Miles, statute	0.33333	leagues, land
Miles, statute	1,609.35	meters
Miles, statute	0.86836	miles, nautical
Miles, statute	1,760.0	yards
Miles per hour (mph)	1.4667	feet per second
Miles per hour	1.6093	kilometers per hour
Miles per hour	0.8684	knots
Miles per hour	0.4470	meters per second
Milligrams (mg)	0.01543	grains
Milligrams	0.001	grams
Milliliters (ml)	0.2705	drams, fluid
Milliliters	0.001	liters
Milliliters	0.0338	ounces, fluid
Millimeters (mm)	0.03937	inches
Millimeters	0.001	meters
Millimeters	1,000.0	microns
Millimeters	39.37	mils
Mils	0.001	inches
Mils	25.4001	microns
Mils	0.0254	millimeters
Minims	0.01667	drams, fluid
Minutes (min)	60.0	seconds
Myriagrams	10,000.0	grams
Myriameters	10,000.0	meters
Ounces (oz), apothecaries'	8.0	drams, apothecaries'
Ounces, avoirdupois	16.0	drams, avoirdupois
Ounces, avoirdupois	437.5	grains
Ounces, avoirdupois	28.3495	grams
Ounces, avoirdupois	1.0971	ounces, troy and apothecaries'
Ounces, avoirdupois	0.0625	pounds, avoirdupois
Ounces, British fluid	28.382	cubic centimeters
Ounces, British fluid	1.732	cubic inches
Ounces, fluid	29.57	milliliters
Ounces, troy	20.0	pennyweights
Ounces, troy and apothecaries'	480.0	grains
Ounces, troy and apothecaries'	31.10348	grams
Ounces, troy and apothecaries'	0.91149	ounces, avoirdupois
Ounces, U.S. fluid	1.805	cubic inches
Ounces, U.S. fluid	8.0	drams, fluid
Ounces, U.S. fluid	0.00781	gallons, U.S.
Ounces, U.S. fluid	0.0296	liters
Pecks (pk)	0.25	bushel, U.S.

Conversions of Weights and Measures (Cont.)

Given	Multiply by	To obtain
Pecks	537.61	cubic inches
Pecks	8.8096	liters
Pecks	8.0	quarts, dry
Pennyweights (dwt)	24.0	grains
Perch (of masonry)	24.75	cubic feet
Pints (pt), dry	0.015625	bushels, U.S.
Pints, dry	33.60	cubic inches
Pints, dry	0.5506	liters
Pints, dry	0.0625	pecks
Pints, dry	0.5	quarts, dry
Pints, liquid	28.875	cubic inches
Pints, liquid	4.0	gills
Pints, liquid	0.4732	liters
Poundals	0.03113	pounds, avoirdupois
Pounds (lb), avoirdupois	0.0160	cubic feet of water
Pounds, avoirdupois	7,000.0	grains
Pounds, avoirdupois	453.5924	grams
Pounds, avoirdupois	16.0	ounces, avoirdupois
Pounds, avoirdupois	32.1740	poundals
Pounds, avoirdupois	0.0311	slugs
Pounds, avoirdupois	0.00045	tons, long
Pounds, avoirdupois	0.0005	tons, short
Pound-feet (lb-ft)	0.1383	kilogram-meters
Pounds per cubic foot (lb per cu ft)	0.01602	grams per cubic centimeter
Pounds per cubic foot	16.0184	kilograms per cubic meter
Pounds per cubic foot	0.00058	pounds per cubic inch
Pounds per foot	1.4882	kilograms per meter
Pounds per square foot (psf)	0.1922	inches of water
Pounds per square foot	4.8824	kilograms per square meter
Pounds per square foot	0.00694	pounds per square inch
Pounds per square inch (psi)	0.0680	atmospheres
Pounds per square inch	2.3066	feet of water
Pounds per square inch	70.3067	grams per square centimeter
Pounds per square inch	27.7	inches of water
Pounds per square inch	2.0360	inches of mercury
Pounds per square inch	703.0669	kilograms per square meter
Pounds per square inch	144.0	pounds per square foot
Pounds, troy and apothecaries'	5,760.0	grains
Pounds, troy and apothecaries'	0.37324	kilograms
Pounds, troy and apothecaries'	12.0	ounces, troy and apothecaries'
Pounds, troy and apothecaries'	0.8229	pounds, avoirdupois
Quadrants	90.0	degrees
Quarts (qt), dry, imperial	1.032	quarts, dry, U.S.

Conversions of Weights and Measures (Cont.)

Given	Multiply by	To obtain
Quarts, dry, U.S.	1.1012	liters
Quarts, dry, U.S.	0.125	pecks
Quarts, dry, U.S.	2.0	pints, dry
Quarts, dry, U.S.	0.968	quarts, dry, imperial
Quarts, dry, U.S.	0.03125	bushel, U.S.
Quarts, dry, U.S.	67.2	cubic inches
Quarts, liquid	57.75	cubic inches
Quarts, liquid	0.94636	liters
Quintals	100,000.0	grams
Quintals	220.46	pounds, avoirdupois
Quire	24.0	sheets
Radians	57.2958	degrees, arc
Radians	3,437.7468	minutes, arc
Radians	0.1591	revolutions
Radians per second	9.4460	revolutions per minute
Ream	480.0	sheets
Ream, printing paper	500.0	sheets
Revolutions	6.2832	radians
Revolutions per minute (rpm)	0.1059	radians per second
Rods	0.25	chains
Rods	16.5	feet
Rods	40.0	furlongs
Rods	25.0	links
Rods	5.029	meters
Rods	5.5	yards
Score	20.0	units
Scruples	20.0	grains
Seconds	0.01667	minutes
Slugs	32.1740	pounds
Spans	9.0	inches
Square centimeters (sq cm or cm²)	0.001076	square feet
Square centimeters	0.1550	square inches
Square centimeters	100.0	square millimeters
Square chains	0.1	acres
Square chains	4,356.0	square feet
Square chains	404.7	square meters
Square chains	0.00016	square miles
Square chains	16.0	square rods
Square chains	484.0	square yards
Square decameters	100.0	square meters
Square decimeters	0.01	square meters
Square feet (sq ft)	0.00002	acres

Conversions of Weights and Measures (*Cont.*)

Given	Multiply by	To obtain
Square feet	929.0341	square centimeters
Square feet	0.00023	square chains
Square feet	144.0	square inches
Square feet	0.0929	square meters
Square feet	0.00368	square rods
Square feet	0.11111	square yards
Square hectometers	10,000.0	square meters
Square inches (sq in.)	1.27324	circular inches
Square inches	6.4516	square centimeters
Square inches	0.00694	square feet
Square inches	645.1625	square millimeters
Square inches	0.00077	square yards
Square kilometers (sq km or km²)	100.0	hectares
Square kilometers	1,000,000.0	square meters
Square kilometers	0.3861	square miles
Square links	0.4356	square feet
Square links	0.0405	square meters
Square links	0.00160	square rods
Square links	0.04840	square yards
Square meters (sq m or m²)	1.0	centiares
Square meters	10.7639	square feet
Square meters	1.1960	square yards
Square miles	2.590	square kilometers
Square miles	640.0	acres
Square miles	6,400.0	square chains
Square millimeters (sq mm or mm²)	0.00155	square inches
Square millimeters	0.000001	square meters
Square rods	0.06250	square chains
Square rods	272.25	square feet
Square rods	625.0	square links
Square rods	25.29	square meters
Square rods	30.25	square yards
Square yards	0.00207	square chains
Square yards	9.0	square feet
Square yards	1,296.0	square inches
Square yards	20.66116	square links
Square yards	0.83613	square meters
Square yards	0.03306	square rods
Tons, long	1,016.0470	kilograms
Tons, long	2,240.0	pounds, avoirdupois
Tons, metric	1,000.0	kilograms
Tons, metric	2,204.62	pounds, avoirdupois
Tons, metric	10.0	quintals

Conversions of Weights and Measures (*Cont.*)

Given	Multiply by	To obtain
Tons, register	100.0	cubic feet
Tons, shipping, British	32.719	bushels, imperial
Tons, shipping, British	32.700	bushels, U.S.
Tons, shipping, British	42.0	cubic feet
Tons, shipping, U.S.	31.16	bushels, imperial
Tons, shipping, U.S.	32.143	bushels, U.S.
Tons, shipping, U.S.	40.0	cubic feet
Tons, short	907.18	kilograms
Tons, short	2,000.0	pounds, avoirdupois
Watts (w)	10,000,000.0	ergs per second
Yards (yd)	0.04545	chains
Yards	0.50000	fathoms
Yards	3.0	feet
Yards	0.004545	furlongs
Yards	36.0	inches
Yards	0.22000	links
Yards	0.9144	meters
Yards	0.000569	miles, statute
Yards	0.18182	rods

Standard Parts, Sizes, Symbols, and Abbreviations

American Standard Unified and American Thread Series[a]

Threads per inch for coarse, fine, extra-fine, 8-thread, 12-thread, and 16-thread series [b] [tap-drill sizes for approximately 75 per cent depth of thread (not American Standard)]

Nominal size (basic major diam.)	Coarse-thd. series UNC and NC[c] in classes 1A, 1B, 2A, 2B, 3A, 3B, 2, 3		Fine-thd. series UNF and NF[c] in classes 1A, 1B, 2A, 2B, 3A, 3B, 2, 3		Extra-fine thd. series UNEF and NEF[d] in classes 2A, 2B, 2, 3		8-thd. series 8N[c] in classes 2A, 2B, 2, 3		12-thd. series 12UN and 12N[d] in classes 2A, 2B, 2, 3		16-thd. series 16UN and 16N[d] in classes 2A, 2B, 2, 3	
	Thd./in.	Tap drill	Thd./in.	Tap drill	Thd./in.	Tap drill	Thd./in.	Tap drill	Thd./in.	Tap drill	Thd./in.	Tap drill
0(0.060)	....	.....	80	$\frac{3}{64}$								
1(0.073)	64	No. 53	72	No. 53								
2(0.086)	56	No. 50	64	No. 50								
3(0.099)	48	No. 47	56	No. 45								
4(0.112)	40	No. 43	48	No. 42								
5(0.125)	40	No. 38	44	No. 37								
6(0.138)	32	No. 36	40	No. 33								
8(0.164)	32	No. 29	36	No. 29								
10(0.190)	24	No. 25	32	No. 21								
12(0.216)	24	No. 16	28	No. 14	32	No. 13						
$\frac{1}{4}$	20	No. 7	28	No. 3	32	$\frac{7}{32}$						
$\frac{5}{16}$	18	Let. F	24	Let. I	32	$\frac{9}{32}$						
$\frac{3}{8}$	16	$\frac{5}{16}$	24	Let. Q	32	$\frac{11}{32}$						
$\frac{7}{16}$	14	Let. U	20	$\frac{25}{64}$	28	$\frac{13}{32}$						
$\frac{1}{2}$	13	$\frac{27}{64}$	20	$\frac{29}{64}$	28	$\frac{15}{32}$	..	...	12	$\frac{27}{64}$		
$\frac{9}{16}$	12	$\frac{31}{64}$	18	$\frac{33}{64}$	24	$\frac{33}{64}$	..	...	12	$\frac{31}{64}$		
$\frac{5}{8}$	11	$\frac{17}{32}$	18	$\frac{37}{64}$	24	$\frac{37}{64}$	..	...	12	$\frac{35}{64}$		
$\frac{11}{16}$	....	.....	..	.....	24	$\frac{41}{64}$	..	...	12	$\frac{39}{64}$		
$\frac{3}{4}$	10	$\frac{21}{32}$	16	$1\frac{1}{16}$	20	$\frac{45}{64}$	..	...	12	$\frac{43}{64}$	16	$1\frac{1}{16}$
$\frac{13}{16}$	....	.....			20	$\frac{49}{64}$	..	...	12	$\frac{47}{64}$	16	$\frac{3}{4}$
$\frac{7}{8}$	9	$\frac{49}{64}$	14	$\frac{13}{16}$	20	$\frac{53}{64}$	..	...	12	$\frac{51}{64}$	16	$1\frac{3}{16}$
$\frac{15}{16}$			..	.....	20	$\frac{57}{64}$	..	...	12	$\frac{55}{64}$	16	$\frac{7}{8}$
1	....	.....	14	$\frac{15}{16}$	..	.....	8	$\frac{7}{8}$				
1	8	$\frac{7}{8}$	12	$\frac{59}{64}$	20	$\frac{61}{64}$	..	...	12	$\frac{59}{64}$	16	$\frac{15}{16}$
1 $\frac{1}{16}$	....	.....	..	.....	18	1	..	...	12	$\frac{63}{64}$	16	1
1 $\frac{1}{8}$	7	$\frac{63}{64}$	12	$1\frac{3}{64}$	18	$1\frac{5}{64}$	8	1	12	$1\frac{3}{64}$	16	$1\frac{1}{16}$
1 $\frac{3}{16}$	....	.....	..	.....	18	$1\frac{9}{64}$	..	...	12	$1\frac{7}{64}$	16	$1\frac{1}{8}$
1 $\frac{1}{4}$	7	$1\frac{7}{64}$	12	$1\frac{11}{64}$	18	$1\frac{3}{16}$	8	$1\frac{1}{8}$	12	$1\frac{11}{64}$	16	$1\frac{3}{16}$
1 $\frac{5}{16}$	....	.....	..	.....	18	$1\frac{17}{64}$	..	...	12	$1\frac{15}{64}$	16	$1\frac{1}{4}$
1 $\frac{3}{8}$	6	$1\frac{7}{32}$	12	$1\frac{19}{64}$	18	$1\frac{5}{16}$	8	$1\frac{1}{4}$	12	$1\frac{19}{64}$	16	$1\frac{5}{16}$
1 $\frac{7}{16}$	....	.....	..	.....	18	$1\frac{3}{8}$	..	...	12	$1\frac{23}{64}$	16	$1\frac{3}{8}$
1 $\frac{1}{2}$	6	$1\frac{11}{32}$	12	$1\frac{27}{64}$	18	$1\frac{7}{16}$	8	$1\frac{3}{8}$	12	$1\frac{27}{64}$	16	$1\frac{7}{16}$
1 $\frac{9}{16}$	....	.....	..	.....	18	$1\frac{1}{2}$	..	...	..	.....	16	$1\frac{1}{2}$
1 $\frac{5}{8}$	....	.....	..	.....	18	$1\frac{9}{16}$	8	$1\frac{1}{2}$	12	$1\frac{35}{64}$	16	$1\frac{9}{16}$
1 $\frac{11}{16}$	....	.....	..	.....	18	$1\frac{5}{8}$	..	...	..	.....	16	$1\frac{5}{8}$

American Standard Unified and American Thread Series (*Cont.*)

Nominal size (basic major diam.)	Coarse-thd. series UNC and NC[c] in classes 1A, 1B, 2A, 2B, 3A, 3B, 2, 3		Fine-thd. series UNF and NF[c] in classes 1A, 1B, 2A, 2B, 3A, 3B, 2, 3		Extra-fine thd. series UNEF and NEF[d] in classes 2A, 2B, 2, 3		8-thd. series 8N[c] in classes 2A, 2B, 2, 3		12-thd. series 12UN and 12N[d] in classes 2A, 2B, 2, 3		16-thd. series 16UN and 16N[d] in classes 2A, 2B, 2, 3	
	Thd. /in.	Tap drill	Thd. /in.	Tap drill	Thd. /in.	Tap drill	Thd. /in.	Tap drill	Thd. /in.	Tap drill	Thd. /in.	Tap drill
$1\frac{3}{4}$	5	$1\frac{9}{16}$	..	.....	16	$1\frac{11}{66}$	8^e	$1\frac{5}{8}$	12	$1\frac{43}{64}$	16	$1\frac{11}{16}$
$1\frac{13}{16}$	....	.....	..	.....	..	.....	..	...			16	$1\frac{3}{4}$
$1\frac{7}{8}$	....	.....	..	.....	..	.....	8	$1\frac{3}{4}$	12	$1\frac{51}{64}$	16	$1\frac{13}{16}$
$1\frac{15}{16}$	....	.....	..	.....	..	.....	..	...			16	$1\frac{7}{8}$
2	$4\frac{1}{2}$	$1\frac{25}{32}$	..	.....	16	$1\frac{15}{16}$	8^e	$1\frac{7}{8}$	12	$1\frac{59}{64}$	16	$1\frac{15}{16}$
$2\frac{1}{16}$	....	.....	..	.....	..	.....	..	...	..	.....	16	2
$2\frac{1}{8}$	....	.....	..	.....	..	.....	8	2	12	$2\frac{3}{64}$	16	$2\frac{1}{16}$
$2\frac{3}{16}$	....	.....	..	.....	..	.....	..	...	..	.....	16	$2\frac{1}{8}$
$2\frac{1}{4}$	$4\frac{1}{2}$	$2\frac{1}{32}$	..	.....	..	.....	8^e	$2\frac{1}{8}$	12	$2\frac{11}{64}$	16	$2\frac{3}{16}$
$2\frac{5}{16}$	....	.....	..	.....	..	.....	..	...	..	.....	16	$2\frac{1}{4}$
$2\frac{3}{8}$									12	$2\frac{19}{64}$	16	$2\frac{5}{16}$
$2\frac{7}{16}$											16	$2\frac{3}{8}$
$2\frac{1}{2}$	4	$2\frac{1}{4}$	..	.....	..	.....	8^e	$2\frac{3}{8}$	12	$2\frac{27}{64}$	16	$2\frac{7}{16}$
$2\frac{5}{8}$									12	$2\frac{35}{64}$	16	$2\frac{9}{16}$
$2\frac{3}{4}$	4	$2\frac{1}{2}$	..	.....	..	.....	8^e	$2\frac{5}{8}$	12	$2\frac{43}{64}$	16	$2\frac{11}{16}$
$2\frac{7}{8}$	....	.....	..	.....			..	...	12	$2\frac{51}{64}$	16	$2\frac{13}{16}$
3	4	$2\frac{3}{4}$	..	.....			8^e	$2\frac{7}{8}$	12	$2\frac{59}{64}$	16	$2\frac{15}{16}$
$3\frac{1}{8}$	....	.....	..	.....			..	...	12	$3\frac{3}{64}$	16	$3\frac{1}{16}$
$3\frac{1}{4}$	4	3	..	.....			8^e	$3\frac{1}{8}$	12	$3\frac{11}{64}$	16	$3\frac{3}{16}$
$3\frac{3}{8}$	....	.....	..	.....			..	...	12	$3\frac{19}{64}$	16	$3\frac{5}{16}$
$3\frac{1}{2}$	4	$3\frac{1}{4}$	..	.....			8^e	$3\frac{3}{8}$	12	$3\frac{27}{64}$	16	$3\frac{7}{16}$
$3\frac{5}{8}$	....	.....	..	.....			..	...	12	$3\frac{35}{64}$	16	$3\frac{9}{16}$
$3\frac{3}{4}$	4	$3\frac{1}{2}$	..	.....			8^e	$3\frac{5}{8}$	12	$3\frac{43}{64}$	16	$3\frac{11}{16}$
$3\frac{7}{8}$	....	.....	..	.....			..	...	12	$3\frac{51}{64}$	16	$3\frac{13}{16}$
4	4	$3\frac{3}{4}$	..	.....			8^e	$3\frac{7}{8}$	12	$3\frac{59}{64}$	16	$3\frac{15}{16}$
$4\frac{1}{4}$	....	.....	..	.....	..	.....	8^e	$4\frac{1}{8}$	12	$4\frac{11}{64}$	16	$4\frac{3}{16}$
$4\frac{1}{2}$	....	.....	..	.....	..	.....	8^e	$4\frac{3}{8}$	12	$4\frac{27}{64}$	16	$4\frac{7}{16}$
$4\frac{3}{4}$	....	.....	..	.....	..	.....	8^e	$4\frac{5}{8}$	12	$4\frac{43}{64}$	16	$4\frac{11}{16}$
5	....	.....	..	.....	..	.....	8^e	$4\frac{7}{8}$	12	$4\frac{59}{64}$	16	$4\frac{15}{16}$
$5\frac{1}{4}$	....	.....	..	.....	..	.....	8^e	$5\frac{1}{8}$	12	$5\frac{11}{64}$	16	$5\frac{3}{16}$
$5\frac{1}{2}$	....	.....	..	.....	..	.....	8^e	$5\frac{3}{8}$	12	$5\frac{27}{64}$	16	$5\frac{7}{16}$
$5\frac{3}{4}$	....	.....	..	.....	..	.....	8^e	$5\frac{5}{8}$	12	$5\frac{43}{64}$	16	$5\frac{11}{16}$
6	....	.....	..	.....	..	.....	8^e	$5\frac{7}{8}$	12	$5\frac{59}{64}$	16	$5\frac{15}{16}$

[a] ASA B1.1—1949. Dimensions are in inches.

[b] Bold type indicates unified combinations.

[c] Limits of size for classes are based on a length of engagement equal to the nominal diameter.

[d] Limits of size for classes are based on a length of engagement equal to nine times the pitch.

[e] These sizes, with specified limits of size, based on a length of engagement of 9 threads in classes 2A and 2B, are designated UN.

Note. If a thread is in both the 8-, 12-, or 16-thread series and the coarse, fine, or extra-fine-thread series, the symbols and tolerances of the latter series apply.

American Standard Square and Hexagon Bolts* and Hexagon Cap Screws †

Nominal size (basic major diam.)	Regular bolts			Heavy bolts		
	Width across flats W, sq.‡ and hex.	Height H		Width across flats W	Height H	
		Unfaced sq. and hex.	Semifin. hex., fin. hex., and hex. screw		Unfaced hex.	Semifin. hex. and fin. hex.
1/4	3/8(sq.), 7/16(hex.)	11/64	5/32			
5/16	1/2	7/32	13/64			
3/8	9/16	1/4	15/64			
7/16	5/8	19/64	9/32			
1/2	3/4	11/32	5/16	7/8	7/16	13/32
9/16	13/16	25/64	23/64	15/16	15/32	7/16
5/8	15/16	27/64	25/64	1 1/16	17/32	1/2
3/4	1 1/8	1/2	15/32	1 1/4	5/8	19/32
7/8	1 5/16	37/64	35/64	1 7/16	23/32	11/16
1	1 1/2	43/64	39/64	1 5/8	13/16	3/4
1 1/8	1 11/16	3/4	11/16	1 13/16	29/32	27/32
1 1/4	1 7/8	27/32	25/32	2	1	15/16
1 3/8	2 1/16	29/32	27/32	2 3/16	1 3/32	1 1/32
1 1/2	2 1/4	1	15/16	2 3/8	1 3/16	1 1/8
1 5/8	2 7/16	1 1/16	1	2 9/16	1 9/32	1 7/32
1 3/4	2 5/8	1 5/32	1 3/32	2 3/4	1 3/8	1 5/16
1 7/8	2 13/16	1 7/32	1 5/32	2 15/16	1 15/32	1 13/32
2	3	1 11/32	1 7/32	3 1/8	1 9/16	1 7/16
2 1/4	3 3/8	1 1/2	1 3/8	3 1/2	1 3/4	1 5/8
2 1/2	3 3/4	1 21/32	1 17/32	3 7/8	1 15/16	1 13/16
2 3/4	4 1/8	1 13/16	1 11/16	4 1/4	2 1/8	2
3	4 1/2	2	1 7/8	4 5/8	2 5/16	2 3/16
3 1/4	4 7/8	2 3/16	2			
3 1/2	5 1/4	2 5/16	2 1/8			
3 3/4	5 5/8	2 1/2	2 5/16			
4	6	2 11/16	2 1/2			

* ASA B18.2—1955. All dimensions in inches.

† ASA B18.6.2—1956. Hexagon-head cap screw in sizes 1/4 to 1 1/2 only.

‡ Square bolts in (nominal) sizes 1/4 to 1 5/8 only.

For bolt-length increments, see table, page 720. Threads are coarse series, class 2A, except for finished hexagon bolt and hexagon cap screw, which are coarse, fine, or 8-pitch, class 2A. Minimum thread length: $2D + 1/4$ in. for bolts 6 in. or less in length; $2D + 1/2$ in. for bolts over 6 in. in length; bolts too short for formula, thread entire length.

American Standard Square and Hexagon Nuts*

Nominal size (basic major diam.)	Reg. nuts						Heavy nuts					Slot		Reg. sq. nuts	
	Width across flats W	Reg. hex.	Reg. hex. jam	Semi-fin. and fin. hex. and hex. slotted	Semi-fin. and fin. hex. jam	Semi-fin. hex. thick, thick slotted,† and castle	Width across flats W	Reg. sq. and hex.	Reg. hex. jam	Semi-fin. hex. and hex. slotted	Semi-fin. hex. jam	Width	Depth	Width across flats W	Thickness T
1/4	7/16	....	....	7/32	5/32	9/32	1/2	1/4	3/16	15/64	11/64	5/64	3/32	7/16	7/32
5/16	1/2	....	....	17/64	3/16	21/64	9/16	5/16	7/32	19/64	13/64	3/32	3/32	9/16	17/64
3/8	9/16	....	....	21/64	7/32	13/32	11/16	3/8	1/4	23/64	15/64	1/8	1/8	5/8	21/64
7/16	11/16	....	....	3/8	1/4	29/64	3/4	7/16	9/32	27/64	17/64	1/8	5/32	3/4	3/8
1/2	3/4	....	....	7/16	5/16	9/16	7/8	1/2	5/16	31/64	19/64	5/32	5/32	13/16	7/16
9/16	7/8	....	....	31/64	5/16	39/64	15/16			35/64	21/64	5/32	3/16		
5/8	15/16	....	....	35/64	3/8	23/32	1 1/16	5/8	3/8	39/64	23/64	3/16	7/32	1	35/64
3/4	1 1/8	21/32	7/16	41/64	27/64	13/16	1 1/4	3/4	7/16	47/64	27/64	3/16	1/4	1 1/8	21/32
7/8	1 5/16	49/64	1/2	3/4	31/64	29/32	1 7/16	7/8	1/2	55/64	31/64	3/16	1/4	1 5/16	49/64
1	1 1/2	7/8	9/16	55/64	35/64	1	1 5/8	1	9/16	63/64	35/64	1/4	9/32	1 1/2	7/8
1 1/8	1 11/16	1	5/8	31/32	39/64	1 5/32	1 13/16	1 1/8	5/8	1 7/64	39/64	1/4	11/32	1 11/16	1
1 1/4	1 7/8	1 3/32	3/4	1 1/16	23/32	1 1/4	2	1 1/4	3/4	1 7/32	23/32	5/16	3/8	1 7/8	1 3/32
1 3/8	2 1/16	1 13/64	13/16	1 11/64	25/32	1 3/8	2 3/16	1 3/8	13/16	1 11/32	25/32	5/16	3/8	2 1/16	1 13/64
1 1/2	2 1/4	1 5/16	7/8	1 9/32	27/32	1 1/2	2 3/8	1 1/2	7/8	1 15/32	27/32	3/8	7/16	2 1/4	1 5/16
1 5/8	2 7/16	....	....	1 25/64	29/32	....	2 9/16	....	....	1 19/32	29/32	3/8	7/16		
1 3/4	2 5/8	....	....	1 1/2	31/32	....	2 3/4	1 3/4	1	1 23/32	31/32	7/16	1/2		
1 7/8	2 13/16	....	....	1 39/64	1 1/32	....	2 15/16	....	....	1 27/32	1 1/32	7/16	9/16		
2	3	....	....	1 23/32	1 3/32	....	3 1/8	2	1 1/8	1 31/32	1 3/32	7/16	9/16		
2 1/4	3 3/8	....	....	1 59/64	1 13/64	....	3 1/2	2 1/4	1 1/4	2 13/64	1 13/64	7/16	9/16		
2 1/2	3 3/4	....	....	2 9/64	1 29/64	....	3 7/8	2 1/2	1 1/2	2 29/64	1 29/64	9/16	11/16		
2 3/4	4 1/8	....	....	2 23/64	1 37/64	....	4 1/4	2 3/4	1 5/8	2 45/64	1 37/64	9/16	11/16		
3	4 1/2	....	....	2 37/64	1 45/64	....	4 5/8	3	1 3/4	2 61/64	1 45/64	5/8	3/4		
3 1/4	....	....	....	....	....	....	5	3 1/4	1 7/8	3 3/16	1 13/16	5/8	3/4		
3 1/2	....	....	....	....	....	....	5 3/8	3 1/2	2	3 7/16	1 15/16	5/8	3/4		
3 3/4	....	....	....	....	....	....	5 3/4	3 3/4	2 1/8	3 11/16	2 1/16	5/8	3/4		
4	....	....	....	....	....	....	6 1/8	4	2 1/4	3 15/16	2 3/16	5/8	3/4		

* ASA B18.2—1955.

† Slot dimensions for regular slotted nuts are same as for heavy slotted nuts.

Thread. Regular and heavy nuts: coarse series, class 2B; finished and semifinished nuts, regular and heavy (all): coarse, fine, or 8-pitch series, class 2B; thick nuts: coarse or fine series, class 2B.

Sizes of Numbered and Lettered Drills

No.	Size	No.	Size	No.	Size	Letter	Size
80	0.0135	53	0.0595	26	0.1470	A	0.2340
79	0.0145	52	0.0635	25	0.1495	B	0.2380
78	0.0160	51	0.0670	24	0.1520	C	0.2420
77	0.0180	50	0.0700	23	0.1540	D	0.2460
76	0.0200	49	0.0730	22	0.1570	E	0.2500
75	0.0210	48	0.0760	21	0.1590	F	0.2570
74	0.0225	47	0.0785	20	0.1610	G	0.2610
73	0.0240	46	0.0810	19	0.1660	H	0.2660
72	0.0250	45	0.0820	18	0.1695	I	0.2720
71	0.0260	44	0.0860	17	0.1730	J	0.2770
70	0.0280	43	0.0890	16	0.1770	K	0.2810
69	0.0292	42	0.0935	15	0.1800	L	0.2900
68	0.0310	41	0.0960	14	0.1820	M	0.2950
67	0.0320	40	0.0980	13	0.1850	N	0.3020
66	0.0330	39	0.0995	12	0.1890	O	0.3160
65	0.0350	38	0.1015	11	0.1910	P	0.3230
64	0.0360	37	0.1040	10	0.1935	Q	0.3320
63	0.0370	36	0.1065	9	0.1960	R	0.3390
62	0.0380	35	0.1100	8	0.1990	S	0.3480
61	0.0390	34	0.1110	7	0.2010	T	0.3580
60	0.0400	33	0.1130	6	0.2040	U	0.3680
59	0.0410	32	0.1160	5	0.2055	V	0.3770
58	0.0420	31	0.1200	4	0.2090	W	0.3860
57	0.0430	30	0.1285	3	0.2130	X	0.3970
56	0.0465	29	0.1360	2	0.2210	Y	0.4040
55	0.0520	28	0.1405	1	0.2280	Z	0.4130
54	0.0550	27	0.1440				

Acme and Stub Acme Threads*

ASA-preferred diameter-pitch combinations

Nominal (major) diam.	Threads/in.	Nominal (major) diam.	Threads/in.	Nominal (major) diam.	Threads/in.	Nominal (major) diam.	Threads/in.
¼	16	¾	6	1½	4	3	2
5⁄16	14	⅞	6	1¾	4	3½	2
⅜	12	1	5	2	4	4	2
7⁄16	12	1⅛	5	2¼	3	4½	2
½	10	1¼	5	2½	3	5	2
⅝	8	1⅜	4	2¾	3		

* ASA B1.5 and B1.8—1952. Diameters in inches.

Buttress Threads

Recommended diam., in.	Assoc. threads/in.
½, 9⁄16, ⅝, 11⁄16	20, 16, 12
¾, ⅞, 1	16, 12, 10
1⅛, 1¼, 1⅜, 1½	16, 12, 10, 8, 6
1¾, 2, 2¼, 2½, 2¾, 3, 3½, 4	16, 12, 10, 8, 6, 5, 4
4½, 5, 5½, 6	12, 10, 8, 6, 5, 4, 3
7, 8, 9, 10	10, 8, 6, 5, 4, 3, 2½, 2
11, 12, 14, 16	10, 8, 6, 5, 4, 3, 2½, 2, 1½, 1¼
18, 20, 22, 24	8, 6, 5, 4, 3, 2½, 2, 1½, 1¼, 1

**American Standard
Round-head Bolts**[a]

Proportions for drawing purposes

Fastener name	Nominal diam.[b] (basic major diam.)	A	H	P or M	B	
Carriage bolts — Round-head square-neck bolt[c]	No. 10, ¼″ to ½″ by (¹⁄₁₆″), ⅝″ to 1″ by (⅛″)	$2D + \frac{1}{16}$	$\frac{D}{2}$	$\frac{D}{2}$	D	
Round-head ribbed-neck bolt[d]	No. 10, ¼″ to ½″ by (¹⁄₁₆″), ⅝″ and ¾″	$2D + \frac{1}{16}$	$\frac{D}{2}$	$\frac{1}{16}$	$D + \frac{1}{16}$	$Q \begin{cases} \frac{3}{16}″ \text{ for } L = \frac{7}{8}″ \text{ or less} \\ \frac{5}{16}″ \text{ for } L = 1″ \text{ and } 1\frac{1}{8}″ \\ \frac{1}{2}″ \text{ for } L = 1\frac{1}{4}″ \text{ or more} \end{cases}$
Round-head fin.-neck bolt[c]	No. 10, ¼″ to ½″ by (¹⁄₁₆″)	$2D + \frac{1}{16}$	$\frac{D}{2}$	$\frac{3}{8}D$	$1\frac{1}{2}D + \frac{1}{16}$	
114° countersunk square-neck bolt[c]	No. 10, ¼″ to ½″ by (¹⁄₁₆″), ⅝″ and ¾″	$2D + \frac{1}{8}$	$\frac{1}{32}$	$D + \frac{1}{32}$	D	
Round-head short square-neck bolt[e]	¼″ to ½″ by (¹⁄₁₆″), ⅝″ and ¾″	$2D + \frac{1}{16}$	$\frac{D}{2}$	$\frac{D}{4} + \frac{1}{32}$	D	
T-head bolt[d]	¼″ to ½″ by (¹⁄₁₆″), ⅝″ to 1″ by (⅛″)	$2D$	$\frac{7}{8}D$	$1\frac{5}{8}D$	D	
Round-head bolt[c] (buttonhead bolt)	No. 10, ¼″ to ½″ by (¹⁄₁₆″), ⅝″ to 1″ by (⅛″)	$2D + \frac{1}{16}$	$\frac{D}{2}$			
Step bolt[c]	No. 10, ¼″ to ½″ by (¹⁄₁₆″)	$3D + \frac{1}{16}$	$\frac{D}{2}$	$\frac{D}{2}$	D	
Countersunk bolt[c] (may be slotted if so specified)	¼″ to ½″ by (¹⁄₁₆″), ⅝″ to 1½″ by (⅛″)	$1.8D$	Obtain by projection			
Elevator bolt, flat head, countersunk[c]	No. 10, ¼″ to ½″ by (¹⁄₁₆″)	$2\frac{1}{2}D + \frac{5}{16}$	$\frac{D}{3}$	$\frac{D}{2} + \frac{1}{16}$	D	Angle $C = 16D + 5°$ (approx.)
Elevator bolt, ribbed head[d] (slotted or unslotted as specified)	¼″, ⁵⁄₁₆″, ⅜″	$2D + \frac{1}{16}$	$\frac{D}{2} - \frac{1}{32}$	$\frac{D}{2} + \frac{3}{64}$	$\frac{D}{8} + \frac{1}{16}$	

[a] The proportions in this table are in some instances approximate and are intended for drawing purposes only. For exact dimensions see ASA B18.5—1951, from which this table was compiled. Dimensions are in inches.

[b] Fractions in parentheses show diameter increments, *e.g.*, ¼ in. to ½ in. by (¹⁄₁₆ in.) includes the diameters ¼ in., ⁵⁄₁₆ in., ⅜ in., ⁷⁄₁₆ in., and ½ in

Threads are coarse series, class 2A.

Minimum thread length l: $2D + \frac{1}{4}$ in. for bolts 6 in. or less in length; $2D + \frac{1}{2}$ in. for bolts over 6 in. in length.

For bolt length increments see table page 720.

[c] Full-size body bolts furnished unless undersize body is specified.

[d] Only full-size body bolts furnished.

[e] Undersize body bolts furnished unless full-size body is specified.

Bolt-length Increments*

Bolt diameter	1/4	5/16	3/8	7/16	1/2	5/8	3/4	7/8	1
Length increments 1/4	3/4–3	3/4–4	3/4–6	1–3	1–6	1–6	1–6	1–4 1/2	....
1/2	3–4	4–5	6–9	3–6	6–13	6–10	6–15	4 1/2–6	3–6
1	4–5	....	9–12	6–8	13–24	10–22	15–24	6–20	6–12
2	....	....	......	...	.....	22–30	24–30	20–30	12–30

* Compiled from manufacturers' catalogues.

Example. 1/4-in. bolt lengths increase by 1/4-in. increments from 3/4- to 3-in. length. 1/2-in. bolt lengths increase by 1/2-in. increments from 6- to 13-in. length. 1-in. bolt lengths increase by 2-in. increments from 12- to 30-in. length.

American Standard Cap Screws[a]—Socket[b] and Slotted Heads[c]

For hexagon-head screws, see page A64.

Nominal diam.	Socket head[d]			Flat head[e]	Fillister head[e]		Round head[e]	
	A	*H*	*J*	*A*	*A*	*H*	*A*	*H*
0	0.096	0.060	0.050					
1	0.118	0.073	0.050					
2	0.140	0.086	1/16					
3	0.161	0.099	5/64					
4	0.183	0.112	5/64					
5	0.205	0.125	3/32					
6	0.226	0.138	3/32					
8	0.270	0.164	1/8					
10	5/16	0.190	5/32					
12	11/32	0.216	5/32					
1/4	3/8	1/4	3/16	1/2	3/8	11/64	7/16	3/16
5/16	7/16	5/16	7/32	5/8	7/16	13/64	9/16	15/64
3/8	9/16	3/8	5/16	3/4	9/16	1/4	5/8	17/64
7/16	5/8	7/16	5/16	13/16	5/8	19/64	3/4	5/16
1/2	3/4	1/2	3/8	7/8	3/4	21/64	13/16	11/32
9/16	13/16	9/16	3/8	1	13/16	3/8	15/16	13/32
5/8	7/8	5/8	1/2	1 1/8	7/8	27/64	1	7/16
3/4	1	3/4	9/16	1 3/8	1	1/2	1 1/4	17/32
7/8	1 1/8	7/8	9/16	1 5/8	1 1/8	19/32		
1	1 5/16	1	5/8	1 7/8	1 5/16	21/32		
1 1/8	1 1/2	1 1/8	3/4					
1 1/4	1 3/4	1 1/4	3/4					
1 3/8	1 7/8	1 3/8	3/4					
1 1/2	2	1 1/2	1					

[a] Dimensions in inches.

[b] ASA B18.3—1954.

[c] ASA B18.6.2—1956.

[d] Thread coarse or fine, class 3A. Thread length *l*: coarse thread, $2D + 1/2$ in.; fine thread, $1\frac{1}{2}D + 1/2$ in.

[e] Thread coarse, fine, or 8-pitch, class 2A. Thread length *l*: $2D + 1/4$ in.

Slot proportions vary with size of screw; draw to look well. All body-length increments for screw lengths 1/4 in. to 1 in. = 1/8 in., for screw lengths 1 in. to 4 in. = 1/4 in., for screw lengths 4 in. to 6 in. = 1/2 in.

American Standard Machine Screws*

Heads may be slotted or recessed

Round Head   Flat Head   Fillister Head   Oval Head   Truss Head

Nominal diam.	Round head A	Round head H	Flat head A	Fillister head A	Fillister head H	Fillister head O	Oval head A	Oval head C	Truss head A	Truss head H
0	0.113	0.053	0.119	0.096	0.045	0.059	0.119	0.021		
1	0.138	0.061	0.146	0.118	0.053	0.071	0.146	0.025	0.194	0.053
2	0.162	0.069	0.172	0.140	0.062	0.083	0.172	0.029	0.226	0.061
3	0.187	0.078	0.199	0.161	0.070	0.095	0.199	0.033	0.257	0.069
4	0.211	0.086	0.225	0.183	0.079	0.107	0.225	0.037	0.289	0.078
5	0.236	0.095	0.252	0.205	0.088	0.120	0.252	0.041	0.321	0.086
6	0.260	0.103	0.279	0.226	0.096	0.132	0.279	0.045	0.352	0.094
8	0.309	0.120	0.332	0.270	0.113	0.156	0.332	0.052	0.384	0.102
10	0.359	0.137	0.385	0.313	0.130	0.180	0.385	0.060	0.448	0.118
12	0.408	0.153	0.438	0.357	0.148	0.205	0.438	0.068	0.511	0.134
1/4	0.472	0.175	0.507	0.414	0.170	0.237	0.507	0.079	0.573	0.150
5/16	0.590	0.216	0.635	0.518	0.211	0.295	0.635	0.099	0.698	0.183
3/8	0.708	0.256	0.762	0.622	0.253	0.355	0.762	0.117	0.823	0.215
7/16	0.750	0.328	0.812	0.625	0.265	0.368	0.812	0.122	0.948	0.248
1/2	0.813	0.355	0.875	0.750	0.297	0.412	0.875	0.131	1.073	0.280
9/16	0.938	0.410	1.000	0.812	0.336	0.466	1.000	0.150	1.198	0.312
5/8	1.000	0.438	1.125	0.875	0.375	0.521	1.125	0.169	1.323	0.345
3/4	1.250	0.547	1.375	1.000	0.441	0.612	1.375	0.206	1.573	0.410

Binding Head   Pan Head   Pan Head (recessed)   Hexagon Head   100° Flat Head

Nominal diam.	Binding head A	Binding head O	Binding head F	Binding head U	Pan head A	Pan head H	Pan head O	Hexagon head A	Hexagon head H	100° flat head A
2	0.181	0.046	0.018	0.141	0.167	0.053	0.062	0.125	0.050	
3	0.208	0.054	0.022	0.162	0.193	0.060	0.071	0.187	0.055	
4	0.235	0.063	0.025	0.184	0.219	0.068	0.080	0.187	0.060	0.225
5	0.263	0.071	0.029	0.205	0.245	0.075	0.089	0.187	0.070	
6	0.290	0.080	0.032	0.226	0.270	0.082	0.097	0.250	0.080	0.279
8	0.344	0.097	0.039	0.269	0.322	0.096	0.115	0.250	0.110	0.332
10	0.399	0.114	0.045	0.312	0.373	0.110	0.133	0.312	0.120	0.385
12	0.454	0.130	0.052	0.354	0.425	0.125	0.151	0.312	0.155	
1/4	0.513	0.153	0.061	0.410	0.492	0.144	0.175	0.375	0.190	0.507
5/16	0.641	0.193	0.077	0.513	0.615	0.178	0.218	0.500	0.230	0.635
3/8	0.769	0.234	0.094	0.615	0.740	0.212	0.261	0.562	0.295	0.762

  * ASA B18.6—1947. Dimensions given are maximum values, all in inches.

  Thread length: screws 2 in. long or less, thread entire length; screws over 2 in. long, thread length $l = 1\frac{3}{4}$ in. Threads are coarse or fine series, class 2. Heads may be slotted or recessed as specified, excepting hexagon form, which is plain or may be slotted if so specified. Slot and recess proportions vary with size of fastener; draw to look well.

American Standard Machine-screw* and Stove-bolt† Nuts‡

Nominal size	0	1	2	3	4	5	6	8	10	12	1/4	5/16	3/8
"W"	5/32	5/32	3/16	3/16	1/4	5/16	5/16	11/32	3/8	7/16	7/16	9/16	5/8
"T"	3/64	3/64	1/16	1/16	3/32	7/64	7/64	1/8	1/8	5/32	3/16	7/32	1/4

* Machine-screw nuts are hexagonal and square.
† Stove-bolt nuts are square.
‡ ASA B18—1951. Dimensions are in inches.
Thread is coarse series for square nuts and coarse or fine series for hexagon nuts; class 2B.

American Standard Hexagon Socket,* Slotted Headless,†
and Square-head‡ Setscrews

Cup Point   Flat Point

Oval Point   Cone Point

Full Dog Point   Half Dog Point

(All six point types are available in all three head types)

Diam. D	Cup and flat-point diam. C	Oval-point radius R	Cone-point angle Y		Full and half dog points			Socket width J
			118° for these lengths and shorter	90° for these lengths and longer	Diam. P	Length Full Q	Length Half q	
5	1/16	3/32	1/8	3/16	0.083	0.06	0.03	1/16
6	0.069	7/64	1/8	3/16	0.092	0.07	0.03	1/16
8	5/64	1/8	3/16	1/4	0.109	0.08	0.04	5/64
10	3/32	9/64	3/16	1/4	0.127	0.09	0.04	3/32
12	7/64	5/32	3/16	1/4	0.144	0.11	0.06	3/32
1/4	1/8	3/16	1/4	5/16	5/32	1/8	1/16	1/8
5/16	11/64	15/64	5/16	3/8	13/64	5/32	5/64	5/32
3/8	13/64	9/32	3/8	7/16	1/4	3/16	3/32	3/16
7/16	15/64	21/64	7/16	1/2	19/64	7/32	7/64	7/32
1/2	9/32	3/8	1/2	9/16	11/32	1/4	1/8	1/4
9/16	5/16	27/64	9/16	5/8	25/64	9/32	9/64	1/4
5/8	23/64	15/32	5/8	3/4	15/32	5/16	5/32	5/16
3/4	7/16	9/16	3/4	7/8	9/16	3/8	3/16	3/8
7/8	33/64	21/32	7/8	1	21/32	7/16	7/32	1/2
1	19/32	3/4	1	1 1/8	3/4	1/2	1/4	9/16
1 1/8	43/64	27/32	1 1/8	1 1/4	27/32	9/16	9/32	9/16
1 1/4	3/4	15/16	1 1/4	1 1/2	15/16	5/8	5/16	5/8
1 3/8	53/64	1 1/32	1 3/8	1 5/8	1 1/32	11/16	11/32	5/8
1 1/2	29/32	1 1/8	1 1/2	1 3/4	1 1/8	3/4	3/8	3/4
1 3/4	1 1/16	1 5/16	1 3/4	2	1 5/16	7/8	7/16	1
2	1 7/32	1 1/2	2	2 1/4	1 1/2	1	1/2	1

* ASA B18.3—1954. Dimensions are in inches. Threads coarse or fine, class 3A. Length increments: 1/4 in. to 5/8 in. by (1/16 in.); 5/8 in. to 1 in. by (1/8 in.); 1 in. to 4 in. by (1/4 in.); 4 in. to 6 in. by (1/2 in.). Fractions in parentheses show length increments; for example, 5/8 in. to 1 in. by (1/8 in.) includes the lengths 5/8 in., 3/4 in., 7/8 in., and 1 in.
† ASA B18.6.2—1956. Threads coarse or fine, class 2A. Slotted headless screws standardized in sizes No. 5 to 3/4 in. only. Slot proportions vary with diameter. Draw to look well.
‡ ASA B18.6.2—1956. Threads coarse, fine, or 8-pitch, class 2A. Square-head setscrews standardized in sizes No. 10 to 1 1/2 in. only.

American Standard Socket-head Shoulder Screws[a]

Shoulder diameter D			Head[b]			Thread		Shoulder lengths[d]
Nominal	Max.	Min.	Diam. A	Height H	Hexagon[c] J	Specification E	Length I	
¼	0.2480	0.2460	⅜	3/16	⅛	10-24NC-3	⅜	¾–2½
5/16	0.3105	0.3085	7/16	7/32	5/32	¼-20NC-3	7/16	1 –3
⅜	0.3730	0.3710	9/16	¼	3/16	5/16-18NC-3	½	1 –4
½	0.4980	0.4960	¾	5/16	¼	⅜-16NC-3	⅝	1¼–5
⅝	0.6230	0.6210	⅞	⅜	5/16	½-13NC-3	¾	1½–6
¾	0.7480	0.7460	1	½	⅜	⅝-11NC-3	⅞	1½–8
1	0.9980	0.9960	15/16	⅝	½	¾-10NC-3	1	1½–8
1¼	1.2480	1.2460	1¾	¾	⅝	⅞-9NC-3	1⅛	1½–8

[a] ASA B18.3—1947. Dimensions are in inches.
[b] Head chamfer is 30°.
[c] Socket depth = ¾H.
[d] Shoulder-length increments: shoulder lengths from ¾ in. to 1 in., ⅛-in. intervals; shoulder lengths from 1 in. to 5 in., ¼-in. intervals; shoulder lengths from 5 in. to 7 in., ½-in. intervals; shoulder lengths from 7 in. to 8 in., 1-in. intervals. Shoulder-length tolerance ±0.005.

American Standard Wood Screws*

Nominal size	Basic diam. of screw D	No. of threads per in.†	Slot width ‡ J (all heads)	Round head		Flat head	Oval head	
				A	H	A	A	C
0	0.060	32	0.023	0.113	0.053	0.119	0.119	0.021
1	0.073	28	0.026	0.138	0.061	0.146	0.146	0.025
2	0.086	26	0.031	0.162	0.069	0.172	0.172	0.029
3	0.099	24	0.035	0.187	0.078	0.199	0.199	0.033
4	0.112	22	0.039	0.211	0.086	0.225	0.225	0.037
5	0.125	20	0.043	0.236	0.095	0.252	0.252	0.041
6	0.138	18	0.048	0.260	0.103	0.279	0.279	0.045
7	0.151	16	0.048	0.285	0.111	0.305	0.305	0.049
8	0.164	15	0.054	0.309	0.120	0.332	0.332	0.052
9	0.177	14	0.054	0.334	0.128	0.358	0.358	0.056
10	0.190	13	0.060	0.359	0.137	0.385	0.385	0.060
12	0.216	11	0.067	0.408	0.153	0.438	0.438	0.068
14	0.242	10	0.075	0.457	0.170	0.491	0.491	0.076
16	0.268	9	0.075	0.506	0.187	0.544	0.544	0.084
18	0.294	8	0.084	0.555	0.204	0.597	0.597	0.092
20	0.320	8	0.084	0.604	0.220	0.650	0.650	0.100
24	0.372	7	0.094	0.702	0.254	0.756	0.756	0.116

Round Head

Flat Head

Oval Head

* ASA B18.6—1947. Dimensions given are maximum values, all in inches. Heads may be slotted or recessed as specified.
† Thread length $l = ⅔L$.
‡ Slot depths and recesses vary with type and size of screw; draw to look well.

Small Rivets*

TINNERS'

COOPERS'

BELT

Tinner's				Cooper's				Belt		
Size No.†	*D* Diam. body	*L* Length		Size No.	*D* Diam. body	*L* Length		Size No.‡	*D* Diam. body	*L* Length
8 oz	0.089	0.16		1 lb	0.109	0.219		7	0.180	From ⅜ to ¾ by ⅛" increments
12	0.105	0.19		1½	0.127	0.256		8	0.165	
1 lb	0.111	0.20		2	0.141	0.292		9	0.148	
1½	0.130	0.23		2½	0.148	0.325		10	0.134	
2	0.144	0.27		3	0.156	0.358		11	0.120	
2½	0.148	0.28		4	0.165	0.392		12	0.109	
3	0.160	0.31		6	0.203	0.466		13	0.095	
4	0.176	0.34		8	0.238	0.571				
6	0.203	0.39		10	0.250	0.606				
8	0.224	0.44		12	0.259	0.608				
10	0.238	0.47		14	0.271	0.643				
12	0.259	0.50		16	0.281	0.677				
14	0.284	0.52								
16	0.300	0.53								

Belt — Approx. proportions:
$A = 2.8 \times D$, $d = 0.9 \times D$
$E = 0.4 \times D$, $H = 0.3 \times D$

Tolerances on the nominal diameter:
$+0.002$
-0.004

Finished rivets shall be free from injurious defects.

Tinner's — Approx. proportions:
$A = 2.25 \times D$
$H = 0.30 \times D$

Cooper's — Approx. proportions:
$A = 2.25 \times D$, $d = 0.90 \times D$
$E = 0.40 \times D$, $H = 0.30 \times D$
Included $\angle\theta = 144°$
$\angle\alpha = 18°$

* ASA B18g1—1942. All dimensions given in inches.
† Size numbers refer to the Trade Name or weight of 1,000 rivets.
‡ Size number refers to the Stubs iron-wire gage number of the stock used in the body of the rivet.

Dimensions of Standard Gib-head Keys, Square and Flat
Approved by ASA *

$L = 4 W$ (Min.)
$L = 16 W$ (Max.)
Taper ⅛" in 12" (1:96)

Diameters of shafts	Square type					Flat type				
	Key		Gib head			Key		Gib head		
	W	*H*	*C*	*D*	*E*	*W*	*H*	*C*	*D*	*E*
½ – 9⁄16	⅛	⅛	¼	7⁄32	5⁄32	⅛	3⁄32	3⁄16	⅛	⅛
⅝ – ⅞	3⁄16	3⁄16	5⁄16	9⁄32	7⁄32	3⁄16	⅛	¼	3⁄16	5⁄32
15⁄16–1¼	¼	¼	7⁄16	11⁄32	11⁄32	¼	3⁄16	5⁄16	¼	3⁄16
1 5⁄16–1⅜	5⁄16	5⁄16	9⁄16	13⁄32	13⁄32	5⁄16	¼	⅜	5⁄16	¼
1 7⁄16–1¾	⅜	⅜	11⁄16	15⁄32	15⁄32	⅜	¼	7⁄16	⅜	5⁄16
1 13⁄16–2¼	½	½	⅞	19⁄32	⅝	½	⅜	⅝	½	7⁄16
2 5⁄16–2¾	⅝	⅝	1 1⁄16	23⁄32	¾	⅝	7⁄16	¾	⅝	½
2 ⅞ –3¼	¾	¾	1 ¼	⅞	⅞	¾	½	⅞	¾	⅝
3 ⅜ –3¾	⅞	⅞	1 ½	1	1	⅞	⅝	1 1⁄16	⅞	¾
3 ⅞ –4½	1	1	1 ¾	1 3⁄16	1 3⁄16	1	¾	1 ¼	1	1 13⁄16
4 ¾ –5½	1¼	1¼	2	1 7⁄16	1 7⁄16	1¼	⅞	1 ½	1¼	1
5 ¾ –6	1½	1½	2 ½	1 ¾	1 ¾	1½	1	1¾	1½	1 ¼

A72

* ASA B17.1—1934. Dimensions in inches.

Widths and Heights of Standard Square- and Flat-stock Keys with Corresponding Shaft Diameters

Approved by ASA *

Shaft diam. d (inclusive)	Square-stock keys W	Flat-stock keys, $W \times H$	Shaft diam. d (inclusive)	Square-stock keys W	Flat-stock keys, $W \times H$
$\frac{1}{2} - \frac{9}{16}$	$\frac{1}{8}$	$\frac{1}{8} \times \frac{3}{32}$	$2\frac{7}{8}-3\frac{1}{4}$	$\frac{3}{4}$	$\frac{3}{4} \times \frac{1}{2}$
$\frac{5}{8} - \frac{7}{8}$	$\frac{3}{16}$	$\frac{3}{16} \times \frac{1}{8}$	$3\frac{3}{8}-3\frac{3}{4}$	$\frac{7}{8}$	$\frac{7}{8} \times \frac{5}{8}$
$\frac{15}{16}-1\frac{1}{4}$	$\frac{1}{4}$	$\frac{1}{4} \times \frac{3}{16}$	$3\frac{7}{8}-4\frac{1}{2}$	1	$1 \times \frac{3}{4}$
$1\frac{5}{16}-1\frac{3}{8}$	$\frac{5}{16}$	$\frac{5}{16} \times \frac{1}{4}$			
$1\frac{7}{16}-1\frac{3}{4}$	$\frac{3}{8}$	$\frac{3}{8} \times \frac{1}{4}$	$4\frac{3}{4}-5\frac{1}{2}$	$1\frac{1}{4}$	$1\frac{1}{4} \times \frac{7}{8}$
$1\frac{13}{16}-2\frac{1}{4}$	$\frac{1}{2}$	$\frac{1}{2} \times \frac{3}{8}$	$5\frac{3}{4}-6$	$1\frac{1}{2}$	$1\frac{1}{2} \times 1$
$2\frac{5}{16}-2\frac{3}{4}$	$\frac{5}{8}$	$\frac{5}{8} \times \frac{7}{16}$			

* ASA B17.1—1934. Dimensions in inches.

Woodruff-key Dimensions

Key* No.	Nominal size $A \times B$	Max. width of key A	Max. diam. of key B	Max. height of key C		Distance below center E
				C	D	E
204	$\frac{1}{16} \times \frac{1}{2}$	0.0635	0.500	0.203	0.194	$\frac{3}{64}$
304	$\frac{3}{32} \times \frac{1}{2}$	0.0948	0.500	0.203	0.194	$\frac{3}{64}$
305	$\frac{3}{32} \times \frac{5}{8}$	0.0948	0.625	0.250	0.240	$\frac{1}{16}$
404	$\frac{1}{8} \times \frac{1}{2}$	0.1260	0.500	0.203	0.194	$\frac{3}{64}$
405	$\frac{1}{8} \times \frac{5}{8}$	0.1260	0.625	0.250	0.240	$\frac{1}{16}$
406	$\frac{1}{8} \times \frac{3}{4}$	0.1260	0.750	0.313	0.303	$\frac{1}{16}$
505	$\frac{5}{32} \times \frac{5}{8}$	0.1573	0.625	0.250	0.240	$\frac{1}{16}$
506	$\frac{5}{32} \times \frac{3}{4}$	0.1573	0.750	0.313	0.303	$\frac{1}{16}$
507	$\frac{5}{32} \times \frac{7}{8}$	0.1573	0.875	0.375	0.365	$\frac{1}{16}$
606	$\frac{3}{16} \times \frac{3}{4}$	0.1885	0.750	0.313	0.303	$\frac{1}{16}$
607	$\frac{3}{16} \times \frac{7}{8}$	0.1885	0.875	0.375	0.365	$\frac{1}{16}$
608	$\frac{3}{16} \times 1$	0.1885	1.000	0.438	0.428	$\frac{1}{16}$
609	$\frac{3}{16} \times 1\frac{1}{8}$	0.1885	1.125	0.484	0.475	$\frac{5}{64}$
807	$\frac{1}{4} \times \frac{7}{8}$	0.2510	0.875	0.375	0.365	$\frac{1}{16}$
808	$\frac{1}{4} \times 1$	0.2510	1.000	0.438	0.428	$\frac{1}{16}$
809	$\frac{1}{4} \times 1\frac{1}{8}$	0.2510	1.125	0.484	0.475	$\frac{5}{64}$
810	$\frac{1}{4} \times 1\frac{1}{4}$	0.2510	1.250	0.547	0.537	$\frac{5}{64}$
811	$\frac{1}{4} \times 1\frac{3}{8}$	0.2510	1.375	0.594	0.584	$\frac{3}{32}$
812	$\frac{1}{4} \times 1\frac{1}{2}$	0.2510	1.500	0.641	0.631	$\frac{7}{64}$
1008	$\frac{5}{16} \times 1$	0.3135	1.000	0.438	0.428	$\frac{1}{16}$
1009	$\frac{5}{16} \times 1\frac{1}{8}$	0.3135	1.125	0.484	0.475	$\frac{5}{64}$
1010	$\frac{5}{16} \times 1\frac{1}{4}$	0.3135	1.250	0.547	0.537	$\frac{5}{64}$
1011	$\frac{5}{16} \times 1\frac{3}{8}$	0.3135	1.375	0.594	0.584	$\frac{3}{32}$
1012	$\frac{5}{16} \times 1\frac{1}{2}$	0.3135	1.500	0.641	0.631	$\frac{7}{64}$
1210	$\frac{3}{8} \times 1\frac{1}{4}$	0.3760	1.250	0.547	0.537	$\frac{5}{64}$
1211	$\frac{3}{8} \times 1\frac{3}{8}$	0.3760	1.375	0.594	0.584	$\frac{3}{32}$
1212	$\frac{3}{8} \times 1\frac{1}{2}$	0.3760	1.500	0.641	0.631	$\frac{7}{64}$

A73

* Dimensions in inches. Key numbers indicate the nominal key dimensions. The last two digits give the nominal diameter B in eighths of an inch, and the digits preceding the last two give the nominal width A in thirty-seconds of an inch. Thus 204 indicates a key $\frac{2}{32}$ by $\frac{4}{8}$, or $\frac{1}{16}$ by $\frac{1}{2}$ in.

Woodruff-key-seat Dimensions

Key* No.	Nominal size	Key slot			
		Width W		Depth H	
		Max.	Min.	Max.	Min.
204	1/16 × 1/2	0.0630	0.0615	0.1718	0.1668
304	3/32 × 1/2	0.0943	0.0928	0.1561	0.1511
305	3/32 × 5/8	0.0943	0 0928	0.2031	0.1981
404	1/8 × 1/2	0.1255	0.1240	0.1405	0.1355
405	1/8 × 5/8	0.1255	0.1240	0.1875	0.1825
406	1/8 × 3/4	0.1255	0.1240	0.2505	0.2455
505	5/32 × 5/8	0.1568	0.1553	0.1719	0.1669
506	5/32 × 3/4	0.1568	0.1553	0.2349	0.2299
507	5/32 × 7/8	0.1568	0.1553	0.2969	0.2919
606	3/16 × 3/4	0.1880	0.1863	0.2193	0.2143
607	3/16 × 7/8	0.1880	0.1863	0.2813	0.2763
608	3/16 × 1	0.1880	0.1863	0.3443	0.3393
609	3/16 × 1 1/8	0.1880	0.1863	0.3903	0.3853
807	1/4 × 7/8	0.2505	0.2487	0.2500	0.2450
808	1/4 × 1	0.2505	0.2487	0.3130	0.3080
809	1/4 × 1 1/8	0.2505	0.2487	0.3590	0.3540
810	1/4 × 1 1/4	0.2505	0.2487	0.4220	0.4170
811	1/4 × 1 3/8	0.2505	0.2487	0.4690	0.4640
812	1/4 × 1 1/2	0.2505	0.2487	0.5160	0.5110
1008	5/16 × 1	0.3130	0.3111	0.2818	0.2768
1009	5/16 × 1 1/8	0.3130	0.3111	0.3278	0.3228
1010	5/16 × 1 1/4	0.3130	0.3111	0.3908	0.3858
1011	5/16 × 1 3/8	0.3130	0.3111	0.4378	0.4328
1012	5/16 × 1 1/2	0.3130	0.3111	0.4848	0.4798
1210	3/8 × 1 1/4	0.3755	0.3735	0.3595	0.3545
1211	3/8 × 1 3/8	0.3755	0.3735	0.4060	0.4015
1212	3/8 × 1 1/2	0.3755	0.3735	0.4535	0.4485

* Dimensions in inches. Key numbers indicate the nominal key dimensions. The last two digits give the nominal diameter B in eighths of an inch, and the digits preceding the last two give the nominal width A in thirty-seconds of an inch. Thus 204 indicates a key 2/32 by 4/8, or 1/16 by 1/2 in.

Dimensions of Pratt and Whitney Keys

Key No.	L	W	H	D	Key No.	L	W	H	D
1	1/2	1/16	3/32	1/16	22	1 3/8	1/4	3/8	1/4
2	1/2	3/32	9/64	3/32	23	1 3/8	5/16	15/32	5/16
3	1/2	1/8	3/16	1/8	F	1 3/8	3/8	9/16	3/8
4	5/8	3/32	9/64	3/32	24	1 1/2	1/4	3/8	1/4
5	5/8	1/8	3/16	1/8	25	1 1/2	5/16	15/32	5/16
6	5/8	5/32	15/64	5/32	G	1 1/2	3/8	9/16	3/8
7	3/4	1/8	3/16	1/8	51	1 3/4	1/4	3/8	1/4
8	3/4	5/32	15/64	5/32	52	1 3/4	5/16	15/32	5/16
9	3/4	3/16	9/32	3/16	53	1 3/4	3/8	9/16	3/8
10	7/8	5/32	15/64	5/32	26	2	3/16	9/32	3/16
11	7/8	3/16	9/32	3/16	27	2	1/4	3/8	1/4
12	7/8	7/32	21/64	7/32	28	2	5/16	15/32	5/16
A	7/8	1/4	3/8	1/4	29	2	3/8	9/16	3/8
13	1	3/16	9/32	3/16	54	2 1/4	1/4	3/8	1/4
14	1	7/32	21/64	7/32	55	2 1/4	5/16	15/16	5/16
15	1	1/4	3/8	1/4	56	2 1/4	3/8	9/16	3/8
B	1	5/16	15/32	5/16	57	2 1/4	7/16	21/32	7/16
16	1 1/8	3/16	9/32	3/16	58	2 1/2	5/16	15/32	5/16
17	1 1/8	7/32	21/64	7/32	59	2 1/2	3/8	9/16	3/8
18	1 1/8	1/4	3/8	1/4	60	2 1/2	7/16	21/32	7/16
C	1 1/8	5/16	15/32	5/16	61	2 1/2	1/2	3/4	1/2
19	1 1/4	3/16	9/32	3/16	30	3	3/8	9/16	3/8
20	1 1/4	7/32	21/64	7/32	31	3	7/16	21/32	7/16
21	1 1/4	1/4	3/8	1/4	32	3	1/2	3/4	1/2
D	1 1/4	5/16	15/32	5/16	33	3	9/16	27/32	9/16
E	1 1/4	3/8	9/16	3/8	34	3	5/8	15/16	5/8

Dimensions in inches. Key is 2/3 in shaft; 1/3 in hub. Keys are 0.001 in. oversize in width to ensure proper fitting in keyway. Keyway size: width = W; depth = $H - D$. Length L should never be less than $2W$.

American Standard Plain Washers*

Size	Light			Medium			Heavy			Extra heavy		
	ID	OD	Thickness	ID	OD	Thickness	ID	OD	Thickness	ID	OD	Thickness
0	5/64	3/16	0.020									
1	3/32	7/32	0.020									
2	3/32	1/4	0.020									
3	1/8	1/4	0.022									
4	1/8	1/4	0.022	1/8	5/16	0.032						
5	5/32	5/16	0.035	5/32	3/8	0.049						
6	5/32	5/16	0.035	5/32	3/8	0.049						
7	11/64	13/32	0.049	3/16	3/8	0.049						
8	3/16	3/8	0.049	3/16	7/16	0.049						
9	13/64	15/32	0.049	7/32	1/2	0.049						
3/16	7/32	7/16	0.049	7/32	1/2	0.049	1/4	9/16	0.049			
10	7/32	7/16	0.049	1/4	9/16	0.049	1/4	9/16	0.065			
11	15/64	17/32	0.049	1/4	9/16	0.049	1/4	9/16	0.065			
12	1/4	1/2	0.049	1/4	9/16	0.049	1/4	9/16	0.065			
14	17/64	5/8	0.049	5/16	3/4	0.065	5/16	7/8	0.065			
1/4	9/32	5/8	0.065	5/16	3/4	0.065	5/16	3/4	0.065	5/16	7/8	0.065
16	9/32	5/8	0.065	5/16	3/4	0.065	5/16	7/8	0.065	5/16	7/8	0.065
18	5/16	3/4	0.065	3/8	3/4	0.065	3/8	7/8	0.083	3/8	1 1/8	0.065
5/16	11/32	11/16	0.065	3/8	3/4	0.065	3/8	7/8	0.083	3/8	1 1/8	0.065
20	11/32	11/16	0.065	3/8	3/4	0.065	3/8	7/8	0.083	3/8	1 1/8	0.065
24	13/32	13/16	0.065	7/16	7/8	0.083	7/16	1	0.083	7/16	1 3/8	0.083
3/8	13/32	13/16	0.065	7/16	7/8	0.083	7/16	1	0.083	7/16	1 3/8	0.083
7/16	15/32	59/64	0.065	1/2	1 1/8	0.083	1/2	1 1/4	0.083	1/2	1 5/8	0.083
1/2	17/32	1 1/16	0.095	9/16	1 1/4	0.109	9/16	1 3/8	0.109	9/16	1 7/8	0.109
9/16	19/32	1 3/16	0.095	5/8	1 3/8	0.109	5/8	1 1/2	0.109	5/8	2 1/8	0.134
5/8	21/32	1 5/16	0.095	11/16	1 1/2	0.134	11/16	1 3/4	0.134	11/16	2 3/8	0.165
3/4	13/16	1 1/2	0.134	13/16	1 3/4	0.148	13/16	2	0.148	13/16	2 7/8	0.165
7/8	15/16	1 3/4	0.134	15/16	2	0.165	15/16	2 1/4	0.165	15/16	3 3/8	0.180
1	1 1/16	2	0.134	1 1/16	2 1/4	0.165	1 1/16	2 1/2	0.165	1 1/16	3 7/8	0.238
1 1/8	.....	.....	.....	1 3/16	2 1/2	0.165	1 1/4	2 3/4	0.165			
1 1/4	.....	.....	.....	1 5/16	2 3/4	0.165	1 3/8	3	0.165			
1 3/8	.....	.....	.....	1 7/16	3	0.180	1 1/2	3 1/4	0.180			
1 1/2	.....	.....	.....	1 9/16	3 1/4	0.180	1 5/8	3 1/2	0.180			
1 5/8	.....	.....	.....	1 11/16	3 1/2	0.180	1 3/4	3 3/4	0.180			
1 3/4	.....	.....	.....	1 13/16	3 3/4	0.180	1 7/8	4	0.180			
1 7/8	.....	.....	.....	1 15/16	4	0.180	2	4 1/4	0.180			
2	.....	.....	.....	2 1/16	4 1/4	0.180	2 1/8	4 1/2	0.180			
2 1/4	.....	.....	.....	.....	....	.....	2 3/8	4 3/4	0.220			
2 1/2	.....	.....	.....	.....	....	.....	2 5/8	5	0.238			
2 3/4	.....	.....	.....	.....	....	.....	2 7/8	5 1/4	0.259			
3	.....	.....	.....	.....	....	.....	3 1/8	5 1/2	0.284			

* ASA B27.2—1949. All dimensions in inches.

American Standard Lock Washers*

Nominal size	Inside diam., min.	Light		Medium		Heavy		Extra heavy	
		Min. thickness	Outside diam., max.	Min. thickness	Outside diam., max.	Min. thickness	Outside diam., max.	Min. thickness	Outside diam., max.
0.086 (No. 2)	0.088	0.015	0.165	0.020	0.175	0.025	0.185	0.027	0.211
0.099 (No. 3)	0.102	0.020	0.188	0.025	0.198	0.031	0.212	0.034	0.242
0.112 (No. 4)	0.115	0.020	0.202	0.025	0.212	0.031	0.226	0.034	0.256
0.125 (No. 5)	0.128	0.025	0.225	0.031	0.239	0.040	0.255	0.045	0.303
0.138 (No. 6)	0.141	0.025	0.239	0.031	0.253	0.040	0.269	0.045	0.317
0.164 (No. 8)	0.168	0.031	0.280	0.040	0.296	0.047	0.310	0.057	0.378
0.190 (No. 10)	0.194	0.040	0.323	0.047	0.337	0.056	0.353	0.068	0.437
0.216 (No. 12)	0.221	0.047	0.364	0.056	0.380	0.063	0.394	0.080	0.500
1/4	0.255	0.047	0.489	0.062	0.493	0.077	0.495	0.084	0.539
5/16	0.319	0.056	0.575	0.078	0.591	0.097	0.601	0.108	0.627
3/8	0.382	0.070	0.678	0.094	0.688	0.115	0.696	0.123	0.746
7/16	0.446	0.085	0.780	0.109	0.784	0.133	0.792	0.143	0.844
1/2	0.509	0.099	0.877	0.125	0.879	0.151	0.889	0.162	0.945
9/16	0.573	0.113	0.975	0.141	0.979	0.170	0.989	0.182	1.049
5/8	0.636	0.126	1.082	0.156	1.086	0.189	1.100	0.202	1.164
11/16	0.700	0.138	1.178	0.172	1.184	0.207	1.200	0.221	1.266
3/4	0.763	0.153	1.277	0.188	1.279	0.226	1.299	0.241	1.369
13/16	0.827	0.168	1.375	0.203	1.377	0.246	1.401	0.261	1.473
7/8	0.890	0.179	1.470	0.219	1.474	0.266	1.504	0.285	1.586
15/16	0.954	0.191	1.562	0.234	1.570	0.284	1.604	0.308	1.698
1	1.017	0.202	1.656	0.250	1.672	0.306	1.716	0.330	1.810
1 1/16	1.081	0.213	1.746	0.266	1.768	0.326	1.820	0.352	1.922
1 1/8	1.144	0.224	1.837	0.281	1.865	0.345	1.921	0.375	2.031
1 3/16	1.208	0.234	1.923	0.297	1.963	0.364	2.021	0.396	2.137
1 1/4	1.271	0.244	2.012	0.312	2.058	0.384	2.126	0.417	2.244
1 5/16	1.335	0.254	2.098	0.328	2.156	0.403	2.226	0.438	2.350
1 3/8	1.398	0.264	2.183	0.344	2.253	0.422	2.325	0.458	2.453
1 7/16	1.462	0.273	2.269	0.359	2.349	0.440	2.421	0.478	2.555
1 1/2	1.525	0.282	2.352	0.375	2.446	0.458	2.518	0.496	2.654

* ASA B27.1—1950. All dimensions in inches.

Tapers. Taper means the difference in diameter or width in 1 ft of length; see figure below. *Taper pins*, much used for fastening cylindrical parts and for doweling, have a standard taper of ¼ in. per ft.

Gage line
SELF-HOLDING (SLOW) TAPER

Machine tapers. The American Standard for self-holding (slow) machine tapers is designed to replace the various former standards. The table below shows its derivation. Detailed dimensions and tolerances for taper tool shanks and taper sockets will be found in ASA B5.10—1937.

Dimensions of Taper Pins

Taper ¼ in. per ft

Size No.	Diam., large end	Drill size for reamer	Max. length
000000	0.072	53	⅝
00000	0.092	47	⅝
0000	0.108	42	¾
000	0.125	37	¾
00	0.147	31	1
0	0.156	28	1
1	0.172	25	1¼
2	0.193	19	1½
3	0.219	12	1¾
4	0.250	3	2
5	0.289	¼	2¼
6	0.341	9/32	3¼
7	0.409	11/32	3¾
8	0.492	13/32	4½
9	0 591	31/64	5¼
10	0.706	19/32	6
11	0.857	23/32	7¼
12	1.013	55/64	8¾
13	1.233	1 1/64	10¾

All dimensions in inches.

American Standard Machine Tapers,* Self-holding (Slow) Taper Series

Basic dimensions

Origin of series	No. of taper	Taper /ft	Diam. at gage line	Means of driving and holding
Brown and Sharpe taper series		0.500	0.239	Tongue drive with shank held in by friction
		0.500	0.299	
		0.500	0.375	
Morse taper series	1	0.600	0.475	
	2	0.600	0.700	
	3	0.602	0.938	Tongue drive with shank held in by key
	4	0.623	1.231	
	4½	0.623	1.500	
	5	0.630	1.748	
¾-in./ft taper series	200	0.750	2.000	
	250	0.750	2.500	
	300	0.750	3.000	Key drive with shank held in by key
	350	0.750	3.500	
	400	0.750	4.000	
	500	0.750	5.000	
	600	0.750	6.000	Key drive with shank held in by drawbolt
	800	0.750	8.000	
	1,000	0.750	10.000	
	1,200	0.750	12.000	

Note: Brown and Sharpe taper series values for No. of taper are 0.239, 0.299, 0.375.

* ASA B5.10—1937. All dimensions in inches.

Wire and Sheet-metal Gages

Dimensions in decimal parts of an inch

No. of gage	American or Brown and Sharpe[a]	Washburn & Moen or American Steel & Wire Co.[b]	Birming-ham or Stubs iron wire[c]	Music wire[d]	Imperial wire gage[e]	U.S. Std. for plate[f]
0000000	. . . . .	0.4900	. . . .	. . . . .	0.5000	0.5000
000000	0.5800	0.4615	. . . . .	0.004	0.4640	0.4688
00000	0.5165	0.4305	0.500	0.005	0.4320	0.4375
0000	0.4600	0.3938	0.454	0.006	0.4000	0.4063
000	0.4096	0.3625	0.425	0.007	0.3720	0.3750
00	0.3648	0.3310	0.380	0.008	0.3480	0.3438
0	0.3249	0.3065	0.340	0.009	0.3240	0.3125
1	0.2893	0.2830	0.300	0.010	0.3000	0.2813
2	0.2576	0.2625	0.284	0.011	0.2760	0.2656
3	0.2294	0.2437	0.259	0.012	0.2520	0.2500
4	0.2043	0.2253	0.238	0.013	0.2320	0.2344
5	0.1819	0.2070	0.220	0.014	0.2120	0.2188
6	0.1620	0.1920	0.203	0.016	0.1920	0.2031
7	0.1443	0.1770	0.180	0.018	0.1760	0.1875
8	0.1285	0.1620	0.165	0.020	0.1600	0.1719
9	0.1144	0.1483	0.148	0.022	0.1440	0.1563
10	0.1019	0.1350	0.134	0.024	0.1280	0.1406
11	0.0907	0.1205	0.120	0.026	0.1160	0.1250
12	0.0808	0.1055	0.109	0.029	0.1040	0.1094
13	0.0720	0.0915	0.095	0.031	0.0920	0.0938
14	0.0641	0.0800	0.083	0.033	0.0800	0.0781
15	0.0571	0.0720	0.072	0.035	0.0720	0.0703
16	0.0508	0.0625	0.065	0.037	0.0640	0.0625
17	0.0453	0.0540	0.058	0.039	0.0560	0.0563
18	0.0403	0.0475	0.049	0.041	0.0480	0.0500
19	0.0359	0.0410	0.042	0.043	0.0400	0.0438
20	0.0320	0.0348	0.035	0.045	0.0360	0.0375
21	0.0285	0.0317	0.032	0.047	0.0320	0.0344
22	0.0253	0.0286	0.028	0.049	0.0280	0.0313
23	0.0226	0.0258	0.025	0.051	0.0240	0.0281
24	0.0201	0.0230	0.022	0.055	0.0220	0.0250
25	0.0179	0.0204	0.020	0.059	0.0200	0.0219
26	0.0159	0.0181	0.018	0.063	0.0180	0.0188
27	0.0142	0.0173	0.016	0.067	0.0164	0.0172
28	0.0126	0.0162	0.014	0.071	0.0148	0.0156
29	0.0113	0.0150	0.013	0.075	0.0136	0.0141
30	0.0100	0.0140	0.012	0.080	0.0124	0.0125
31	0.0089	0.0132	0.010	0.085	0.0116	0.0109
32	0.0080	0.0128	0.009	0.090	0.0108	0.0102
33	0.0071	0.0118	0.008	0.095	0.0100	0.0094
34	0.0063	0.0104	0.007	0.100	0.0092	0.0086
35	0.0056	0.0095	0.005	0.106	0.0084	0.0078
36	0.0050	0.0090	0.004	0.112	0.0076	0.0070
37	0.0045	0.0085	. . . . .	0.118	0.0068	0.0066
38	0.0040	0.0080	. . . . .	0.124	0.0060	0.0063
39	0.0035	0.0075	. . . . .	0.130	0.0052	
40	0.0031	0.0070	. . . . .	0.138	0.0048	

[a] Recognized standard in the United States for wire and sheet metal of copper and other metals except steel and iron.

[b] Recognized standard for steel and iron wire. Called the "U.S. steel wire gage."

[c] Formerly much used, now nearly obsolete.

[d] American Steel & Wire Co.'s music wire gage. Recommended by U.S. Bureau of Standards.

[e] Official British Standard.

[f] Legalized U.S. Standard for iron and steel plate, although plate is now always specified by its thickness in decimals of an inch.

Preferred thicknesses for uncoated thin flat metals (under 0.250 in.): ASA B32—1941 gives recommended sizes for sheets.

Preferred Basic Sizes for Cylindrical Fits*

...	0.0100	...	...	...	0.80	5½	5.5000	5.5
...	0.0125	...	⅞	0.8750	...	5¾	5.7500	5.75
¹⁄₆₄	0.015625	...	...	...	0.90	6	6.0000	6.0
...	0.0200	...	1	1.0000	1.0	6½	6.5000	6.5
...	0.0250	...	...	...	1.1	7	7.0000	7.0
¹⁄₃₂	0.03125	...	1⅛	1.1250	...	7½	7.5000	7.5
...	0.0400	0.04	...	...	...	8	8.0000	8.0
...	0.0500	...	1¼	1.2500	1.25	8½	8.5000	8.5
...	...	0.06	1⅜	1.3750	...	9	9.0000	9.0
¹⁄₁₆	0.0625	...	...	...	1.40	9½	9.5000	9.5
...	0.0800	...	1½	1.5000	1.50	10	10.0000	10.0
³⁄₃₂	0.09375	...	1⅝	1.6250	...	10½	10.5000	10.5
...	0.1000	0.10	1¾	1.7500	1.75	11	11.0000	11.0
⅛	0.1250	...	1⅞	1.8750	...	11½	11.5000	11.5
...	...	0.15	2	2.0000	2.0	12	12.0000	12.0
⁵⁄₃₂	0.15625	...	2⅛	2.1250	...	12½	12.5000	12.5
³⁄₁₆	0.1875	...	2¼	2.2500	2.25	13	13.0000	13.0
...	...	0.20	2⅜	2.3750	...	13½	13.5000	13.5
¼	0.2500	0.25	2½	2.5000	2.5	14	14.0000	14.0
...	...	0.30	2⅝	2.6250	...	14½	14.5000	14.5
⁵⁄₁₆	0.3125	...	2¾	2.7500	2.75	15	15.0000	15.0
...	...	0.35	2⅞	2.8750	...	15½	15.5000	15.5
⅜	0.3750	...	3	3.0000	3.0	16	16.0000	16.0
...	...	0.40	3¼	3.2500	3.25	16½	16.5000	16.5
⁷⁄₁₆	0.4375	...	3½	3.5000	3.5	17	17.0000	17.0
½	0.5000	0.50	3¾	3.7500	3.75	17½	17.5000	17.5
⁹⁄₁₆	0.5625	...	4	4.0000	4.0	18	18.0000	18.0
...	...	0.60	4¼	4.2500	4.25	18½	18.5000	18.5
⅝	0.6250	...	4½	4.5000	4.5	19	19.0000	19.0
¹¹⁄₁₆	0.6875	...	4¾	4.7500	4.75	19½	19.5000	19.5
...	...	0.70	5	5.0000	5.0	20	20.0000	20.0
¾	0.7500	0.75	5¼	5.2500	5.25	20½	20.5000	...
						21	21.0000	...

* Adapted from ASA B4.1—1955

TABLES OF LIMITS FOR CYLINDRICAL FITS*

Table 1. Running and Sliding Fits

Nominal size, in.	Class RC 1 Clearance	Class RC 1 Std. lim. Hole	Class RC 1 Std. lim. Shaft	Class RC 2 Clearance	Class RC 2 Std. lim. Hole	Class RC 2 Std. lim. Shaft	Class RC 3 Clearance	Class RC 3 Std. lim. Hole	Class RC 3 Std. lim. Shaft	Class RC 4 Clearance	Class RC 4 Std. lim. Hole	Class RC 4 Std. lim. Shaft
0.04–0.12	0.1	+0.2	−0.1	0.1	+0.25	−0.1	0.3	+0.25	−0.3	0.3	+0.4	−0.3
	0.45	0	−0.25	0.55	0	−0.3	0.8	0	−0.55	1.1	0	−0.7
0.12–0.24	0.15	+0.2	−0.15	0.15	+0.3	−0.15	0.4	+0.3	−0.4	0.4	+0.5	−0.4
	0.5	0	−0.3	0.65	0	−0.35	1.0	0	−0.7	1.4	0	−0.9
0.24–0.40	0.2	+0.25	−0.2	0.2	+0.4	−0.2	0.5	+0.4	−0.5	0.5	+0.6	−0.5
	0.6	0	−0.35	0.85	0	−0.45	1.3	0	−0.9	1.7	0	−1.1
0.40–0.71	0.25	+0.3	−0.25	0.25	+0.4	−0.25	0.6	+0.4	−0.6	0.6	+0.7	−0.6
	0.75	0	−0.45	0.95	0	−0.55	1.4	0	−1.0	2.0	0	−1.3
0.71–1.19	0.3	+0.4	−0.3	0.3	+0.5	−0.3	0.8	+0.5	−0.8	0.8	+0.8	−0.8
	0.95	0	−0.55	1.2	0	−0.7	1.8	0	−1.3	2.4	0	−1.6
1.19–1.97	0.4	+0.4	−0.4	0.4	+0.6	−0.4	1.0	+0.6	−1.0	1.0	+1.0	−1.0
	1.1	0	−0.7	1.4	0	−0.8	2.2	0	−1.6	3.0	0	−2.0
1.97–3.15	0.4	+0.5	−0.4	0.4	+0.7	−0.4	1.2	+0.7	−1.2	1.2	+1.2	−1.2
	1.2	0	−0.7	1.6	0	−0.9	2.6	0	−1.9	3.6	0	−2.4
3.15–4.73	0.5	+0.6	−0.5	0.5	+0.9	−0.5	1.4	+0.9	−1.4	1.4	+1.4	−1.4
	1.5	0	−0.9	2.0	0	−1.1	3.2	0	−2.3	4.2	0	−2.8
4.73–7.09	0.6	+0.7	−0.6	0.6	+1.0	−0.6	1.6	+1.0	−1.6	1.6	+1.6	−1.6
	1.8	0	−1.1	2.3	0	−1.3	3.6	0	−2.6	4.8	0	−3.2

Nominal size, in.	Class RC 5 Clear.	Class RC 5 Hole	Class RC 5 Shaft	Class RC 6 Clear.	Class RC 6 Hole	Class RC 6 Shaft	Class RC 7 Clear.	Class RC 7 Hole	Class RC 7 Shaft	Class RC 8 Clear.	Class RC 8 Hole	Class RC 8 Shaft	Class RC 9 Clear.	Class RC 9 Hole	Class RC 9 Shaft
0.04–0.12	0.6	+0.4	−0.6	0.6	+0.6	−0.6	1.0	+1.0	−1.0	2.5	+1.6	−2.5	4.0	+2.5	−4.0
	1.4	0	−1.0	1.8	0	−1.2	2.6	0	−1.6	5.1	0	−3.5	8.1	0	−5.6
0.12–0.24	0.8	+0.5	−0.8	0.8	+0.7	−0.8	1.2	+1.2	−1.2	2.8	+1.8	−2.8	4.5	+3.0	−4.5
	1.8	0	−1.3	2.2	0	−1.5	3.1	0	−1.9	5.8	0	−4.0	9.0	0	−6.0
0.24–0.40	1.0	+0.6	−1.0	1.0	+0.9	−1.0	1.6	+1.4	−1.6	3.0	+2.2	−3.0	5.0	+3.5	−5.0
	2.2	0	−1.6	2.8	0	−1.9	3.9	0	−2.5	6.6	0	−4.4	10.7	0	−7.2
0.40–0.71	1.2	+0.7	−1.2	1.2	+1.0	−1.2	2.0	+1.6	−2.0	3.5	+2.8	−3.5	6.0	+4.0	−6.0
	2.6	0	−1.9	3.2	0	−2.2	4.6	0	−3.0	7.9	0	−5.1	12.8	0	−8.8
0.71–1.19	1.6	+0.8	−1.6	1.6	+1.2	−1.6	2.5	+2.0	−2.5	4.5	+3.5	−4.5	7.0	+5.0	−7.0
	3.2	0	−2.4	4.0	0	−2.8	5.7	0	−3.7	10.0	0	−6.5	15.5	0	−10.5
1.19–1.97	2.0	+1.0	−2.0	2.0	+1.6	−2.0	3.0	+2.5	−3.0	5.0	+4.0	−5.0	8.0	+6.0	−8.0
	4.0	0	−3.0	5.2	0	−3.6	7.1	0	−4.6	11.5	0	−7.5	18.0	0	−12.0
1.97–3.15	2.5	+1.2	−2.5	2.5	+1.8	−2.5	4.0	+3.0	−4.0	6.0	+4.5	−6.0	9.0	+7.0	−9.0
	4.9	0	−3.7	6.1	0	−4.3	8.8	0	−5.8	13.5	0	−9.0	20.5	0	−13.5
3.15–4.73	3.0	+1.4	−3.0	3.0	+2.2	−3.0	5.0	+3.5	−5.0	7.0	+5.0	−7.0	10.0	+9.0	−10.0
	5.8	0	−4.4	7.4	0	−5.2	10.7	0	−7.2	15.5	0	−10.5	24.0	0	−15.0
4.73–7.09	3.5	+1.6	−3.5	3.5	+2.5	−3.5	6.0	+4.0	−6.0	8.0	+6.0	−8.0	12.0	+10.0	−12.0
	6.7	0	−5.1	8.5	0	−6.0	12.5	0	−8.5	18.0	0	−12.0	28.0	0	−18.0

Table 2. Clearance Locational Fits

Nominal size, in.	Class LC 1	Class LC 1 Hole	Class LC 1 Shaft	Class LC 2	Class LC 2 Hole	Class LC 2 Shaft	Class LC 3	Class LC 3 Hole	Class LC 3 Shaft	Class LC 4	Class LC 4 Hole	Class LC 4 Shaft	Class LC 5	Class LC 5 Hole	Class LC 5 Shaft
0.04–0.12	0	+0.25	+0	0	+0.4	+0	0	+0.6	+0	0	+1.0	+0	0.1	+0.4	−0.1
	0.45	−0	−0.2	0.65	−0	−0.25	1	−0	−0.4	2.0	−0	−1.0	0.75	−0	−0.35
0.12–0.24	0	+0.3	+0	0	+0.5	+0	0	+0.7	+0	0	+1.2	+0	0.15	+0.5	−0.15
	0.5	−0	−0.2	0.8	−0	−0.3	1.2	−0	−0.5	2.4	−0	−1.2	0.95	−0	−0.45
0.24–0.40	0	+0.4	+0	0	+0.6	+0	0	+0.9	+0	0	+1.4	+0	0.2	+0.6	−0.2
	0.65	−0	−0.25	1.0	−0	−0.4	1.5	−0	−0.6	2.8	−0	−1.4	1.2	−0	−0.6
0.40–0.71	0	+0.4	+0	0	+0.7	+0	0	+1.0	+0	0	+1.6	+0	0.25	+0.7	−0.25
	0.7	−0	−0.3	1.1	−0	−0.4	1.7	−0	−0.7	3.2	−0	−1.6	1.35	−0	−0.65
0.71–1.19	0	+0.5	+0	0	+0.8	+0	0	+1.2	+0	0	+2.0	+0	0.3	+0.8	−0.3
	0.9	−0	−0.4	1.3	−0	−0.5	2	−0	−0.8	4	−0	−2.0	1.6	−0	−0.8
1.19–1.97	0	+0.6	+0	0	+1.0	+0	0	+1.6	+0	0	+2.5	+0	0.4	+1.0	−0.4
	1.0	−0	−0.4	1.6	−0	−0.6	2.6	−0	−1	5	−0	−2.5	2.0	−0	−1.0
1.97–3.15	0	+0.7	+0	0	+1.2	+0 ·	0	+1.8	+0	0	+3	+0	0.4	+1.2	−0.4
	1.2	−0	−0.5	1.9	−0	−0.7	3	−0	−1.2	6	−0	−3	2.3	−0	−1.1
3.15–4.73	0	+0.9	+0	0	+1.4	+0	0	+2.2	+0	0	+3.5	+0	0.5	+1.4	−0.5
	1.5	−0	−0.6	2.3	−0	−0.9	3.6	−0	−1.4	7	−0	−3.5	2.8	−0	−1.4
4.73–7.09	0	+1.0	+0	0	+1.6	+0	0	+2.5	+0	0	+4	+0	0.6	+1.6	−0.6
	1.7	−0	−0.7	2.6	−0	−1.0	4.1	−0	−1.6	8	−0	−4	3.2	−0	−1.6

Nominal size, in.	Class LC 6	Class LC 6 Hole	Class LC 6 Shaft	Class LC 7	Class LC 7 Hole	Class LC 7 Shaft	Class LC 8	Class LC 8 Hole	Class LC 8 Shaft	Class LC 9	Class LC 9 Hole	Class LC 9 Shaft	Class LC 10	Class LC 10 Hole	Class LC 10 Shaft	Class LC 11	Class LC 11 Hole	Class LC 11 Shaft
0.04–0.12	0.3	+0.6	−0.3	0.6	+1.0	−0.6	1.0	+1.6	−1.0	2.5	+2.5	−2.5	4	+4	−4	5	+6	−5
	1.5	−0	−0.9	2.6	−0	−1.6	3.6	−0	−2.0	7.5	−0	−5.0	12	−0	−8	17	−0	−11
0.12–0.24	0.4	+0.7	−0.4	0.8	+1.2	−0.8	1.2	+1.8	−1.2	2.8	+3.0	−2.8	4.5	+5	−4.5	6	+7	−6
	1.8	−0	−1.1	3.2	−0	−2.0	4.2	−0	−2.4	8.8	−0	−5.8	14.5	−0	−9.5	20	−0	−13
0.24–0.40	0.5	+0.9	−0.5	1.0	+1.4	−1.0	1.6	+2.2	−1.6	3.0	+3.5	−3.0	5	+6	−5	7	+9	−7
	2.3	−0	−1.4	3.8	−0	−2.4	5.2	−0	−3.0	10.0	−0	−6.5	17	−0	−11	25	−0	−16
0.40–0.71	0.6	+1.0	−0.6	1.2	+1.6	−1.2	2.0	+2.8	−2.0	3.5	+4.0	−3.5	6	+7	−6	8	+10	−8
	2.6	−0	−1.6	4.4	−0	−2.8	6.4	−0	−3.6	11.5	−0	−7.5	20	−0	−13	28	−0	−18
0.71–1.19	0.8	+1.2	−0.8	1.6	+2.0	−1.6	2.5	+3.5	−2.5	4.5	+5.0	−4.5	7	+8	−7	10	+12	−10
	3.2	−0	−2.0	5.6	−0	−3.6	8.0	−0	−4.5	14.5	−0	−9.5	23	−0	−15	34	−0	−22
1.19–1.97	1.0	+1.6	−1.0	2.0	+2.5	−2.0	3.0	+4.0	−3.0	5	+6	−5	8	+10	−8	12	+16	−12
	4.2	−0	−2.6	7.0	−0	−4.5	9.5	−0	−5.5	17	−0	−11	28	−0	−18	44	−0	−28
1.97–3.15	1.2	+1.8	−1.2	2.5	+3.0	−2.5	4.0	+4.5	−4.0	6	+7	−6	10	+12	−10	14	+18	−14
	4.8	−0	−3.0	8.5	−0	−5.5	11.5	−0	−7.0	20	−0	−13	34	−0	−22	50	−0	−32
3.15–4.73	1.4	+2.2	−1.4	3.0	+3.5	−3.0	5.0	+5.0	−5.0	7	+9	−7	11	+14	−11	16	+22	−16
	5.8	−0	−3.6	10.0	−0	−6.5	13.5	−0	−8.5	25	−0	−16	39	−0	−25	60	−0	−38
4.73–7.09	1.6	+2.5	−1.6	3.5	+4.0	−3.5	6	+6	−6	8	+10	−8	12	+16	−12	18	+25	−18
	6.6	−0	−4.1	11.5	−0	−7.5	16	−0	−10	28	−0	−18	44	−0	−28	68	−0	−43

* Adapted from ASA B4.1—1955. Limits for hole and shaft are applied algebraically to basic size to obtain limits of size for parts. Data in boldface in accordance with ABC agreements.

Table 3. Transition Locational Fits

Nominal size, in.	Class LT 1			Class LT 2			Class LT 3			Class LT 4			Class LT 6			Class LT 7		
	Fit†	Hole	Shaft	Fit	Hole	Shaft	Fit	Hole	Shaft	Fit	Hole	Shaft	Fit	Hole	Shaft	Fit	Hole	Shaft
0.04–0.12	−0.15	+0.4	+0.15	−0.3	+0.6	+0.3							−0.55	+0.6	+0.55	−0.5	+0.4	+0.5
	+0.5	−0	−0.1	+0.7	−0	−0.1							+0.45	−0	+0.15	+0.15	−0	+0.25
0.12–0.24	−0.2	+0.5	+0.2	−0.4	+0.7	+0.4							−0.7	+0.7	+0.7	−0.6	+0.5	+0.6
	+0.6	−0	−0.1	+0.8	−0	−0.1							+0.5	−0	+0.2	+0.2	−0	+0.3
0.24–0.40	−0.3	+0.6	+0.3	−0.4	+0.9	+0.4	−0.5	+0.6	+0.5	−0.7	+0.9	+0.7	−0.8	+0.9	+0.8	−0.8	+0.6	+0.8
	+0.7	−0	−0.1	+1.1	−0	−0.2	+0.5	−0	+0.1	+0.8	−0	+0.1	+0.7	−0	+0.2	−0.2	−0	+0.4
0 40–0.71	−0.3	+0.7	+0.3	−0.5	+1.0	+0.5	−0.5	+0.7	+0.5	−0.8	+1.0	+0.8	−1.0	+1.0	+1.0	−0.9	+0.7	+0.9
	+0.8	−0	−0.1	+1.2	−0	−0.2	+0.6	−0	+0.1	+0.9	−0	+0.1	+0.7	−0	+0.3	+0.2	−0	+0.5
0.71–1.19	−0.3	+0.8	+0.3	−0.5	+1.2	+0.5	−0.6	+0.8	+0.6	−0.9	+1.2	+0.9	−1.1	+1.2	+1.1	−1.1	+0.8	+1.1
	+1.0	−0	−0.2	+1.5	−0	−0.3	+0.7	−0	+0.1	+1.1	−0	+0.1	+0.9	−0	+0.3	+0.2	−0	+0.6
1.19–1.97	−0.4	+1.0	+0.4	−0.6	+1.6	+0.6	−0.7	+1.0	+0.7	−1.1	+1.6	+1.1	−1.4	+1.6	+1.4	−1.3	+1.0	+1.3
	+1.2	−0	−0.2	+2.0	−0	−0.4	+0.9	−0	+0.1	+1.5	−0	+0.1	+1.2	−0	+0.4	+0.3	−0	+0.7
1.97–3.15	−0.4	+1.2	+0.4	−0.7	+1.8	+0.7	−0.8	+1.2	+0.8	−1.3	+1.8	+1.3	−1.7	+1.8	+1.7	−1.5	+1.2	+1.5
	+1.5	−0	−0.3	+2.3	−0	−0.5	+1.1	−0	+0.1	+1.7	−0	+0.1	+1.3	−0	+0.5	+0.4	−0	+0.8
3.15–4.73	−0.5	+1.4	+0.5	−0.8	+2.2	+0.8	−1.0	+1.4	+1.0	−1.5	+2.2	+1.5	−1.9	+2.2	+1.9	−1.9	+1.4	+1.9
	+1.8	−0	−0.4	+2.8	−0	−0.6	+1.3	−0	+0.1	+2.1	−0	+0.1	+1.7	−0	+0.5	+0.4	−0	+1.0
4.73–7.09	−0.6	+1.6	+0.6	−0.9	+2.5	+0.9	−1.1	+1.6	+1.1	−1.7	+2.5	+1.7	−2.2	+2.5	+2.2	−2.2	+1.6	+2.2
	+2.0	−0	−0.4	+3.2	−0	−0.7	+1.5	−0	+0.1	+2.4	−0	+0.1	+1.9	−0	+0.6	+0.4	−0	+1.2

† "Fit" represents the maximum interference (minus values) and the maximum clearance (plus values).

Table 4. Interference Locational Fits

Nominal size, in.	Class LN 2			Class LN 3		
	Interference	Hole	Shaft	Interference	Hole	Shaft
0.04–0.12	0	+0.4	+0.65	0.1	+0.4	+0.75
	0.65	−0	+0.4	0.75	−0	+0.5
0.12–0.24	0	+0.5	+0.8	0.1	+0.5	+0.9
	0.8	−0	+0.5	0.9	−0	+0.6
0.24–0.40	0	+0.6	+1.0	0.2	+0.6	+1.2
	1.0	−0	+0.6	1.2	−0	+0.8
0.40–0.71	0	+0.7	+1.1	0.3	+0.7	+1.4
	1.1	−0	+0.7	1.4	−0	+1.0
0.71–1.19	0	+0.8	+1.3	0.4	+0.8	+1.7
	1.3	−0	+0.8	1.7	−0	+1.2
1.19–1.97	0	+1.0	+1.6	0.4	+1.0	+2.0
	1.6	−0	+1.0	2.0	−0	+1.4
1.97–3.15	0.2	+1.2	+2.1	0.4	+1.2	+2.3
	2.1	−0	+1.4	2.3	−0	+1.6
3.15–4.73	0.2	+1.4	+2.5	0.6	+1.4	+2.9
	2.5	−0	+1.6	2.9	−0	+2.0
4.73–7.09	0.2	+1.6	+2.8	0.9	+1.6	+3.5
	2.8	−0	+1.8	3.5	−0	+2.5

Table 5. Force and Shrink Fits

Nominal size	Class FN 1			Class FN 2			Class FN 3			Class FN 4			Class FN 5		
0.04–0.12	0.05	+0.25	+0.5	0.2	+0.4	+0.85				0.3	+0.4	+0.95	0.5	+0.4	+1.3
	0.5	−0	+0.3	0.85	−0	+0.6				0.95	−0	+0.7	1.3	−0	+0.9
0.12–0.24	0.1	+0.3	+0.6	0.2	+0.5	+1.0				0.4	+0.5	+1.2	0.7	+0.5	+1.7
	0.6	−0	+0.4	1.0	−0	+0.7				1.2	−0	+0.9	1.7	−0	+1.2
0.24–0.40	0.1	+0.4	+0.75	0.4	+0.6	+1.4				0.6	+0.6	+1.6	0.8	+0.6	+2.0
	0.75	−0	+0.5	1.4	−0	+1.0				1.6	−0	+1.2	2.0	−0	+1.4
0.40–0.56	0.1	+0.4	+0.8	0.5	+0.7	+1.6				0.7	+0.7	+1.8	0.9	+0.7	+2.3
	0.8	−0	+0.5	1.6	−0	+1.2				1.8	−0	+1.4	2.3	−0	+1.6
0.56–0.71	0.2	+0.4	+0.9	0.5	+0.7	+1.6				0.7	+0.7	+1.8	1.1	+0.7	+2.5
	0.9	−0	+0.6	1.6	−0	+1.2				1.8	−0	+1.4	2.5	−0	+1.8
0.71–0.95	0.2	+0.5	+1.1	0.6	+0.8	+1.9				0.8	+0.8	+2.1	1.4	+0.8	+3.0
	1.1	−0	+0.7	1.9	−0	+1.4				2.1	−0	+1.6	3.0	−0	+2.2
0.95–1.19	0.3	+0.5	+1.2	0.6	+0.8	+1.9	0.8	+0.8	+2.1	1.0	+0.8	+2.3	1.7	+0.8	+3.3
	1.2	−0	+0.8	1.9	−0	+1.4	2.1	−0	+1.6	2.3	−0	+1.8	3.3	−0	+2.5
1.19–1.58	0.3	+0.6	+1.3	0.8	+1.0	+2.4	1.0	+1.0	+2.6	1.5	+1.0	+3.1	2.0	+1.0	+4.0
	1.3	−0	+0.9	2.4	−0	+1.8	2.6	−0	+2.0	3.1	−0	+2.5	4.0	−0	+3.0
1.58–1.97	0.4	+0.6	+1.4	0.8	+1.0	+2.4	1.2	+1.0	+2.8	1.8	+1.0	+3.4	3.0	+1.0	+5.0
	1.4	−0	+1.0	2.4	−0	+1.8	2.8	−0	+2.2	3.4	−0	+2.8	5.0	−0	+4.0
1.97–2.56	0.6	+0.7	+1.8	0.8	+1.2	+2.7	1.3	+1.2	+3.2	2.3	+1.2	+4.2	3.8	+1.2	+6.2
	1.8	−0	+1.3	2.7	−0	+2.0	3.2	−0	+2.5	4.2	−0	+3.5	6.2	−0	+5.0
2.56–3.15	0.7	+0.7	+1.9	1.0	+1.2	+2.9	1.8	+1.2	+3.7	2.8	+1.2	+4.7	4.8	+1.2	+7.2
	1.9	−0	+1.4	2.9	−0	+2.2	3.7	−0	+3.0	4.7	−0	+4.0	7.2	−0	+6.0
3.15–3.94	0.9	+0.9	+2.4	1.4	+1.4	+3.7	2.1	+1.4	+4.4	3.6	+1.4	+5.9	5.6	+1.4	+8.4
	2.4	−0	+1.8	3.7	−0	+2.8	4.4	−0	+3.5	5.9	−0	+5.0	8.4	−0	+7.0
3.94–4.73	1.1	+0.9	+2.6	1.6	+1.4	+3.9	2.6	+1.4	+4.9	4.6	+1.4	+6.9	6.6	+1.4	+9.4
	2.6	−0	+2.0	3.9	−0	+3.0	4.9	−0	+4.0	6.9	−0	+6.0	9.4	−0	+8.0
4.73–5.52	1.2	+1.0	+2.9	1.9	+1.6	+4.5	3.4	+1.6	+6.0	5.4	+1.6	+8.0	8.4	+1.6	+11.6
	2.9	−0	+2.2	4.5	−0	+3.5	6.0	−0	+5.0	8.0	−0	+7.0	11.6	−0	+10.0
5.52–6.30	1.5	+1.0	+3.2	2.4	+1.6	+5.0	3.4	+1.6	+6.0	5.4	+1.6	+8.0	10.4	+1.6	+13.6
	3.2	−0	+2.5	5.0	−0	+4.0	6.0	−0	+5.0	8.0	−0	+7.0	13.6	−0	+12.0
6.30–7.09	1.8	+1.0	+3.5	2.9	+1.6	+5.5	4.4	+1.6	+7.0	6.4	+1.6	+9.0	10.4	+1.6	+13.6
	3.5	−0	+2.8	5.5	−0	+4.5	7.0	−0	+6.0	9.0	−0	+8.0	13.6	−0	+12.0

American Standard Pipe[a, b]

Welded wrought iron

Nominal pipe size	Actual outside diam. D	Tap-drill size S	Thd. /in. T	Distance pipe enters fittings L	Wall thickness X Standard 40[c]	Wall thickness X Extra strong 80[d]	Wall thickness X Double extra strong[e]	Weight, lb/ft[f] Standard 40[c]	Weight, lb/ft[f] Extra strong 80[d]	Weight, lb/ft[f] Double extra strong[e]
⅛	0.405	11⁄32	27	3⁄16	0.070	0.098	....	0.25	0.32	
¼	0.540	7⁄16	18	9⁄32	0.090	0.122	....	0.43	0.54	
⅜	0.675	37⁄64	18	19⁄64	0.093	0.129	....	0.57	0.74	
½	0.840	23⁄32	14	3⁄8	0.111	0.151	0.307	0.86	1.09	1.714
¾	1.050	59⁄64	14	13⁄32	0.115	0.157	0.318	1.14	1.48	2.440
1	1.315	1 5⁄32	11½	½	0.136	0.183	0.369	1.68	2.18	3.659
1¼	1.660	1 ½	11½	35⁄64	0.143	0.195	0.393	2.28	3.00	5.214
1½	1.900	147⁄64	11½	9⁄16	0.148	0.204	0.411	2.72	3.64	6.408
2	2.375	2 7⁄32	11½	37⁄64	0.158	0.223	0.447	3.66	5.03	9.029
2½	2.875	2 ⅝	8	⅞	0.208	0.282	0.565	5.80	7.67	13.695
3	3.5	3 ¼	8	15⁄16	0.221	0.306	0.615	7.58	10.3	18.583
3½	4.0	3 ¾	8	1	0.231	0.325	....	9.11	12.5	
4	4.5	4 ¼	8	1 1⁄16	0.242	0.344	0.690	10.8	15.0	27.451
5	5.563	5 5⁄16	8	1 5⁄32	0.263	0.383	0.768	14.7	20.8	38.552
6	6.625	6 5⁄16	8	1 ¼	0.286	0.441	0.884	19.0	28.6	53.160
8	8.625	.....	8	115⁄32	0.329	0.510	0.895	28.6	43.4	72.424
10	10.75	.....	8	143⁄64	0.372	0.606	....	40.5	64.4	
12	12.75	.....	8	1 ⅞	0.414	0.702	....	53.6	88.6	
14 OD	14.0	.....	8	2	0.437	0.750	....	62.2	104.	
16 OD	16.0	.....	8	213⁄64	0.500	....	....	82.2		
18 OD	18.0	.....	8	213⁄32	0.562	....	....	103.		
20 OD	20.0	.....	8	219⁄32	0.562	....	....	115.		
24 OD	24.0	.....	8	3						

[a] For welded and seamless steel pipe. See ASA B36.10—1939. Dimensions in inches.

[b] A pipe size may be designated by giving the nominal pipe size and wall thickness or by giving the nominal pipe size and weight per linear foot.

[c] Refers to American Standard schedule numbers, approximate values for the expression $1{,}000 \times P/S$. Schedule 40—standard weight.

[d] Schedule 80—extra strong.

[e] Not American Standard, but commercially available in both wrought iron and steel.

[f] Plain ends.

American Standard 150-lb Malleable-iron Screwed Fittings[a]

90° ELBOW

TEE   CROSS

45° ELL   Y BRANCH

PLUG

Nominal pipe size	A	B	C	E	F	G	H	J	K	L	M
⅛	0.69	0.25	....	0.200	0.405	0.090	0.693	1.00[b]	....	0.264	
¼	0.81	0.32	0.73	0.215	0.540	0.095	0.844	1.19	0.94	0.402	1.00
⅜	0.95	0.36	0.80	0.230	0.675	0.100	1.015	1.44	1.03	0.408	1.13
½	1.12	0.43	0.88	0.249	0.840	0.105	1.197	1.63	1.15	0.534	1.25
¾	1.31	0.50	0.98	0.273	1.050	0.120	1.458	1.89	1.29	0.546	1.44
1	1.50	0.58	1.12	0.302	1.315	0.134	1.771	2.14	1.47	0.683	1.69
1¼	1.75	0.67	1.29	0.341	1.660	0.145	2.153	2.45	1.71	0.707	2.06
1½	1.94	0.70	1.43	0.368	1.900	0.155	2.427	2.69	1.88	0.724	2.31
2	2.25	0.75	1.68	0.422	2.375	0.173	2.963	3.26	2.22	0.757	2.81
2½	2.70	0.92	1.95	0.478	2.875	0.210	3.589	3.86	2.57	1.138	3.25
3	3.08	0.98	2.17	0.548	3.500	0.231	4.285	4.51	3.00	1.200	3.69
3½	3.42	1.03	2.39	0.604	4.000	0.248	4.843	5.09[b]	....	1.250	4.00
4	3.79	1.08	2.61	0.661	4.500	0.265	5.401	5.69	3.70	1.300	4.38
5	4.50	1.18	3.05	0.780	5.563	0.300	6.583	6.86[b]	....	1.406	5.12
6	5.13	1.28	3.46	0.900	6.625	0.336	7.767	8.03[b]	....	1.513	5.86

Nominal pipe size	N	P	T	U	V	W	X	Y	Z[c]	O[d]	Thickness of ribs on caps, couplings
⅛	0.20	....	....	....	....	0.96	0.37	0.24	9⁄32	....	0.090
¼	0.26	....	....	....	....	1.06	0.44	0.28	⅜	....	0.095
⅜	0.37	....	0.50	1.43	1.93	1.16	0.48	0.31	7⁄16	....	0.100
½	0.51	0.87	0.61	1.71	2.32	1.34	0.56	0.38	9⁄16	0.16	0.105
¾	0.69	0.97	0.72	2.05	2.77	1.52	0.63	0.44	⅝	0.18	0.120
1	0.91	1.16	0.85	2.43	3.28	1.67	0.75	0.50	1 3⁄16	0.20	0.134
1¼	1.19	1.28	1.02	2.92	3.94	1.93	0.80	0.56	1 5⁄16	0.22	0.145
1½	1.39	1.33	1.10	3.28	4.38	2.15	0.83	0.62	1 ⅛	0.24	0.155
2	1.79	1.45	1.24	3.93	5.17	2.53	0.88	0.68	1 5⁄16	0.26	0.173
2½	2.20	1.70	1.52	4.73	6.25	2.88	1.07	0.74	1 ½	0.29	0.210
3	2.78	1.80	1.71	5.55	7.26	3.18	1.13	0.80	1 11⁄16	0.31	0.231
3½	3.24	1.90	....	....	....	3.43	1.18	0.86	1 ⅞	0.34	0.248
4	3.70	2.08	2.01	6.97	8.98	3.69	1.22	1.00	2 ⅛	0.37	0.265
5	4.69	2.32	....	....	....	....	1.31	1.00	2 5⁄16	0.46	0.300
6	5.67	2.55	....	....	....	....	1.40	1.25	2 ½	0.52	0.336

[a] ASA B16c—1939. Street tee not made in ⅛-in. size. Dimensions in inches. Left-hand couplings have four or more ribs. Right-hand couplings have two ribs. [b] Street ell only.

[c] These dimensions are the nominal size of wrench (ASA B18.2—1941). Square-head plugs are designed to fit these wrenches.

[d] Solid plugs are provided in sizes ⅛ to 3½ in. inclusive; cored plugs ½ to 3½ in. inclusive. Cored plugs have min. metal thickness at all points equal to dimension O except at the end of thread.

90° STREET ELBOW

45° STREET ELBOW

STREET TEE

COUPLING

REDUCING COUPLING

CAP

American Standard 150-lb Malleable-iron Screwed Fittings: Dimensions of Close-, Medium-, and Open-pattern Return Bends*†

CLOSE

MEDIUM

OPEN

Nominal pipe size	Length of thread, min. B	Width of band, min. E	Inside diam. of fittings F		Metal thickness ‡ G	Outside diam. of band, min. H	Center to center (close pattern) R_1	Center to center (medium pattern) R_2	Center to center (open pattern) R_3
			Max.	Min.					
½	0.43	0.249	0.840	0.897	0.116	1.197	1.000	1.250	1.50
¾	0.50	0.273	1.050	1.107	0.133	1.458	1.250	1.500	2.00
1	0.58	0.302	1.315	1.385	0.150	1.771	1.500	1.875	2.50
1¼	0.67	0.341	1.660	1.730	0.165	2.153	1.750	2.250	3.00
1½	0.70	0.368	1.900	1.970	0.178	2.427	2.188	2.500	3.50
2	0.75	0.422	2.375	2.445	0.201	2.963	2.625	3.000	4.00
2½	0.92	0.478	2.875	2.975	0.244	3.589	....	....	4.50
3	0.98	0.548	3.500	3.600	0.272	4.285	....	....	5.00
4	1.08	0.661	4.500	4.600	0.315	5.401	....	....	6.00

All dimensions given in inches.

* Adapted from ASA B16.3—1951.

† It is permissible to furnish close-pattern return bends not banded. Close-pattern return bends will not make up parallel coils, as the distance center to center of two adjacent bends is greater than the center to center of openings of a single bend.

‡ Patterns shall be designed to produce castings of metal thicknesses given in the table. Metal thickness at no point shall be less than 90 per cent of the thickness given in the table.

American Standard Cast-iron Screwed Fittings*

For maximum working saturated steam pressure of 125 and 250 lb per sq in.

ELBOW   TEE

CROSS   45°ELBOW

Nominal pipe size	A	B min.	C	E min.	F Min.	F Max.	G min.	H min.
¼	0.81	0.32	0.73	0.38	0.540	0.584	0.110	0.93
⅜	0.95	0.36	0.80	0.44	0.675	0.719	0.120	1.12
½	1.12	0.43	0.88	0.50	0.840	0.897	0.130	1.34
¾	1.31	0.50	0.98	0.56	1.050	1.107	0.155	1.63
1	1.50	0.58	1.12	0.62	1.315	1.385	0.170	1.95
1¼	1.75	0.67	1.29	0.69	1.660	1.730	0.185	2.39
1½	1.94	0.70	1.43	0.75	1.900	1.970	0.200	2.68
2	2.25	0.75	1.68	0.84	2.375	2.445	0.220	3.28
2½	2.70	0.92	1.95	0.94	2.875	2.975	0.240	3.86
3	3.08	0.98	2.17	1.00	3.500	3.600	0.260	4.62
3½	3.42	1.03	2.39	1.06	4.000	4.100	0.280	5.20
4	3.79	1.08	2.61	1.12	4.500	4.600	0.310	5.79
5	4.50	1.18	3.05	1.18	5.563	5.663	0.380	7.05
6	5.13	1.28	3.46	1.28	6.625	6.725	0.430	8.28
8	6.56	1.47	4.28	1.47	8.625	8.725	0.550	10.63
10	8.08	1.68	5.16	1.68	10.750	10.850	0.690	13.12
12	9.50	1.88	5.97	1.88	12.750	12.850	0.800	15.47

* ASA B16d—1941. Dimensions in inches.

Globe, Angle-globe, and Gate Valves*

Size	A (globe only)	B (open)	C	D (angle only)	E	F (open)	G
⅛	2	4	1¾	1			
¼	2	4	1¾	1	1⅞	5⅛	1¾
⅜	2¼	4½	2	1⅛	2	5⅛	1¾
½	2¾	5¼	2½	1¼	2⅛	5½	2
¾	3³⁄₁₆	6	2¾	1½	2⅜	6⅝	2½
1	3¾	6¾	3	1¾	2⅞	7⅞	2¾
1¼	4¼	7¼	3⅝	2	3¼	9½	3
1½	4¾	8¼	4	2¼	3½	10⅞	3⅝
2	5¾	9½	4¾	2¾	3⅞	13⅛	4
2½	6¾	11	6	3¼	4½	15⅜	4¾
3	8	12¼	7	3¾	5	17⅞	5⅜

* Dimensions in inches and compiled from manufacturers' catalogues for drawing purposes.

Lengths of Pipe Nipples*

Size	Length		Size	Length		Size	Length		Size	Length	
	Close	Short		Close	Short		Close	Short		Close	Short
⅛	¾	1½	½	1⅛	1½	1¼	1⅝	2½	2½	2½	3
¼	⅞	1½	¾	1⅜	2	1½	1¾	2½	3	2⅝	3
⅜	1	1½	1	1½	2	2	2	2½			

* Compiled from manufacturers' catalogues. Dimensions in inches.

Long-nipple lengths: from short-nipple lengths to 6 in. in ½ in. increments; from 6 in. nipple lengths to 12 in. in 1 in. increments; from 12 in. nipple lengths to 24 in. in 2 in. increments.

Pipe Bushings*

Dimensions of outside-head, inside-head, and face bushings in inches

FACE BUSHING   OUTSIDE HEAD   INSIDE HEAD

Size	Length of external thread,† min., A	Height of head, min., D	Width of head,‡ min., C Outside	Width of head,‡ min., C Inside	Size	Length of external thread,‡ min., A	Height of head, min., D	Width of head,† min., C Outside	Width of head,† min., C Inside
¼ × ⅛	0.44	0.14	0.64		1½ × ¼	0.83	0.37	....	1.12
⅜ × ¼	0.48	0.16	0.68		2 × 1½	0.88	0.34	2.48	
⅜ × ⅛	0.48	0.16	0.68		2 × 1¼	0.88	0.34	2.48	
½ × ⅜	0.56	0.19	0.87		2 × 1	0.88	0.41	....	1.95
½ × ¼	0.56	0.19	0.87		2 × ¾	0.88	0.41	....	1.63
½ × ⅛	0.56	0.19	0.87		2 × ½	0.88	0.41	....	1.34
¾ × ½	0.63	0.22	1.15		2 × ⅜	0.88	0.41	....	1.12
¾ × ⅜	0.63	0.22	1.15		2 × ¼	0.88	0.41	....	1.12
¾ × ¼	0.63	0.22	1.15		2½ × 2	1.07	0.37	2.98	
¾ × ⅛	0.63	0.22	1.15		2½ × 1½	1.07	0.44	2.68	
1 × ¾	0.75	0.25	1.42		2½ × 1¼	1.07	0.44	....	2.39
1 × ½	0.75	0.25	1.42		2½ × 1	1.07	0.44	....	1.95
1 × ⅜	0.75	0.30	....	1.12	2½ × ¾	1.07	0.44	....	1.63
1 × ¼	0.75	0.30	....	1.12	2½ × ½	1.07	0.44	....	1.34
1 × ⅛	0.75	0.30	....	1.12	3 × 2½	1.13	0.40	3.86	
1¼ × 1	0.80	0.28	1.76		3 × 2	1.13	0.48	3.28	
1¼ × ¾	0.80	0.28	1.76		3 × 1½	1.13	0.48	....	2.68
1¼ × ½	0.80	0.34	....	1.34	3 × 1¼	1.13	0.48	....	2.39
1¼ × ⅜	0.80	0.34	....	1.12	3 × 1	1.13	0.48	....	1.95
1¼ × ¼	0.80	0.34	....	1.12	3 × ¾	1.13	0.48	....	1.63
1½ × 1¼	0.83	0.31	2.00		3 × ½	1.13	0.48	....	1.34
1½ × 1	0.83	0.31	2.00						
1½ × ¾	0.83	0.37	....	1.63					
1½ × ½	0.83	0.37	....	1.34					
1½ × ⅜	0.83	0.37	....	1.12					

* ASA B16.14—1949.

† In the case of outside-head bushings, length *A* includes provisions for imperfect threads.

‡ Heads of bushings shall be hexagonal or octagonal, except that on the larger sizes of outside-head bushings the heads may be made round with lugs instead of hexagonal or octagonal.

American Standard Cast-iron Pipe Flanges and Flanged Fittings*

For maximum working saturated steam pressure of 125 lb per sq in. (gage)

90° ELL   LONG RAD ELL   45° ELL   REDUCING ELL   SIDE OUTLET ELL   TRUE "Y"   TEE

SIDE OUTLET TEE   CROSS   LATERAL   REDUCER   ECCENTRIC REDUCER   FLANGES

Nominal pipe size N	A	B	C	D	E	F	G	H	K min.
1	3½	5	1¾	7½	5¾	1¾	....	4¼	7/16
1¼	3¾	5½	2	8	6¼	1¾	....	4⅝	½
1½	4	6	2¼	9	7	2	....	5	9/16
2	4½	6½	2½	10½	8	2½	5	6	⅝
2½	5	7	3	12	9½	2½	5½	7	11/16
3	5½	7¾	3	13	10	3	6	7½	¾
3½	6	8½	3½	14½	11½	3	6½	8½	13/16
4	6½	9	4	15	12	3	7	9	15/16
5	7½	10¼	4½	17	13½	3½	8	10	15/16
6	8	11½	5	18	14½	3½	9	11	1
8	9	14	5½	22	17½	4½	11	13½	1 ⅛
10	11	16½	6½	25½	20½	5	12	16	1 3/16
12	12	19	7½	30	24½	5½	14	19	1 ¼

Nominal pipe size N	L	M	No. of bolts	Diam. of bolts	Length of bolts	X min.	Y min.	Wall thickness	V
1	3⅛	⅝	4	½	1¾	1 15/16	1 1/16	5/16	⅜
1¼	3½	⅝	4	½	2	2 5/16	1 3/16	5/16	7/16
1½	3⅞	⅝	4	½	2	2 9/16	⅞	5/16	½
2	4¾	¾	4	⅝	2¼	3 1/16	1	5/16	9/16
2½	5½	¾	4	⅝	2½	3 9/16	1 ⅛	5/16	⅝
3	6	¾	4	⅝	2½	4 ¼	1 3/16	⅜	11/16
3½	7	¾	8	⅝	2¾	4 13/16	1 ¼	7/16	¾
4	7½	¾	8	⅝	3	5 5/16	1 5/16	½	⅞
5	8½	⅞	8	¾	3	6 7/16	1 7/16	½	⅞
6	9½	⅞	8	¾	3¼	7 9/16	1 9/16	9/16	15/16
8	11¾	⅞	8	¾	3½	9 11/16	1 ¾	⅝	1 1/16
10	14¼	1	12	⅞	3¾	11 15/16	1 15/16	¾	1 ⅛
12	17	1	12	⅞	3¾	14 1/16	2 3/16	13/16	

* ASA B16a—1939. Dimensions in inches.

Lengths of Malleable-iron Unions*

Ground joint

Nominal size........	⅛	¼	⅜	½	¾	1	1¼	1½	2	2½	3
End to end	1½	1 9/16	1⅝	1 13/16	2 1/16	2¼	2½	2⅝	3	3 9/16	3 15/16

* Compiled from manufacturers' catalogues. Dimensions in inches.

American Standard Steel Butt-welding Fittings*, †

Elbows, tees, caps, and stub ends

Nominal pipe size	Outside diam. at bevel	Center to end			Welding caps E	Lapped-joint stub ends		
		90° welding elbow A	45° welding elbow B	Of run, welding tee C		Lengths F	Radius of fillet R	Diameter of lap G
1	1.310	1½	⅞	1½	1½	4	⅛	2
1¼	1.660	1⅞	1	1⅞	1½	4	3/16	2½
1½	1.900	2¼	1⅛	2¼	1½	4	¼	2⅞
2	2.375	3	1⅜	2½	1½	6	5/16	3⅝
2½	2.875	3¾	1¾	3	1½	6	5/16	4⅛
3	3.500	4½	2	3⅜	2	6	⅜	5
3½	4.000	5¼	2¼	3¾	2½	6	⅜	5½
4	4.500	6	2½	4⅛	2½	6	7/16	6 3/16

Butt-welding reducers

Nominal pipe size	Outside diam. at bevel		End to end H
	Large end	Small end	
1 × ¾	1.315	1.050	2
1 × ½		0.840	
1 × ⅜		0.675	
1¼ × 1	1.660	1.315	2
1¼ × ¾		1.050	
1¼ × ½		0.840	
1½ × 1¼	1.900	1.660	2½
1½ × 1		1.315	
1½ × ¾		1.050	
1½ × ½		0.840	
2 × 1½	2.375	1.900	3
2 × 1¼		1.660	
2 × 1		1.315	
2 × ¾		1.050	
2½ × 2	2.875	2.375	3½
2½ × 1½		1.900	
2½ × 1¼		1.660	
2½ × 1		1.315	

Nominal pipe size	Outside diam. at bevel		End to end H
	Large end	Small end	
3 × 2½	3.500	2.875	3½
3 × 2		2.375	
3 × 1½		1.900	
3 × 1¼		1.660	
3½ × 3	4.000	3.500	4
3½ × 2½		2.875	
3½ × 2		2.375	
3½ × 1½		1.900	
3½ × 1¼		1.660	
4 × 3½	4.500	4.000	4
4 × 3		3.500	
4 × 2½		2.875	
4 × 2		2.375	
4 × 1½		1.900	
5 × 4	5.563	4.500	5
5 × 3½		4.000	
5 × 3		3.500	
5 × 2½		2.875	

* For larger sizes, see ASA B16.
† ASA B16.9—1940. Dimensions in inches.

Threaded Cast-iron Pipe*

Dimension of pipe and drainage hubs

Pipe size	Pipe			Drainage hubs					Nominal weights	
	Nominal diam.		Wall thick-ness, min.,	Thread length*	Diam. of groove, max.,	End to shoulder †	Min. band		Type A and barrel of type B per foot	Addi-tional weight of hubs for type B
	Outside	Inside					Diam.	Length		
	D	A	G	B	K	C	H	E		
1¼	1.66	1.23	0.187	0.42	1.73	0.71	2.39	0.71	3.033	0.60
1½	1.90	1.45	0.195	0.42	1.97	0.72	2.68	0.72	3.666	0.90
2	2.38	1.89	0.211	0.43	2.44	0.76	3.28	0.76	5.041	1.00
2½	2.88	2.32	0.241	0.68	2.97	1.14	3.86	1.14	7.032	1.35
3	3.50	2.90	0.263	0.76	3.60	1.20	4.62	1.20	9.410	2.80
4	4.50	3.83	0.294	0.84	4.60	1.30	5.79	1.30	13.751	3.48
5	5.56	4.81	0.328	0.93	5.66	1.41	7.05	1.41	19.069	5.00
6	6.63	5.76	0.378	0.95	6.72	1.51	8.28	1.51	26.223	6.60
8	8.63	7.63	0.438	1.06	8.72	1.71	10.63	1.71	39.820	10.00
10	10.75	9.75	0.438	1.21	10.85	1.92	13.12	1.93	50.234	
12	12.75	11.75	0.438	1.36	12.85	2.12	15.47	2.13	60.036	

* ASA A40.5—1943. All dimensions are given in inches, except where otherwise stated. Type A has external threads both ends. Type B as shown.

† The length of thread B and the end to shoulder C shall not vary from the dimensions shown by more than plus or minus the equivalent of the pitch of one thread.

American Standard Class-125 Cast-iron and 150-lb Steel Valves: Valves with Class-125 or 150-lb End Flanges, or with Welding Ends—Face-to-face and End-to-end Dimensions[a]

PLAIN FACE — A · RAISED FACE — A · BUTT WELDING END — B · RING JOINT — C

Nominal valve size	Class-125 cast iron — Flanged end—plain face — Gate Solid wedge (A)	Gate Double disc (A)	Plug Short pattern (A)	Plug Regular (A)	Plug Venturi (A)	Globe and lift check (A)	Swing check[b] (A)	Control[c] (A)	150-lb steel — Flanged end[d] (1/16 in. raised face) and welding end — Gate[e] Solid wedge (A)	Gate Double disc (A)	Gate Solid wedge (B)	Gate Double disc (B)	Plug[f] Short pattern (A)	Plug Regular (A)	Plug Venturi (A)	Round port full bore (A)
¼	...	...	...	...	...	...	...	...	4	4	4	4	...	...	...	...
⅜	...	...	...	...	...	...	...	...	4	4	4	4	...	...	...	...
½	...	...	...	...	...	...	...	...	4¼	4¼	4¼	4¼	...	...	...	...
¾	...	...	...	...	...	...	...	...	4⅝	4⅝	4⅝	4⅝	...	...	...	...
1	...	...	5½	5½	...	...	...	7¼	5	5	5	5	5½	...	...	7
1¼	...	...	...	6½	...	...	...	...	5½	5½	5½	5½	...	...	...	...
1½	...	...	6½	6½	...	...	...	8¾	6½	6½	6½	6½	6½	...	...	8¾
2	7	7	7	7½	...	8	8	10	7	7	8½	8½	7	...	...	10½
2½	7½	7½	7½	8¼	...	8½	8½	10⅞	7½	7½	9½	9½	7½	...	...	11¾
3	8	8	8	9	...	9½	9½	11¾	8	8	11⅛	11⅛	8	...	...	13½
3½	8½	8½	...	...	...	...	...	...	...	...	...	...	...	...	...	...
4	9	9	9	9	...	11½	11½	13⅞	9	9	12	12	9	...	...	17
5	10	10	10	14	...	13	13	...	10	10	15	15	...	...	...	...
6	10½	10½	10½	15½	15½	14	14	17¾	10½	10½	15⅞	15⅞	10½	15½	...	21
8	11½	11½	11½	18	18	19½	19½	21⅜	11½	11½	16½	16½	11½	18	...	25

150-lb steel

Nominal valve size	Flanged end[d] (1/16 in. raised face) and welding end — Globe and lift check (A & B)	Swing check (A & B)	"Y" pattern globe (A & B)	Control[c,f] (A)	Flanged end (ring joint) — Gate[e] Solid wedge (C)	Gate Double disc (C)	Plug Short pattern (C)	Plug Regular (C)	Plug Venturi (C)	Round port full bore (C)	Globe and lift check (C)	Swing check (C)
¼	4	4	...	...	...	...	...	...	...	...	...	...
⅜	4	4	...	...	...	...	...	...	...	...	...	...
½	4¼	4¼	5½	...	4 11/16	4 11/16	...	...	...	...	4 11/16	4 11/16
¾	4⅝	4⅝	6	...	5⅛	5⅛	...	...	...	...	5⅛	5⅛
1	5	5	6½	7¼	5½	5½	6	...	...	7½	5½	5½
1¼	5½	5½	7¼	...	6	6	...	...	...	...	6	6
1½	6½	6½	8	8¾	7	7	7	...	...	9¼	7	7
2	8	8	9	10	7½	7½	7½	...	...	11	8½	8½
2½	8½	8½	11	10⅞	8	8	8	...	...	12¼	9	9
3	9½	9½	12½	11¾	8½	8½	8½	...	...	14	...	10
3½	...	...	...	...	...	...	...	...	...	...	...	...
4	11½	11½	14½	13⅞	9½	9½	9½	...	...	17½	12	12
5	14	13	...	...	10½	10½	...	...	...	...	14½	13½
6	16	14	18½	17¾	11	11	11	16	...	21½	16½	14½
8	19½	19½	23½	21⅜	12	12	12	18½	...	25½	20	20

[a] Adapted from ASA B16.10—1957. API Standards 6D and 600 conform to the dimensions shown for corresponding sizes, valve type and flange class or welding end.

[b] These dimensions are not intended to cover the type of check valve having the seat angle at approximately 45 deg to the run of the valve or the "Underwriter Pattern" or other patterns where large clearances are required.

[c] Instrument Society of America Tentative Standard ISA RP4.1 face-to-face conforms to dimensions shown in column 10 and column 23.

[d] 150-lb corrosion-resistant valves covered by MSS SP-42 have *plain faces*.

[e] 150-lb Steel conduit-type gate valves are not standardized.

[f] These valves are flanged end only.

Beam Connections

36"	33"	30"	27"	24"
2ℓs-4"x3½"x $\frac{7}{16}$"x2'-5½"	2ℓs-4"x3½"x $\frac{7}{16}$"x2'-2½"	2ℓs-4"x3½"x $\frac{7}{16}$"x1'-11½"	2ℓs-4"x3½"x $\frac{7}{16}$"x1'-8½"	2ℓs-4"x3½"x $\frac{7}{16}$"x1'-5½"
Weight 52 lbs.	Weight 47 lbs.	Weight 42 lbs.	Weight 36 lbs.	Weight 31 lbs.
21"-20"	18"-15"	14"-12"	10"-8"	7"-5"
2ℓs-4"x3½"x $\frac{7}{16}$"x1'-2½"	2ℓs-4"x3½"x $\frac{3}{8}$"x0'-11½"	2ℓs-4"x3½"x $\frac{3}{8}$"x0'-8½"	2ℓs-6"x4"x $\frac{3}{8}$"x0'-5½"	2ℓs-6"x4"x $\frac{3}{8}$"x0'-3"
Weight 26 lbs.	Weight 18 lbs.	Weight 13 lbs.	Weight 12 lbs.	Weight 7 lbs.

Driving Clearances for Riveting

	Diam. of rivet								
	½	$\frac{5}{8}$	¾	$\frac{7}{8}$	1	1$\frac{1}{8}$	1¼	1$\frac{3}{8}$	1½
D	1¾	2	2¼	2½	2¾	3	3¼	3½	3¾
C	1	1$\frac{1}{8}$	1¼	1$\frac{3}{8}$	1½	1$\frac{5}{8}$	1¾	1$\frac{7}{8}$	2

Dimensions in inches.

Gage and Maximum Rivet Size for Angles

Leg	8	7	6	5	4	3½	3	2½	2	1¾	1½	1$\frac{3}{8}$	1¼	1
g	4½	4	3½	3	2½	2	1¾	1$\frac{3}{8}$	1$\frac{1}{8}$	1	$\frac{7}{8}$	$\frac{7}{8}$	¾	$\frac{5}{8}$
g_1	3	2½	2¼	2										
g_2	3	3	2½	1¾										
Max. rivet	1$\frac{1}{8}$	1$\frac{1}{8}$	1	1	$\frac{7}{8}$	$\frac{7}{8}$	$\frac{7}{8}$	¾	$\frac{5}{8}$	½	$\frac{3}{8}$	$\frac{3}{8}$	$\frac{3}{8}$	¼

Dimensions in inches.

Selected Structural Shapes*

Dimensions for detailing

Name	Depth of section, in.	Weight per foot, lb	Flange Width, in.	Flange Mean thickness, in.	Web Thickness, in.	Web Half thickness, in.	T, in.	k, in.	g_1, in.	c, in.	Grip, in.	Max. flange rivet, in.	Usual gage g, in.	Clearance m
Channels	18	58.0	4¼	⅝	11/16	⅜	15⅜	1 5/16	2¾	¾	⅝	1	2½	
	15	40.0	3½	⅝	9/16	¼	12⅜	1 5/16	2¾	⅝	⅝	1	2	
	12	30.0	3⅛	½	½	¼	9⅞	1 1/16	2½	9/16	½	⅞	1¾	
	10	15.3	2⅝	7/16	¼	⅛	8⅛	15/16	2½	5/16	7/16	¾	1½	
	9	13.4	2⅜	7/16	¼	⅛	7¼	⅞	2½	5/16	⅜	¾	1⅜	
	8	18.75	2½	⅜	½	¼	6⅜	13/16	2¼	9/16	⅜	¾	1½	
	7	12.25	2¼	⅜	5/16	3/16	5⅜	13/16	2	⅜	⅜	⅝	1¼	
	6	10.5	2	⅜	5/16	3/16	4½	¾	2	⅜	⅜	⅝	1⅛	
	5	9.0	1⅞	5/16	5/16	3/16	3⅝	11/16	2	⅜	5/16	½	1⅛	
	4	7.25	1¾	5/16	5/16	3/16	2¾	⅝	2	⅜	5/16	½	1	
	3	6.0	1⅝	¼	⅜	3/16	1¾	⅝	...	7/16	5/16	½	⅞	
WF shapes	21†(21¼)	127	13	1	9/16	5/16	17¾	1 ¾	3	⅜	.....	.....	5½	25
	16 (16⅜)	96	11½	⅞	9/16	5/16	13⅛	1 ⅝	2¾	⅜	.....	.....	5½	20
	14 (14⅛)	84	12	¾	7/16	¼	11⅜	1 ⅜	2¾	5/16	.....	.....	5½	18⅝
	14 (13¾)	48	8	9/16	⅜	3/16	11⅜	1 3/16	2½	¼	.....	.....	5½	16
	12 (12¼)	50	8⅛	⅝	⅜	3/16	9¾	1 ¼	2½	¼	.....	.....	5½	14⅝
	10 (10)	49	10	9/16	⅜	3/16	7⅞	1 1/16	2½	¼	.....	.....	5½	14⅛
	10 (9¾)	33	8	7/16	5/16	3/16	7⅞	15/16	2¼	¼	.....	.....	5½	12⅝
	8 (8)	28	6½	7/16	5/16	⅛	6⅜	13/16	2¼	3/16	.....	.....	3½	10½
Beams	24	120.0	8	1 ⅛	13/16	7/16	20⅛	1 15/16	3¼	½	1 ⅛	1	4	
	20	85.0	7	15/16	11/16	5/16	16½	1 ¾	3¼	⅜	⅞	1	4	
	18	70.0	6¼	11/16	¾	⅜	15¼	1 ⅜	2¾	7/16	11/16	⅞	3½	
	15	50.0	5⅝	⅝	9/16	5/16	12½	1 ¼	2¾	⅜	9/16	¾	3½	
	12	31.8	5	9/16	⅜	3/16	9¾	1 ⅛	2½	¼	½	¾	3	
	10	35.0	5	½	⅝	5/16	8	1	2½	⅜	½	¾	2¾	
	8	23.0	4⅛	7/16	7/16	¼	6¼	⅞	2¼	5/16	7/16	¾	2¼	
	7	20.0	3⅞	⅜	7/16	¼	5⅜	13/16	2	5/16	⅜	⅝	2¼	
	6	17.25	3⅝	⅜	½	¼	4½	¾	2	5/16	⅜	⅝	2	
	5	10.0	3	5/16	¼	⅛	3⅝	11/16	2	3/16	5/16	½	1¾	
	4	9.5	2¾	5/16	5/16	3/16	2¾	⅝	2	¼	5/16	½	1½	
	3	7.5	2½	¼	⅜	3/16	1⅞	9/16	...	¼	¼	⅜	1½	

* From Steel Construction Handbook.
† Nominal depth; ( ) indicates actual depth.

CHANNEL

WF SHAPE

BEAM

RENEWABLE SLIP   RENEWABLE FIXED

LINER
(used with Renewable Type bushings)

Standard Jig Bushings*

Renewable Slip Type and Renewable Fixed Type													Liners		
Slip type Hole size A	Fixed type Hole size A	Tolerance on hole	Body diameter limits B	Lengths available C	Head dimensions							Lock screw no.	Hole limits A	OD limits B	Lengths
					F	G		H	J	L	R				
						Slip type	Fixed type								
0.052 to 0.089	0.055 to 0.089	+0.0004	0.3125 / 0.3123	5/16, 1/2 / 3/4, 1	3 5/64	3/8	1/4	1/8	11/64	65°	1/2		0.3126 / 0.3129	0.5017 / 0.5014	Same as the bushing
0.0935 to 0.1562	0.0935 to 0.1562	+0.0001		5/16, 1/2 / 3/4, 1											
0.1406 to 0.3437	0.1570 to 0.3125	Incl 1/4 +0.0004 +0.0001 Over 1/4 +0.0005 +0.0001	0.5000 / 0.4998	5/16, 1/2, 3/4 / 1, 1 3/8, 1 3/4	5 1/64	7/16	1/4	1/8	19/64	65°	5/8	1	0.5002 / 0.5005	0.7518 / 0.7515	
0.2812 to 0.5312	0.3160 to 0.5000	+0.0005	0.7500 / 0.7498	1/2, 3/8, 1 / 1 3/8, 1 3/4, 2 1/8	1 3/64	7/16	1/4	1/8	27/64	50°	3/4		0.7503 / 0.7506	1.0015 / 1.0018	
0.4687 to 0.7812	0.5156 to 0.750	+0.0001	1.0000 / 0.9998	3/4, 1, 1 3/8 / 1 3/4, 2 1/8, 2 1/2	1 27/64	7/16	3/8	3/16	19/32	35°	5 9/64	2	1.0004 / 1.0007	1.3772 / 1.3768	
0.7817 to 1.0312	0.7656 to 1.0000	+0.0006	1.3750 / 1.3747	3/4, 1, 1 3/8 / 1 3/4, 2 1/8, 2 1/2	1 51/64	7/16	3/8	3/16	25/32	30°	1 7/64		1.3756 / 1.3760	1.7523 / 1.7519	
0.9687 to 1.4062	1.0156 to 1.3750	+0.0002	1.7500 / 1.7497	1, 1 3/8, 1 3/4 / 2 1/8, 2 1/2, 3	2 19/64	5/8	3/8	3/16	1	30°	1 25/64	3	1.7508 / 1.7512	2.2521 / 2.2525	
1.3437 to 1.7812	1.3906 to 1.750	Incl 1 1/2 +0.0006 +0.0002 Over 1 1/2 +0.0007 +0.0003	2.2500 / 2.2496	1, 1 3/8, 1 3/4 / 2 1/8, 2 1/2, 3	2 51/64	5/8	3/8	3/16	1 1/4	25°	1 41/64		2.2510 / 2.2515	2.7526 / 2.7522	

Dimensions in inches.
*ASA B5.6—1941.
Head design in accordance with manufacturer's practice; slip type usually knurled.

Lock Screws

Screw No.	A	B	C	D	E	F	ASA thd
1	5/8	3/8	5/8	1/16	1/4	.138 / .132	5/16–18
2	7/8	3/8	5/8	3/32	3/8	.200 / .194	5/16–18
3	1	7/16	3/4	1/8	3/8	.200 / .194	3/8–16

Standard Jig Bushings (Cont.)

Press-fit Headless and Press-fit Head Types

Hole size *A*	Tolerance on hole	OD limits *B*	Lengths available *C*	Head type dimension *F*	Head type dimension *G*
0.055 to 0.0995		0.2046 / 0.2043	5/16, 1/2	19/64	3/32
0.1015 to 0.1360	+0.0004 +0.0001	0.2516 / 0.2513	5/16, 1/2	23/64	3/32
0.1405 to 0.1875		0.3141 / 0.3138	5/16, 1/2 3/4, 1	27/64	1/8
0.1890 to 0.2500		0.4078 / 0.4075	5/16, 1/2 3/4, 1	1/2	5/32
0.2570 to 0.3125		0.5017 / 0.5014	1 3/8, 1 3/4	39/64	7/32
0.316 to 0.4219		0.6267 / 0.6264	1/2, 3/4 1, 1 3/8	51/64	7/32
0.4375 to 0.500	+0.0005 +0.0001	0.7518 / 0.7515	1 3/4, 2 1/8	59/64	7/32
0.5156 to 0.625		0.8768 / 0.8765	3/4, 1	1 7/64	1/4
0.6406 to 0.7500		1.0018 / 1.0015	1 3/8, 1 3/4	1 15/64	5/16
0.7656 to 1.0000	+0.0006 +0.0002	1.3772 / 1.3768	2 1/8, 2 1/2	1 39/64	3/8
1.0156 to 1.3750		1.7523 / 1.7519	1, 1 3/8	1 63/64	3/8
1.3906 to 1.7500	Incl 1 1/2 +0.0006 +0.0002 Over 1 1/2 +0.0007 +0.0003	2.2525 / 2.2521	1 3/4, 2 1/8 2 1/2, 3	2 31/64	3/8

PRESS FIT HEADLESS TYPE

PRESS FIT HEAD TYPE

59°

Slight Radius

CROSS   TEE   COUPLING   ECCENTRIC COUPLING

90° ELL   45° ELL

American Standard Brass Solder-joint Fittings*

Tubing size	A	B	C	D	Reducing size	F	E	G
3/8	5/16	11/16	3/16	1/8	3/4 × 1/2	5/8	1	13/16
1/2	7/16	13/16	3/16	1/8	1 × 3/4	11/16	11/16	1
3/4	9/16	1	1/4	1/8	1 × 1/2	1/2	11/16	13/16
1	3/4	11/16	5/16	1/8	2 × 1 1/2	1 1/8	1 3/8	1 3/16
1 1/2	1	1 3/16	1/2	1/8	2 1/2 × 2	1 3/16	1 5/8	1 3/8
2	1 1/4	1 3/8	9/16	3/16	2 1/2 × 1 1/2	15/16	1 5/8	1 3/16
2 1/2	1 1/2	1 5/8	5/8	3/16	3 × 2 1/2	1 1/4	1 7/8	1 5/8
3	1 3/4	1 7/8	3/4	3/16	3 1/2 × 3	1 1/8	2 1/16	1 7/8
3 1/2	2	2 1/16	7/8	3/16	3 1/2 × 2 1/2	1 5/16	2 1/16	1 5/8
4	2 1/4	2 1/4	15/16	1/4	4 × 3 1/2	1 3/16	2 1/4	2 1/16

* Adapted from ASA B16.18—1950.

SAE STANDARD COTTER PINS

MITER   EXTENDED MITER   DOUBLE MITER   SQUARE CUT   BEVEL POINT   HAMMER LOCK

Pin diameter A			Eye diameter, min.		Recommended hole diam., drill size
Nominal	Max.	Min.	Inside B	Outside C	
1/32 (0.031)	0.032	0.028	1/32	1/16	3/64 (0.0469)
3/64 (0.047)	0.048	0.044	3/64	3/32	1/16 (0.0625)
1/16 (0.062)	0.060	0.056	1/16	1/8	5/64 (0.0781)
5/64 (0.078)	0.076	0.072	5/64	5/32	3/32 (0.0937)
3/32 (0.094)	0.090	0.086	3/32	3/16	7/64 (0.1094)
1/8 (0.125)	0.120	0.116	1/8	1/4	9/64 (0.1406)
5/32 (0.156)	0.150	0.146	5/32	5/16	11/64 (0.1719)
3/16 (0.188)	0.176	0.172	3/16	3/8	13/64 (0.2031)
7/32 (0.219)	0.207	0.202	7/32	7/16	15/64 (0.2344)
1/4 (0.250)	0.225	0.220	1/4	1/2	17/64 (0.2656)
5/16 (0.312)	0.280	0.275	5/16	5/8	5/16 (0.3125)
3/8 (0.375)	0.335	0.329	3/8	3/4	3/8 (0.3750)
1/2 (0.500)	0.473	0.467	1/2	1	1/2 (0.5000)

American Standard Graphic Symbols for Piping and Heating*

PIPING

Piping, General ——————— (Lettered with name of material conveyed) ———————

Non-intersecting Pipes ———

(To differentiate lines of piping on a drawing the following symbols may be used.)

Air	Cold Water	Steam
Gas	Hot Water	Condensate
Oil	Vacuum	Refrigerant

PIPE FITTINGS AND VALVES

	Flanged	Screwed	Bell and Spigot	Welded	Soldered
Joint					
Elbow—90 deg					
Elbow—45 deg					
Elbow—Turned Up					
Elbow—Turned Down					
Elbow—Long Radius					
Side Outlet Elbow Outlet Down					
Side Outlet Elbow Outlet Up					
Base Elbow					
Double Branch Elbow					
Reducing Elbow					
Reducer					
Eccentric Reducer					
Tee-Outlet Up					
Tee-Outlet Down					
Tee					
Side Outlet Tee Outlet Up					
Side Outlet Tee Outlet Down					
Single Sweep Tee					
Double Sweep Tee					
Cross					
Lateral					
Gate Valve					

* ASA Z14.2—1935.

Symbols for Piping and Heating (*Cont.*)

PIPING

	Flanged	Screwed	Bell and Spigot	Welded	Soldered
Globe Valve					
Angle Globe Valve					
Angle Gate Valve					
Check Valve					
Angle Check Valve					
Stop Cock					
Safety Valve					
Quick Opening Valve					
Float Operating Valve					
Motor Operated Gate Valve					
Motor Operated Globe Valve					
Expansion Joint Flanged					
Reducing Flange					
Union	(See Joint)				
Sleeve					
Bushing					

HEATING AND VENTILATING

Lock and Shield Valve		Tube Radiator	(Plan) (Elev.)	Exhaust Duct, Section	
Reducing Valve		Wall Radiator	(Plan) (Elev.)	Butterfly Damper	(Plan or Elev.) (Elev. or Plan)
Diaphragm Valve		Pipe Coil	(Plan) (Elev.)	Deflecting Damper Rectangular Pipe	
Thermostat	(T)	Indirect Radiator	(Plan) (Elev.)	Vanes	
Radiator Trap	(Plan) (Elev.)	Supply Duct, Section		Air Supply Outlet	
				Exhaust Inlet	

HEAT-POWER APPARATUS

Flue Gas Reheater (Intermediate Superheater)		Steam Turbine		Automatic By-pass Valve	
Steam Generator (Boiler)		Condensing Turbine		Automatic Valve Operated by Governor	
Live Steam Superheater		Open Tank		Pumps Air Service Boiler Feed Condensate Circulating Water Reciprocating	
Feed Heater With Air Outlet		Closed Tank			
Surface Condenser		Automatic Reducing Valve		Dynamic Pump (Air Ejector)	

American Standard Plumbing Symbols*

Corner Bath	Recessed Bath	Roll Rim Bath	Sitz Bath
Foot Bath	Bidet	Shower Stall	Shower Head (Plan) (Elev.)
Overhead Gang Shower (Plan) (Elev.)	Manicure Lavatory Medical Lavatory	Corner Lavatory	Wall Lavatory
DENTAL LAV Dental Lavatory	Plain Kitchen Sink	Kitchen Sink R&L Drain Board	Pedestal Lavatory
Kitchen Sink L.H. Drain Board	Combination Sink and Dishwasher	Combination Sink and Laundry Tray	Service Sink
Laundry Tray	Wash Sink (Wall Type)	Water Closet (No Tank)	Wash Sink
Water Closet (Low Tank)	Urinal (Pedestal Type)	Urinal (Corner Type)	Urinal (Wall Type)
Drinking Fountain (Pedestal Type)	Drinking Fountain (Wall Type)	Urinal (Stall Type)	Urinal (Trough Type)

Drinking Fountain (Trough Type)	Hot Water Tank	Water Heater	Meter	Hose Rack
Vacuum Outlet	Hose Bib	Gas Outlet	Drain	Grease Separator
Oil Separator	Cleanout	Garage Drain	Floor Drain With Backwater Valve	Roof Sump

* A Z14.2—1935.

American Standard Wiring Symbols*

Ceiling Outlet	Branch Circuit, Run Exposed
" " for Extensions	Run Concealed Under Floor
" Lamp Receptacle, Specifications	" " " Floor Above
to describe type, as Key, Keyless or Pull Chain	Feeder Run Exposed
Ceiling Fan Outlet	Run Concealed Under Floor
Pull Switch	" " " Floor Above
Drop Cord	Telephone, Interior, Public
Wall Bracket	Clock, Secondary, Master
" Outlet for Extensions	Time Stamp
" Lamp Receptacle, as specified	Electric Door Opener
" Fan Outlet	Local Fire Alarm Gong
Single Convenience Outlet	City Fire Alarm Station
Double " " "	Local " " "
Junction Box	Fire Alarm Central Station
Special Purpose Outlets	Speaking Tube
Lighting, Heating and Power	Nurse's Signal Plug
as described in specifications	Maid's Plug
Exit Light	Horn Outlet
Floor Outlet	District Messenger Call
Floor Elbow, Floor Tee	Watchman Station
Local Switch, Single Pole S^1	Watchman Central Station Detector
Double Pole S^2, 3-Way S^3, 4-Way S^4	Public Telephone-P.B.X. Switchboard
Automatic Door Switch S^D	Interior Telephone Central Switchboard
Key Push Button Switch S^K	Interconnection Cabinet
Electrolier Switch S^E	Telephone Cabinet
Push Button Switch and Pilot S^P	Telegraph "
Remote Control Push Button Switch S^R	Special Outlet for Signal System as Specified
Tank Switch T.S.	Battery
Motor, Motor Controller M.C.	Signal Wires in Conduit Under Floor
Lighting Panel	" " " " " Floor Above
Power Panel	This Character Marked on Tap Circuits Indicates
Heating Panel	2 No. 14 Conductors in $\frac{1}{2}$" Conduit ‖
Pull Box	3 " 14 " " $\frac{1}{2}$" " ‖‖
Cable Supporting Box	4 " 14 " " $\frac{3}{4}$" " (Unless Marked $\frac{1}{2}$") ‖‖‖
Meter	5 " 14 " " $\frac{3}{4}$" " ‖‖‖‖
Transformer	6 " 14 " " 1" " (Unless Marked $\frac{3}{4}$") ‖‖‖‖‖
Push Button	7 " 14 " " 1" " ‖‖‖‖‖‖
Pole Line	8 " 14 " " 1" " ‖‖‖‖‖‖‖
Buzzer, Bell	(Radio Outlet)
Annunciator	(Public Speaker Outlet)

* ASA C10.

American Standard Graphic Symbols for Electrical Diagrams*

Single-line symbols are shown at the left, complete symbols at the right, and symbols for both purposes are centered in each column.
Listing is alphabetical.

ADJUSTABLE
CONTINUOUSLY ADJUSTABLE (Variable)
The shaft of the arrow is drawn at about 45 degrees across the body of the symbol.

AMPLIFIER
See also MACHINE, ROTATING

General
The triangle is pointed in the direction of transmission.
Amplifier type may be indicated in the triangle by words, standard abbreviations, or a letter combination from the following list.

BDG	Bridging	MON	Monitoring
BST	Booster	PGM	Program
CMP	Compression	PRE	Preliminary
DC	Direct Current	PWR	Power
EXP	Expansion	TRQ	Torque
LIM	Limiting		

Applications

Booster amplifier with two inputs

Monitoring amplifier with two outputs

Amplifier with associated power supply

ANTENNA

General
Types or functions may be indicated by words or abbreviations adjacent to the symbol.

Dipole

ARRESTER (Electric Surge, Lightning, etc.)
GAP

General

Carbon block
The sides of the rectangle are to be approximately in the ratio of 1 to 2 and the space between rectangles shall be approximately equal to the width of a rectangle.

Electrolytic or aluminum cell
This symbol is not composed of arrowheads.

Protective gap
These arrowheads shall not be filled.

Sphere gap

Multigap, general

ATTENUATOR
See also PAD

General

Balanced, general

Unbalanced, general

BATTERY
The long line is always positive, but polarity may be indicated in addition.
Example:

Generalized direct-current source

BREAKER, CIRCUIT
If it is desired to show the condition causing the breaker to trip, the relay-protective-function symbols may be used alongside the breaker symbol.

General
Note 1—Use appropriate number of single-line diagram symbols.

SEE NOTE 1

Air or, if distinction is needed, for alternating-current circuit breaker rated at 1,500 volts or less and for direct-current circuit breaker.

SEE NOTE 1

CAPACITOR
See also TERMINATION

General
If it is necessary to identify the capacitor electrodes, the curved element shall represent the outside electrode in fixed paper-dielectric and ceramic-dielectric capacitors, the negative electrode in electrolytic capacitors, the moving element in adjustable and variable capacitors, and the low-potential element in feed-through capacitors.

Application: shielded capacitor

Application: adjustable or variable capacitor

If it is necessary to identify trimmer capacitors, the letter T should appear adjacent to the symbol.

Application: adjustable or variable capacitors with mechanical linkage of units

Shunt capacitor

Feed-through capacitor (with terminals shown on feed-through element)
Commonly used for bypassing high-frequency currents to chassis.

Application: feed-through capacitor between 2 inductors with third lead connected to chassis

CELL, PHOTOSENSITIVE (Semiconductor)

λ indicates that the primary characteristic of the element within the circle is designed to vary under the influence of light.

Asymmetrical photoconductive transducer (resistive)
This arrowhead shall be solid.

Symmetrical photoconductive transducer; selenium cell

CHASSIS
FRAME
See also GROUND
The chassis or frame is not necessarily at ground potential.

COIL, BLOWOUT

COIL, OPERATING
See also INDUCTOR; WINDING

Note 3—The asterisk is not a part of the symbol. Always replace the asterisk by a device designation.

* SEE NOTE 3

CONNECTION, MECHANICAL –
MECHANICAL INTERLOCK
The preferred location of the mechanical connection is as shown in the various applications, but other locations may be equally acceptable.

Mechanical connection (*short dashes*)

* Adapted from ASA Y32.2—1954.

Symbols for Electrical Diagrams (*Cont.*)

Mechanical connection or interlock with fulcrum (*short dashes*)

Mechanical interlock, other

INDICATE BY A NOTE

CONNECTOR
DISCONNECTING DEVICE
The connector symbol is not an arrowhead. It is larger and the lines are drawn at a 90-degree angle.

Female contact

Male contact

Connector assembly, movable or stationary portion; jack, plug, or receptacle
Note 4—Use appropriate number of contact symbols.

SEE NOTE 4

Commonly used for a jack or receptacle (usually stationary)

SEE NOTE 4 OR

Commonly used for a plug (usually movable)

SEE NOTE 4 OR

Separable connectors (engaged)

SEE NOTE 4 OR

Application: engaged 4-conductor connectors; the plug has 1 male and 3 female contacts

Communication switchboard-type connector

2-conductor (jack)

2-conductor (plug)

Jacks with circuit normalled through one way

Jacks with circuit normalled through both ways

Jacks in multiple, one set with circuit normalled through both ways

Connectors of the type commonly used for power-supply purposes (convenience outlets and mating connectors)

Female contact

Male contact

2-conductor nonpolarized connector with female contacts

2-conductor nonpolarized connector with male contacts

2-conductor polarized connector with female contacts

2-conductor polarized connector with male contacts

3-conductor polarized connector with female contacts

3-conductor polarized connector with male contacts

4-conductor polarized connector with female contacts

4-conductor polarized connector with male contacts

Test blocks

Female portion with short-circuiting bar (with terminals shown)

Male portion (with terminals shown)

CONTACT, ELECTRIC
For build-ups or forms using electric contacts, see applications under CONNECTOR

Fixed contact

Fixed contact for jack, key, relay, etc.

Fixed contact for switch

Fixed contact for momentary switch
See SWITCH

Sleeve

Moving contact

Adjustable or sliding contact for resistor, inductor, etc.

Locking

Nonlocking

Closed contact (break)

Open contact (make)

Transfer

Make-before-break

Application: open contact with time closing (TC or TDC) feature

Application: closed contact with time opening (TO or TDO) feature

Time sequential closing

COUPLER, DIRECTIONAL
Commonly used in coaxial and waveguide diagrams.
The arrows indicate the direction of power flow.
Number of coupling paths, type of coupling, and transmission loss may be indicated.

General

Symbols for Electrical Diagrams (Cont.)

Applications

E-plane aperture coupling, 30-decibel transmission loss

Loop coupling, 30-decibel transmission loss

Probe coupling, 30-decibel transmission loss

Resistance coupling, 30-decibel transmission loss

DIRECTION OF FLOW OF POWER, SIGNAL, OR INFORMATION

One-way

Note 10—The lower symbol is used if it is necessary to conserve space. The arrowhead in the lower symbol shall be filled.

OR

SEE NOTE 10

Both ways

OR

SEE NOTE 10

DISCONTINUITY

A component that exhibits throughout the frequency range of interest the properties of the type of circuit element indicated by the symbol within the triangle.

Commonly used for coaxial and waveguide transmission.

Equivalent series element, general

Capacitive reactance

ELEMENT, CIRCUIT (General)

Note 12—The asterisk is not a part of the symbol. Always indicate the type of apparatus by appropriate words or letters in the rectangle.

* SEE NOTE 12

Accepted abbreviations in the latest edition of American Standard Z32.13 may be used in the rectangle.

The following letter combinations may be used in the rectangle.

CB	Circuit breaker	NET	Network
DIAL	Telephone dial	PS	Power supply
EQ	Equalizer	RU	Reproducing unit
FAX	Facsimile set		
FL	Filter	RG	Recording unit
FL-BE	Filter, band elimination	TEL	Telephone station
FL-BP	Filter, band pass	TPR	Teleprinter
FL-HP	Filter, high pass	TTY	Teletypewriter
FL-LP	Filter, low pass		

ELEMENT, THERMAL
Thermomechanical transducer

Note 13—Use appropriate number of single-line diagram symbols.

SEE NOTE 13

FUSE

SEE NOTE 14

Note 14—Use appropriate number of single-line diagram symbols.

Fusible element

SEE NOTE 14

GROUND
See also CHASSIS; FRAME

INDUCTOR
WINDING
General

Either symbol may be used in the following subparagraphs.

OR

If it is desired especially to distinguish magnetic-core inductors

LAMP

Ballast lamp; ballast tube

The primary characteristic of the element within the circle is designed to vary nonlinearly with the temperature of the element.

Fluorescent lamp

2-terminal

4-terminal

Glow lamp; cold-cathode lamp; neon lamp

Alternating-current type

Direct-current type
See also TUBE, ELECTRON

Incandescent-filament illuminating lamp

MACHINE, ROTATING

Basic

Generator, general

Motor, general

Motor, multispeed

USE BASIC MOTOR
SYMBOL AND NOTE
SPEEDS

Rotating armature with commutator and brushes

Wound rotor

Field, generator or motor

Compensating or commutating

Series

Shunt, or separately excited

Permanent magnet

Winding symbols

Motor and generator winding symbols may be shown in the basic circle using the following representations.

1-phase

2-phase

3-phase wye (ungrounded)

3-phase wye (grounded)

3-phase delta

6-phase diametrical

6-phase double-delta

MOTION, MECHANICAL

Translation, one direction

Translation, both directions

Rotation, one direction

Rotation, both directions

Symbols for Electrical Diagrams (Cont.)

NETWORK

General

NET

OSCILLATOR
GENERALIZED ALTERNATING-CURRENT SOURCE

PAD

See also ATTENUATOR

General

Balanced, general

Unbalanced, general

PATH, TRANSMISSION

Air or space path

Dielectric path other than air

Commonly used for coaxial and waveguide transmission.

DIEL

Crossing of paths or conductors not connected
The crossing is not necessarily at a 90-degree angle.

Junction of paths or conductors

Junction (if desired)

Application: junction of different-size cables

Junction of connected paths, conductors, or wires

OR

OR ONLY IF REQUIRED BY SPACE LIMITATION

RELAY
See also CONTACT

Fundamental symbols for contacts, mechanical connections, coils, etc., are the basis of relay symbols and should be used to represent relays on complete diagrams.

Basic

®

Relay coil

Note 21—The asterisk is not a part of the symbol. Always replace the asterisk by a device designation.

* SEE NOTE 21

Application: 2-pole double-make

RESISTOR

Note 22—The asterisk is not a part of the symbol. Always add identification within or adjacent to the rectangle.

General

* SEE NOTE 22

Tapped resistor

* SEE NOTE 22

Application: with adjustable contact

* SEE NOTE 22

Application: adjustable or continuously adjustable (variable) resistor

* SEE NOTE 22

Heating resistor

* SEE NOTE 22

SWITCH

Fundamental symbols for contacts, mechanical connections, etc., may be used for switch symbols.

The standard method of showing switches is in a position with no operating force applied. For switches that may be in any one of two or more positions with no operating force applied and for switches actuated by some mechanical device (as in air-pressure, liquid-level, rate-of-flow, etc., switches), a clarifying note may be necessary to explain the point at which the switch functions.

Single throw, general

Double throw, general

Application: 2-pole double-throw switch with terminals shown

Knife switch, general

Switch, nonlocking; momentary or spring return

The symbols to the left are commonly used for spring buildups in key switches, relays, and jacks. The symbols to the right are commonly used for toggle switches.

Circuit closing (make)

OR

Circuit opening (break)

OR

Switch, locking

The symbols to the left are commonly used for spring buildups in key switches, relays, and jacks. The symbols to the right are commonly used for toggle switches.

Circuit closing (make)

OR

Circuit opening (break)

OR

Transfer, 2-position

OR

TERMINAL, CIRCUIT

Terminal board or terminal strip with 4 terminals shown; group of 4 terminals

Number and arrangement as convenient.

TRANSFORMER

General

Either winding symbol may be used.

Additional windings may be shown or indicated by a note.

For power transformers, use polarity marking H_1-X_1, etc., from American Standard C6.1.

In coaxial and waveguide circuits, this symbol will represent a taper or step transformer without mode change.

OR

If it is desired especially to distinguish a magnetic-core transformer

TUBE, ELECTRON

Tube-component symbols are shown first. These are followed by typical applications showing the use of these specific symbols in the various classes of devices such as thermionic, cold-cathode, and photoemissive tubes of varying structures and combinations of elements (triodes, pentodes, cathode-ray tubes, magnetrons, etc.).

Lines outside of the envelope are not part of the symbol but are electrical connections thereto.

Connections between the external circuit and electron tube symbols within the envelope may be located as required to simplify the diagram.

Emitting electrode

Directly heated (filamentary) cathode
Note—Leads may be connected in any convenient manner to ends of the ∧ provided the identity of the ∧ is retained.

Indirectly heated cathode
Lead may be connected to either extreme end of the ⌐ or, if required, to both ends, in any convenient manner.

Cold cathode (including ionically heated cathode)

Photocathode

Pool cathode

Ionically heated cathode with provision for supplementary heating

Symbols for Electrical Diagrams (Cont.)

Controlling electrode

Grid (including beam-confining or beam-forming electrodes)

Deflecting electrodes (used in pairs); reflecting or repelling electrode (used in velocity-modulated tube)

Ignitor (in pool tubes) (should extend into pool)
Starter (in gas tubes)

Excitor (contactor type)

Collecting electrode

Anode or plate (including collecting electrode and fluorescent target)

Target or X-ray anode
Drawn at about a 45-degree angle.

Collecting and emitting electrode

Dynode

Alternately collecting and emitting

Composite anode-photocathode

Composite anode-cold cathode

Composite anode-ionically heated cathode with provision for supplementary heating

Heater

Envelope (shell)

The general envelope symbol identifies the envelope or enclosure regardless of evacuation or pressure. When used with electron-tube component symbols, the general envelope symbol indicates a vacuum enclosure unless otherwise specified. A gas-filled electron device may be indicated by a dot within the envelope symbol.

General

OR

Split envelope
If necessary, envelope may be split.

Gas-filled
The dot may be located as convenient.

Shield

This is understood to shield against electric fields unless otherwise noted.

Any shield against electric fields that is within the envelope and that is connected to an independent terminal

Outside envelope of X-ray tube

Coupling by loop (electromagnetic type)
Coupling loop may be shown inside or outside envelope as desired, but if inside it should be shown grounded.

Resonators (cavity type)

Single-cavity envelope and grid-type associated electrodes

Double-cavity envelope and grid-type associated electrodes

Multicavity magnetron anode and envelope

Associated parts of a circuit, such as focusing coils, deflecting coils, field coils, etc., are not a part of the tube symbol but may be added to the circuit in the form of standard symbols. For example, resonant-type magnetron with permanent magnet may be shown:

PM

External and internal shields, whether integral parts of tubes or not, shall be omitted from the circuit diagram unless the circuit diagram requires their inclusion.

In line with standard drafting practice, straight-line crossovers are recommended.

Typical applications

Triode with directly heated filamentary cathode and envelope connection to base terminal

Equipotential-cathode pentode showing use of elongated envelope

---

Typical wiring figure
This figure illustrates how tube symbols may be placed in any convenient position in a circuit.

For tubes with keyed bases
Explanatory word and arrow are not a part of the symbol shown.

KEY

For tubes with bayonets, bosses, and other reference points

Base terminals
Explanatory words and arrows are not a part of the symbol.

SMALL PIN

LARGE PIN

Envelope terminals
Explanatory words and arrows are not a part of the symbol.

RIGID TERMINAL

FLEXIBLE LEAD

Applications

Triode with indirectly heated cathode and envelope connected to base terminal

Triode-heptode with rigid envelope connection

Symbols for Materials (Exterior)

Brick

Stone

Transparent Material
Glass. Celluloid. Etc.

Wood

Symbols for Materials (Section)

Cast Iron

Steel

Bronze, Brass, Copper
and Composition

White Metal, Zinc,
Lead, Babbitt & Alloys

Aluminum

(Show solid for narrow sections)

Electric Insulation, Mica,
Fibre, Vulcanite, Bakelite, Etc.

Sound or Heat Insulation
Cork, Asbestos, Packing, Etc.

Flexible Material
Fabric, Rubber, Etc.

Fire Brick and
Refractory Material

Concrete

Brick or Stone
Masonry

Marble, Slate, Glass,
Porcelain, Etc.

Earth

Rock

Sand

Water & Other Liquids

Weights of Materials

Metals	lb/cu in.	Wood	lb/cu in.
Aluminum alloy, cast	0.099	Ash	0.024
Aluminum, cast	0.094	Balsa	0.0058
Aluminum, wrought	0.097	Cedar	0.017
Babbitt metal	0.267	Cork	0.009
Brass, cast or rolled	0.303–0.313	Hickory	0.0295
Brass, drawn	0.323	Maple	0.025
Bronze, aluminum cast	0.277	Oak (white)	0.028
Bronze, phosphor	0.315–0.321	Pine (white)	0.015
Chromium	0.256	Pine (yellow)	0.025
Copper, cast	0.311	Poplar	0.018
Copper, rolled, drawn or wire	0.322	Walnut (black)	0.023
Dowmetal *A*	0.065	**Miscellaneous materials**	**lb/ cu ft**
Duralumin	0.101	Asbestos	175
Gold	0.697	Bakelite	79.5
Iron, cast	0.260	Brick, common	112
Iron, wrought	0.283	Brick, fire	144
Lead	0.411	Celluloid	86.4
Magnesium	0.063	Earth, packed	100
Mercury	0.491	Fiber	89.9
Monel metal	0.323	Glass	163
Silver	0.379	Gravel	109
Steel, cast or rolled	0.274–0.281	Limestone	163
Steel, tool	0.272	Plexiglass	74.3
Tin	0.263	Sandstone	144
Zinc	0.258	Water	62.4

ABBREVIATIONS FOR USE ON DRAWINGS

Abbreviations are shortened forms of words or expressions and their use on drawings is entirely for the purpose of conserving space and drafting time. Since they must be interpreted by shopmen, assemblers, construction men, and others, abbreviations should not be used where the meaning may not be clear. In case of doubt, spell out. Only words that are abbreviated on drawings are included in this list, which is selected from the more complete list given in ASA Z32.13—1950.

The same abbreviation is used for all forms of a given word. Periods are used only to avoid misinterpretation of an abbreviation. Spaces between letters are for clarity only;

the abbreviation of word combinations or phrases is sometimes spaced. The use of hyphens and slant bars has been avoided where practicable. Upper-case letters are used for abbreviations. Subscripts are not used in abbreviations. Whenever a special abbreviation is used (one not appearing in ASA Z32.13), it should be explained in a table on the drawing. For metals, chemicals, formulas, and equations, the abbreviations, symbols, and rules in general use and established by long acceptance are employed.

Abbreviations for colors and a partial list of chemical symbols are given after the general abbreviations.

Word	Abbreviation	Word	Abbreviation
Abbreviate	ABBR	American Wire Gage	AWG
Absolute	ABS	Ammeter	AM
Accelerate	ACCEL	Amount	AMT
Acceleration due to gravity	G	Ampere	AMP
Access panel	AP	Ampere hour	AMP HR
Accessory	ACCESS.	Amplifier	AMPL
Actual	ACT.	Anneal	ANL
Adapter	ADPT	Antenna	ANT.
Addendum	ADD.	Apparatus	APP
Adjust	ADJ	Approved	APPD
Advance	ADV	Approximate	APPROX
After	AFT.	Arc weld	ARC/W
Aggregate	AGGR	Area	A
Aileron	AIL	Armature	ARM.
Air-break switch	ABS	Arrange	ARR.
Air-circuit breaker	ACB	Arrester	ARR.
Aircraft	ACFT	Asbestos	ASB
Airplane	APL	Assemble	ASSEM
Airtight	AT	Assembly	ASSY
Alarm	ALM	Atomic	AT
Allowance	ALLOW	Attach	ATT
Alloy	ALY	Audio-frequency	AF
Alteration	ALT	Automatic	AUTO
Alternate	ALT	Auto-transformer	AUTO TR
Alternating current	AC	Auxiliary	AUX
Alternator	ALT	Average	AVG
Altitude	ALT		
Aluminum	AL	Babbitt	BAB
American Standard	AMER STD	Back to back	B to B

Word	Abbreviation	Word	Abbreviation
Baffle	BAF	Cast (used with other materials)	C
Balance	BAL	Cast iron	CI
Ball bearing	BB	Cast-iron pipe	CIP
Base line	BL	Cast steel	CS
Base plate	BP	Casting	CSTG
Battery	BAT.	Castle nut	CAS NUT
Bearing	BRG	Cement	CEM
Bent	BT	Center	CTR
Between	BET.	Center line	CL
Between centers	BC	Center to center	C to C
Between perpendiculars	BP	Centering	CTR
Bevel	BEV	Centigrade	C
Bill of material	B/M	Centigram	CG
Birmingham Wire Gage	BWG	Centiliter	CL
Blank	BLK	Centimeter	CM
Block	BLK	Centrifugal	CENT.
Blueprint	BP	Centrifugal force	CF
Bolt circle	BC	Ceramic	CER
Bottom	BOT	Chain	CH
Bottom chord	BC	Chamfer	CHAM
Brake	BK	Change	CHG
Brass	BRS	Change notice	CN
Brazing	BRZG	Change order	CO
Break	BRK	Channel	CHAN
Breaker	BKR	Check	CHK
Brinnell hardness	BH	Check valve	CV
British Standard	BR STD	Chemical	CHEM
British thermal units	BTU	Chord	CHD
Broach	BRO	Chrome molybdenum	CR MOLY
Bronze	BRZ	Chromium plate	CR PL
Brown & Sharp	B&S	Chrome vanadium	CR VAN
Brush	BR	Circle	CIR
Burnish	BNH	Circuit	CKT
Bushing	BUSH.	Circular	CIR
Bypass	BYP	Circular pitch	CP
		Circulate	CIRC
Cadmium plate	CD PL	Circumference	CIRC
Calculate	CALC	Clamp	CLP
Calibrate	CAL	Class	CL
Calking	CLKG	Clear	CLR
Capacitor	CAP	Clearance	CL
Capacity	CAP	Clockwise	CW
Cap screw	CAP. SCR	Closing	CL
Carburize	CARB	Clutch	CL
Caseharden	CH	Coated	CTD
Casing	CSG	Coaxial	COAX

Word	Abbreviation	Word	Abbreviation
Coefficient	COEF	Counterbore	CBORE
Cold drawn	CD	Counterdrill	CDRILL
Cold-drawn steel	CDS	Counterpunch	CPUNCH
Cold rolled	CR	Countersink	CSK
Cold-rolled steel	CRS	Countersink other side	CSK-O
Column	COL	Coupling	CPLG
Combination	COMB.	Cover	COV
Combustion	COMB	Crank	CRK
Communication	COMM	Cross connection	XCONN
Commutator	COMM	Cross section	XSECT
Complete	COMPL	Cubic	CU
Composite	CX	Current	CUR
Composition	COMP	Cyanide	CYN
Compressor	COMPR	Cycle	CY
Concentric	CONC	Cycles per minute	CPM
Concrete	CONC	Cycles per second	CPS
Condition	COND	Cylinder	CYL
Conduct	COND		
Conductor	COND	Decibel	DB
Conduit	CND	Decimal	DEC
Connect	CONN	Dedendum	DED
Constant	CONST	Deep drawn	DD
Contact	CONT	Deflect	DEFL
Container	CNTR	Degree	(°) DEG
Continue	CONT	Density	D
Continuous wave	CW	Describe	DESCR
Contract	CONT	Design	DSGN
Contractor	CONTR	Designation	DESIG
Control	CONT	Detail	DET
Control relay	CR	Detector	DET
Control switch	CS	Detonator	DET
Controller	CONT	Develop	DEV
Convert	CONV	Diagonal	DIAG
Conveyor	CNVR	Diagram	DIAG
Cooled	CLD	Diameter	DIA
Copper oxide	CUO	Diametral pitch	DP
Copper plate	COP. PL	Diaphragm	DIAPH
Cord	CD	Differential	DIFF
Correct	CORR	Dimension	DIM.
Corrosion resistant	CRE	Diode	DIO
Corrosion-resistant steel	CRES	Direct current	DC
Corrugate	CORR	Directional	DIR
Cotter	COT	Discharge	DISCH
Counter	CTR	Disconnect	DISC.
Counterclockwise	CCW	Distance	DIST
Counterbalance	CBAL	Distribute	DISTR

Word	Abbreviation	Word	Abbreviation
Ditto	DO.	Fahrenheit	F
Double	DBL	Fairing	FAIR.
Dovetail	DVTL	Farad	F
Dowel	DWL	Far side	FS
Down	DN	Feed	FD
Drafting	DFTG	Feeder	FDR
Draftsman	DFTSMN	Feet	(′) FT
Drain	DR	Feet per minute	FPM
Drawing	DWG	Feet per second	FPS
Drawing list	DL	Female	FEM
Drill	DR	Fiber	FBR
Drill rod	DR	Field	FLD
Drive	DR	Figure	FIG.
Drive fit	DF	Filament	FIL
Drop	D	Fillet	FIL
Drop forge	DF	Filling	FILL.
Duplex	DX	Fillister	FIL
Duplicate	DUP	Filter	FLT
Dynamic	DYN	Finish	FIN.
Dynamo	DYN	Finish all over	FAO
		Fireproof	FPRF
Each	EA	Fitting	FTG
Eccentric	ECC	Fixture	FIX.
Effective	EFF	Flange	FLG
Electric	ELEC	Flashing	FL
Elevation	EL	Flat	F
Enclose	ENCL	Flat head	FH
End to end	E to E	Flexible	FLEX.
Envelope	ENV	Float	FLT
Equal	EQ	Floor	FL
Equation	EQ	Fluid	FL
Equipment	EQUIP.	Fluorescent	FLUOR
Equivalent	EQUIV	Flush	FL
Estimate	EST	Focus	FOC
Evaporate	EVAP	Foot	(′) FT
Excavate	EXC	Force	F
Exhaust	EXH	Forging	FORG
Expand	EXP	Forward	FWD
Exterior	EXT	Foundation	FDN
External	EXT	Foundry	FDRY
Extra heavy	X HVY	Fractional	FRAC
Extra strong	X STR	Frame	FR
Extrude	EXTR	Freezing point	FP
		Frequency	FREQ
Fabricate	FAB	Frequency, high	HF
Face to face	F to F	Frequency, low	LF

Word	Abbreviation	Word	Abbreviation
Frequency, medium	MF	Harden	HDN
Frequency modulation	FM	Hardware	HDW
Frequency, super high	SHF	Head	HD
Frequency, ultra high	UHF	Headless	HDLS
Frequency, very high	VHF	Heat	HT
Frequency, very low	VLF	Heat treat	HT TR
Friction horsepower	FHP	Heater	HTR
From below	FR BEL	Heavy	HVY
Front	FR	Height	HGT
Fuel	F	Henry	H
Furnish	FURN	Hexagon	HEX
Fusible	FSBL	High	H
Fusion point	FNP	High frequency	HF
		High point	H PT
Gage or Gauge	GA	High pressure	HP
Gallon	GAL	High speed	HS
Galvanize	GALV	High-speed steel	HSS
Galvanized iron	GI	High tension	HT
Galvanized steel	GS	High voltage	HV
Galvanized steel wire rope	GSWR	Highway	HWY
Gas	G	Holder	HLR
Gasket	GSKT	Hollow	HOL
Gasoline	GASO	Horizontal	HOR
General	GEN	Horsepower	HP
Glaze	GL	Hot rolled	HR
Government	GOVT	Hot-rolled steel	HRS
Government furnished equipment	GFE	Hour	HR
Governor	GOV	Hydraulic	HYD
Grade	GR		
Graduation	GRAD	Identify	IDENT
Gram	G	Ignition	IGN
Graphic	GRAPH.	Illuminate	ILLUM
Graphite	GPH	Illustrate	ILLUS
Grating	GRTG	Impact	IMP
Gravity	G	Impedance	IMP.
Grid	G	Inch	(") IN.
Grind	GRD	Inches per second	IPS
Groove	GRV	Include	INCL
Ground	GRD	Increase	INCR
		Indicate	IND
Half hard	½H	Inductance or induction	IND
Half round	½RD	Industrial	IND
Handle	HDL	Information	INFO
Hanger	HGR	Injection	INJ
Hard	H	Inlet	IN
Hard-drawn	HD	Inspect	INSP

Word	Abbreviation	Word	Abbreviation
Install	INSTL	Lacquer	LAQ
Instantaneous	INST	Laminate	LAM
Instruct	INST	Lateral	LAT
Instrument	INST	Lead-coated metal	LCM
Insulate	INS	Lead covered	LC
Interchangeable	INTCHG	Leading edge	LE
Interior	INT	Left	L
Interlock	INTLK	Left hand	LH
Intermediate	INTER	Length	LG
Intermittent	INTMT	Length over all	LOA
Internal	INT	Letter	LTR
Interrupt	INTER	Light	LT
Interrupted continuous wave	ICW	Limit	LIM
Interruptions per minute	IPM	Line	L
Interruptions per second	IPS	Linear	LIN
Intersect	INT	Link	LK
Inverse	INV	Liquid	LIQ
Invert	INV	Liter	L
Iron	I	Locate	LOC
Iron-pipe size	IPS	Long	LG
Irregular	IRREG	Longitude	LONG.
Issue	ISS	Low explosive	LE
		Low frequency	LF
Jack	J	Low pressure	LP
Job order	JO	Low tension	LT
Joint	JT	Low voltage	LV
Junction	JCT	Low speed	LS
		Low torque	LT
Kelvin	K	Lubricate	LUB
Key	K	Lubricating oil	LO
Keyseat	KST	Lumen	L
Keyway	KWY	Lumens per watt	LPW
Kilo	K		
Kilocycle	KC	Machine	MACH
Kilocycles per second	KC	Magnet	MAG
Kilogram	KG	Main	MN
Kiloliter	KL	Male and female	M&F
Kilometer	KM	Malleable	MALL
Kilovolt	KV	Malleable iron	MI
Kilovolt-ampere	KVA	Manual	MAN.
Kilovolt-ampere hour	KVAH	Manufacture	MFR
Kilowatt	KW	Manufactured	MFD
Kilowatt-hour	KWH	Manufacturing	MFG
Kip (1000 lb)	K	Material	MATL
Knots	KN	Material list	ML
		Maximum	MAX
Laboratory	LAB		

Word	Abbreviation	Word	Abbreviation
Maximum working pressure	MWP	Mounted	MTD
Mean effective pressure	MEP	Mounting	MTG
Mechanical	MECH	Multiple	MULT
Mechanism	MECH	Multiple contact	MC
Medium	MED		
Mega	M	National	NATL
Megacycles	MC	Natural	NAT
Megawatt	MW	Near face	NF
Megohm	MEG	Near side	NS
Melting point	MP	Negative	NEG
Metal	MET.	Network	NET
Meter (instrument or measure		Neutral	NEUT
of length)	M	Nickel-silver	NI-SIL
Micro	μ or U	Nipple	NIP.
Microampere	μA or UA	Nominal	NOM
Microfarad	μF or UF	Normal	NOR
Microhenry	μH or UH	Normally closed	NC
Micro-inch-root-mean square	μ-IN-RMS or	Normally open	NO
	U-IN-RMS	Not to scale	NTS
Micrometer	MIC	Number	NO.
Micron	μ or U		
Microvolt	μV or UV	Obsolete	OBS
Microwatt	μW or UW	Octagon	OCT
Miles	MI	Ohm	Ω
Miles per gallon	MPG	Oil-circuit breaker	OCB
Miles per hour	MPH	Oil insulated	OI
Milli	M	Oil switch	OS
Milliampere	MA.	On center	OC
Milligram	MG	One pole	1 P
Millihenry	MH	Opening	OPNG
Millimeter	MM	Operate	OPR
Milliseconds	MS	Opposite	OPP
Millivolt	MV	Optical	OPT
Milliwatt	MW	Ordnance	ORD
Minimum	MIN	Orifice	ORF
Minute	(') MIN	Original	ORIG
Miscellaneous	MISC	Oscillate	OSC
Mixture	MIX.	Ounce	OZ
Model	MOD	Out to Out	O to O
Modify	MOD	Outlet	OUT.
Modulated continuous wave	MCW	Output	OUT.
Modulator	MOD	Outside diameter	OD
Molecular weight	MOL WT	Outside face	OF
Monument	MON	Outside radius	OR
Morse taper	MOR T	Over-all	OA
Motor	MOT	Overhead	OVHD

Word	Abbreviation	Word	Abbreviation
Overload	OVLD	Pounds per cubic foot	PCF
Overvoltage	OVV	Pounds per square foot	PSF
Oxidized	OXD	Pounds per square inch	PSI
		Pounds per square inch absolute	PSIA
Pack	PK	Power	PWR
Packing	PKG	Power amplifier	PA
Painted	PTD	Power directional relay	PDR
Pair	PR	Power factor	PF
Panel	PNL	Preamplifier	PREAMP
Parallel	PAR.	Precast	PRCST
Part	PT	Prefabricated	PREFAB
Pattern	PATT	Preferred	PFD
Perforate	PERF	Premolded	PRMLD
Permanent	PERM	Prepare	PREP
Permanent magnet	PM	Press	PRS
Perpendicular	PERP	Pressure	PRESS.
Phase	PH	Pressure angle	PA.
Phosphor bronze	PH BRZ	Primary	PRI
Photograph	PHOTO	Process	PROC
Physical	PHYS	Production	PROD
Piece	PC	Profile	PF
Piece mark	PC MK	Project	PROJ
Pierce	PRC	Punch	PCH
Pipe Tap	PT	Purchase	PUR
Pitch	P	Push-pull	P-P
Pitch circle	PC		
Pitch diameter	PD	Quadrant	QUAD
Plastic	PLSTC	Quality	QUAL
Plate	PL	Quantity	QTY
Plotting	PLOT.	Quart	QT
Pneumatic	PNEU	Quarter	QTR
Point	PT	Quarter hard	¼ H
Point of compound curve	PCC	Quarter round	¼ RD
Point of curve	PC	Quartz	QTZ
Point of intersection	PI		
Point of reverse curve	PRC	Radial	RAD
Point of switch	PS	Radio frequency	RF
Point of tangent	PT	Radius	R
Polar	POL	Reactive	REAC
Pole	P	Reactive kilovolt-ampere	KVAR
Polish	POL	Reactive volt-ampere	VAR
Port	P	Reactive voltmeter	RVM
Position	POS	Reactor	REAC
Positive	POS	Ream	RM
Potential	POT.	Reassemble	REASM
Pound	LB	Received	RECD

Word	Abbreviation	Word	Abbreviation
Receiver	REC	Saddle	SDL
Receptacle	RECP	Safe working pressure	SWP
Recriprocate	RECIP	Safety	SAF
Recirculate	RECIRC	Sand blast	SD BL
Reclosing	RECL	Saturate	SAT.
Record	REC	Schedule	SCH
Rectangle	RECT	Schematic	SCHEM
Rectifier	RECT	Scleroscope hardness	SH
Reduce	RED.	Screen	SCRN
Reference	REF	Screw	SCR
Reference line	REF L	Second	SEC
Regulator	REG	Section	SECT
Reinforce	REINF	Segment	SEG
Relay	REL	Select	SEL
Release	REL	Semifinished	SF
Relief	REL	Semifixed	SFXD
Remove	REM	Semisteel	SS
Repair	REP	Separate	SEP
Replace	REPL	Sequence	SEQ
Reproduce	REPRO	Serial	SER
Require	REQ	Series	SER
Required	REQD	Serrate	SERR
Resistance	RES	Service	SERV
Resistor	RES	Set screw	SS
Retainer	RET.	Shaft	SFT
Retard	RET.	Shield	SHLD
Return	RET.	Shipment	SHPT
Reverse	REV	Shop order	SO
Revise	REV	Short wave	SW
Revolution	REV	Shunt	SH
Revolutions per minute	RPM	Side	S
Revolutions per second	RPS	Signal	SIG
Rheostat	RHEO	Sink	SK
Right	R	Sketch	SK
Right hand	RH	Sleeve	SLV
Ring	R	Slide	SL
Rivet	RIV	Slotted	SLOT.
Rockwell hardness	RH	Small	SM
Roller bearing	RB	Smoke	SMK
Root diameter	RD	Smokeless	SMKLS
Root mean square	RMS	Socket	SOC
Rotary	ROT.	Soft	S
Rotate	ROT.	Solder	SLD
Rough	RGH	Solenoid	SOL
Round	RD	Sound	SND
Rubber	RUB.	South	S

Word	Abbreviation	Word	Abbreviation
Space	SP	Tangent	TAN.
Spare	SP	Taper	TPR
Speaker	SPKR	Technical	TECH
Special	SPL	Tee	T
Specific	SP	Teeth per inch	TPI
Specific gravity	SP GR	Television	TV
Specific heat	SP HT	Temperature	TEMP
Specification	SPEC	Template	TEMP
Speed	SP	Tensile strength	TS
Spherical	SPHER	Tension	TENS.
Spindle	SPDL	Terminal	TERM.
Split phase	SP PH	Terminal board	TB
Spot-faced	SF	That is	IE
Spring	SPG	Theoretical	THEO
Square	SQ	Thermal	THRM
Stabilize	STAB	Thermostat	THERMO
Stainless	STN	Thick	THK
Standard	STD	Thousand	M
Static pressure	SP	Thread	THD
Station	STA	Throttle	THROT
Stationary	STA	Through	THRU
Steel	STL	Time	T
Stiffener	STIFF.	Time delay	TD
Stock	STK	Time-delay closing	TDC
Storage	STG	Time-delay opening	TDO
Straight	STR	Tinned	TD
Strip	STR	Tobin bronze	TOB BRZ
Structural	STR	Toggle	TGL
Substitute	SUB	Tolerance	TOL
Suction	SUCT	Tongue and groove	T&G
Summary	SUM.	Tool steel	TS
Supervise	SUPV	Tooth	T
Supply	SUP	Total	TOT
Surface	SUR	Total indicator reading	TIR
Survey	SURV	Trace	TR
Switch	SW	Tracer	TCR
Symbol	SYM	Transfer	TRANS
Symmetrical	SYM	Transformer	TRANS
Synchronous	SYN	Transmission	XMSN
Synthetic	SYN	Transmitter	XMTR
System	SYS	Transmitting	XMTG
		Transportation	TRANS
Tabulate	TAB.	Transverse	TRANSV
Tachometer	TACH	Trimmer	TRIM.
Tandem	TDM	Triode	TRI

Word	Abbreviation	Word	Abbreviation
True air speed	TAS	Voltmeter	VM
Truss	T	Volts per mil	VPM
Tubing	TUB	Volume	VOL
Tuned radio frequency	TRF		
Turbine	TURB	Washer	WASH
Typical	TYP	Water	W
		Water line	WL
Ultimate	ULT	Watertight	WT
Ultra-high frequency	UHF	Watt	W
Under voltage	UV	Watt-hour	WHR
Unit	U	Watt-hour meter	WHM
United States Gage	USG	Wattmeter	WM
United States Standard	USS	Weight	WT
Universal	UNIV	West	W
		Wet bulb	WB
Vacuum	VAC	Width	W
Vacuum tube	VT	Wind	WD
Valve	V	Winding	WDG
Vapor proof	VAP PRF	Wire	W
Variable	VAR	With	W/
Variable-frequency oscillator	VFO	With equipment and spare parts	W/E&SP
Velocity	V	Without	W/O
Ventilate	VENT.	Without equipment and spare parts	W/O E&SP
Versed sine	VERS		
Versus	VS	Wood	WD
Vertical	VERT	Woodruff	WDF
Very-high frequency	VHF	Working point	WP
Very-low frequency	VLF	Working pressure	WP
Video-frequency	VDF	Wrought	WRT
Vibrate	VIB	Wrought iron	WI
Viscosity	VISC		
Vitreous	VIT	Yard	YD
Voice frequency	VF	Year	YR
Volt	V	Yield point	YP
Volt-ampere	VA	Yield strength	YS

Abbreviations for Colors

Amber	AMB	Green	GRN
Black	BLK	Orange	ORN
Blue	BLU	White	WHT
Brown	BRN	Yellow	YEL

Partial List of Chemical Symbols

Word	Abbreviation	Word	Abbreviation
Aluminum	Al	Molybdenum	Mo
Antimony (stibium)	Sb	Neon	Ne
Barium	Ba	Nickel	Ni
Beryllium	Be	Nitrogen	N
Bismuth	Bi	Oxygen	O
Boron	B	Phosphorus	P
Bromine	Br	Platinum	Pt
Cadmium	Cd	Potassium (kalium)	K
Calcium	Ca	Radium	R
Carbon	C	Rhodium	Rh
Chlorine	Cl	Ruthenium	Ru
Chromium	Cr	Selinium	Se
Cobalt	Co	Silicon	Si
Copper	Cu	Silver (argentum)	Ag
Fluorine	F	Sodium (natrium)	Na
Gold (aurium)	Au	Strontium	St
Helium	He	Sulfur	S
Hydrogen	H	Tantalum	Ta
Indium	In	Tellurium	Te
Iodine	I	Thallium	Th
Iridium	Ir	Tin (stannum)	Sn
Iron (ferrum)	Fe	Titanium	Ti
Lead (plumbum)	Pb	Tungsten (walfranium)	W
Lithium	Li	Uranium	U
Magnesium	Mg	Vanadium	V
Manganese	Mn	Zinc	Z
Mercury (hydrargyrum)	Hg	Zirconium	Zr

Index